THE BIBLICAL WO

— ·◆· —

The Biblical World is a comprehensive guide to the contents, historical setting and social context of the Bible. It presents the fruits of years of specialist study in accessible form, and is essential reading for anyone who reads the Bible and would like to know more about how and why it came to be.

Volume I begins with an overview of the full range of Biblical material (Old Testament, Apocrypha and New Testament), before going on to more detailed discussion of the major genres of biblical literature – from myth and prophecy to poetry and proverbs. The contributors also consider the ways in which the texts have been transmitted, the significance of parallel and related versions, and past interpretations of the Bible.

Explorations of the historical background are complemented by the findings of archaeology, and discussion of matters such as language, law, administration, social life and the arts offers a fuller understanding of the social and cultural setting of ancient Israel and the early Christian churches. Major figures in the Bible – including Abraham, Jesus and Paul – are studied in detail, as are its central religious concepts, such as salvation and purity. Volume II concludes with a survey of how the Bible is studied and seen today.

Written by an international collection of acknowledged experts, this monumental work will be an invaluable resource for students, academics and clergy, and for all to whom the Bible is important as a religious or cultural document.

John Barton is Oriel and Laing Professor of the Interpretation of Holy Scripture, University of Oxford, and Fellow of Oriel College, Oxford. He is the author of numerous books and articles on biblical texts, and is also the editor of *The Cambridge Companion to Biblical Interpretation* (1998) and (with John Muddiman) of *The Oxford Bible Commentary* (2001).

THE BIBLICAL WORLD

Volume I

Edited by

John Barton

Routledge
Taylor & Francis Group

LONDON AND NEW YORK

Every attempt has been made to obtain permission to reproduce copyright material. If any proper acknowledgement has not been made, we would invite copyright holders to inform us of the oversight.

First published 2002
by Routledge
2 Park Square, Milton Park, Abingdon, Oxon OX14 4RN

Simultaneously published in the USA and Canada
by Routledge
270 Madison Avenue, New York, NY 10016

Routledge is an imprint of the Taylor & Francis Group

First published in paperback 2004

Typeset in Garamond 3 by
Florence Production Ltd, Stoodleigh, Devon
Printed and bound in Great Britain by
TJ International Ltd, Padstow, Cornwall

British Library Cataloguing in Publication Data
A catalogue record for this book is available from the British Library

Library of Congress Cataloging in Publication Data

ISBN 0–415–34954–0 (2 vol. set)
ISBN 0–415–35090–5 (Vol. 1)

CONTENTS

———·◆·———

Volume I

PART I: THE BIBLE

PART II: GENRES

PART III: DOCUMENTS

PART IV: HISTORY

Volume II

PART V: INSTITUTIONS

PART VI: BIBLICAL FIGURES

PART VII: RELIGIOUS IDEAS

PART VIII: THE BIBLE TODAY

ILLUSTRATIONS

———◆———

CONTRIBUTORS

———•◆•———

Rainer Albertz is Professor of the Old Testament at the Westfälische Wilhelms-Universität in Münster, Germany. He has written on various topics in biblical studies, especially in the fields of biblical theology and of ancient Near Eastern history of religion. His books include *Weltschöpfung und Menschenschöpfung bei Hiob, Deuterojesaja und in den Psalmen* (1974), *Persönliche Frömmigkeit und Offizielle Religion* (1978), *Der Gott des Daniel* (1988), *A History of Israelite Religion*, 2 vols (1996) and *Die Exilszeit* (2001).

Graeme Auld is Professor of Hebrew Bible at the University of Edinburgh. He has written mainly on the prophets and the narrative books. His books include *Joshua, Moses and the Land* (1980), *Amos* (1986), *Kings Without Privilege* (1994) and *Joshua Retold* (1998).

John Barton is Oriel and Laing Professor of the Interpretation of the Holy Scripture at the University of Oxford. He has written on various topics in biblical studies, especially the prophets, Old Testament ethics and the formation of the biblical canon. His books include *Reading the Old Testament* (2nd edn, 1996), *Oracles of God* (1986), *People of the Book?* (1988), *The Spirit and the Letter* (1997) and *Ethics and the Old Testament* (1998).

Joseph Blenkinsopp is John A. O'Brien Professor Emeritus at the University of Notre Dame, Indiana, USA, where he has taught intermittently since 1970. He has also taught at Vanderbilt University, Chicago Theological Seminary, Hartford Seminary Foundation and, most recently, at the Biblical Institute, Rome. He served as Rector at the Ecumenical Institute, Tantur, Israel in 1978, and has excavated at Tel Dan and other sites in Israel. He was President of the Catholic Biblical Association, USA, in 1989, and President of the Society for Old Testament Study in 1999–2000. He was born in Bishop Auckland, Durham, was educated at the Universities of London and Oxford, and is married with two children.

Thomas M. Bolin is Associate Professor in the Theology Department of St Mary's University in San Antonio, Texas. His research and publications deal with questions concerning Israelite history and the development of biblical tradition. In addition to several articles and essays he is the author of *Freedom Beyond Forgiveness: The Book of Jonah Re-examined* (1997), and is writing a commentary on Ezra–Nehemiah.

George J. Brooke is Rylands Professor of Biblical Criticism and Exegesis at the University of Manchester. He is Co-Director of the Manchester–Sheffield Centre for Dead Sea Scrolls Research and since 1992 has been a member of the international team of editors of the scrolls. He is a founding editor of the journal *Dead Sea Discoveries*, and among his publications are *Exegesis at Qumran* (1985), *Temple Scroll Studies* (editor, 1989), *Septuagint, Scrolls and Cognate Writings* (co-editor, 1992), *New Qumran Texts and Studies* (editor, 1994) and *The Allegro Qumran Collection* (1996). He was an area editor for the *Encyclopaedia of the Dead Sea Scrolls* (2000).

Andrew Chester is University Lecturer in Divinity and Fellow of Selwyn College at the University of Cambridge. He has written on a number of themes within the area of early Judaism and Christianity, especially messianism and eschatology, and the interpretation of scripture.

Felicity J. Cobbing is Curator at the Palestine Exploration Fund in London. She lectures regularly and has written several articles on various aspects of the archaeology of the region and the history of the Palestine Exploration Fund. She has acted as a consultant on a number of popular and children's publications, most recently *The Atlas of the Bible* (1999) and *The Eyewitness Travel Guide to the Holy Land* (2000).

Dan Cohn-Sherbok is Professor of Judaism at the University of Wales, Lampeter. He is the author of *Biblical Hebrew for Beginners* (1996), *The Hebrew Bible* (1996) and *The Jewish Messiah* (1997).

John J. Collins is Holmes Professor of Old Testament Criticism and Interpretation at Yale University. He has written extensively on apocalyptic literature, Hellenistic Judaism, Dead Sea Scrolls and wisdom literature. His books include the commentary on *Daniel* in the Hermeneia series (1993), *The Scepter and the Star* (1995), *Apocalypticism in the Dead Sea Scrolls* (1997), *Jewish Wisdom in the Hellenistic Age* (1997), *The Apocalyptic Imagination* (rev. edn, 1998) and *Between Athens and Jerusalem* (rev. edn, 2000).

Stephanie Dalley is Shillito Fellow in Assyriology at the Oriental Institute of the University of Oxford. She has published editions of cuneiform tablets from various excavations and museums; more general works include *Mari and Karana, Two Old Babylonian Cities* (1984), *Myths from Mesopotamia* (rev. edn, 2000), *The Legacy of Mesopotamia* (1998).

Graham Davies is Professor of Old Testament studies at the University of Cambridge and Director of Studies in Theology at Fitzwilliam College. His books include *The Way of the Wilderness* (1979), *Megiddo* (1986), *Ancient Hebrew Inscriptions: Corpus and Concordance* (1991) and a commentary and study guide on the prophet Hosea (1992, 1993). He is preparing the *International Critical Commentary* volume on Exodus. From 1990 to 2000 he was the editor of the *Palestine Exploration Quarterly*.

Katharine Dell is Lecturer in Old Testament Studies in the Faculty of Divinity at the University of Cambridge, and Fellow of St Catherine's College. She specializes in the wisdom literature and is the author of a number of articles on that and other topics and of two books on Job, *The Book of Job as Sceptical Literature* (1991) and *Shaking a Fist at God: Understanding Suffering through the Book of Job* (1995). She has written a number of 'overview' articles on wisdom and an introductory textbook on wisdom literature entitled *Get Wisdom, Get Insight: An Introduction to Israel's Wisdom Literature* (2000).

J. Duncan M. Derrett is Emeritus Professor of Oriental Laws at the University of London. He is interested in the overlap between religion, ethics and law, and in the uses made by different cultures of their law codes. He has written *Law in the New Testament* (1970), *Studies in the New Testament* (1977–95), *The Sermon on the Mount* (1994), *Two Masters* (1995), *Law and Morality* (1998) and *The Bible and the Buddhists* (2000).

Mark Edwards is Tutor in Theology at Christ Church, Oxford. He is the author of *Apologetics in the Roman Empire* (1999; co-edited with Simon Price and Martin Goodman) and *Ancient Christian Commentary on Scripture.* Vol. 8: *Galatians, Ephesians, Philippians* (1999).

Jarl Fossum, born 1946 (Oslo, Norway). MA from the University of Bergen 1971; ThD from the University of Utrecht 1982; Assistant Lecturer in Religion in Bergen. Professor of new Testament Studies at the University of Michigan 1988–99. Now retired; lives and works in Spain. Author of *The Name of God and the Angel of the Lord* (WUNT 36, 1985) and *The Image of the Invisible God* (NTOA 1995) and numerous articles in scholarly periodicals.

Harry Gamble is Professor of Religious Studies at the University of Virginia, Charlottesville, Virginia, and Chair of the Department of Religious Studies. He has written articles and books on diverse subjects in the field of New Testament studies, including *The Textual History of the Letter to the Romans* (1977), *The New Testament Canon: Its Making and Meaning* (1985) and *Books and Readers in the Early Church: A History of Early Christian Texts* (1995).

Susan Gillingham is Fellow and Tutor in Theology at Worcester College, Oxford, and University Lecturer in Old Testament. Her teaching and writing interests include prophecy, psalmody and feminist studies of the Old Testament. Her publications include *The Poems and Psalms of the Hebrew Bible* (1994) and *One Bible, Many Voices* (1998). She is working on a reception-history commentary on the Psalms.

Lester L. Grabbe is Professor of Hebrew Bible and Early Judaism and Director of the Graduate School at the University of Hull. His books include *Judaism from Cyrus to Hadrian*, 2 vols (1992), *Priests, Prophets, Diviners, Sages* (1995), and *Judaic Religion in the Second Temple Period* (2000).

Leonard J. Greenspoon holds the Philip M. and Ethel Klutznick Chair in Jewish Civilization at Creighton University in Omaha, Nebraska. An acknowledged expert on the Septuagint and, more generally, the history of Bible translations, he has authored or edited eight volumes and contributed more than a hundred scholarly and popular articles in these and related fields.

Jo Ann Hackett is Professor of the Practice of Biblical Hebrew and Northwest Semitic Epigraphy at Harvard University. She publishes on biblical topics, especially the history of women in ancient Israel, Transjordanian religion, and the era of the Judges, as well as Hebrew, Phoenician and Northwest Semitic epigraphic finds (*The Balaam Text from Deir 'Alla*, 1984).

David G. Horrell is Senior Lecturer in New Testament Studies in the Department of Theology, University of Exeter. His main interests are in the use of social sciences in New Testament interpretation and the Pauline and Petrine epistles. He is currently working on Pauline ethics. His books include *The Social Ethos of the Corinthian Correspondence* (1996), *The Epistles of Peter and Jude* (1998), *An Introduction to the Study of Paul* (2000) and an edited collection entitled *Social-Scientific Approaches to New Testament Interpretation* (1999).

John Huehnergard is Professor of Semitic Philosophy at Harvard University. His research covers the various linguistic aspects of individual ancient Semitic languages and of the Semitic language family in general. His books include *Ugaritic Vocabulary in Syllabic Transcription* (1987), *The Akkadian of Ugarit* (1989), and *A Grammar of Akkadian* (1996).

Gwilym H. Jones was, until his retirement in 1995, Professor and Head of the School of Theology and Religious Studies at the University of Wales, Bangor. He has published a number of books in Welsh on Old Testament studies. Among his other works are *1 and 2 Kings*, *The New Century Bible Commentary* (1984), *The Nathan Narratives* (1990) and *1 and 2 Chronicles* (1993).

Alastair H. B. Logan is Senior Lecturer in the Department of Theology at the University of Exeter. He is particularly interested in the relation of 'orthodoxy' and 'heresy' in the early church and has published articles on gnosticism, Origen and Marcellus of Ancyra. His major monograph *Gnostic Truth and Christian Heresy* (1996) reconsiders the generally accepted view of the origins and development of the gnostic religious phenomenon.

Carmel McCarthy is Senior Lecturer in Hebrew and Syriac at the Department of Near Eastern Languages at University College Dublin, Ireland. She has written on various topics in biblical studies, especially on textual criticism and early Syriac texts. She has published a major work on *The Tiqqune Sopherim in the Masoretic Text of the Old Testament* (1981) and is editing the book of Deuteronomy for a new edition of the Hebrew Bible (*Biblia Hebraica, Editio quinta funditus renovata*). Other books include the first English translation of the unique Syriac Chester Beatty Manuscript 709 of St Ephrem's Commentary on Tatian's Diatessaron (1993, repr. 2000) and (with William Riley) *The Old Testament Short Story* (1986).

Rex Mason is Emeritus Fellow of Regent's Park College, Oxford, and was, until retirement, Lecturer in Old Testament and Hebrew at the University of Oxford. His publications include *Preaching the Tradition: Homily and Hermeneutic after the Exile* (1990), *Micah, Nahum, Obadiah* (1991), *Zephaniah, Habakkuk, Joel* (1994) and *Propaganda and Subversion in the Old Testament* (1997).

A. D. H. Mayes is Erasmus Smith's Professor of Hebrew in the University of Dublin. His writing has been chiefly on early Israelite history and the historical books of the Old Testament. His books include *Israel in the Period of the Judges* (1974), *Deuteronomy* (1979), *The Story of Israel from Settlement to Exile* (1983), *Judges* (1986) and *The Old Testament in Sociological Perspective* (1989).

Justin J. Meggitt is College Lecturer in Theology at Corpus Christi College, Cambridge. He has written *Paul, Poverty and Survival* (1998) and is working on *Christ and the Universe of Disease* and *The New Testament and Ancient Popular Culture*.

J. Maxwell Miller is Professor Emeritus of Emory University and Curator for Middle Eastern Archaeology at Fernbank Museum of Natural History in Atlanta, Georgia. He has participated in archaeological excavations in Israel, Jordan and Syria, and written on various topics related to the history and archaeology of biblical times. His books include *The Old Testament and the Historian* (1975), *Introducing the Holy Land* (1982), *A History of Ancient Israel and Judah* (1986; co-authored with J. Hayes), and *An Archaeological Survey of the Kerak Plateau* (1991).

Robert Morgan is Reader in New Testament Theology at the University of Oxford. He has written on biblical topics, the history of interpretation, and modern theology, including *The Nature of New Testament Theology* (1973), *Ernst Troeltsch: Writings on Theology and Religion* (1977; with Michael Pye), *Biblical Interpretation* (1985; with John Barton), and *Romans* (1998).

John Muddiman is G. B. Caird Fellow in New Testament Studies at Mansfield College and lectures in the Oxford Faculty of Theology. He has written on various topics in biblical studies, especially on the Gospels, Pauline letters and biblical interpretation. His books are *The Bible, Fountain and Well of Truth* (1983) and *A Commentary on the Epistle to the Ephesians* (2001).

Bustanay Oded received his doctoral degree from the Hebrew University in 1967. He is a professor at the University of Haifa, teaching various subjects in biblical studies and ancient Near Eastern civilizations. He has published articles and reviews as well as monographs. His books include *Mass Deportations and Deportees in the Neo-Assyrian Empire* (1972), *History of Israel during the First Temple Period* (1983–4) and *War, Peace and Empire* (1992).

David Parker is Reader in New Testament Textual Criticism and Palaeography at the University of Birmingham, where he is also Director of the Centre for the Editing of Texts in Religion. He is Co-Editor of the International Greek New Testament Project and, as well as translating and editing sixteenth-century commentaries, has written on various aspects of New Testament textual and manuscript studies. His books include

Paul's Letter to the Colossians by Philip Melanchthon (1989), *Codex Bezae: An Early Christian Manuscript and its Text* (1992), *The Living Text of the Gospels* (1997), *The Gospel According to St John.* Vol. 1: *The Papyri* (1995; with W. J. Elliott) and *Iohannis Calvini Commentarius in Epistolam Pauli ad Romanos* (1999; with T. H. L. Parker).

Sarah Pearce is Ian Karten Lecturer in Jewish History at the University of Southampton. She has written on various areas of ancient Jewish history and literary culture including Josephus, Philo and the Septuagint. She is co-editor of *Jewish Local Patriotism and Self-Identification in the Graeco-Roman Period* (1998) and *Cultures of Ambivalence and Contempt* (1998).

George W. Ramsey is the Kristen Herrington Professor of Bible at the Presbyterian College, Clinton, South Carolina. He is the author of *The Quest for Historical Israel* (1981), and his writings have appeared in periodicals such as the *Journal of Biblical Literature*, *Catholic Biblical Quarterly* and *Perspectives in Religious Studies*. He is also a contributor to the *Anchor Bible Dictionary*.

Stefan C. Reif is the Director of the Genizah Research Unit and Head of the Oriental Division at the University Library, Professor of Medieval Hebrew Studies in the Faculty of Oriental Studies, and Fellow of St John's College, all at the University of Cambridge. His major fields of research are Jewish liturgy and the Cairo Genizah, and he is the author/editor of seven books and of over two hundred scholarly articles. His most recent are *Hebrew Manuscripts at Cambridge University Library*, 2 vols (1997) and *A Jewish Archive from Old Cairo* (2000).

Adele Reinhartz is Professor of New Testament and Second Temple Judaism in the Department of Religious Studies, McMaster University, Hamilton, Ontario. She has published extensively on the Gospel of John, apocryphal literature, feminist biblical criticism and literary criticism of biblical narrative. Recent books include *'Why Ask My Name?' Anonymity and Identity in Biblical Narrative* (1998) and *Befriending the Beloved Disciple: A Jewish Reading of the Gospel of John* (2001).

Christopher Rowland is the Dean Ireland's Professor of the Exegesis of Holy Scripture at the University of Oxford. He has written on apocalypticism in Christianity and Second Temple Judaism and is writing a commentary on the reception-history of the Apocalypse. His books include *The Open Heaven* (1982), *Christian Origins* (2nd edn, 2001) and the commentary on the Apocalypse for the *New Interpreter's Bible* (1998).

Alison Salvesen is Fellow of the Oxford Centre for Hebrew and Jewish Studies. She is interested in early Jewish and Christian Bible translations and exegesis. She has published a book on Greek Bible translation, *Symmachus in the Pentateuch* (1991); and on a late Syriac version, *The Books of Samuel in the Syriac Version of Jacob of Edessa* (1999).

William R. Telford is Senior Lecturer in Religious Studies (Christian Origins and the New Testament) at the University of Newcastle, England. His research interests include the historical Jesus, pre-Synoptic traditions, the Gospels, methods of biblical interpretation, and the Bible and literature and film. He has published in these areas, especially on the Gospel of Mark. His books include *The Barren Temple and the Withered Tree* (1980), *Mark* (1995), *The Interpretation of Mark* (2nd edn, 1995) and *The Theology of the Gospel of Mark* (1999).

Christopher Tuckett is Professor of New Testament Studies at the University of Oxford. He has written on a number of topics on aspects of study of the New Testament and early Christian literature, especially the Synoptic Gospels and the non-canonical traditions about Jesus. His books include *The Revival of the Griesbach Hypothesis* (1983), *Reading the New Testament* (1987), *Luke* (1996), *Q and the History of Early Christianity* (1996), and *Christology and the New Testament* (2001).

John Van Seters is Distinguished University Professor Emeritus at the University of North Carolina, Chapel Hill, NC. He is retired and now living in Waterloo, Canada. His books include *The Life of Moses: The Yahwist as Historian in Exodus–Numbers* (1994) and *The Pentateuch: A Social-Scientific Commentary* (1999).

Henry Wansbrough is a Benedictine monk of Ampleforth. He is Master of St Benet's Hall, Oxford, and teaches New Testament in the Theology Faculty there. He is General Editor of the New Jerusalem Bible, and is the only English member of the Pontifical Biblical Commission. He has lectured widely in America, Africa and Jerusalem.

Gordon Wenham is Professor of Old Testament at the Cheltenham and Gloucester College of Higher Education. He has written commentaries on Genesis, Leviticus and Numbers, and a book on Old Testament ethics entitled *Story as Torah: Reading the Old Testament Ethically* (2000).

Keith W. Whitelam is Professor of Biblical Studies and Head of the Department of Biblical Studies at the University of Sheffield. His books include *The Invention of Ancient Israel: The Silencing of Palestinian History* (1996), *The Emergence of Early Israel in Historical Perspective* (1987; co-authored with Robert Coote) and *The Just King: Royal Judicial Authority in Ancient Israel* (1979). He has published a series of articles on ancient Israelite and Palestinian history.

Catrin H. Williams teaches New Testament at the University of Wales, Bangor. She has written on the Fourth Gospel and is the author of *I Am He: The Interpretation of Anî Hû in Jewish and Early Christian Literature* (2000).

Lawrence M. Wills is Professor of Biblical Studies at Episcopal Divinity School, Cambridge, Massachusetts. His research areas include Judaism in the Persian and Graeco-Roman periods and the New Testament, especially the early Gospel traditions. His books include *The Jew in the Court of the Foreign King: Ancient Jewish Court Legends* (1990), *The Jewish Novel in the Ancient World* (1995) and *The Quest of the Historical Gospel: Mark, John and the Origins of the Gospel Genre* (1997).

PREFACE

———•◆•———

This book has been several years in the making, and much is owed to many advisers and helpers, as well as to the contributors. I am particularly indebted to its commissioning editor, Richard Stoneman, who first conceived the idea, and to his assistants Coco Stevenson and Catherine Bousfield who have seen it through to publication.

John Barton
Oriel College, Oxford
January 2001

ABBREVIATIONS

————•◆•————

AB	Anchor Bible
ABC	*Assyrian and Babylonian Chronicles*, A. K. Grayson (Locust Valley, New York, 1975)
ABD	The *Anchor Bible Dictionary*, D. N. Freedman (ed.) (Doubleday, 1992)
ABL	*Assyrian and Babylonian Letters Belonging to the Kouyunjik Collections of the British Museum*, R. F. Harper (ed.), 14 vols (Chicago, 1892–1914)
AGJU	*Arbeiten zur Geschichte des antiken Judentums und des Urchristentums*
AIA	Archaeolgical Institute of America
AJA	*American Journal of Archaeology*
AnBib	Analecta biblica
ANEP	*The Ancient Near East in Pictures Relating to the Old Testament*, J. B. Pritchard (ed.) (Princeton, 1969)
ANET	*Ancient Near Eastern Texts Relating to the Old Testament*, J. B. Pritchard (ed.) (Princeton, 3rd edn, 1969)
ANRW	*Aufstieg und Niedergang der römischen Welt: Geschichte und Kultur Roms im Spiegel der neueren Forschung*, H. Temporini and W. Haase (eds) (Berlin, 1972–)
ANTF	Arbeiten zur neutestamentlichen Textforschung
ARAB	*Ancient Records of Assyria and Babylonia*, D. D. Luckenbill, 2 vols (Chicago, 1926–7)
ASTI	*Annual of the Swedish Theological Institute*
ATANT	Abhandlungen zur Theologie des Alten und Neuen Testaments
AThR	*Anglican Theological Review*
BA	*Biblical Archaeologist*
BAG	Bauer, W., Arndt, W. F., Gingrich F. W. and Danker, F. W., *Greek–English Lexicon of the New Testament and Other Early Christian Literature* (Chicago, 1957)
BAR	*Biblical Archaeology Review*
BASOR	*Bulletin of the American Schools of Oriental Research*
BBB	Bonner biblische Beiträge
BDF	Blass, F., Debrunner A. and Funk, R. W., *A Greek Grammar of the New Testament and Other Early Christian Literature* (Chicago, 1961)

BETL	Bibliotheca ephemeridum theologicarum lovaniensium
Bib	*Biblica*
BibInt	*Biblical Interpretation*
BJRL	*Bulletin of the John Rylands University Library of Manchester*
BMes	Bibliotheca mesopotamica
BNTC	Black's New Testament Commentaries
BR	*Bible Review*
BWANT	Beiträge zur Wissenschaft vom Alten und Neuen Testament
BZAW	Beihefte zur Zeitschrift für die alttestamentliche Wissenschaft
BZNW	Beihefte zur Zeitschrift für die neutestamentliche Wissenschaft
CAH	Cambridge Ancient History
CBQ	*Catholic Biblical Quarterly*
CBQMS	Catholic Biblical Quarterly Monograph Series
CPJ	*Corpus papyrorum judaicorum*, V. Tcherikover (ed.), 3 vols (Cambridge, 1957–64)
CRBR	*Critical Review of Books in Religion*
CRINT	Compendia rerum iudaicarum ad novum testamentum
CTA	*Corpus des tablettes en cunéiformes alphabétiques découvertes à Ras Shamra-Ugarit de 1929 à 1939*, A. Herdner (ed.) (Paris, 1963)
CurBS	*Currents in Research: Biblical Studies*
DJD	Discoveries in the Judaean Desert
EBib	*Etudes bibliques*
ErIsr	*Eretz-Israel*
EsBíb	*Estudios bíblicos*
ET	English Translation
ExpTim	*Expository Times*
FRLANT	Forschungen zur Religion und Literatur des Alten und Neuen Testaments
HTR	*Harvard Theological Review*
HUCA	*Hebrew Union College Annual*
ICC	International Critical Commentary
IDBSup	Interpreter's Dictionary of the Bible: Supplementary Volume
IEJ	*Israel Exploration Journal*
Int	*Interpretation*
JBL	*Journal of Biblical Literature*
JBR	*Journal of Bible and Religion*
JCS	*Journal of Cuneiform Studies*
JJS	*Journal of Jewish Studies*
JR	*Journal of Religion*
JRS	*Journal of Roman Studies*
JSJ	*Journal for the Study of Judaism in the Persian, Hellenistic and Roman Periods*
JSNT	*Journal for the Study of the New Testament*
JSNTSup	Journal for the Study of the New Testament: Supplement Series
JSOT	*Journal for the Study of the Old Testament*
JSOTSup	Journal for the Study of the Old Testament: Supplement Series

JSP	*Journal for the Study of the Pseudepigrapha*
JTS	*Journal of Theological Studies*
KAI	*Kanaanäische und aramäische Inschriften*, H. Donner and W. Röllig (Wiesbaden, 2nd edn, 1966–9)
KAR	*Keilschrifttexte aus Assur religiösen Inhalts*, E. Ebeling (Wiesbaden, 2nd edn, 1966–9)
KJV	King James Version
KTU	*Die Keilalphabetischen Texte aus Ugarit*, M. Dietrich, O. Loretz and J. Sanmartín (eds) (Neukirchen-Vluyn, 1976)
LXX	Septuagint
MBPF	Münchener Beiträge zur Papyrusforschung und antiken Rechtsgeschichte
MT	Masoretic Text
ND	Nimrud Documents
NEAEHL	*The New Encyclopedia of Archaeological Excavations in the Holy Land*, E. Stern (ed.), 4 vols (Jerusalem, 1993)
NHC	Nag Hammadi Codices
NHMS	Nag Hammadi and Manichaean Studies
NHS	Nag Hammadi Studies
NIV	New International Version
NovT	*Novum Testamentum*
NovTSup	Novum Testamentum Supplements
NRSV	New Revised Standard Version
NTG	New Testament Guides
NTOA	Novum Testamentum et Orbis Antiquus
NTS	*New Testament Studies*
NTT	*Norsk Teologisk Tidsskrift*
OBO	Orbis biblicus et orientalis
PTMS	Pittsburgh Theological Monograph Series
RB	*Revue biblique*
RGG	*Religion in Geschichte und Gegenwart*, K. Galling (ed.), 7 vols (Tübingen, 3rd edn, 1957–65)
RIDA	*Revue internationale des droits de l'antiquité*
RIMA	The Royal Inscriptions of Mesopotamia, Assyrian Periods
RSV	Revised Standard Version
SAA	State Archives of Assyria
SBLDS	Society of Biblical Literature Dissertation Series
SD	Studies and Documents
SJT	*Scottish Journal of Theology*
SJOT	*Scandinavian Journal of the Old Testament*
SNTSMS	Society for New Testament Studies Monograph Series
SNTW	Studies of the New Testament and its World
SR	*Studies in Religion*
TA	*Tel Aviv*
TDNT	*Theological Dictionary of the New Testament*, G. Kittel and G. Friedrich (eds), trans. by G. W. Bromiley, 10 vols (Grand Rapids, 1964–76)

TLZ	*Theologische Literatur Zeitung*
TPIII	*The Inscriptions of Tiglath-pileser III, King of Assyria*, H. Tadmor (Jerusalem, 1994)
TRev	*Theologische Revue*
TRu	*Theologische Rundschau*
TS	*Theological Studies*
TSSI	*Textbook of the Syrian Semitic Inscriptions*, C. L. Gibson (Oxford, 1971)
TU	Texte und Untersuchungen
TUAT	Texte aus der Umwelt des Alten Testaments
VT	*Vetus Testamentum*
VTSup	Vetus Testamentum Supplements
WMANT	Wissenschaftliche Monographien zum Alten und Neuen Testament
WUNT	Wissenschaftliche Untersuchungen zum Neuen Testament
ZAW	*Zeitschrift für die alttestamentliche Wissenschaft*
ZNW	*Zeitschrift für die neutestamentliche Wissenschaft*
ZPE	*Zeitschrift für Papyrologie und Epigraphik*

INTRODUCTION

———— •◆• ————

John Barton

To the religious believer, the Bible is a 'fountain and well of truth' (Cranmer 1908; cf. Muddiman 1983). To the literary critic, it is an immense cultural artefact that 'sit[s] there inscrutably in the middle of our cultural heritage . . . frustrating all our efforts to walk around it' (Northrop Frye 1982: xviii). To both it is essentially a monolith: a single book consisting of many thousands of words between two covers, all in a similar style, with consistent pagination and typeface.

However, to those who study it historically the Bible is not one thing, but many things. It is a library of books from, perhaps, a millennium of human history, deriving from two related but quite distinct faith systems, Judaism and Christianity. It invites the reader to walk around it, observing it from many sides and in many different perspectives. This book is an attempt to suggest what some of these perspectives might be.

First it is essential to have an overall grasp of the sweep of the biblical material, as currently organized into Old Testament (or Hebrew Bible), Apocrypha, and New Testament. For these three collections do have a certain coherence, and can be studied as subsets of the whole Scripture (see chapters 1–3). But we also need, secondly, to break them down into certain major genres: myths, historiographical texts, prophecies, Gospels, letters, and so on (see chapters 4–11).

Once this is done, questions arise that justify us in referring not simply to 'The Bible' but to 'The Biblical World'. Foremost among these is the process by which the biblical texts have been transmitted, as studied by the discipline known as textual criticism (chapters 12 and 13). But at once questions arise about parallel and related ancient texts, many of which were discovered in the late nineteenth and twentieth centuries – texts such as the Gnostic Gospels and the Dead Sea Scrolls (chapters 14–17). No one can study the Bible today without an awareness of this material. Nor can the contemporary task of interpreting the Bible be undertaken without knowing something of how it was interpreted in the past, by both Jews and Christians (chapters 18 and 19).

There was a time when the Bible was the only source for the history of the ancient world outside the 'classical' cultures of Greece and Rome. But modern discoveries, achieved principally through the work of archaeologists in the literal sense and of 'archaeologists' of the text – those who have analysed biblical tradition through various modern literary techniques – have yielded much more information than was available in earlier ages. Sometimes this serves only to show that we cannot trust the biblical record to guide us, but at other times it shows it to be the tip of an iceberg, at least some of whose underlying structures we can reconstruct. Chapters 20–6 outline what can be known at present about the cultural and political world in which the Bible came to be.

The institutions of ancient Israel and of the early Christian churches have come increasingly under scrutiny in the last few decades, partly through applying the techniques and questions of the social sciences to the biblical text. A section entitled 'Institutions' surveys some of these developments, together with the modern study of the languages (Hebrew, Aramaic and Greek) in which the texts are written.

Such study makes clear that the Bible cannot be studied merely as the product of certain principal characters, as a story of heroes and villains. Nevertheless modern study has thrown light on some of the central figures in biblical tradition, and these are surveyed in chapters 37–41. Abraham, Isaac and Jacob, together with their wives; Moses, David and Solomon; and Paul and Jesus: these are characters to whom biblical research returns again and again, sometimes with scepticism about the extent of our possible historical knowledge, sometimes in a surprisingly optimistic frame of mind.

The Bible is religious literature through and through, containing not everything written in Israel or within the early churches but only their theological literature. A complete guide to the religious ideas of the Bible would be a large book in itself, but the present volume offers a guide to a few of the more obvious concepts that the reader needs to know in order to make some sense of the text (chapters 42–6).

Finally there is a survey of how the Bible is seen and studied today, both in its theological and literary interpretation and through the many translations that proliferated particulary in the last century (chapters 47–9). Biblical translation is in many ways the stage on which interpretation is played out, and readers of this volume need to have a modern version of the Bible to accompany them as they read it.

BIBLIOGRAPHY

Cranmer, Thomas (1908) 'A Fruitful Exhortation to the Reading of Holy Scripture', *First Book of Homilies*. London: SPCK.

Muddiman, J. (1983) *The Bible, Fountain and Well of Truth*. Oxford: Basil Blackwell.

Northrop Frye, C. (1982) *The Great Code: The Bible and Literature*. London: Routledge & Kegan Paul.

PART I
THE BIBLE

CHAPTER ONE

THE OLD TESTAMENT/ HEBREW BIBLE

———·◆·———

Rex Mason

The fact that this article appears under a dual heading reveals that there has been disagreement about the title, the extent, and, to some degree, the function of the Old Testament. 'Old Testament' is a Christian name for the sacred writings of Judaism, writings already venerated and regarded as authoritative by the time of Jesus of Nazareth, a veneration continued by most early Christians and encouraged by the reported respect for them of Jesus himself. In spite of the objections of some that they had been superseded by the new revelation God had made of himself in Jesus, it became the firm conviction of the early church that they remained a valid and authoritative set of texts, a valued part of its Jewish heritage. Nevertheless, such veneration was often achieved by exegetical methods of reading the Old Testament books that saw them as in some way 'prophetic' of the coming of Jesus, a valuable, but preparatory, pointer to the 'New Testament', which God had established with both Jews and Gentiles through the life and work of Jesus 'the Christ' ('Messiah'). Christian ways of reading and understanding the 'Old Testament', at both consciously theological and popular levels, have therefore often differed markedly from Jewish understanding. For this reason many Christian scholars now tend to avoid the term and to speak and write more often of 'the Hebrew Scriptures'.

However, this raises the issue of the extent of just what it is we mean when we speak of the 'Old Testament'. We know remarkably little about the process of how certain writings came to be vested with 'canonical' status in either the Jewish or the Christian communities. It seems, however, that the first five books of the Old Testament, the 'Torah' (meaning 'law' or 'instruction'), were accepted as supremely authoritative in the post-exilic Jewish community by perhaps as early as the fourth century BCE, although such a view would have resulted from a cumulative appreciation and use of them developed over a long period. There is some evidence that the prophetic books, both 'former' and 'latter' prophets (see below), had established themselves as similarly authoritative by the end of the third century BCE (although 'Torah', then and later, was always regarded as *the* supremely important authority). The others, known as 'the Writings', including Psalms, the Wisdom literature and Daniel, because many of them were mainly of later date (at least in their present form) than the other collections, were regarded as more marginal. Nevertheless, as with all writings that achieve 'canonical' status, they must have been widely used and admired.

All these works which thus made up the Jewish 'Scriptures' by the beginning of the Common Era were written in Hebrew, except for a few excerpts in the 'Writings' (Ezra 4:8 – 6:18; 7:12–26; Daniel 2:4 – 7:28), which were in Aramaic. By this time, however, Hebrew had become mainly only the 'classical' language of the Scriptures. Most Jewish people in Palestine actually spoke Aramaic, which had become the vernacular language throughout the Assyrian, Babylonian and Persian empires, while many Jews living abroad, in such places as Egypt, spoke Greek, the vernacular language of the Greek and, to some extent, the Roman empires. A number of popular works therefore appeared in Greek, and many of these were included in a translation of the Hebrew Scriptures into Greek, a translation made in Egypt from about the third century BCE onwards, known as 'the Septuagint' (LXX). This was the form of the Hebrew Scriptures known mainly to the writers of the New Testament, and it is therefore no surprise that a number of those additional Greek works it contained, such as 'The Wisdom of Solomon' and 'Ecclesiasticus', achieved considerable popularity among Christian communities.

In course of time Judaism decided to accept only those works written in Hebrew as authoritative, but the Christian church, in spite of the objections of some, accepted also the works that existed only in Greek, sometimes known as 'the deutero-canonical books'. However, at the time of the Reformation, Protestants asserted their belief that only the Hebrew works were truly authoritative, and this has remained their position since, while the Roman Catholic Church still includes the Greek works. (The Orthodox Churches have always taken a similar view of the 'deutero-canonical' works, even including a few that do not figure in the Catholic canon.) Thus the term 'Old Testament' raises not only questions of the nature of the texts between Jews and Christians, but questions of content between different branches of the christian church. (For the books in the various 'canons', see the lists as the end of this chapter.) To call it 'the Hebrew Bible' is thus not entirely satisfactory, since, however defined, it is also part of the 'Christian' Bible. Perhaps, when referring more narrowly to 'the Hebrew Scriptures', the Jewish term TANAK is preferable. This is an acronym formed from the Hebrew names for the three main parts of the canon, Torah (law), N^{e}bi'im (prophets), and K^{e}thubim (writings).

Whatever title we give it, and whatever canon we accept, it is clear that the 'Old Testament' (the name used here for convenience) was a long time in reaching its present form. Few of the individual books that comprise it can be thought of as the work of a single author. Even where, as is probably the case with most of the prophetic books, an individual's thoughts and teaching lay behind it, the books that bear the name of those individuals have resulted from a long process of oral and written tradition, and have been subject to editing processes designed to make the 'message' of the prophet relevant to people of later times. The same may be said of many of the other books, even where tradition may, or may have not, have associated them with a specific historical figure. It is true of the Pentateuch (Torah), traditionally assigned to Moses, and the so-called history books. The Psalter, linked in tradition with David, contains many compositions from times later than his, while the Wisdom literature, again traditionally associated with Solomon, contains work from many hands continuing late into the post-exilic period.

While, therefore, the composition of the books of the Old Testament was a complex, continuing process stretching over centuries, modern biblical scholarship sees in general three main stages to its emergence. It is clear that Yahwism became the State religion of the pre-exilic kingdom of Judah, and a good deal of literature, while containing, as it did, much ancient material, was produced in the period of the monarchy to bolster claims for the divine origin and sanction of the royal house of David that ruled over it. In the manner of those days, the tie between the divine world and the royal house, which was thought to rule in the name of the gods and as their representative, was seen to be a very close one. Much in the Pentateuch, therefore, especially the so-called Yahwistic strand (see below), which, in spite of some contemporary scholarly disagreement, still seems most likely to have originated in the Judean court during the monarchic period, is designed to show how the emergence of the nation of Israel, under the leadership of the Davidic kings, was in the mind and purpose of God from the very earliest times. All is presented as the 'story' of Israel, a story that runs through the Pentateuch and continues in the books of Joshua and Judges. The climax to it all comes in the books of Samuel and the early chapters of Kings, which tell how God chose David and his line to rule over this people and made a covenant with him assuring him of the everlasting nature of the dynasty. This covenant was sealed with the building by Solomon of the temple of Jerusalem, the city David had captured, thus ensuring God's presence at the heart of the national life, a presence that guaranteed the eternal security, not only of the Davidic dynasty, but of the city of Jerusalem itself. Such a 'theology' of royal house and temple is also enshrined in a number of Psalms (e.g. 2, 21, 89, 110, 132), which no doubt had their liturgical origins in the worship of the temple. All of this is entirely in line with the way other nations at that time saw the status and security of their identity as a result of a pact between the gods and their royal representatives on earth. The actual historical process by which 'Israel' emerged as a national identity and came to occupy the area we now know as Palestine is shrouded in uncertainty. But the 'story' presented in this first level of the Old Testament Scriptures was the one by which self-understanding and self-confidence was established and expressed.

Such confidence came to be severely shaken, however, as this tiny nation was threatened by the expansionary aims of powerful neighbours, in particular first from the Assyrians in the eighth century, and then from the Babylonians in the seventh and sixth centuries BCE. Under the latter, Jerusalem was destroyed, the royal Davidic line removed and many society leaders deported into exile. It is remarkable that such a shattering of the whole royal ideology did not mark the end of Yahwism as a living religion. That it did not is due in part to those who put a much heavier emphasis on the ethical implications of Yahwism, already a strong feature of the 'covenant' obligations by which Israel was seen to be bound to Yahweh as his 'special' people, than on its political ramifications. Foremost among these were the prophets who, in the name of the very Yahwism by which the rulers claimed their power and vested interests, challenged them with its obligations of justice and compassion. From Amos in the eighth century BCE onwards, there was a strong prophetic challenge to what were seen as abuses of power.

Such prophetic voices claimed that God had given power to kings, priests and other leaders in the community, in order to establish a society in which the rights and interests of the poor and weakest members were safeguarded. Such prophetic complaints were taken up by those scholars referred to as 'the Deuteronomists', so called because they not only produced our book of Deuteronomy, but also edited the 'history' books and some of the prophetic books from their own particular theological stance and in their own distinctive language. They stressed that the 'covenant' relationship between God and Israel, and between God and the royal house of David, had always been *conditional* upon their keeping the terms of the ethical laws of the covenant. Further, they believed that that same covenant demanded of king and people the worship of Yahweh *alone*, and they strongly attacked every form of what they saw as syncretism, that is, the worship of both Yahweh and other gods. In their hands this became a powerful tool with which to criticize the foreign policy of many kings who sought military and political alliances with other nations, alliances that presumably, at least in their eyes, involved acknowledgement of those nations' tutelary deities. Thus they were able to explain why the apparent breaking of God's promise to David and the nation was not due to either the fickleness or the powerlessness of Yahweh. The religious and moral conditions of the covenant had been broken. That is why God allowed this disaster to come upon the nation. It was judgement on them for sin. The same belief, however, enabled them to hold out hope for the future. If only the nation would return to the conditions of the covenant, then they might hope, in the grace of God, to experience again its blessings. This is the message that has informed the Deuteronomistic editing of the 'historical' and prophetic books of the Old Testament, much of the book of Deuteronomy and some prophetic books like Jeremiah. These 'Deuteronomists', then, strongly influenced by much pre-exilic prophecy, are the ones responsible for this second stage of the development of the Old Testament.

The third stage is that which followed the exile and the partial restoration of the community in Jerusalem and Judah under the Persians. In spite of early hopes there was no restoration of the Davidic monarchy, and Judah was now a subservient part of the Persian empire. What did Yahwism mean now that it was no longer the religion of a nation state? This was the time when priests came more and more to the fore in the conduct of the community's life and, with the rebuilding of the temple, they established what may best be described as a 'theocracy'. It was the people's status as a people of God that mattered now above all else, and this status was more and more defined in obedience to the law and the proper observance of the worship of God in the temple. Here, through the correct observance of the sacrifices and religious festivals, God dealt with the sins of his people and so maintained that vital level of communication between deity and people by which they could experience his grace and know his presence. This outlook prevails in all those long sections of the Pentateuch that deal in great detail with the various sacrifices and correct forms and observances of the temple worship, sections making up what scholars call 'the Priestly Code' (see below), and it also finds expression in the final form of the book of Ezekiel, the post-exilic prophets and in the books of Chronicles, Ezra and Nehemiah. This 'third' stage of the emergence of the Old Testament Scriptures thus represented a brave attempt to redefine Yahwism and make it a living force and reality for the post-exilic community. It was the need to keep their life and identity distinctive that, no doubt, led to as great an emphasis on laws of ritual cleanliness and observance as on those that relate to what we would call 'moral' or 'ethical' matters, thus presenting a strange contrast to the pre-exilic prophets who emphasized the far greater importance of the latter.

Included in this 'third' stage of development have to be those Wisdom writings (Job, Ecclesiastes, Wisdom) that wrestled more and more with the problems of suffering and injustice in human affairs; stories that urged people living under foreign rule to keep the faith (e.g. Esther, Tobit); and books that express more far-reaching 'apocalyptic' hopes for a time when God would intervene once again drastically to deliver his people (e.g. Daniel). Yet, as we have seen, all the works of the Old Testament, even those that had their origin before the exile, bear evidence of all three stages in the final edited form in which we now have them.

To turn in more detail to the various components of the Old Testament 'canon' it is natural to begin with Torah. This section of the canon comprises five books, Genesis, Exodus, Leviticus, Numbers and Deuteronomy. They include some generally identifiable broad sections. Genesis 1–11, often referred to as 'the Primeval History', tells of the creation of the world and of humankind, the threat to that creation through the sin of human beings that brings the judgement of the flood, the salvation of Noah and his family and enough animals to restart creation, yet of persistent sin symbolized by the building of the tower of Babel with the resultant division of languages between nations. These chapters draw on myths and traditional material that in some form or other were widely known in the ancient Near East. Yet they are told from a distinctive theological slant and, with the inclusion of the genealogies that trace the descent of Abraham from Adam, they aim to show that Israel has been in the mind and purpose of the Creator from the first.

Genesis 12–50 narrates the stories of the patriarchs beginning with the migration of Abraham from Ur at the command of God. They draw on a large range of saga-like and related material, much of which originally related to quite distinctive clan groupings, centred on various local shrines, but which have now been brought together by portraying Abraham, Isaac and Jacob as all members of one family. They thus stress the 'all-Israel' theme so important at the time of the monarchy and at later periods of Israel's history, while, by showing that God has promised the land of Canaan to the descendants of these patriarchs, they establish Israel's title deeds to the land. The Joseph narrative links the patriarchal stories to the account of Israel's slavery in Egypt and the delivery from that bondage by the redemptive act of God, an act that became the foundation stone of the covenant of faith of later Israel. This is told in Exodus 1–18, and then follows the account of the foundation of the covenant between God and Israel at Mount Sinai. The legal obligations of that covenant are stressed in two law codes, the Decalogue (Exod. 20:1–17) and the 'Book of the Covenant' (Exod. 21–23). There follow detailed instructions to Moses concerning the making of a 'tabernacle' (clearly based on the later temple in Jerusalem), the institution of the Aaronic priesthood and the major sacrifices and festivals of Israel's religious calendar. These are continued in even greater detail in Leviticus and Numbers where liturgical matters are interspersed with the story of Israel's forty years of 'wandering in the wilderness', a period of delay that was seen as judgement for the unfaithfulness of the people. This contains another law code, dealing with both ritual and ethical matters, known as 'the Code of Holiness' (Lev. 17–26).

Deuteronomy is presented as a series of sermons by Moses spoken as the people stand at last on the threshold of the promised land of Canaan, recalling God's past mercies and urging them to renewed obedience to the covenant in the terms of a new law code, found in Deuteronomy 12–26. The book ends with the death of Moses following his commission to Joshua to lead the people into the land he had seen but not entered.

On the face of it all this might seem to be a seamless garment of woven narrative, but inner tensions and contradictions, variations in terminology and theological outlook, and other characteristics have long since led scholars to believe that it is a complex amalgam of material from many different ages. In general many have detected four major strands of tradition within it. The first is the 'Yahwistic Source' (J), so called because it assumes that God was known by the name Yahweh from the first (Gen. 4:26). It represents mainly a southern, Judean outlook and is concerned to authenticate the rule of the Davidic dynasty and so dates from some time in the monarchic period. A second narrative intertwines with it from Genesis 15 onwards, called the 'Elohistic Source' (E), which believes the name Yahweh was first revealed only to Moses (Exod. 3:13–15). This seems to show greater interest in the northern kingdom of Israel and expresses something of the outlook of the eighth-century prophetic movement. Deuteronomy (D), with its distinctive style, vocabulary and theological emphases, contains a law code so closely followed in the account of King Josiah's religious reforms in the seventh century, especially in its insistence that legitimate worship could only be carried out in the one central sanctuary of Jerusalem (2 Kings 22:8 – 23:25), that it is felt this must have been the law book that was 'found' in the temple, which inspired those reforms. 'D' therefore is to be dated in the seventh century. The final source is known as the 'Priestly Code' (P) comprising narratives and legal sections that deal with matters relating to the cult. This seems to reflect the interest of the priests whose task was to reconstruct the theocracy after the rebuilding of the temple following the exile and so must itself be post-exilic in date. All this is still a matter of keen scholarly debate and disagreement but may be said to represent something of a broad 'consensus'. The fact that the Pentateuch reads as it does, however, is due in no small degree to the skill and theological convictions of its final redactors (editors) and certainly those who insist that we must take seriously the final form of the Torah, and not merely analyse it into its consituent elements, have a strong case to argue.

The prophetic section of the canon falls into two parts, 'Former' and 'Latter' prophets. At first glance it may appear strange that what we might call the 'history books' (Joshua, Judges, Samuel, Kings) are designated as 'prophets' of any kind. They cover a vast range, from the account of the conquest of Canaan under Joshua, its distribution among the tribes of Israel, the period of the Judges, the introduction of monarchy, the division of the kingdom after the death of Solomon, and the fortunes of the two kingdoms until the fall of northern Israel to Assyria in the eighth century and the fall of Judah to the Babylonians in 586 BCE. They draw also on a wide range of source material, some of it named, some of it to be deduced from the form the history takes. But the whole has been edited by the 'Deuteronomists' with the aim of showing why it was that these disasters befell the people of God who had been promised the protection of Yahweh. To that extent the work is a kind of 'preaching', accounting for the disaster and pointing their contemporaries in the exilic period to the path of penitence by which they might know a deliverance again as, so often, their fathers had done in the past. It is this 'message' that makes the place of these books in the 'prophetic' section apposite.

While 'prophecy' in many forms was a phenomenon widely known throughout the ancient Near East, only Israel has produced such a remarkable corpus of written 'prophetic' literature as that found in the 'Latter Prophets'. While many prophets served the courts and temples that employed them in order to secure the divine favour and warn of conduct that might lead to divine disfavour, only Israel appears to have seen the emergence of individual prophets, by no means all of them in any apparent 'official' position, who so fiercely criticized the conduct of king, priests, court prophets and the rich and powerful in society, threatening them in the name of God with dire consequences for their sin. From the time of Amos in the north in the eighth century onwards a succession of such prophets followed (including Hosea in the north, Micah, Isaiah and Jeremiah in the south) with very similar messages. Presumably they spoke most of their oracles (only a very few instances are given of prophets writing their words), and these were remembered by groups of followers and, as time went on, committed to writing. The reason that some were so immortalized while others, whom they often condemned as 'false' prophets, were not, was probably not a little due to the fact that their words appeared to have been proved true when the disasters they had threatened actually happened.

It is clear that all the prophetic books underwent a long process of editing and development as oracles were arranged in ways that the editors found appropriate and were given fresh interpretation to adapt them to the needs of later situations. The result is a unique collection of three major books, Isaiah, Jeremiah and Ezekiel, together with a collection of twelve 'minor' prophets (so called because they were much shorter) known as 'The Book of the Twelve'. It is interesting that, after the exile, while prophecy seems to have known a brief period of revival (Haggai, Zechariah, Malachi), it faded away to be replaced, later, by more 'apocalyptic' writings. The reasons for this are doubtless complex but the very process of writing may have helped to 'fix' the prophetic corpus and accelerate its acceptance as having 'canonical' authority, an authority that would have discouraged the emergence of 'new' prophecy. To be accepted, later works had to be issued under the 'pseudonym' of some great authority from the past.

The 'Writings' cover a wide range of literary genres. The Psalms express the language of worship and include compositions that must have formed part of the liturgy in the royal temple in pre-exilic times. As the collection stands, however, it also obviously includes later psalms that lament the disasters of the exile and also reflect post-exilic 'Torah' piety. At this time psalms that obviously referred to the pre-exilic Davidic king (e.g. 2, 21, 45, 89, 110, 132) must have been given an eschatological interpretation, or 'democratized' by finding the fulfilment of their promises in the emergence of the post-exilic theocratic community (cf. Isa. 55:3–5), a situation helped by the fact that traditionally their composition was associated with David. The collection has been arranged in five 'books', possibly on analogy with the five books of the Torah and, in its present form, represents the hymn-book of the post-exilic 'second' temple.

The 'Wisdom' books also represent post-exilic developments. The collections of proverbial sayings and proverbs to be found in Proverbs 10–31 include many that date back to early times and that doubtless had their origin in clan life, in court 'instruction' and in temple circles. There are many parallels to such collections in the ancient Near East. In Proverbs 1–9, however, there is to be found a more 'theological' investigation into the nature and authority of 'Wisdom', in which Wisdom is thought of as a distinct 'being', a female figure, created by God from before the beginning of the world, and destined by him to bring illumination to human beings. Several factors may be at work here. Again, we may see foreign influences being adapted to the special needs of Israel since Ma'at was the Egyptian goddess of wisdom who plays a similar role in the Egyptian wisdom literature. A growing sense that there is only one God, Yahweh (as opposed to the view that Yahweh is the only god, among others, with whom Israel has to do), probably led to the idea of intermediaries between a transcendent God and his created world. Again, the wisdom thinkers were probably speculating on the revelation God makes of himself in the world of creation, the world of human observation and experience, in addition to the 'supernatural' revelation celebrated in his great saving deeds in history and the divinely given prophetic word. Divine authority is being claimed for the teaching of the wise in the idea that this has itself been revealed by the divinely begotten figure of Wisdom. In fact, in the book of Ecclesiasticus, otherwise known as 'The Wisdom of ben Sirach' (c. 190 BCE), 'Torah' and 'Wisdom' are equated (24:23). To a growing conviction that there is only one God can also be traced Wisdom's preoccupation with questions of theodicy as found in the books of Job and Ecclesiastes (Qoheleth). How can evil exist in a world that has been made by the one good God? The same theological concern also begins to give rise to a kind of modified dualism that attributes evil in God's world to malevolent supernatural powers (see 1 Chron. 21:1; cf. 2 Sam. 24:1; Dan. 10:14).

In addition to liturgical and wisdom material the Writings contain 'historical' compositions in the books of Chronicles, Ezra and Nehemiah. Chronicles, using the books of Samuel and Kings, and possibly other historical records, as source material, reconstructs the development of Israel before the exile in such a way as to show that the post-exilic theocratic community is the true 'heir' to the promises of God, the true 'Israel'. The book of Nehemiah recounts the rebuilding of the walls of Jerusalem by Nehemiah. Ezra, like a post-exilic Moses, brings the law with him to Jerusalem and instigates a renewed 'covenant' between the people and God, thus sealing the authentic line of continuity between pre- and post-exilic 'Israel'. The genre is further represented by the books of Maccabees, which tell the story of the struggles within Judaism in the time of the Greek empire, works that again express a very clear religious and political agenda.

Popular stories of individuals also figure in the Writings, with such stories as Ruth, Esther, Judith, Tobit and of Susanna (in an addition to the book of Daniel, itself an 'apocalyptic'-type representative of 'prophecy' in the Writings whose late date meant it was not included in the already established canon of 'Prophecy'). Such stories are always popular and were mostly designed to encourage faithfulness to Torah in the often adverse and difficult circumstances in which the faithful found themselves under foreign control at home or living in an alien cultural and religious environment abroad.

The Hebrew Bible   *The Greek Bible*

Torah   **Historical Books**   **Prophetic Books**
Genesis   Genesis   Twelve Minor Prophets
Exodus   Exodus   Hosea
Leviticus   Leviticus   Amos
Numbers   Numbers   Micah
Deuteronomy   Deuteronomy   Joel
                         Joshua   Obadiah
'Former' Prophets   Judges   Jonah
Joshua   Ruth   Nahum
Judges   1 Samuel   Habakkuk
Samuel   2 Samuel   Zephaniah
Kings   1 Kings   Haggai
                         2 Kings   Zechariah
'Latter' Prophets   1 Chronicles   Malachi
Isaiah   2 Chronicles   Isaiah
Jeremiah   *1 Esdras*   Jeremiah
Ezekiel   Ezra   *Baruch 1–5*
The Twelve   Nehemiah   Lamentations
  Hosea   Esther (*with*   *Letter of Jeremiah*
  Joel   *additions*)   *(= Baruch 6)*
  Amos   *Judith*   Ezekiel
  Obadiah   *Tobit*   *Susanna*
  Jonah   *1 Maccabees*   *(= Daniel 13)*
  Micah   *2 Maccabees*   Daniel 1–12
  Nahum   *3 Maccabees*   (with additions of
  Habakkuk   *4 Maccabees*   *Song of Azariah*
  Zephaniah   and *Song of the Three Jews*)
  Haggai   **Didactic Books**   *Bel* and *The Dragon*
  Zechariah   Psalms   *(= Daniel 14)*
  Malachi   Proverbs
                         Ecclesiastes
Writings   Song of Songs
Psalms   Job
Job   *Wisdom of Solmon*
Proverbs   *Ecclesiasticus*
Ruth
Song of Songs
Ecclesiastes
Lamentations
Esther
Daniel
Ezra–Nehemiah
Chronicles

Books additional to the Hebrew Bible are in italics.

Books are given the names familiar to English readers. Samuel and Kings in the Greek Bible are called 'The Four Books of the Kingdoms' and Ezra–Nehemiah is '2 Esdras'.

Figure 1.1   Books of the Hebrew and Greek Bibles in their canonical order.

If, finally, we ask about the enduring value of the Old Testament, the signals are mixed. It has to be admitted that there is a good deal of national and political chauvinism expressed in it, and the idea of the warrior God who fights in the interests of one people and one political system and urges the destruction of their enemies, widespread as such views were in the ancient Near East, can seem only ethically and religiously repugnant now. Nevertheless, the Old Testament also contains the views of those who came to see that Yahweh, as the only God, was also concerned for all peoples, and that his purpose was to establish justice and righteousness for all. Prophets, law-givers and others affirmed that the 'enemies' of such a God were not just, conveniently, the enemies of a particular state or dynasty, but all who failed to act in compassion for the poor and underprivileged. They warned that God would not let human opposition thwart his purposes for justice on the earth, even when those who opposed him claimed to bear his name and stand in a specially favoured relationship with him. In place of crude (and hopelessly unrealistic) earlier dreams of world domination in the name of Yahweh, at least some in Israel came to see their place among the nations as being bearers of the revelation of God's name and nature. It is very largely because the sacred Scriptures of the Old Testament express such ethical and religious insights that this is in fact what happened, and the Old Testament has fathered three of the world's major monotheistic religions: Judaism, Christianity and Islam.

For Christians the Old Testament has to occupy a special place as the Bible of Jesus and all the writers of the New Testament. This means, at the least, that its language, imagery and religious ideas, as well as having much intrinsic value of their own, form an indispensable key for unlocking the meaning of the New Testament itself. Neglect of the Old Testament in worship, in the pulpit and lecture room, inevitably brings a diminution in understanding and appreciation of the New Testament and the story of the Christian church itself.

BIBLIOGRAPHY

Barr, J. (1999) *The Concept of Biblical Theology: An Old Testament Perspective*. London: SCM Press.

Barton, J. (1996) *Reading the Old Testament: Method in Biblical Study*, rev. edn. London: Darton, Longman & Todd/Louisville, KY: Westminster John Knox Press.

—— (1997) *Making the Christian Bible*. London: Darton, Longman & Todd.

—— (1997) *The Spirit and the Letter: Studies in the Biblical Canon*. London: SPCK.

Blenkinsopp, J. (1996) *A History of Prophecy in Israel from the Settlement in the Land to the Hellenistic Period*, rev. edn. Louisville, KY: Westminster John Knox Press.

Brueggemann, W. (1997) *Theology of the Old Testament: Testimony, Dispute, Advocacy*. Minneapolis, MN: Fortress Press.

Coogan, M. (1998) *The Oxford History of the Biblical World*. Oxford: Oxford University Press.

Crenshaw, J. (1981) *Old Testament Wisdom: An Introduction*. Atlanta, GA: John Knox Press.

Gillingham, S. (1994) *The Poems and Psalms of the Hebrew Bible*. Oxford: Oxford University Press.

Noth, M. (1966) *The Laws in the Pentateuch and Other Essays*. Edinburgh: Oliver & Boyd.

Theissen, G. (1984) *Biblical Faith: An Evolutionary Perspective*. London: SCM Press.

CHAPTER TWO

THE APOCRYPHA

——— ·◆· ———

Adele Reinhartz

INTRODUCTION

The term 'apocrypha' stems from the Greek, meaning 'hidden away.' Within the
context of the biblical canon, however, the term refers to a set of Jewish texts
from the second-temple period (second century BCE to first century CE) whose canonicity
is disputed. These texts are not to be found in the Hebrew scriptures – the
Tanakh[1] – nor are they generally included in Protestant Bibles, but they are present
in Bibles intended for use in Roman Catholic, Orthodox Christian, and, increasingly,
in academic settings. Furthermore, the specific list of apocryphal works itself
varies. The books of Tobit, Judith, Additions to Esther, Wisdom of Solomon,
Ecclesiasticus (Wisdom of Jesus Son of Sirach), Baruch, Letter of Jeremiah, Additions
to Daniel (Prayer of Azariah and the Song of the Three Young Jews, Susanna, Bel
and The Dragon), 1 and 2 Maccabees are included in all listings. Greek and Slavonic
Orthodox Bibles add the Prayer of Manasseh, Psalm 151, 1 Esdras (called 2 Esdras
in the Slavonic canon), and 3 Maccabees. The Greek Orthodox canon includes 4
Maccabees in an appendix; Slavonic Orthodox Bibles include 3 Esdras, often known
as 4 Ezra according to its designation in the Vulgate. Hence those who considered
the texts canonical considered them to have been hidden or withdrawn from common
use because they contained mysteries too profound for the general reader to comprehend.
This understanding is hinted at in 2 Esdras (4 Ezra) 14:45–6, in which God
tells Ezra to 'make public the twenty-four books [of the canonical Hebrew scriptures]
that you wrote first, and let the worthy and the unworthy read them; but
keep the seventy that were written last, in order to give them to the wise among
your people.'[2] Those who abhorred the Apocrypha, on the other hand, believed that
they should be hidden away as heretical or spurious texts (Metzger 1957: 5).

In our own day, general readers of the Bible might well add a third meaning to
'apocrypha,' as texts tucked into the space between the Old Testament and New
Testament portions of their Bibles, which, unlike Genesis and historical Jesus questions,
rarely see the light of public discussion and are apparently too esoteric for any
but the most dedicated scholar. This chapter is intended to dispel such notions by
providing a general introduction to the admittedly complex history of the Apocrypha
as a collection, to the individual books therein, and to some of their major themes
and ideas.

THE APOCRYPHA AS A COLLECTION

With the exception of 2 Esdras (4 Ezra), the apocryphal books are present in the Septuagint, the Greek translation of the Hebrew Bible that was used widely in diaspora Greek-speaking Jewish communities in the second-temple period. The scant references to apocryphal books in rabbinic sources suggest that there was a period during which the canonicity of at least the Wisdom of Ben Sira was debated in Jewish circles. Ultimately, none was admitted to the canon, due in part perhaps to awareness of their late date *vis-à-vis* most biblical books (De Lange 1978: 9). Because the Septuagint itself fell out of Jewish usage in the early centuries of the common era, the Apocrypha, though the product of second-temple Judaism, were read, preserved, and transmitted by Christians. Yet from the beginning of the process of canonization of Christian scripture, these texts were the subject of controversy, in large measure because of the discrepancies between the Hebrew Bible, from which these texts were absent, and the Septuagint, in which they are scattered among the books whose canonicity was not disputed.

The apocryphal texts are quoted by the church fathers as authoritative scripture, particularly by those who did not know Hebrew and relied on the Septuagint alone. In preparing the Vulgate, however, Jerome distinguished between biblical texts that could be used as a basis for establishing doctrine, and apocryphal texts that are edifying but not decisive from a doctrinal perspective (Metzger 1957: 179–80). In the Old Testament section Jerome called the reader's attention to the apocryphal additions to the books of Esther and Daniel by means of prefaces, and included translations of Tobit and Judith. Later Latin-speaking Christians added translations of the other books that had been current in Latin before Jerome's time. Other texts, namely, the Prayer of Manasseh, 1 Esdras and 2 Esdras, were included as an appendix. Copyists often omitted Jerome's prefaces, however, and hence blurred the lines between the canonical and apocryphal material. Later editions of the Vulgate incorporated the Apocrypha, probably using the Old Latin version, within the sequence of the Old Testament, but continued to relegate the Prayer of Manasseh and 1 and 2 Esdras to an appendix. Hence for readers of the Vulgate, there was little to distinguish most of the Apocrypha from the undisputed biblical books.

Protestant and Catholic viewpoints on the canonicity of the Apocrypha were entangled in the polemics between these two groups. In the sixteenth century Luther and the early Protestants rejected the canonicity of the Apocrypha, because they had been used by the Catholic Church to support views such as apocalypticism (2 Esdras), purgatory (2 Maccabees 12:43–5) or works' righteousness (Tobit). The Roman Catholic Church, at the Council of Trent (April 8, 1546), in turn pronounced an anathema upon anyone who did not accept the apocryphal books (with the exception of the Prayer of Manasseh and 1 and 2 Esdras) as sacred and canonical (Metzger 1957: 189). To this day these texts are considered 'deuterocanonical,' inspired, though later in date than other books of the Old Testament. The Orthodox Churches were also divided in their stance towards these texts. Some leaders of Eastern Orthodoxy emphasized the distinction between the canonical and apocryphal books while others placed the latter on a level with the former (Metzger 1957: 193). These variations in the status of the Apocrypha are apparent in the array of Christian Bibles in any bookstore. Depending upon their sponsorship and intended audience, Bibles may or may not contain the Apocrypha, may relegate them to a separate section between the Old and New Testament (e.g., New Revised Standard Version) or include some of them within the sequence of Old Testament books (e.g., Jerusalem Bible).

Despite their marginal and disputed place in the canon, the Apocrypha have exercised a strong hold on the cultural imagination, as the subject of numerous paintings, dramas, poems, and novels (cf. Metzger 1957: 205–38). They have even had an impact on the history of the western world. Apparently Ferdinand and Isabella of Spain were persuaded to finance Christopher Columbus's voyage of 1492 after he cited 2 Esdras (4 Ezra) 6:42. On the basis of this passage, which indicates six-sevenths of the oceanic waters were dried up by God to create land, Columbus argued that the ocean between the west coast of Europe and the east coast of Asia could be no great width and might be navigated in a few days with a fair wind (Metzger 1957: 232–4).

THE BOOKS OF THE APOCRYPHA

The headings employed below pertain primarily to literary genres. These categories are not watertight, however. In many cases, the literary and theological features of the text bear their strongest similarities not to other texts within this collection but to biblical, pseudepigraphical, or Greco-Roman texts.

Historical writings

These books are written in a historiographic style modeled after the historical biblical books such as Chronicles, Ezra, and Nehemiah. They are often used – with caution – as historical sources for specific events in the second-temple period.

1 Esdras reproduces the substance of 2 Chronicles 35:1 – 36:23, Ezra, and Nehemiah 7:38 – 8:12, with some variation in detail, order, and content. Its purpose is unclear, though it may reflect the rivalry between the Jerusalem temple and its rivals, namely, the Oniad temple at Leontopolis in Egypt and the Tobiad temple at 'Araq-e-Amir in Transjordan (Attridge 1984: 160). 1 Esdras is independent of the Septuagint translation of Ezra–Nehemiah and was used by the first-century Jewish historian Josephus as his source for the events that it covers. Its latest possible date is therefore the mid-first century CE. Its close parallels to the book of Daniel (e.g., 1 Esdras 4:40 = Daniel 2:37) suggest a date after 165 BCE, the date generally assigned to Daniel. Its provenance is uncertain.

1 Maccabees is a brief account of the Hellenistic period, from the Alexandrian conquest to the reign of John Hyrcanus I. It is extant in Greek and Latin translations of the original Hebrew and is likely of Palestinian Jewish provenance. It dates from shortly after the death of John Hyrcanus (1 Maccabees 16:23–4), who was the High Priest in the Hasmonean state between 134 and 104 BCE, though chapters 14–16 may be an addition written after 70 CE. It is often used as a historical source for the causes, events, and aftermath of the Maccabean revolt, with some allowances made for its decidedly pro-Hasmonean perspective (cf. 5:55–62; 14:27–45; 7:8; 1:11).

2 Maccabees is an epitome or abridgment of a five-volume history written by Jason of Cyrene (2:23–8), which covers the same period as 1 Maccabees 1:10 – 78:50, namely, the reigns of the High Priest Onias III and Seleucus IV to the defeat of Nicanor's army (180–61 BCE). Greek is the original language. The epitome idealizes the piety of Judas and provides a theological interpretation of history as well as a celebration of martyrdom. The earliest possible date for Jason's history is 110 BCE, after Nicanor's victory. The epitomator's statement in 15:37, that Jerusalem had remained in Jewish hands, dates the epitome to the period before 63 BCE, when Rome took over direct rule of Judea.

Despite its name, 3 Maccabees is not about the Maccabees, nor is it related to the other books named after them, though it may have been composed for an annual commemoration of the martyrs' deaths (Young 1998: 330). It describes three episodes in the relationship between the Jews and Ptolemy IV Philopator, king of Egypt from 221 to 204 BCE: an attempted assassination of Ptolemy foiled by an apostate Jew named Dositheus, an unsuccessful attempt by the king to enter the Jerusalem temple, and Ptolemy's persecution of Egyptian Jews. It has been used as a historical source, though strong legendary features raise doubts about its accuracy. It was written in Greek, in Alexandria between 30 BCE and 70 CE.

Moralistic narratives

Like modern novels, and the Greco-Roman novels of the Hellenistic period, these books were intended for entertainment as well as to convey a moralistic or didactic message (Wills 1995: 5).

Tobit tells of a pious man of the Diaspora, who becomes blind after providing proper burial for a fellow Jew. Believing that he will soon die, he sends his son Tobias, accompanied by 'Azariah' – the angel Raphael – to redeem a sum of money in a distant land. Tobias returns not only with the money, but with a remedy for his father's blindness and with a fitting bride named Sarah, having vanquished – with Raphael's help – the demon who had caused Sarah's seven previous bridegrooms to die in the marriage bed. The narrative employs well-known folk motifs such as the Grateful Dead Man, and the Monster in the Bridal Chamber (Wills 1995: 73; Zimmerman 1958: 6–12). Fragments found at Qumran, four in Aramaic and one in Hebrew, suggest a Hebrew or Aramaic original. Tobit is generally dated to the second century BCE, but the absence of references to the Torah and Prophets as collected works may imply an earlier date (Nickelsburg 1984: 45). The provenance may be Jerusalem, Antioch, or Alexandria.

Judith is a lengthy novella set during a dire, if fictional, military crisis facing the town of Bethulia at the hands of Nebuchadnezzar's Assyrian army and his general Holofernes.[3] Judith, a wealthy widow, saves Bethulia when she develops and successfully carries out a risky and gruesome plan for killing Holofernes. The book was probably written in Hebrew during the latter part of the second century BCE. It was transmitted in three slightly different Greek versions, two Latin versions, a Syriac version, and several later Hebrew recensions.

Greek Esther, like its Hebrew counterpart, tells of the Jewish queen to the Persian king Artaxerxes, who saves the Jewish people from a pogrom engineered by the

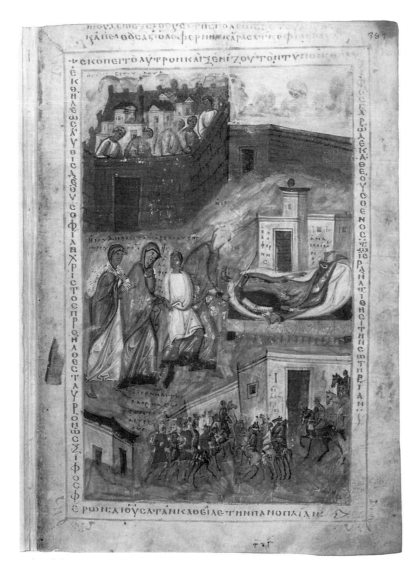

Figure 2.1   A miniature from the Bible of Patricius Leo in Rome, Codex Reg. Gr. 1, fol. 383, showing the decapitation of Holofernes (from the book of Judith). Copyright Biblioteca Apostolica Vaticana.

king's chamberlain Haman and thus institutes the festival of Purim. It differs from Hebrew Esther in two principal ways. First, it contains six additional sections, which add narrative content as well as amplify aspects of the Hebrew story, and, second, it adds approximately fifty references to God to the Hebrew story in which God is not mentioned in any explicit way. A colophon attributes the Greek text to one Lysimachus, an Alexandrian Jew who lived in Jerusalem, though opinions are divided as to the historicity of this attribution. Additions B and E, ostensibly the texts of

Figure 2.2 *Judith and her Maidservant.* Sandro Botticelli (1444–1510), Uffizi, Florence. Copyright Alinari/Art Resource, New York.

Persian edicts, were composed in Greek; the others may have had a Hebrew source. The latest possible date is the late first century CE, when the additions were used by Josephus in his paraphrase of the Esther story.

Susanna is one of three additions to the biblical book of Daniel. It focuses on the plight of a beautiful and pious woman married to a wealthy and influential man in Babylonia. One hot day Susanna is entrapped in her garden by two elders who offer her an unsavory ultimatum: either she lies with them or they report that she has had a rendezvous with a young man. She refuses, is accused, tried, and about to be

Figure 2.3 *Susanna and the Elders.* Jacob Jordaens, 1653. Photo Hans Petersen.
Copyright Statens Museum for Kunst, Copenhagen.

executed for adultery when she is saved by the young Daniel who exposes the duplicity of the elders. In the Septuagint and the Vulgate the story of Susanna follows the last chapter of Daniel and is numbered chapter 13. In Theodotion, Old Latin, Coptic and Arabic it is a prefix to the first chapter of Daniel or an insert before Daniel 2. The latest possible date is the Old Greek text of Daniel, early first century BCE. The original language was likely Greek.

Two other additions to Daniel, Bel and The Dragon, are stories that ridicule idolatry. In Bel, Daniel uncovers the artifice which made it appear that the idol Bel was consuming copious amounts of food and drink, thereby proving to Cyrus of Persia that Bel is a mere statue unworthy of worship. In The Dragon, Daniel proves that the revered dragon is mortal by feeding him a concoction of boiled pitch, fat, and hair and thereby causing the dragon to burst. As punishment, Daniel is thrown into the lion's den, where he survives a week with God's assistance. In Greek versions of Daniel these tales appear at the end of chapter 12; in the Vulgate they appear after Susanna, as chapter 14 of Daniel. Their date, provenance, and original language are uncertain.

Didactic

These wisdom texts have close analogues in the biblical wisdom texts of Proverbs, Ecclesiastes, and Job.

The Wisdom of Solomon is a wisdom text that professes to be written by King Solomon and touches on a range of topics including theology, Torah, observance, nature, history, and society. Internal evidence suggests that it was written in Greek, probably in Alexandria in the first century BCE, and draws on the language and theories of Stoicism, as well as traditional Jewish wisdom material.

The Wisdom of Ben Sira (Sirach), also referred to as Ecclesiasticus, deals extensively with a variety of issues pertaining to social and religious life. It is somewhat notorious for its derogatory statements about women (Eisenbaum 1998: 299). It was written in Jerusalem by a Jewish scribe named Joshua ben Sira in approximately 180 BCE, during the reign of the High Priest Simon II (cf. Sirach 50:1–24). The book was translated from Hebrew into Greek by Ben Sira's grandson in 132 BCE. Four fragmentary early medieval Hebrew manuscripts were found in Egypt at the end of the nineteenth century, and several other Hebrew fragments were found at Qumran.

Devotional/liturgical

The Prayer of Manasseh is a brief penitential prayer attributed to the wicked King Manasseh of Judah (cf. 2 Chronicles 33:11–13). It is dated to the last two centuries BCE and survives in Greek, Latin, Syriac, Armenian, and Ethiopic. The original language is uncertain.

The Prayer of Azariah and Song of the Three Young Jews are two short additions to Daniel that are inserted in the Vulgate between Daniel 3:23 and 24. They are attributed to Azariah and his two friends, Hananiah and Mishael, after they had been thrown into fiery furnace. The prayer echoes the national laments of the canonical psalms such as 74, 79, 80. These texts were probably composed in Hebrew in the second or first century BCE.

Others

The Letter of Jeremiah claims to have been sent by Jeremiah in 597 BCE to the Israelites about to be taken as captives to Babylon, to warn them against idolatry. The original language is probably Hebrew. It is dated to the early second century BCE, based on the manuscript found in Cave 7 at Qumran from 100 BCE. The provenance is uncertain, although familiarity with Babylonian religion implies Mesopotamia.

2 Esdras (4 Ezra), the sole example of apocalyptic literature in the Apocrypha, has its closest parallels in the pseudepigraphical Enoch literature. The main part of the text is a series of seven revelations in which the seer is instructed by the angel Uriel. The book has a complicated history of transmission. The author of chapters 3–14 was an unknown Palestinian Jew who probably wrote in Hebrew or Aramaic near the end of the first century CE, a dating based on the identification of the three

heads of the eagle in chapter 13 with the Flavian emperors. The Semitic original and almost all of the Greek translation have been lost and are known only from translations into Syriac, Coptic, Ethiopic, Arabic, Armenian, and Georgian and several Old Latin versions. 2 Esdras is not in the Septuagint; the Latin versions have two additional chapters before and two after, written later by unknown Christian authors.

Baruch purports to have been written during the Babylonian captivity by the companion and secretary of Jeremiah (Jeremiah 32:12; 36:4), as a confessional reading for feast days (1:14). In the Septuagint it is an appendix to the book of Jeremiah. Composite authorship has been suggested, due to variety in viewpoint, literary form, and language. The original language is Hebrew; the final redaction can be dated to the mid-second century BCE.

Psalm 151, attributed to David on the occasion of his conquest of Goliath, is extant in Hebrew, Greek, Latin, and Syriac. The psalm is found in the Hebrew scroll of biblical psalms from Qumran Cave 11 (11QPs^a) dating to the early first century CE.

4 Maccabees is an appendix in the Slavonic Orthodox canon and is present in some Septuagint manuscripts. The first, and shorter, part (1:1 – 3:18) is a discourse on the superiority of 'religious reason' over the emotions and the former's compatibility with Mosaic law. The second part, 3:19 – 18:24, illustrates these points by describing the torture and martyrdom of the elderly priest Eleazar, seven brothers, and their mother during the prelude to the Maccabean revolt. The source for this section is 2 Maccabees. The book was written in Greek, perhaps at Alexandria or Antioch, in the mid-first century to early second century CE.

MAJOR THEMES

The Apocrypha are important not only for the history of the canonization process but also, perhaps primarily, for insight into the concerns, beliefs, and traditions of second-temple Judaism. For this reason they provide a crucial link between biblical religion and the normative forms of Judaism and Christianity as they developed in the first centuries of the common era. We shall focus on four themes that illustrate this point: reflections on biblical events and figures, the understanding of the covenantal relationship between God and Israel, views of death and afterlife, and the issue of Jewish identity in a Hellenistic environment.

Biblical events and figures

Apocryphal books situate themselves explicitly *vis-à-vis* biblical events and figures in a number of ways. First, works such as the Letter of Jeremiah, Baruch, and the Additions to Daniel and Esther build on or add to biblical books. Second, some historical books, most notably 1 Esdras, retell portions of biblical history. Third, several books feature recitations of biblical history. Sirach 44–50 describes the achievements of the 'fathers', beginning with Enoch and concluding with a lengthy paean to Simon son of Onias, High Priest from 219 to 196 BCE, as the climax of this long line. Wisdom 10 and 11 summarizes primordial history to demonstrate that just as wisdom was the instrument through which God helped the righteous in the past (9:17), so too will she help those who cleave to her in the present. Achior, the leader of Ammonites who converts to Judaism at the conclusion of the book of Judith, recites a brief summary of Israelite history in order to convey to the general Holofernes that success or failure in battle against Bethulia will depend not so much on the prowess of his own troops as on the status of Israel's relationship with God (5:17–21).

Finally, specific individuals are singled out. In 2 Esdras (4 Ezra) 6:7–10 the patriarchs mark the division of the ages: 'From Abraham to Isaac, because from him were born Jacob and Esau, for Jacob's hand held Esau's heel from the beginning. Now Esau is the end of this age, and Jacob is the beginning of the age that follows.' More chillingly, Judith seeks to emulate Simeon (Genesis 34), who murderously avenged the rape of his sister Dinah (Judith 9:2). Judith also resembles Deborah (Judges 4:4) in her leadership role among the people of Bethulia (Judith 8:9–36), and Jael (Judges 4:17–22; 5:24–7) in using decapitation as the means by which she vanquishes the foe (Judith 13). These biblical figures are role models for personal action and for understanding Israel's covenantal relationship with God.

Covenantal relationship between God and Israel

As Achior explains to Holofernes, Israel's success or failure in the world is entirely determined by her status *vis-à-vis* God. If Israel sins, she is punished by God through a particular military power. This view is expressed in Azariah's lament 'We have sinned and broken your law . . . So all that you have brought upon us, and all that you have done to us, you have done by a true judgment. You have handed us over to our enemies, lawless and hateful rebels, and to an unjust king, the most wicked in all the world' (Prayer of Azariah 5–8). If Israel repents, however, she will be rescued from her enemies. In the words of Tobit to his son Tobias, 'God will again have mercy on them and God will bring them back . . . so now, my children, serve God faithfully and do what is pleasing in his sight' (Tobit 14:5, 9).

Death and resurrection

Personal sin and righteousness, punishment and reward, are discussed in terms of the individual's death and afterlife. The most pathetic example is Manasseh, who confesses to innumerable sins and implores the Lord for kindness, begging that he not be destroyed or condemned 'to the depths of the earth' (Prayer of Manasses 13). Specific beliefs concerning death and afterlife vary. According to Sirach 41:10–11, 'Whatever comes from earth returns to earth; so the ungodly go from curse to destruction . . . The human body is a fleeting thing, but a virtuous name will never be blotted out.' Wisdom of Solomon concurs: 'these mortals . . . made of earth . . . after a little while go to the earth from which all mortals are taken' (15:8). These sentiments echo the views of biblical wisdom texts (e.g., Ecclesiastes 9:1–6).

A more elaborate view is found in 2 Esdras (4 Ezra): 'When the decisive decree has gone out from the Most High that a person shall die, as the spirit leaves the body to return again to him who gave it, first of all it adores the glory of the Most

High. If it is one of those who have shown scorn and have not kept the way of the Most High . . . such spirits . . . shall immediately wander about in torments, always grieving and sad, in seven ways' (7:78–80). The righteous, on the other hand, while similarly separated from their mortal bodies, will see glory and have rest in seven orders, in which they will enjoy their immortality (7:88–96).

Most striking, however, are the numerous and explicit references to resurrection. Resurrection is not explicitly mentioned in the biblical corpus though it is used as a metaphor for the restoration of Israel (e.g., Ezekiel 37). Second Maccabees attributes belief in resurrection to the seven martyred brothers. The second brother, for example, declares that 'the King of the universe will raise us up to an everlasting renewal of life, because we have died for his laws' (2 Maccabees 7:9; cf. 7:14). The author of 2 Maccabees declares that Judas Maccabaeus also believed in the resurrection, as indicated by the collection of 2,000 drachmas of silver that he took up as a sin offering for the dead, 'For if he were not expecting that those who had fallen would rise again, it would have been superfluous and foolish to pray for the dead' (12:43–5).

Jewish identity in a Hellenistic world

The apocryphal texts demonstrate acute awareness of the Babylonian conquest, which left a sizeable Jewish population living outside the land of Israel. Tobit, for example, instructs his son Tobias to take his children to Media, for 'all of our kindred, inhabitants of the land of Israel, will be scattered and taken as captives from the good land; and the whole land of Israel will be desolate, even Samaria and Jerusalem will be desolate. And the temple of God in it will be burned to the ground and it will be desolate for a while' (14:3–4).

A major threat to the exiled community is idolatry. The Letter of Jeremiah warns the exiles in Babylonia 'To beware of becoming at all like the foreigners or of letting fear for these gods possess you when you see the multitude before and behind them worshipping them' (5–6). As in prophetic texts (e.g., Isaiah 48), idols and idolaters come in for critique and mockery. Wisdom 13:10, for example, describes idolaters as miserable beings with their hopes set on dead things, namely, 'the works of human hands, gold and silver fashioned with skill, and the likenesses of animals, or a useless stone, the work of an ancient hand.' Bel and The Dragon gleefully narrate the discrediting of these two pagan gods. In a different vein, the emphasis on prayer in the moralistic narratives (e.g., Judith 9; Esther Addition C), and on God's providential care for his people whether in the land or outside it may also be intended to deter idolatry (e.g., Wisdom 19:22).

Apocryphal texts provide concrete guidance for maintaining Jewish identity in these circumstances. Keeping the law is paramount. Ben Sira urges his readers, 'Do not be ashamed of the law of the Most High and his covenant (42:2; cf. Baruch 4:1). Wisdom is equated with Torah; the wise is the one who studies and observes Torah (Sirach 24:23; Wisdom 9:18; cf. Marcus 1966).

In their piety and knowledge of the Law, the heroes of the apocryphal narratives exemplify the ideal Jew (e.g., Susanna 3; Tobit 1:8). Esther (Addition C; 14:16) and Judith (10:5; 12:19) maintain the dietary laws under the most adverse circumstances.

Also important was the observance of holidays such as Purim (Greek Esther) and Hanukkah (2 Maccabees 2:16–19), which commemorate victories of Israel against foreign political, military and spiritual forces. Such victory sometimes required compromising laws such as Sabbath observance. As the Maccabean leader Mattathias noted, 'If we all do as our kindred have done and refuse to fight with the Gentiles for our lives and for our ordinances, they will quickly destroy us from the earth … Let us fight against anyone who comes to attack us on the Sabbath day; let us not all die as our kindred died in their hiding places' (1 Maccabees 2:40–1).

But it is the practice of endogamy that receives the greatest attention. In 1 Esdras 8:69–70, as in the late biblical books of Ezra and Nehemiah, Ezra laments that 'the holy race has been mixed with the alien peoples of the land.' Tobit emphatically instructs his son Tobias to 'marry a woman from among the descendants of your ancestors; do not marry a foreign woman, who is not of your father's tribe; for we are the descendants of the prophets' (4:12). Most poignant is Esther, who confides to God about her marriage to the Persian king Artaxerxes, 'You have knowledge of all things, and you know that I hate the splendour of the wicked and abhor the bed of the uncircumcised and of any alien' (Addition C; 14:15).

As the example of Esther illustrates, the apocryphal women are positive paradigms of diaspora Jewish behavior. From the moralistic narratives in particular we learn that the ideal diaspora Jew is learned, pious, observant of the Law, and, above all, married to a kinsman.[4] Not that apocryphal women are entirely benign in their relationships with men. True, the taint of adultery that Susanna brings to her household, and the fatal effects of marriage on Sarah's first seven bridegrooms (Tobit 3:8) were not the fault of these two women. On the other hand, Esther's actions quite intentionally led to the death of Haman and to a pogrom in which many non-Jews died (Esther 9:11–15) and Judith's decapitation of Holofernes was meticulously planned (Judith 8:32–4; 9:9–10). The danger that these women pose affects primarily the impious (in the case of Susanna) or the enemy, but not righteous members of their own communities. They therefore represent the ideal Israel, which vanquishes the enemy and fiercely protects its own unique identity in partnership with God.

CONCLUSION

The Apocrypha are fascinating not only for their role in the vagaries and controversies that surrounded the lengthy canonization processes within Jewish and Christian communities but also for the insight they provide into the travails, concerns, and beliefs of second-temple Jews as they considered their place in the culture, politics, and religious systems of the Hellenistic world. These texts both illustrate the development of biblical beliefs such as covenant and provide a backdrop against which the beliefs of Christians and Jews in the first centuries of the Common Era may be understood. Perhaps most interesting is the fact that in reflecting the reality of a sizeable Jewish Diaspora, these texts sound some contemporary notes concerning the ways and means of maintaining religious identity in the face of a dominant culture.

NOTES

1   *TaNaKh* is the Hebrew acronym that summarizes the three-part content of the Jewish canon: *Torah* (Pentateuch), *Neviim* (the prophets), and *Ketubim* (miscellaneous writings).

2   All quotations from the Bible and Apocrypha are taken from *The HarperCollins Study Bible: New Revised Standard Version*, Wayne A. Meeks (general ed.), New York: HarperCollins, 1993.

3   The reference to Nebuchadnezzar as the Assyrian emperor signals that Judith is not historiography but fiction (Wills 1995: 134).

4   According to the Septuagint, Esther, though married to Artaxerxes, may have been Mordecai's intended. The Septuagint describes Esther explicitly as Mordecai's wife (2:7), in contrast to the Masoretic Text, which states that he took her to be his daughter. Moore (1977: 186) argues that the Greek may be the translator's midreading of the Hebrew consonants (*bt*), which are the same for 'daughter' as for 'house' (Moore 1977: 186). Nevertheless, the Greek is suggestive of the need to associate Esther as closely as possible with Mordecai.

BIBLIOGRAPHY

Attridge, Harold (1984) 'Historiography,' in M. E. Stone (ed.) *Jewish Writings of the Second Temple Period*. Assen: Van Gorcum.

Bow, Beverly and Nickelsburg, George W. E. (1991) 'Patriarchy with a Twist: Men and Women in Tobit,' in Amy-Jill Levine (ed.) *'Women Like This': New Perspectives on Jewish Women in the Greco-Roman World*. Atlanta: Scholar Press.

Clines, David J. A. (1984) *The Esther Scroll: The Story of the Story*. Sheffield: JSOT Press.

De Lange, Nicholas (1978) *Apocrypha: Jewish Literature of the Hellenistic Age*. New York: Viking.

Eisenbaum, Pamela (1998) 'Sirach,' in Carol A. Newsom and Sharon H. Ringe (eds) *Women's Bible Commentary*, expanded edn. Louisville, Ky.: Westminster John Knox Press.

Marcus, Ralph (1966) *Law in the Apocrypha*. New York: AMS Press.

Metzger, Bruce M. (1957) *An Introduction to the Apocrypha*. New York: Oxford University Press.

Moore, Carey A. (1977) *Daniel, Esther and Jeremiah: The Additions*. Anchor Bible 44. New York: Doubleday.

Nickelsburg, George W. E. (1984) 'Stories of Biblical and Early Post-Biblical Times,' in Michael E. Stone (ed.) *Jewish Writings of the Second Temple Period: Apocrypha, Pseudepigrapha, Qumran Sectarian Writings, Philo, Josephus*. Assen: Van Gorcum.

Spolsky, Ellen (ed.) (1996) *The Judgment of Susanna: Authority and Witness*. Atlanta: Scholars Press.

VanderKam, James C. (ed.) (1992) *'No One Spoke Ill of Her': Essays on Judith*. Atlanta: Scholar Press.

Wills, Lawrence M. (1995) *The Jewish Novel in the Ancient World*. Ithaca: Cornell University Press.

Young, Robin Darling (1998) '4 Maccabees,' in Carol A. Newsom and Sharon H. Ringe (eds) *Women's Bible Commentary*, expanded edn. Louisville, Ky.: Westminster John Knox Press.

Zimmerman, Frank (1958) *The Book of Tobit*. New York: Harper & Brothers.

CHAPTER THREE

THE NEW TESTAMENT

——— ·◆· ———

Christopher Tuckett

The collection we call 'the New Testament' is something of a mixed bag. The New Testament today comprises 27 different texts that vary considerably in terms of their length, their scope, their aims, and their genre. It contains four 'gospels', giving narrative accounts of parts of the life and ministry of Jesus; there is one book (Acts) that presents a (somewhat selective!) account of the history of the early Christian church in its first 30 or so years. There are then a number of letters, many purporting to be by the apostle Paul, as well as others written under the name of other leading figures (e.g. Peter, James) or anonymously (e.g. Hebrews); and within the group of letters in the New Testament there is considerable variation in that some are genuine letters written to specific communities in specific situations (virtually all of Paul's own letters), whereas others are more like general treatises where the letter form seems to be more peripheral (e.g. James). The last book of the New Testament, Revelation, has the form of an 'apocalypse' comprising for the most part a great series of visions of the heavenly realm. The one thing all these writings have in common is that they all stem from a very early period in the history of the Christian movement. Indeed they do (by and large) represent the earliest Christian writings we possess, and they provide our prime sources for seeking to gain information about the start of the Christian movement and its 'founder', Jesus of Nazareth. Nevertheless (like almost every assertion in biblical studies today!) such a claim may need some qualification. How early is the 'early period' from which they come? And how broad is the period?

DATES

Almost all the New Testament documents can be confidently dated to the first century CE, with only the occasional exception such as 2 Peter, which may come from the second. However, it is also clear that they do not date from the *very* earliest period in the history of early Christianity.

The earliest New Testament writings are probably the letters of Paul. These were probably written during a period from c.48/49 until the mid-50s. The precise dating of each letter is of course debated. But clearly, the letters of Paul do not come from his earliest time as a Christian: Paul had been 'converted' to the Christian movement some 15 years or so before the time of the earliest letter we have from him (probably 1 Thessalonians). Thus Paul's letters let us see something of himself only as a Christian of some years' standing.

The dates of the other letters in the New Testament are much less certain. A number of letters purportedly written by Paul were probably written in his name by a later writer and hence stem from a later period after Paul's death (see below). Some of the more general letters (e.g. James, Hebrews), simply by virtue of the fact that they are so general, are notoriously difficult to date. In part, too, assigning a date to them is dependent on other decisions about their authorship. It is though very unlikely that any of these other letters are to be dated any earlier than Paul's letters, and they all come from a time no earlier than the second half of the first century.

The same probably applies in the case of the more overtly 'historical' books of the New Testament, that is, the gospels and Acts, which purport to give accounts of earlier historical events in the life of Jesus or in the life of the earliest Christian community. The earliest gospel is almost certainly the gospel of Mark, probably to be dated to around 70 CE. (There is dispute about whether Mark was written before or after the fall of the city of Jerusalem in 70 CE.) Further, Mark's gospel was probably one of the sources used by the writers of the gospels of Matthew and Luke: hence these two gospels must have been written after Mark, probably in the 80s (or perhaps 90s). John's gospel presents many peculiar difficulties of interpretation, not least of which is the fact that it is so different at almost every level from the other three (so-called 'synoptic') gospels. Again, most scholars today would date the gospel well into the last quarter of the first century, since it appears to presuppose some kind of formal, institutionalized split between the Christian community and the Jewish synagogues (cf. John 9.22; 16.2), which, as far as we can tell, did not take place until the mid-80s (or perhaps even later). Acts was written by Luke as a 'sequel' to his gospel, and hence probably also stems from the 80s at the earliest.

Thus all the 'historical' books of the New Testament are describing events that lie some 40 years or more in the past from the point of view of their authors at the time of writing. Some may be written 60–70 years after the events concerned. These texts, as mentioned earlier, are probably the earliest sources for the history concerned that we have available. But we must not lose sight of the fact that they are themselves not documents coming from the very earliest period itself. They are from a generation, or two generations, later. And this will inevitably at times colour our assessment of their value as historical sources for the events they describe.

AUTHORSHIP

Who wrote these books? Just as the documents themselves represent something of a mixed bag, so too their authors comprise a somewhat miscellaneous group. Indeed, we should probably go further and say that in a large number of instances we simply do not know who wrote these texts. For example, a striking feature of all four gospels is that they are anonymous. Unlike a large number of similar writings in the Graeco-Roman world, the Christian gospel writers never reveal their identity. (The sole exception may be John's gospel, where, in a note clearly added by someone other than the writer of the bulk of the gospel, it is said that the so-called 'beloved disciple' was the author of the gospel: see John 21.24. But this does not help very much since, notoriously, the 'beloved disciple' in John remains a tantalizingly unclear figure who is never explicitly named. In any case, most scholars today would regard with some scepticism the claim that a companion of Jesus wrote the whole of the fourth gospel, if only because it is so unlike the other gospels and seems to show no knowledge of key events in Jesus' life.)

We call the gospel writers Matthew, Mark, Luke and John by tradition, and these names are today always used to refer to these gospels. However, the traditional identification of them seems implausible. The author of the gospel of Mark is unlikely to have been the John Mark of Acts (as is probably implied by the naming of him as 'Mark' in the tradition) if only because he seems at times blissfully unaware of details of Palestinian geography and customs (see Mark 5.1, where Gerasa seems to be assumed to be near the Sea of Galilee, whereas it is in fact some 30 miles away; or Mark 10.11–12, where it seems to be assumed that Jewish women could divorce their husbands, whereas in fact they could not). The author of Matthew's gospel seems to have to rely on Mark for information and is thus unlikely to have been the Matthew who was one of Jesus' own closest companions. The author of Luke's gospel is almost certainly also the author of Acts; he *may* have been a companion of Paul (as the tradition claims), though there are formidable difficulties with such a view due to the great differences between the portrait of Paul that emerges from Acts and the picture of Paul we get from his own letters. The author of John's gospel is, as we have noted already, unlikely to have been an immediate disciple of Jesus, if only because so much of the material in the synoptic gospels is missing from John.

The likelihood is therefore that all the historical books of the New Testament are not eyewitness accounts of the events described. They are all written by people some time after the events, a fact that must affect one's assessment of the books concerned.

The authorship of the letters is also disputed. Several are written in the name of the apostle Paul. However, it seems clear that not all the letters attributed to Paul are by Paul himself. Significant differences of style, language and at times important ideas make this extremely likely. The so-called 'Pastoral epistles' (1 Timothy, 2 Timothy and Titus) form a group of three letters, very similar to each other but in turn very different in style, tone and at times theology from Paul's own. They are thus the work of a later writer, writing in Paul's name, claiming Paul's authority (perhaps even writing to rehabilitate Paul at a time when Paul's authority was being questioned), but not written by Paul himself. The exact extent of the corpus of such letters in the New Testament, purportedly by Paul but in fact written by someone else, is disputed. (The technical word for such letters is 'pseudonymous'.) Most would include Ephesians in this category of pseudonymous Pauline letters; many would also include Colossians and 2 Thessalonians. The unquestionably genuine Pauline corpus thus comprises only seven letters (Romans, 1 Corinthians, 2 Corinthians, Galatians, Philippians, 1 Thessalonians and Philemon).

The authorship of other letters in the New Testament is also disputed. The letter to the Hebrews (traditionally ascribed to Paul) is anonymous. Its ideas, especially its highly distinctive presentation of the person of Jesus in the category of a high priest, are very different from Paul's, and hence the author is almost certainly not

Paul, though some link with a Pauline circle is not impossible. (At the end of the text, 'Timothy' is mentioned [Heb 13.23], and Timothy was evidently a well-known member of the Pauline circle.) The letters ascribed to Peter may also be pseudonymous. (In any case, 1 Peter and 2 Peter are not by the same author, as is fairly clear on grounds of style.) The Johannine letters (1–3 John) are stylistically and thematically very close to the fourth gospel, and hence may stem from the same 'circle'. The so-called 'letter of James' *may* come from James the brother of Jesus: the author probably intended that to be understood in using the name, but whether it is accurate or not is unclear. (There is, for example, virtually no reference to Jesus at all in the letter of James.) The book of Revelation claims to be by a 'John' (Rev 1.4), but further identification of who is meant by this (very common!) name is not clear from the book.

All in all, large parts of the New Testament are not written by people directly connected with Jesus or the very earliest period of the Christian church. (This could apply even to Paul: Paul was 'converted' after the death of Jesus.) Rather, many New Testament books stem from second- or third-generation Christians, writing a little time after the foundational events of the Christian church and reflecting on them. Some of the authors would clearly like to be seen as earlier authoritative figures in that they write in the name of such figures. But the fact remains that large parts of the New Testament were written by Christians *after* the initial period.

Despite all these caveats, it remains the case that the New Testament texts are the earliest Christian writings we have, at least for the most part. They are not uniformly early, as we have seen. Moreover, there are one or two writings from early Christians that are not now part of the New Testament but are probably earlier in date than the latest New Testament writings. There is a small manual of church order known as the *Didache*, the full text of which was only discovered in the nineteenth century and which many today would regard as a very early, first-century document. So too the letter known as *1 Clement*, a document written by the bishop of Rome in the 90s to the Christian church at Corinth, is to be dated at the end of the first century. Both texts probably pre-date a New Testament text such as 2 Peter. Nevertheless, the New Testament texts by and large constitute the earliest Christian texts we have.

GAPS IN OUR KNOWLEDGE

It is however also clear that the New Testament texts do not give us anything like a comprehensive picture of the earliest days of the Christian movement. The New Testament is dominated, directly or indirectly, by the figure of Paul. As we have seen, there are seven undisputed genuine letters of Paul in the New Testament; in addition, there are several letters written in his name; further, the story in the book of Acts is dominated for the second half (and more) of its compass by the figure of Paul as Luke focuses almost exclusively on Paul's exploits in telling his story.

All this may have its own 'justification' at one level in that Paul was clearly an important figure within the new Christian movement. On the other hand, we should not lose sight of the fact that Paul's real influence in the first century may not have been quite so all-powerful. We can see very clearly from his letters (much less easily from Acts!) that Paul was frequently engaged in fierce arguments with other Christians, and the likelihood is that he did not always win such arguments. Paul's own theology was clearly controversial in the first century, and not accepted by all Christians. A lot of evidence suggests that within early Christianity Paul may have been something of an isolated figure whose influence may have been somewhat peripheral. Certainly we know that, at a later period, Paul was regarded by some Christians with intense suspicion, and it may have been in such a situation that the Pastoral letters were written in Paul's name, seeking to show that Paul really was 'safe' and 'sound'. The picture we get from the New Testament texts alone may thus give us a potentially slightly misleading picture of earliest Christianity.

We should also note that the New Testament does not give us anything like a comprehensive coverage of the writings of early Christians. As already noted, there may well be a few texts from the first century that are not in the New Testament. But we also know of the existence of other texts now lost. It seems that Paul wrote a letter to the Laodiceans (see Col 4.16): if this letter really did exist, it has not survived. We know from Paul's letters to the Corinthians that he must have written other letters to them, apart from the ones we have in the New Testament (see 1 Cor 5.9; 2 Cor 2.3); it is clear too that the Corinthians wrote to him (see 1 Cor 7.1). Clearly then we do not have all the letters Paul wrote (and none he received). Similarly, Luke mentions in the preface to his gospel that he knew of 'many' who had already undertaken an enterprise similar to the one he himself was starting in beginning his account of Jesus' life (Luke 1.1); and presumably the 'many' cannot have been just Mark! It would seem that there may have been a number of such texts in circulation at the time. So, too, many scholars have suggested that both Matthew and Luke had access to another source apart from Mark: this source is usually known as 'Q', but if (as seems likely) it existed in written form, no copy of it has survived. In addition, we know of the existence of a number of other texts, for example the 'Gospel of the Hebrews', from the fact that various church fathers quote them, even though no manuscript of the texts survives today. It is then clear that the texts that have survived represent only a part of the literature produced by the earliest Christians.

Further, we know of great gaps in our knowledge of early Christianity that are shown, but not filled, by the New Testament. The origins of Egyptian Christianity, or Roman Christianity, remain totally obscure to us. The New Testament documents indicate that Christianity reached Egypt, and Rome, very early. (For Egypt, see Acts 18.24ff. where Apollos suddenly appears in the story as a Christian from Alexandria; for Rome, one has the evidence of Paul's letter to Rome for the existence of a church there in the mid-50s.) Yet on the questions how or when these communities were founded, we are entirely in the dark.

The New Testament writings then give us a somewhat haphazard collection of first-century Christian texts. They provide us with (mostly) our only sources for discovering information about the early days of the new Christian movement; but as sources they are at times tantalizingly incomplete.

THE NEW TESTAMENT AS A CHRISTIAN COLLECTION

One element however that binds all the New Testament texts together is the fact that they are all Christian texts. They are all written by people who were adherents of the new Christian movement. In one way this is of course trite and obvious. But it does have further implications, for example, if one wishes to use these texts to discover aspects of the history of the period. All the accounts of Jesus' life in the gospels are 'biased' in that they are written by Christians. Sadly perhaps, we have virtually nothing written about Jesus by contemporary non-Christian writers. So too the earliest history of the church evidently made almost no impact on other authors in the Hellenistic or Jewish environment. (The Jewish historian Josephus never mentions the Christian movement, except in one paragraph about Jesus, though the authenticity of this is heavily disputed, and in a brief note about the execution of James. Hellenistic authors of the period do not mention the new Christian movement prior to the references to Christians being blamed for the fire at Rome during the reign of Nero in the mid-60s.)

In the case of the gospels, in particular, this does have a potentially enormous effect on the nature of these texts. The one common element in the (at times very great) variety shown by early Christians was the claim made by them all in relation to the 'resurrection' of Jesus. Christians believed that the Jesus who had lived and preached in Palestine and been crucified on a Roman cross had been 'raised' to a new kind of life by God. As such, he was alive and still speaking to his followers in the present. For the gospel writers, therefore, any distinction some might make as historians between past and present, between what Jesus might have said in the past and what could be said today, would have appeared rather unreal. For the evangelists, it was the same Jesus who had worked in Palestine prior to his death who was now alive and still speaking to his followers. As a result, the evangelists evidently felt free to change their traditions to reflect their beliefs about the aliveness of Jesus with a freedom that many people find on first encounter a little disconcerting.

Perhaps this is clearest in the case of the gospel of John, where it seems that the original Jesus tradition has been transposed and transformed into a completely new setting, with the language and categories changed to reflect that setting. Thus Jesus now talks in long discourses, rather than in short parables or aphorisms; and he ceases to talk of a future 'Kingdom of God', but rather of 'eternal life' available in the present, and of himself as the direct object of faith and commitment. All this is quite different from the picture in the synoptic gospels, so much so that the two pictures can scarcely be reconciled at the level of the pre-Easter Jesus. Nevertheless, the picture in John reflects one way in which the fundamental conviction of the aliveness of Jesus after Easter, and the basic belief that Jesus was still speaking to his church, enabled at least one Christian writer to refashion and re-present the gospel story in a radically different way. Rewriting on a less radical, but no less real, scale can also be seen in the other gospels; for example, Matthew and Luke rewrite Mark's account, at times with considerable freedom. All this means that, as source books for the past, the Christian gospels may tell us as much, if not more, about their authors and their situations as they do about the events they are purportedly describing, namely the life and ministry of Jesus prior to the resurrection.

The other thing to bear in mind is that the New Testament is not only a collection of Christian texts; it is also a collection made by Christians. The process of separating off these books and forming them into a 'New Testament' was one undertaken in the church by Christians for Christians. The details of that process are often not very clear. It seems likely that the process was not always very self-conscious. Often the process, like the New Testament itself, may have been more than a little haphazard. Some books may simply have been lost in the course of time. Others were simply accepted, almost without any self-conscious evaluation at all. Why in the end some books 'made it' into the New Testament canon and others did not is unclear. Perhaps whether or not a book was written by an 'apostle' was significant, though this is by no means certain. (For example, the gospels of Mark and Luke were never claimed to have been written by apostles, yet no one really worried too much!) Antiquity was certainly important for some: the New Testament books were valued because they were the oldest documents available. Also their historical reliability was important (even though today one might assess that 'reliability' rather differently!). So too their theological 'orthodoxy' was relevant, though it is notoriously difficult to define what is meant by orthodoxy, especially in the earliest period of Christian history. Nevertheless, at least one book, the *Gospel of Peter*, was, according to a story in Eusebius's *Church History* (a fourth-century account of the history of the church), barred from use in public worship by a bishop Serapion in the second century because it was felt to be doctrinally suspect. (It implies the idea that Jesus had not really died on the cross.) Above all though what seemed to count was whether a document was used everywhere and universally in the church.

The main bulk of the New Testament canon was implicitly agreed very early and with a remarkable lack of controversy. For example, the fourfold gospel canon was accepted by the end of the second century and no one thereafter appears to question it (even though it is clear that there were a number of other texts claiming to be 'gospels' current at the time). Discussions about the precise limits of the canon, at the 'edges' so to speak, continued on for a very long time. The book of Revelation, for example, remained a matter of dispute for several centuries. Nevertheless, the main outline of the New Testament canon was agreed by the middle of the fourth century and has remained fixed ever since.

That said, it should not be forgotten that the process of forming the books of the New Testament into a single 'canonical' collection only starts some time after the writing of the New Testament texts themselves. The New Testament writers themselves were scarcely conscious of the fact that they were writing texts that would become part of sacred scripture for the whole Christian church. For first-century Christians, 'scripture' meant primarily the Jewish scriptures. Paul no doubt intended his letters to be read, and to be taken, very seriously. Yet he does not appear to think that he is supplementing and expanding Jewish scriptures with his letters. So too the freedom with which, say, Matthew and Luke use Mark as a source in writing their gospels shows clearly that they at least did not regard Mark as any very sacred text. The freedom they exercise implies precisely the opposite. Perhaps the only New Testament book that shows any self-awareness of claiming some kind of 'scriptural' authority for itself is the book of Revelation: see Revelation 22.18–19 and the warning about adding anything to, or subtracting anything from, what has been written, a claim similar to others made elsewhere about Jewish scripture (cf. Deut 4.2).

IDEAS IN THE NEW TESTAMENT

The New Testament texts show at times a bewildering diversity in their 'theologies' and ideas. The very nature of the Christian movement as something new within Judaism meant that the early Christians were inevitably struggling from the start to determine what was normative for their beliefs and what was debatable, what was acceptable and what was 'out of bounds', how one could determine what was right and what was wrong.

Christianity grew out of Judaism, and so Christians could – and did – draw on Judaism for ideas and norms in this respect. Indeed, many of those norms and ideas were accepted in toto without any questioning at all. Christians adopted the Jewish ideas of God (i.e. 'theo-logy' strictly speaking) without ever questioning it in any way: ideas such as monotheism (God as Creator) were simply assumed as axiomatic. The same is the case in relation to a Jewish eschatological framework of thought: Christians such as Paul simply assumed this as self-evidently true and never stopped to discuss or defend it, even when writing to non-Jews. So too much of Jewish ethical teaching was assumed.

Yet soon a major issue forced Christians to ask awkward questions about their Jewish roots. This was the influx of non-Jews (i.e. Gentiles) into the Christian movement, leading to the question being raised: should Gentiles become Jews before/when they became Christians? This of course had very practical consequences for males because it involved the question of circumcision: should Gentiles have to be circumcised if they wished to join the Christian movement? The answer ultimately was no. But this inevitably led to an awareness of some difference between Christians and Jews. At a very visible level (e.g. in public baths), not all Christian men looked like Jewish men any longer.

As Christians struggled to resolve such issues, they were inevitably forced to reassess different parts of their traditions, Jewish and non-Jewish, to see what could/should be maintained, what jettisoned, what arguments were justified, what were not, how one could/should argue, and so on. And it is this state of what is at times quite a turbulent situation that one sees reflected in the New Testament, especially in the Pauline letters.

It is perhaps not in the least surprising to find a lack of uniformity in the New Testament. At times there is even what seems like outright contradiction. For example, Paul argues passionately for the priority of what he calls 'faith' over what he terms 'works', or 'works of the law', as the basis for salvation (see Rom 4). The author of the letter of James on the other hand claims that 'works' are all important and that faith without works is dead (James 2.20). The disagreement is in one way rather formal and artificial: James and Paul do not necessarily mean precisely the same thing by the same words 'faith'/'works'. Nevertheless, there is an element of tension here, which in James is quite explicit (and James is probably in part responding to Pauline Christianity). As already noted, we see Paul himself in his letters frequently having heated debates with other Christians about what are regarded as key issues of the day, not the least of which is very often the question of how far some of the Jewish practices are still to be regarded as obligatory in the Christian church.

We also see Christians in the New Testament coming out with 'answers' to 'questions' that are at best tentative and certainly at times tangential to each other. For example, early Christians were convinced that in some way or other, Jesus' death on the cross was to be seen not just a judicial execution, nor even as only a miscarriage of justice perpetrated on an innocent man. Rather, it came to be seen as somehow having positive significance in itself, effecting a real change in the human situation and in the relationship between God and human beings. But precisely what had been achieved, and how Jesus' death on the cross had achieved it, was not so clear. Different writers use different images. Even a single writer like Paul used a riot of different images and 'language games' to describe it. Thus Jesus' death is referred to as a sacrifice, similar to the sin offerings of the Jewish cult (Rom 3.25), or as a Passover sacrifice implying a new act of liberation by God similar to the rescue of the Israelites from Egypt (1 Cor 5.7); it was also a new covenant sacrifice, inaugurating a new covenant relationship, similar to that which brought the Jewish people into existence as the people of God (1 Cor 11.24); it was also a 'price paid' (though it is never said to whom!), leading to the transfer of ownership of Christians who then, like slaves bought in the market place for a price, are now the property of a new master, Christ (1 Cor 6.20; 7.23). All these used images and ideas current at the time to try to express aspects of the new life Christians believed they experienced as a result of Jesus' life and death. There is little if any attempt in the New Testament itself to synthesize all these ideas. And it was the task of later Christians in the early church to try to bring some kind of synthesis in the later creeds and doctrinal statements of the church.

Further, we should remember in reading the New Testament that, when the later process of synthesizing and systematizing took place, it was often undertaken in a thought world and with presuppositions very different from those of the New Testament writers. At the very least, key words and phrases were used in ways, and with meanings, rather different from their usage in the New Testament. For example, language of Jesus as Son of God, used later by Christians to express their conviction that Jesus was fully divine, one in being with the Father, also occurs in the New Testament but arguably with no such clear overtones of divinity attached to the phrase. Talk about individuals as a 'son of God' is thoroughly at home in Judaism, referring variously to a royal figure (see 2 Sam 7.14) or perhaps a righteous person who remains obedient to God through suffering (see Wisd 2–5). No doubt the same language when applied to Jesus was in a state of flux, and may have taken on some significantly new overtones of meaning. But we should always be aware of the dangers of anachronistically reading back the meanings that key phrases came to have in later Christianity into the earlier documents of the New Testament itself.

IMPORTANCE OF THE NEW TESTAMENT

In the course of time, the New Testament books were gradually accorded the position and status of holy scripture alongside, and in addition to, the books of Jewish
scripture. They came to form a 'New Testament' alongside what came then to be
called the 'Old Testament' (though it should be noted that the existence of a New
Testament never led to the displacement of Jewish scripture from the Christian Bible:
however much Christians wished to stress their differences from Judaism, Christians
have never given up their claim to the Jewish scriptures as an integral part of their
own Bibles). The status of these books as holy scripture meant that they profoundly
affected the whole subsequent history of the Christian church. Any religious tradition in its history constantly relates back to its past to establish elements of
continuity, to define itself and to regulate developments. The documents of the New
Testament inevitably occupy a key role in these respects in the Christian religion.
They are the earliest documents of Christianity that we possess; the 'scriptural' status
accorded them reinforces their significance. For all those interested in the Christian
religion, these texts will therefore be of foundational significance. Further, for all
those interested in the historical roots of the Christian religion, in the historical
events, supremely the life, death and resurrection of Jesus, that provided the initial
impetus inaugurating the new Christian movement, the New Testament texts will
provide us with our primary historical sources (even if, as I have tried to indicate,
they must be used with some care).

But equally, in an age that has become suspicious and critical of some old authorities or dogmatic claims, it can be just as important to return to the roots of the
Christian tradition, in one way to see how the earliest Christians struggled with the
problems and issues facing them at a time when old authorities were being called
into question and new structures had to be developed, and in another way to be able
to view critically later developments in Christian history. As we look at the earliest
Christians once again, we may for example find that some of the more dogmatic
claims alleged to be based on their ideas and beliefs are perhaps not as securely
founded as others have claimed. It is as part of this constant search for truth, as well
as the perennial fascination of the earliest days of the new Christian movement, that
the New Testament texts need to be read and studied afresh in every generation.

PART II

GENRES

CHAPTER FOUR

NEAR EASTERN MYTHS
AND LEGENDS

——•◆•——

Stephanie Dalley

HISTORICAL BACKGROUND

During the Bronze Age, before the Judaean monarchy was established in Jerusalem, some royal courts at cities in Palestine and Canaan were literate in Akkadian cuneiform, a complex system of writing that uses logograms, determinatives and syllables. This spread of literacy is known from a variety of inscribed clay tablets found on archaeological sites in modern Israel, Lebanon and Syria. We now know that the ancient Mesopotamian tradition of writing and literature permeated the whole of western Asia through sites such as Ebla and Byblos in the Early Bronze Age; Mari, Hazor, Megiddo and Hebron in the Middle Bronze Age; Emar, Ugarit and Tell Aphek in the Late Bronze Age, even when Egypt ruled Palestine. It was then largely superseded by Hebrew and Aramaic, written in linear alphabetic script. Briefly intermediate between the Akkadian cuneiform and the linear ways of writing was the cuneiform alphabetic script written on clay, known mainly from Ugarit and so named Ugaritic. It was applied not only to the west Semitic language of that city, but was certainly used far beyond, as we know from finds at Tell Aphek, and it flourished rather briefly in the fourteenth to thirteenth century alongside Akkadian cuneiform. Another script that did not long survive the spread of alphabets was the Hittite hieroglyphic writing used for the Luwian (Indo-European) language, but it persisted into the eighth century at Hamath, for instance. The kings of city-states who still wrote in Hittite hieroglyphs were called by traditional Hittite dynastic names, and these survivals may imply that Hittite mythology too survived into the early Iron Age. Aramaic gradually replaced Ugaritic, Luwian and Akkadian.

Systems of writing

The complex Akkadian and the alphabetic Ugaritic systems of writing and their separate literatures were not linked to political or military domination, and traces of influence from each have been found in different books of the Old Testament. In the case of Akkadian cuneiform, these vestiges have survived partly because they were 'set texts' in the curriculum of scribes in Palestine at the time when Akkadian cuneiform had not yet given way to local alphabetic scripts there, so it was inevitable that old genres and modes of expression were adapted to new material. The new alphabetic scripts were soon adapted for particular languages and nationalities, so that literary work, both for training scribes and for their compositions, became less international and more nationalistic during the early Iron Age. As far as we can tell, the new alphabetic scripts were used for recording relatively local literature. We find cuneiform Akkadian myths translated into cuneiform Hittite and Hurrian, but we do not find them in alphabetic Ugaritic or Hebrew, nor do we find Ugaritic myths translated into Akkadian. No Egyptian literature has been found in Palestine, nor was it translated in the royal cities of western Asia.

From the early Iron Age onwards the new alphabetic writing was very largely restricted to perishable materials: papyrus, parchment and wooden writing boards, and so the picture we now have is shockingly incomplete. No Phoenician or non-biblical Hebrew myths or legends survive from this time. But literature certainly existed, for the well-structured alphabetic text written on the Moabite Stone in the early ninth century, the Deir Alla inscription written on plaster perhaps in the eighth century, and the inscription on stone from Tell Dan of the late ninth century, all show that the scribes of Syro-Palestine were indeed composing quite sophisticated works in Moabite-Hebrew and Aramaic languages using alphabetic script, early in the Iron Age.

This chapter aims to survey the various myths and legends that circulated in different parts of the ancient Near East. From this wealth of material a few stories are given in outline, and unequivocal biblical connections are pointed out. But it cannot be emphasized too strongly that new material and improved understanding of texts alters the state of scholarship at a fast pace, rendering out of date good editions, translations and the assessments published by scholars in the recent past.

Mesopotamian texts

Sumerian (non-Semitic) and Akkadian (east-Semitic) myths and legends developed during at least 2,000 years in Mesopotamia. Sumerian works, emanating in particular from the cities of Eridu, Ur, Uruk (Erech) and Nippur, were often translated or adapted into Akkadian, and were assimilated into the Semitic tradition of literature. Sumerian gods either keep their Sumerian names in Akkadian works, such as Ninurta, or they are transferred directly into Akkadian; for example, the goddess Inanna becomes Ishtar, the moon-god Nanna becomes Sin, and the sun-god Utu becomes Shamash. It is therefore not often appropriate to try to distinguish Sumerian from Akkadian themes or texts, or to separate 'Semitic' characteristics from non-Semitic. Translation skills developed early through the use of bilingual and trilingual manuals found on sites both in Mesopotamia and far abroad, for instance at Tell el-Amarna in Egypt and Tell Aphek in Palestine, and several major myths are known to us from bilingual texts in which each line of Sumerian is translated or paraphrased with a line of Akkadian.

Sumerian and Akkadian compositions are preserved on clay tablets that are usually copies of older texts. For this reason we can seldom put an accurate date to a composition; in any case, texts evolved through time and seldom if ever reach a static, canonical form. Indications of date are therefore approximate in this chapter.

However, scenes from known myths are thought to be recognizable on cylinder seals of c.2300 BC, showing that some themes from the basic stories presumably go back to that time at least, and writing at Ebla in Syria around 2300 BC was based on Mesopotamian cuneiform, although it quickly developed its own character. These facts may support a presumption that Canaanite literature, with its unmistakeably different forms and emphases, developed under some influence from the literature of Mesopotamia. Issues of influence are therefore complex. The difficulties are exacerbated by the damaged condition in which most tablets are found, with the result that our knowledge of complete texts is slowly and painfully acquired. All our knowledge of Sumerian, Akkadian, Hittite and Canaanite literature comes primarily from clay tablets that are usually damaged and incomplete.

Canaanite texts

The terms 'Canaanite' and 'Phoenician' are both words that refer to murex-purple. This dye, extracted from sea-shells along the Levantine coast from the mid-second millennium onwards, together with the organization for its use, distribution and trade, allowed great cities along the east Mediterranean coast to grow extremely wealthy. As a result, court life and the patronage of arts and crafts, including technical skills in metal working and literature, flourished to a high level. Such centres were Tyre, Sidon, Acco, Beirut and Ugarit. The population was ethnically mixed: west-Semitic people from the Amorite tribal movements of the Middle Bronze Age, east-Semitic people who had emigrated from Mesopotamia, and Achaean and Anatolian people who blended with them as a result of various forces including the migrations associated with the break-up of the Hittite empire, and the so-called Dark Age, linked to the movements of the Sea Peoples. They all eventually adopted some form of west-Semitic alphabet, which spread to Greece, so that essentially the same writing system was used for both Semitic and Indo-European languages and their literatures.

Of Canaanite literature we have only a glimpse from the cuneiform alphabetic texts found at Ugarit and nearby sites. They date to the end of the Late Bronze Age. How much of its tradition came down from Amorites who dominated the area in the Middle Bronze Age remains unknown for lack of evidence. How much of its tradition then fed into Phoenician literate culture in the great cities of Tyre and Sidon is also undocumented, although the later account given by Philo of Byblos shows connections as well as significant differences. Nevertheless, the texts from Ugarit suffice to show that Canaanite myths have some very close connections with biblical imagery and forms of poetic expression.

Hittite texts

Hittite myths and legends were eclectic, drawing upon Mesopotamian, Hurrian and Canaanite materials. The names of non-Hittite gods and cities from those materials are easily recognized in Hittite myths, and archaeologists have uncovered Akkadian and Hurrian originals from which translations were made at the capital city Hattusa in central Anatolia. The Hurrians were a non-Semitic, non-Indo-European people who lived in eastern Anatolia; we do not yet have texts from any of their major cities. As in Palestine and the Levant, traditions of literacy in Anatolia in the Middle and Late Bronze Age drew upon the conventions and compositions that emanated from scribal schools in Mesopotamia. Therefore it is very difficult to isolate strictly Hittite material from Mesopotamian and Canaanite when we are looking at biblical texts. Since Hittite rule never penetrated Palestine, direct Hittite influence may well be lacking, although the name Tidal in Genesis 14.1, 9 may come from Tudhaliya (IV? 1254–1220 BC). Hittite writings are, however, especially interesting because they draw attention to the importance of Mesopotamian and Canaanite myths beyond the borders of native cities. They also show some of the processes by which myths from one country were adopted and adapted by another.

Egyptian texts

Egypt had a border in common with Palestine, which it dominated or influenced at certain periods. Its contribution to culture there is readily observable in iconography, particularly in metalwork and seals, and we can be sure that Phoenician culture acted as intermediary in conveying Egyptian influence to Palestine. But Egyptian writing was never adopted by indigenous scribes in the way that Akkadian cuneiform was, and Egyptian myths and other kinds of literature did not penetrate the educational system as Akkadian myths did. Although the seals of many individuals are Egyptianizing in style, the Bronze Age seals of Levantine kings are remarkably Syro-Mesopotamian in design. The names of Egyptian cities and gods are not found in the books of the Old Testament except in the immediate context of historical events. This seems to indicate that high culture in Palestine was connected to that of Canaan and Mesopotamia, whereas in general popular culture was influenced from Egypt.

Even though, during the Amarna period of the Late Bronze Age, Egyptian governors were installed in the cities of Palestine, cuneiform Akkadian, often in local dialects, was the language of international communication. This means that scribes were trained using set pieces from Mesopotamian myths and legends. We know this because cuneiform dictionary lists, epics and scribal exercises were found in the palace at Tell el-Amarna. The Egyptians had wisdom dialogues, proverbs and creation myths quite similar in form and content to those popular in Mesopotamia, and it is not always possible to distinguish which has influenced biblical texts.

Northern Syria and south-eastern Turkey

Patriarchal stories in Genesis mention on the one hand cities such as Erech and Ur in southern Mesopotamia, which have yielded literary material to the archaeologist's spade, and on the other hand cities such as Harran, Nahor and Serug in northern Syria, modern south-east Turkey, where virtually no excavation has taken place. The present-day scholar needs to be aware that this imbalance of discovery may skew our sense of proportion, and may drastically be rectified in future. Surprises may well be in store both from Amorite culture in the Middle Bronze Age and from Hurrian culture in the Late Bronze Age. The literature of neo-Hittite Luwian in the early Iron Age remains unknown, but Luwian was written and spoken in Anatolia during the Middle and Late Bronze Age; now that continuity through the so-called Dark Age has been discovered for dynasties in cities governed by Hittites (for instance at Carchemish), some continuity of myths and legends in Luwian can safely be deduced. Luwian inscriptions are found as far south as Hamath during the ninth century BC. Aramaic material of the Iron Age, now coming to light on stone from Syro-Palestine, and on papyri from Egypt, Qumran and elsewhere, is beginning to show that there was a rich literature in that language, some of it independent of both biblical and cuneiform traditions.

Non-textual evidence

Some themes from the early literature of western Asia and Egypt would have been familiar from pictures. Wall-paintings from Egypt, the Levant, Syria and Mesopotamia, sculptured stone panels in temples and palaces, especially in Assyria and the neo-Hittite cities of Syria and Cilicia; cylinder seals from Syria and Mesopotamia; metal bowls decorated in repoussé work, of which particularly fine examples were made in Phoenicia (see Figures 4.1, 4.2), illustrate how the world was visualized in terms that relate to mythology; likewise woven and embroidered textiles, which have only survived in Egyptian tombs but were certainly made and used all over western Asia.

Figure 4.1   Apsu, the ocean of fresh water, represented by a stone basin in the temple of Assur, c.700 BC. Copyright Staatliche Museen zu Berlin.

Figure 4.2   The Legend of Etana shown on a cylinder seal c.2300 BC.
Copyright Pergamum Museum, Berlin.

The prime elements of creation were represented in temples: the Apsu was a basin standing for watery chaos and the father of the first gods, and the holy mound or mountain Duku was there too. The tablet and seal of destinies may also have had a physical presence in the shrine of destinies. As trophies of the victorious gods, many of the composite creatures who had fought with the forces of chaos were displayed in various temples.

THE TEXTS

Sumerian myths and legends

The Sumerian language is not related to any other known language, so that the process of decipherment has been slow. To this difficulty should be added the problems of reading the script, with its many ambiguities, correctly, as well as the poor state of preservation of many tablets. Most of the works identified have been reconstructed from fragments that do not necessarily come from the same recension, and many words and phrases will not be understood until enough variants make the reading clear.

A Sumerian literary account of the Flood story is found in The Eridu Genesis (Kramer 1983; Jacobsen 1987: 145–50). Its details, though fragmentary, seem similar to those in the much better preserved Akkadian versions, although the gods are given their Sumerian names and the hero who corresponds to the biblical Noah is called Ziusudra. Since Berossus, a priest of the Seleucid period who recorded Babylonian traditions in Greek, used this Sumerian version of the name, we may suppose that the Sumerian version of the Flood story remained in circulation after the death of Alexander the Great. The poor state of preservation allows few useful comparisons to be made with the story of the Flood in Genesis, except that the text now known as the Sumerian king-list (Borger et al. 1982: 328–37) inserts a reference to the Flood between legendary kings with fabulous lifespans, and dynasties that lead into known historical periods, and the Flood marks a similar transition in the Bible. The king-list may first have been drawn up around 2100 BC, but was certainly completed a couple of centuries later. We can therefore be confident that some kind of Flood story was well established in early Mesopotamian tradition, where it is attached to the Sumerian city Shuruppak in lower Mesopotamia. Sumerian literary texts are notoriously difficult to understand, and this is especially true of BMes 120011 (Kramer 1979: 30–6), which may possibly refer to humanity's defiance and disgraceful sexual behaviour as a preliminary to the Flood. If so, it provides an antecedent to the motive found in the biblical account of the Flood that is absent from the main cuneiform accounts of the Flood. This type of variety in important details shows that many different versions of a work could exist at the same time, even though they might be contradictory. There was no single, consistent tradition. This means, for instance, that the naming of Mount Ararat (Urartu, in E. Anatolia) in Genesis 8 does not allow the biblical account to be dated; no extant Sumerian or Akkadian version gives that name for the mountain. Ararat is named also by Berossus in the third century BC. Berossus certainly did not invent this detail, and appears to have used a Sumerian version of the Flood story that is unknown to us.

A legend recounting the birth of Sargon of Agade in Akkadian is probably a translation of the opening to a Sumerian legend about his life, the Legend of Sargon (Lewis 1980; Afanas'eva 1987). It tells how his mother was a high priestess who bore him in secret and put him on the river in a reed basket. He floated down and was rescued by a water-drawer, who raised him as his adopted son. He found favour with the goddess Ishtar, and became the king's cup-bearer, from which position he eventually became king and performed great deeds. This theme is found in the biblical story of Moses, and was also used for Cyrus the Great. The Legend of Sargon also contains the motif of the messenger who unwittingly bears a letter requiring the recipient to put him to death, known later in the biblical story of Uriah in 2 Samuel 11.

Various Sumerian myths recount the exploits of gods and goddesses. Particular themes include amorous encounters that resulted in offspring, such as the myths of Enki and Ninhursag, and Enlil and Ninlil, which explain the relationship between different deities and connections between their cults. There are cultic journeys that sometimes show a transfer of power from one city to another, such as Inanna and Enki (Farber, in Hallo 1997: 522–6). There are visits to the Underworld that provide an explanation for the changing seasons, such as Inanna's Descent (Sladek 1974), and short stories about Dumuzi and Inanna (Alster 1972; Jacobsen 1987: 3–56). There are heroic battles led by a single god, notably Ninurta, against superior, evil forces, such as the Return of Ninurta to Nippur, also called Angim (Cooper 1978), which explains the presence of trophies in his temple, and Lugal-e (van Dijk 1983; Jacobsen 1987: 233–72), which assigns powers to different minerals once they have been conquered in a cosmic battle. The latter category was often adapted to fit the requirements of other cities, and we find allusions to other gods such as Nergal and Marduk slipping into the heroic role originally played by Ninurta. These allusions are often found in Akkadian literature, emphasizing the very close relationship between Sumerian and Akkadian myths. As a bilingual myth, Lugal-e was present in several copies in the great libraries of late Assyrian kings, which shows that it was still important in the Iron Age. It belongs to an important 'scientific' tradition in Mesopotamia that assigned characters and functions to different stones and metals.

Some of the myths are introduced with a few lines giving an account of how the world was created. Such introductions are also used for other types of literature such as Incantations (Romer, in Farber 1987: 163–211), and Debate dialogues (Clifford 1994: 25–7).

Frequently used as a theme in Sumerian myths was the journey of a god from one cult centre to another. Enki's Journey to Nippur (al-Fouadi 1969), Nanna-Suen's Journey to Nippur (Ferrara 1973) and Inanna's Descent to the Underworld (Sladek 1974), in which the Underworld is represented by the temple of Nergal in Cuthah, are three examples. Such visits are thought to reflect actual cultic journeys in which the cult statue travelled by water on a ceremonial boat, and such myths may serve as aetiologies for a regular event in the cultic calendar explaining the division or transfer of powers between cities and their patron deities. The myths represent the gods as members of an extended family, each individual having human weaknesses: getting drunk, tricking each other, seducing, and manoeuvring amorous liaisons.

Other Sumerian myths recount episodes in the lives of legendary kings of Uruk, notably Enmerkar, Lugal-banda and Gilgamesh. The Lugal-banda Epic (Wilcke 1969), features the goddess of beer, Nin-kasi, who plays the part of a wise guide and advisor, similar to the role played by Siduri in the Akkadian Epic of Gilgamesh. This character seems to be ancestral to Wisdom the woman of Proverbs 8. Some of the short Sumerian myths about Gilgamesh were worked into the Akkadian Epic of Gilgamesh, but others, such as Gilgamesh and Akka (Katz 1993 and in Hallo 1997: 550–51), were excluded. The latter is one of very few Mesopotamian myths to involve the wars of men. The myth known as Gilgamesh, Enkidu and the Netherworld (Shaffer 1963) was taken over directly into an Akkadian translation to form tablet XII of the Epic of Gilgamesh.

It has become clear as more texts have come to light that stories and motivations were different in the various cities of Sumer. Accounts of creation, which so often introduce other kinds of text – myths, incantations and hymns – vary greatly. For instance, in Nippur it was the cosmic marriage of Heaven and Earth that started the long process of evolution, perhaps reflecting the position of a city in the centre of lower Mesopotamia where the sky and the horizon of earth seemed limitless; but in Eridu, which lay at the shore of the Arabian Gulf, creation was initiated when Earth was fertilized by Water. The myth Enki and the World Order (Benito 1969) ascribed the creation of crafts, technologies and human institutions such as kingship to the god Enki, who then was tricked into allowing them to enter cities of which other deities were patrons. In early periods each city drew up a list of gods in an order that reflected its local cosmogony, but later these lists were apparently blended into a standard form that reflected the eminence of Uruk, Nippur and Babylon. This makes it difficult to pin down precise influences from cuneiform texts upon the Bible, but parts of Genesis and Exodus suggest familiarity with material from Mesopotamia, and they name some of its most ancient cities: Ur, Erech, Babel (Babylon) and Irad (Eridu). We know from Hittite texts that Mesopotamian scholars resided in foreign capitals to teach cuneiform writing, and that they used Sumerian myths as well as Akkadian ones in the training process in the Middle and the Late Bronze Age. A Sumerian myth of creation, *KAR* 4 (Clifford 1994: 49–51), describing the original separation of Heaven and Earth, the origin of the rivers Tigris and Euphrates, and how humans were made to work for the gods, has come from

Assyria around 1100 BC, and shows how important Sumerian myths still were at that time.

Sumerian stories accounted for the creation of humankind in at least two ways: by sexual union, and by agricultural work. In the Hymn to E-Engura (Clifford 1994: 29–30), as in other Sumerian tales, people sprouted like plants from the earth, engendered apparently by Sky; according to KAR 4.54 the seed for them was sown by Sky. In The Praise of the Pickaxe (= The Song of the Hoe: Farber, in Hallo 1997: 511–13) Enlil, god of Nippur, used a pickaxe or hoe and a brick-mould to create a human from soil.

In Genesis 11 is found the idea that people once spoke a single language. Later, God deliberately introduced confusion into language as different tongues came into being. This distinctive concept is described in the Sumerian work known as Enmerkar and the Lord of Aratta (Jacobsen, in Hallo 1997: 547–49), Enmerkar being a legendary king of Uruk two generations before Gilgamesh. Enki (Ea), god of Eridu, is responsible: 'In those days . . . the people . . . could address Enlil in a single tongue . . . (but later) Enki . . . the lord of wisdom, the country's clever one, the leader of the gods, altered the speech in their mouths, as many as were there, the tongues of men which had been one'.

One of the most notable genres in Sumerian, which may not have any equivalent in Akkadian, is the City Lament. Laments for Ur, Eridu, Uruk, Agade and Nippur (e.g. Cooper 1983; Michalowski 1989) are all known as independent compositions in which the fall of a great city is described in rhetorical detail, and the catastrophe, related to actual historical events, is directly attributed to the wrath of various gods, thus transferring a real event into the realm of legend and referring occasionally to the city as a person. Although no first-millennium versions of these texts are known, in contrast to many other Sumerian literary works, influence upon Lamentations has been proposed. A text of the Seleucid period, written in Akkadian, and normally entitled A Lament for Dumuzi (Foster 1993: 838–39), is in fact a lamentation for various cities damaged or destroyed in times long past, and shows that the genre persisted well into the period of the Exile.

In general, Sumerian literature is known at its earliest from copies made during the early second millennium BC. The originals from which they were taken are of unknown date, presumably during the late third millennium or even earlier. Many of the compositions remained in libraries where they were still being copied, studied and translated in the Seleucid period.

Akkadian (east-Semitic) myths and legends

With Akkadian literary texts we reach a better level of understanding because the language is related to better-known languages such as Hebrew, which makes grammar and vocabulary easier to understand, and because the texts are written in a less laconic form than is the case for Sumerian. Akkadian is a term comprising all the dialects of Babylonian and Assyrian, written in cuneiform. Our sign-lists and dictionaries are well advanced, and many of the main myths and legends are relatively complete. Mesopotamian tradition ascribed its earliest literature to the Seven Sages, divine beings who were sent down to earth to bring the arts and institutions of civilization to humankind before the Flood, and to semi-divine sages of historical times, such as Lu-Nanna, the sage of Shulgi (king of Ur 2150–2103 BC by the long chronology) who was credited with writing the Legend of Etana (Dalley 1989: 189–202), the king who wanted an heir and flew to heaven on an eagle's back to find the plant of birth; and Asalluhi-mansum, sage of Hammurabi (king of Babylon 1848–1806 BC). The hero of another myth, Adapa (Dalley 1989: 182–88), describes how humankind lost the chance of immortality; Adapa himself was a legendary character, the first sage, and was also known as Uan. In Greek the name is given as Oannes, and by a cunning word-play Uan was related to the word used in Akkadian for a craftsman or sage, *ummiānu*. A Syro-Phoenician version of the same concept is described in The Phoenician History recorded by Philo of Byblos (Attridge and Oden 1981), showing how this basic and important tradition is found beyond Mesopotamia. It is therefore especially interesting that a reference to the seven sages, *ummânu* in later Akkadian, has been found embedded in Proverbs 9. The biblical figure of Enoch in Genesis 5, the wise man who occupied a place intermediate between God and men, and achieved a certain degree of immortality, may be linked to this tradition.

Some well-known myths have no perceptible echoes in Old Testament writing; such are the Descent of Ishtar to the Underworld (Dalley 1989: 154–62), Nergal and Ereshkigal (Dalley 1989: 163–81), Adapa, and the Legend of Etana, of which the last-named envisages a time when human society existed without cities or the institution of kingship. Other works, however, have been much discussed in connection with the Old Testament. The Babylonian Epic of Creation (Dalley 1989: 228–77), known from texts of the first millennium, played a vital part in national ritual, both in Assyria and in Babylonia, and was regularly recited at major festivals. The story begins at a time when heaven and earth had not been created, when the water of the sea (Tiamat) and subterranean sweet water (Apsu) mingled and gave birth to the great gods. The children became too noisy, and when Apsu planned to kill them, he himself was killed. Then Tiamat rose up to avenge his death, and she created an army of composite creatures (see Figure 4.3) who represented both chaos and evil. Their leader Qingu obtained control of the Tablet of Destinies, without which the great gods were powerless. The hero-god is Marduk who defeated the forces of evil embodied in the primeval Tiamat and her monstrous army, using a magical spell and an impressive array of weaponry. He regained the stolen Tablet of Destinies, captured and controlled the monstrous army, and then set about putting the world in order. He put the heavenly bodies in place, regulating their movements; he built Babylon and its temples as the centre of religion for the world, and he created humankind with the help of his father Ea's magic, using the blood of the defeated enemy Qingu. To celebrate his works, the other gods proclaimed his many names, some of which imply syncretism with other deities such as the storm-god, agricultural gods and healing deities. He also receives the epithet Bel, 'Lord', as supreme leader of the assembly of great gods.

A Seleucid tablet, which describes the ritual required for the New Year festival at Babylon in the month of Nisan (the first month of the year starting in spring), states that the Epic of Creation was recited or enacted on several occasions during the days of celebration. Another text, quite recently discovered, shows that a rather

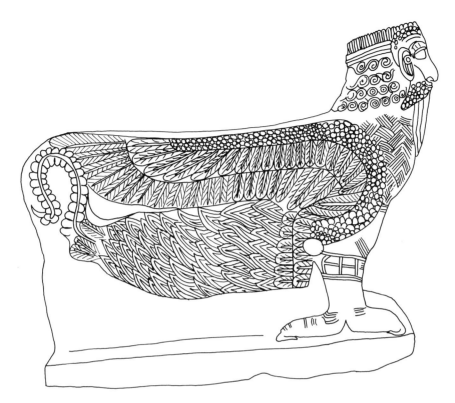

Figure 4.3 Scorpion-man from Tell Halaf in Syria, Early Iron Age.
Drawing by S. Dalley after A. Parrot, *Nineveh and Babylon* (1961), pl. 91.

different version of the epic, involving, for instance, the goddess Ishtar, was
performed during the month of Kislimu (the ninth month of the year) in another,
unidentified, city of Mesopotamia (Çagirgan and Lambert 1994). Fragments from
the city of Ashur, probably dating to around 700 BC, show that there was an Assyrian
version in which Ashur played the hero-god and took the title 'Bel'; and this version
can be linked to a building inscription of Sennacherib, who decorated the doors of
his new festival-house in Ashur with a scene from the great battle, stating that he,
as king, took the part of Ashur, and was accompanied into battle by various other
gods. This contrasts with the version we have from Babylon, in which Marduk faces
the enemy Tiamat alone (Klein 1992).

The cherubim and seraphim, which are described in the visions of Ezekiel, may
ultimately be derived from the subjugated composite creatures which fought beside
Tiamat, and were on display as gigantic sculpture in Assyrian palaces and temples
visited by envoys and deportees from Palestine (see Figure 4.4). One of the composite
creatures, the *mušḫuššu* (literally 'red dragon') was taken over by Marduk as his
personal beast. The seven-headed red dragon of Revelation 12.3 may come from this
tradition; for the cult of Marduk in Babylon survived into the Christian era (Dalley
et al. 1997: 95); and at Tarsus Roman coins show that an Assyrian cult of the patron-

Figure 4.4 Winged, human-headed bull from Assyrian palace of Assurnasirpal II at Nimrud.
Copyright The British Museum.

Figure 4.5 Seven-headed dragon, shown on a cylinder seal, late third millennium BCE.
Copyright D. Collon. Photo reproduced by kind permission of D. Collon.

god, identified with Marduk, still flourished in the early Roman empire (Dalley et al. 1997: 163). The seven-headed serpent is one of the trophies of Ninurta in The Return of Ninurta to Nippur (Cooper 1978: 154) (see Figure 4.5). In the Apocrypha Daniel's destruction of the dragon of Babylon in the story of Bel and The Dragon is a reworking of a similar theme in an explicitly Babylonian context.

Some of the themes in the Babylonian Epic of Creation have come from myths about the heroic deeds of Ninurta, in particular the Epic of Anzu (Dalley 1989: 203–27) in which Ninurta attacks Anzu and retrieves the stolen Tablet of Destinies, (see Figure 4.6), and some have been traced less specifically to national myths of the kingdom of Eshnunna, east of the Tigris. Several of the captured monsters are found as trophies of the god Ninurta in a Sumerian myth The Return of Ninurta to Nippur (Cooper 1978). These myths date back at the latest to the early second millennium, and the date of composition for the Epic of Creation may itself go back to that period. The same theme was used at an early period to the west of Mesopotamia: a letter from Mari alludes to a defeat of the Sea by the west-Semitic storm-god Addu in his cult centre Aleppo, ancient Halab, in the time of Hammurabi of Babylon (Durand 1993). Some scholars think that the essence of the composition is Amorite in origin; others still maintain that the composition arose from the ceremony conducted when a statue of Marduk, looted by raiding Elamites, returned to Babylon in the reign of Nebuchadnezzar I (1125–1104 BC). The links between these different stories of hero-gods who defeat the forces of chaos and establish order in the universe make it difficult to identify with certainty particular characters or scenes depicted on cylinder seals, terracotta plaques and other media.

It is likely that there were many versions of this story of Creation and the ordering of the world in different cities. The moon-god of Harran, Ashur in Assyria, the storm-god of Aleppo, and other important deities in their various cult centres, were also known locally as Bel, 'Lord', and presumably acted the part of the hero-god, earning the title through victory. At Palmyra in the Roman period the chief god, perhaps a storm-god, was called Bel, and a sculptured frieze showed him shooting Tiamat from his chariot (see Figure 4.7). At Hatra the contemporary sun-god was called Bel

Figure 4.6 Ninurta attacking Anzu. Drawing from stone sculpture from Assyrian temple of Ninurta, Nimrud. Early Iron Age. British Museum Original Drawing I 54. Copyright The British Museum.

Figure 4.7 Frieze from the great temple at Palmyra showing Bel shooting Tiamat. Early Roman empire period. Drawing by Marion Cox, after H. Seyrig, 'Bas-reliefs monumentaux du temple de Bêl à Palmyre', *Syria* 15 (1934), pl. 20.

and his temple was named after that of Marduk in Babylon, Esagila; at the same period the temple of the New Year festival in Ashur was rebuilt. An Aramaic version of the story of Creation may have accompanied the ritual in those cities.

The Epic of Atrahasis (Dalley 1989: 1–38; Foster 1983: 158–201), written in the mid-second millennium BC, tells how the gods created humankind for labour and then periodically had to reduce overpopulation by causing natural disasters. The creator-god is Enki (Ea) who, with the wise goddess Nintu/Mami, mixed clay with the blood of a slain god and recited an incantation. The epithet 'wise', always given to Mami here, may be compared with the figure of Wisdom, as a woman who was present beside Yahweh at the creation, in Proverbs 8. The story of a universal Flood is an episode integral to the structure of the story.

The Babylonian Theodicy (Foster 1983: 806–14), a wisdom dialogue written in the late second millennium BC, contains a passage ascribing the creation of mankind to Narru (a name of Enlil), with Zulummar (a name of Ea) as the provider of clay, and Mami the goddess who give them shape. These gods were all responsible for introducing twisted words and falsehood into the speech of men. The bilingual Poem of Early Rulers (Alster 1990) begins creation with the god Enki/Ea and his designs or plans. The Theogony of Dunnu (Dalley 1989: 278–81; Hallo 1997: 404–15) treats creation as an agricultural process.

The Epic of Gilgamesh (Dalley 1989: 39–153), in its seventh-century version found at Nineveh, has a long textual history to which various earlier fragments bear witness. A tablet of the Bronze Age, perhaps around 1500 BC, has been found at Megiddo, which shows that an earlier version of that time was studied in Palestine. The later, so-called 'standard' work, still incompletely known, tells the story of Gilgamesh, king of Uruk, son of a king and a goddess, whose insufferable behaviour induces the gods to send down Enkidu, an innocent, unsophisticated man whose deep sense of outrage at injustice combines with friendship to reform Gilgamesh. They team

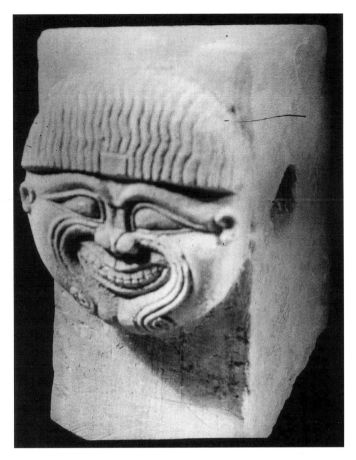

Figure 4.8 Humbaba, divine guardian of the Pine Forest in the Epic of Gilgamesh, from Tell el-Rimah, c.1800 BC. See T. Howard-Carter, *Iraq* 45 (1983), pl. Va. Photo reproduced by kind permission of David Oates.

up for an expedition to the Pine Forest to win fame by adventure, but commit sacrilege in killing Humbaba, the monstrous guardian, and in cutting down his trees. (see Figure 4.8). When Gilgamesh spurns the amorous advances of the goddess Ishtar, whose passion was aroused by his heroism and beauty, Enkidu insults her and so his death is decreed by the gods. Gilgamesh, inconsolable at the death and bodily corruption of his friend, wanders beyond the borders of the known world to cosmic regions where he meets the wise ale-wife Siduri and gets advice on how he can meet Utnapishtim who achieved immortality because he survived the Flood. But the latter explains that such a Flood will never be allowed again, and so Gilgamesh cannot avoid death. On his return to Uruk, Gilgamesh is cheated, by a snake and his own carelessness, of a chance to obtain the plant of rejuvenation. He arrives home knowing that humanity's lot is restricted to happiness in human relationships and achievement in urban culture. An extra episode, in which Enkidu rises up from the Underworld to relate his experiences to Gilgamesh, is clearly a late addition.

In its seventh-century form, the Epic of Gilgamesh is divided into twelve tablets, although the matching prologue and epilogue enclose only the first eleven tablets. Fragments of text from various earlier dates allow us to see that this version is an elaboration of an earlier version known in Megiddo in the mid-second millennium, and that the older version was constructed by using themes from a selection of Sumerian stories about the hero Gilgamesh. As a possibly historical king of Uruk, Gilgamesh is listed in the Sumerian king-list.

Certain echoes of this epic have been found in the Bible. The city of Gilgamesh, Uruk, is named in Genesis as one of the great cities of early antiquity. Ecclesiastes 9.7–9 gives a paraphrase of Siduri's speech to Gilgamesh as it is known in the Bronze Age version of the text; and a proverb used by Enkidu to encapsulate his assertion that two people acting together are stronger than two separate individuals comes into Ecclesiastes 4.9–12. The motif of committing sacrilege by cutting down trees is found describing the acts of Sennacherib in 2 Kings 19.23. An early version of the Book of Enoch (Beyer 1994), written in Aramaic and found at Qumran, has contributed to showing that a reworking of the story of Gilgamesh, Humbaba and Ut-napishtim was embedded in the narrative, and that the character of Enoch seems to owe something to the person of Enkidu; later, Manichaean, versions of the same themes in the Book of Giants (Reeves 1992: 51–164; Reeves 1993) confirm this, and there are vestiges of themes from Gilgamesh also in the Apocryphon of Jannes and Jambres (Pietersma 1994).

The story of the Flood in the Epic of Gilgamesh seems to have been taken over from the Epic of Atra-hasis, for the way in which the Flood story is inserted into the narrative suggests that it was not, originally, an integral part of the epic. The mountain on which the ark rests is named as Nimush only in the version in the Epic of Gilgamesh. A version of the Flood story in Akkadian cuneiform is known from fragments found at Ugarit.

Allusions to episodes in the Epic of Gilgamesh have been found in incantations of various periods, written in various languages. Akkadian Incantations (Foster 1983), like their Sumerian predecessors, often begin with a brief account of the creation of the world from prime elements, and sometimes allude to well-known myths. A few examples have been found beyond the borders of Mesopotamia, including Palestine.

Akkadian literature also produced battle epics based on the deeds of individual, historical kings. The best-known of these is the Epic of Tukulti-Ninurta (Foster 1983: 209–29) who ruled Assyria in the thirteenth century, but the genre is known from the time of Hammurabi, from an Epic of Zimri-Lim, king of Mari (still unpublished). This genre may have originated among the west-Semitic Amorites rather than in the cuneiform tradition of Mesopotamia proper. Since these epics do not seem to have entered the canon of educational literature, and so were not copied by scribes through the generations that followed their composition, we mostly know of them from very fragmentary tablets of a single period. Features of their style are long and aggressive speeches made by the opposing heroes to justify their actions, and battle scenes reminiscent of the climax to the Epic of Creation, with the great gods playing a major role. The Song of Deborah in Judges 5 may be connected to this genre.

A genre that began in Sumerian but is known mainly in Akkadian is the Poem or Chant of self-praise (e.g. Foster 1983: 74 and 901), in which a deity, usually a goddess, proclaims her own excellence. In other ways this type of composition is like a hymn in which the pious worshipper proclaims the virtues of the deity. Both types are found among the Hebrew Psalms.

In the Poem of Erra and Ishum (Dalley 1989: 282–315), probably composed in the eighth century BC, the merciless god Erra rants and rages, destroying men and animals, but is appeased by his helper Ishum. Some of the passages of rhetorical speech are similar in style to speeches of Yahweh in Ezekiel.

During the late Assyrian period at least one new myth seems to have been composed to account for the deportation of Marduk and Ishtar from Babylon after Sennacherib sacked the city. A rough draft for such a composition seems to have been made in the text now called The Marduk Ordeal (Livingstone 1989: 82–91), and there are some other fragments that may be related to the same episode in history and the need to justify it in mythological terms. In particular, an allusion linked to a non-standard version of the Epic of Creation names the great enemy as Anu, rather than Apsu, refers to the villain Qingu as the father of seven wicked sons, and features the goddess Ishtar as Marduk's fervent supporter. This group of texts contributed material to the story in the book of Esther, with its tale of Esther (Ishtar) and Mordecai (Marduk) as people deported from their homeland, resident at the court of an alien monarch (Dalley forthcoming).

Ugaritic-Canaanite (west-Semitic) myths and legends

For our knowledge of this material we are dependent upon two very different kinds of source: on the one hand, clay tablets of the fourteenth/thirteenth century found at Ugarit, written in the alphabetic cuneiform known as Ugaritic, and on the other hand a Hellenistic account of Phoenician traditions recorded by Philo of Byblos (Attridge and Oden 1981). The latter was based upon records said to have been made by a priest in Beirut, and so presumably some of the differences can be attributed to the individual traditions of Beirut and of Ugarit. Philo also acknowledges the Mesopotamian tradition of the Seven Sages. Some of the characteristics of Philo's work may be due to Hellenistic interpretation, but certain traits once thought to be Hellenistic, such as euhemerism (which maintains that the gods were originally men who built cities etc.), have since been recognized in indigenous Near Eastern traditions. Primordial elements such as air, water and mist, which are represented by god-names in all Near Eastern myths, are demythologized and given as common nouns by Philo, so that they can be related to the writings of early Greek philosophers. Some god-names are left in their Near Eastern form, but others are translated into their Greek equivalents. Some of the information Philo relays has been verified by the myths found at Ugarit, and so can definitely be attributed to the Late Bronze Age, pre-biblical, traditions of Canaan.

Ugaritic myths reflect a background of luxury and strife in the region between the sea and the mountains. Chief among them is the Myth of Baʿal (Pardee, in Hallo 1997: 241–73), probably a single composition of some 2,350 lines. Its story about Baʿal, a storm-god, and Yam, the Sea, portrays a stormy environment in which the great gods live on Mt Zephon, a dramatic peak to the north of Ugarit, beneath which lies the source of the rivers, the cosmic wellspring of fresh water where El, father of the gods, resides. Ba'al rides the clouds and battles for supremacy with the help of the virgin goddess Anat. His enemies Yam, 'Sea', and Mot, 'Death', are both male, and his defeat of them justifies the building of his new palace in Ugarit, using all the skills of the craftsman god Kothar-wa-Hasis. The details of smelting, plating and decorating, and the selection of precious materials from all over the earth, echo building inscriptions rather than Mesopotamian myths, but Athirat's role as the one who moulds bricks has Mesopotamian overtones. The great banquet of deities who drink wine to excess from fine vessels also reminds one of a major theme in the Epic of Creation, but the Ugaritic work has added music and minstrels to the scene. El, father of the gods, lives at the source of the rivers, a concept similar to that expressed in Genesis 2 and Ezekiel 28 and 32. The overarching theme is comparable with Marduk's battle and building works as recited in the Epic of Creation, but many of the details are very different. Names for the enemy are also found in the Psalms: Lotan, Rahab, Yam and Tannin are all specific to the Ugaritic myths. Psalm 29 in particular is thought to have been written under Canaanite influence (Day 1990: 42). The stories of Ba'al abound with goddesses including Athirat (biblical Asherah), 'Anat, Pidray, Tallay and Arsay. It is possible that versions of these myths were recited in temples throughout Syria and Palestine in the same way as we know, from clear written evidence, that versions of the Babylonian Epic of Creation were recited in major cult centres in Mesopotamia, but proof is lacking.

The name Ba'al is an epithet meaning 'Lord' in west Semitic, which corresponds to the east-Semitic Bel, 'Lord'. It could be used for any god as head of the pantheon in his own city, but is most frequently found of the storm-god in the Levant, and of Marduk in Mesopotamia (Fleming 1993). Ba'al's father is usually called by his epithet El, 'god', and at Ugarit El may stand for the chthonic god Dagan. A similar practice in naming hero-gods by such epithets is found in the Akkadian Epic of Anzu, the early version of which calls the hero-god *ilu* (cognate with El), 'god' and the later version calls the hero-god *bēl* (cognate with Ba'al), 'lord'.

The manner in which the myths of Ba'al are told, with short lines, frequent divine epithets and alternative names for gods; parallelism in which a pair of lines repeats the sense using alternate vocabulary, and various other stylistic features, have found many echoes in the Psalms and in parts of Isaiah. The closest parallels in biblical material can be made among such poetic conventions, and in the name and nature of the sea-serpent Lotan (probably Leviathan), which represents the powers of chaos. The parallels are mainly found in the Psalms, especially Psalm 29, and in the Prophets.

Allusions to myths of creation and the defeat of the serpent are found in Ugaritic incantations. Particularly important in this respect is the Ugaritic Liturgy against Venomous Reptiles (Pardee, in Hallo 1997: 295–98)

The Legend of Aqhat (Pardee, in Hallo 1997: 343–55) is the story of Daniel, 'man of Rapiu', a just king who was unable to produce a son and heir until Ba'al interceded and Aqhat was born. The event was celebrated with a feast. The divine craftsman Kothar-wa-Hasis made a bow for Aqhat which was so fine that the goddess 'Anat coveted it. Unable to get it by fair means, she resorted to force, turning her servant into an eagle which killed and ate Aqhat. Daniel eventually recovered the bones and buried his son. He cursed three towns in whose vicinity the murder occurred, but proved unable to exact vengeance on the gods. The story shares with the myth of Etana the theme of a king's childlessness until a god intercedes, but there are no other specific resemblances. The character of the wise king Daniel may perhaps be connected with the later sage of Jewish legend called Daniel, to whom the passages Ezekiel 14.14, 20 and 28.3 refer, but no connections have been found with the biblical book of Daniel.

The Legend of Kirta (or Keret) (Pardee, in Hallo 1997: 333–42) also deals with the theme of childlessness. Keret was a just king who had lost seven wives. The great god El appeared to him in a dream and told him to extract by force a new wife of royal blood. The myth deals with the nature of kingship and its effect upon the fertility of the land and upon human behaviour. A kernel of historical fact is thought likely for the setting, but has not been identified.

The Myth of Nikkal and the Kotharat (Gibson 1977: 128–29) tells how the marriage was arranged between Nikkal (a pronunciation of Ningal, the Sumerian moon-goddess) and Yarikh the west-Semitic god of the new moon, and how the birth of a son is foretold. Gifts are given, and hymns of praise sung. The story names a human bride and commends her to El and to the Kotharat, who are divine midwives and wise attendants, indicating that the myth accompanied a ceremony for a mortal rite of passage.

Other fragments of myths from Ugarit suggest that we possess only a small proportion of the whole quantity of such material as would have been available in Ugarit and other Levantine cities in the Late Bronze Age. No Canaanite myth telling the whole story of creation or the creation of humankind has been found among the tablets at Ugarit, but indirect evidence from a Hittite myth, Elkunirsha and Ashertu (Beckman, in Hallo 1997: 149), shows that the Canaanites were not lacking in this respect, for Elkunirsha is a phonetic rendering of the Canaanite name and epithet *El qōnē ereṣ*, 'El creator of the earth', and it is found much later in Aramaic at Palmyra and Hatra in the first century AD (Clifford 1994: 126 n. 25). It shows that a Canaanite myth about the creation of the world, handed down into Aramaic, still remains undiscovered. The birth of the great gods is told in the Ugaritic Myth of Dawn and Dusk (Pardee, in Hallo 1997: 274–83), giving insight into one episode in the story of creation.

Hittite myths

Most of the myths that have come to light in the Hittite capital Hattusa are written in the Hittite language in cuneiform script. The scribes who worked there bore Mesopotamian names, but their particular use of the writing system indicates that they were trained in the writing traditions of Bronze Age cities in North Syria. This may partly explain why the Hittites had such a mixture of material in their corpus of myths. The tablets from Hattusa were found in a very fragmentary state. Nevertheless, it has proved possible to assign the Hittite material to several distinct categories.

Several myths concern the storm-god, his deeds, his irrational anger, and the means required to pacify him. As in the Ugaritic myths, there is a strong connection with seasonal activities and festivals, although in the Hittite myths the story is explicitly connected to a festival. The Wrath of Telepinu (Beckman, in Hallo

1997: 151–53) tells how Telepinu, a storm-god , disappeared in a rage, causing fertility on earth to cease. An eagle and a bee were despatched to find him and bring him back, and he was pacified with great difficulty and much magic. The Storm-god and the serpent Illuyanka (Beckman, in Hallo 1997: 150–51) concerns a sequence of encounters between the storm-god of Nerik, a city in the Hittite heart-land, and a serpent who seems to represent the forces of chaos. The story is told as an accompaniment to the *purulli*-festival.

Some Mesopotamian myths were known in Hittite translations with modifica-tions. The Epic of Gilgamesh was translated into both Hittite and Hurrian, but the fragments we have are too small for us to assess how much divergence separated them from the Akkadian versions that we have. One remarkable detail seems to diverge from the Mesopotamian versions that are extant: Gilgamesh and Enkidu are explicitly referred to in Hittite as giants, which links them to the early version of the book of Enoch, found at Qumran. But we cannot tell how direct or indirect Hittite influence was upon the Aramaic composition.

Some Mesopotamian and Hurrian deities feature in Hittite myths. The Myth of Appu and his two sons (Hoffner, in Hallo 1997: 153–55) involves the sun-god of Sippar, Marduk of Babylon, and Shawushka, goddess of Nineveh, as well as the Hurrian storm-god Teshub of Kummiya, a major cult centre on the upper Tigris. The Song of Kumarbi (Hoffner 1990: 40–2) involves the Hurrian storm-god Teshub as well as Mesopotamian deities, and describes how generation succeeded generation of gods by violence; comparisons have been made with the Theogony of Hesiod. It may belong to a cycle of songs that includes the Song of Silver and the Song of Ullikummi (Hoffner 1990: 45–60).

Canaanite myths were known in Hittite. The myth Elkunirsha and Ashertu (Beckman, in Hallo 1997: 149), preserved only in small fragments, concerns rival-ries among the great deities of the Syrian pantheon: the gods El and Baʿal, and the goddesses Ashertu and Astarte.

Egyptian myths and legends

Different texts from various cities in Egypt give accounts of cosmogony that empha-size the role played by the patron god of a particular city. As in other parts of the ancient Near East, each account had its place and was not perceived as conflicting with or contradicting other accounts. Some syncretism connected the different tradi-tions, and different groupings of gods drew together important aspects of creation. All the traditions begin by trying to express a time before creation, and they indi-cate a primeval, watery formlessness; but then they envisage a single entity from which the diversity of creation emerges, whether by speech, by separation, by spit-ting, or by masturbation. The sun-god always plays a vital role. The Pyramid Texts and the Coffin Texts of the third millennium, and the Book of the Dead of the second millennium, as well as prayers and rituals (Lichtheim 1975; Clifford 1994), are the main sources of information for the following myths.

At Heliopolis the god Atum, symbolized by the *bnbn*-stone (an obelisk repre-senting the primordial mound that caught the rays of the rising sun), generated nine gods, the Ennead, by masturbation or, alternatively, spit.

Figure 4.9 Ivory carving from Samaria showing Horus on a lotus flower, early Iron Age.
Drawing by S. Dalley after J. W. Crowfoot, *Samaria – Sebaste 2 Early Ivories* (1938).

At Memphis, Ptah, the god of craft skills, gave material form to a mental image
or word, and so created Atum and the Ennead. This is closest to the biblical creation
in which the Creator-God stands outside the universe at the beginning, and so it is
thought that the theology of Memphis may have influenced Genesis 1 and Psalm
104.

At Hermopolis the sun-god Re was born from an egg that lay in a watery chaos,
and Re was the prime mover, creating four pairs of primeval gods resembling frogs
and snakes. In an alternative tradition from the same city, a lotus bud opened to
reveal Horus, who was then the prime mover (see Figure 4.9).

Cosmological concepts are found in hymns, including in The Great Hymn to the
Aten (Lichtheim, in Hallo 1997: 44–6), written in the Amarna period. It has been
compared closely with Psalm 104.

An important legend in Egyptian traditions was the Legend of Osiris (Cooke
1979) to which Egyptian texts refer in passing; a coherent account is given in Greek
by Plutarch. Osiris, a wise man who introduced wine into Egypt, was put in a chest
in the Nile and drowned by his brother Seth. The chest was washed up in Byblos;
Isis, their sister, collected bits of his body, and she with Nephthys reconstituted it
and brought it back to life. Osiris became a fertility god, acted as ruler of the
Underworld and judge of the Dead, and was equated with the Pharaoh as one who
was resurrected. His links with the city of Abydos were especially strong.
Connections with the story of Moses are not now favoured.

No story of a universal Flood is found in any Egyptian myth or tradition. A
Canaanite-influenced myth that features the goddess Astarte and the threatening sea,
Yam, is The Legend of Astarte (Ritner, in Hallo 1997: 35–6). Incorporated into a
spell is an account, The Repulsing of the Dragon (Ritner, in Hallo 1997: 32), of

how the sun-god Re had to overcome a gigantic serpent each day. In this tale the serpent presumably represents darkness and chaos.

Aramaic myths and legends

From Egypt comes an Aramaic text written in Egyptian demotic script (Steiner, in Hallo 1997: 309–26), which was addressed to an audience consisting partly of Israelites living in Egypt. It recounts the liturgy for a New Year festival in Upper Egypt in which the main deities have been identified as Nanay (a Babylonian goddess of Uruk) and Nebo (the Babylonian/Assyrian god Nabu). The text ends with a legend about the Assyrian king Ashurbanipal and how his brother Sarmuge (Shamash-shum-ukin) was king in Babylon but rebelled against his brother, despite the intercession of their sister Saritrah. The story explains why Ashurbanipal had to capture Babylon. The text seems to have been revised for use in a new situation, perhaps when Cyrus defeated Nabonidus and needed to justify his capture of Babylon.

The Legend of Ahiqar (VanderKam 1992) is a court narrative, which is now thought to go back to an Aramaic original. The story is set in the court of the Assyrian kings Sennacherib and Esarhaddon, and attached to it is a series of proverbs, ostensibly composed by the wise Ahiqar. The collection in general, and a few in detail, have been compared with the biblical book of Proverbs, especially 23.13–14. Ahiqar is mentioned in the Book of Tobit, an Aramaic story in the Apocrypha, as an Israelite relative of Tobit at an earlier Assyrian court. Sections of text in Ahiqar are reused in the story of Aesop, with its attached proverbs and fables, known in Greek, which is set in the court of a legendary king of Babylon.

Court legends of the type known from the book of Esther have been identified in Aramaic fragments from Qumran (White Crawford 1996).

Many of these texts appear to begin with a historical situation arising from court life in the Late Assyrian period. Some of them are then adapted to later courts: to the neo-Babylonian court of Nebuchadnezzar and Nabonidus, or to the Persian courts of Cyrus, Darius and Artaxerxes. The Prayer of Nabonidus (Levine and Robertson, in Hallo 1997: 285–6), an Aramaic text found at Qumran, seems to be antecedent to the story of Nebuchadnezzar's madness in the book of Daniel; the court is still in Babylon, but the name of the king changed.

Aramaic literature, with its reworking of themes for new political backgrounds, has as important a role as the older literatures of western Asia for illustrating the background to the biblical world.

BIBLIOGRAPHY

J. B. Pritchard (ed.), *Ancient Near Eastern Texts Relating to the Old Testament*, is now very largely outdated by substantial new discoveries. The books of Clifford, Dalley, Foster, Hallo, Hoffner, TUAT, and various editions of Sumerian texts, listed below, give more up-to-date translations and bibliography. Where interpretations differ widely, two different references have been supplied for translations.

Afanas'eva, V. K. (1987) 'Das sumerische Sargon-Epos', *Altorientalische Forschungen* 14: 237–46.
Alster, B. (1972) *Dumuzi's Dream*. Copenhagen.

—— (1990) 'The Sumerian Poem of Early Rulers and Related Poems', Orientalia lovaniensia Periodica 21: 5–25.

Attridge, H. W. and Oden, R. A. (1981) *Philo of Byblos: The Phoenician History*. Catholic Biblical Quarterly Monograph Series 9. Washington, D.C.

Benito, C. A. (1969) '"Enki and Ninmah" and "Enki and the World Order".' PhD diss., Pennsylvania.

Beyer, K. (1994) *Die aramäischen Texte vom Toten Meer, Ergänzungsband*. Göttingen.

Black, J. A., Cunningham, G., Robson, E. and Zólyomi, G. *The Electronic Text Corpus of Sumerian Literature*. http://www-etcsl.orient.ox.ac.uk

Borger, R., Lutzmann, H., Römer, W. H. P. and von Schuler, E. (1982) *Texte aus der Umwelt des Alten Testaments*. Vol. 1: *Historische-chronologische Texte*. Gütersloh.

Bottéro, J., and Kramer, S. N. (1989) *Lorsque les dieux faisaient l'homme: Mythologie mésopotamienne*. Paris.

Çagirgan, G. and Lambert, W. G. L. (1994) 'The Late Babylonian Kislimu Ritual for Esagila', *Journal of Cuneiform Studies* 43/45: 89–106.

Clifford, R. J. (1994) *Creation Accounts in the Ancient Near East and in the Bible*. Catholic Biblical Quarterly Monograph Series 26. Washington, D.C.

Cooke, H. P. (1979) *Osiris: A Study in Myths, Mysteries and Religion*. Chicago.

Cooper, J. S. (1978) *The Return of Ninurta to Nippur*, Analecta orientalia 52. Rome.

—— (1983) *The Curse of Agade*. Baltimore.

Dalley, S. (1999) 'Sennacherib and Tarsus', *Anatolian Studies* 49: 73–80.

—— (2000) *Myths from Mesopotamia: Creation, the Flood, Gilgamesh and Others* rev. edn. Oxford.

—— (forthcoming) 'An Assyrian Background to the Book of Esther'. Oxford.

Dalley, S. et al. (1997) *The Legacy of Mesopotamia*. Oxford.

Day, J. (1990) *Psalms*. Sheffield.

Durand, J.-M. (1993) 'Le mythologème du combat entre le dieu de l'orage et la mer en Mesopotamie', *Mari Annales de Recherche Internationale* 7: 41–61.

Farber, W., Kümmel, H. M. and Romer, W. H. P. (1987) *Texte aus der Umwelt des Alten Testaments* Vol. 2/2: *Religiose Texte*. Gütersloh.

Ferrara, A. J. (1973) *Nanna-suen's Journey to Nippur*. Studia Pohl, series maior 2. Rome.

Fleming, D. E. (1993) 'Baʿal and Dagan in Ancient Syria', *Zeitschrift für Assyriologie* 83: 88–98.

Foster, B. R. (1983) *Before the Muses: An Anthology of Akkadian Literature*. Bethesda, Md.

al-Fouadi, A.-H. (1969) 'Enki's Journey to Nippur.' PhD diss., Pennsylvania.

George, Andrew (1999) *The Epic of Gilgamesh: A New Translation*. London.

Gibson, J. C. L. (1977) *Canaanite Myths and Legends*. Edinburgh.

Greenfield, J. C. (1985) 'The Seven Pillars of Wisdom (Prov. 9:1) – A Mistranslation', *Jewish Quarterly Review* 76: 13–20.

Hallo, W. W. (ed.), (1997) *The Context of Scripture*. Leiden.

Hillers, D. (1992) 'LAMENTATIONS', *The Anchor Bible Dictionary* 4: 137–41. New York.

Hoffner, H. A. (1990) *Hittite Myths*. Atlanta.

Jacobsen, T. (1987) *The Harps that Once . . . Sumerian Poetry in Translation*. New Haven.

Katz, D. (1993) *Gilgamesh and Akka*. Groningen.

Klein, J. (1992) 'AKITU', *The Anchor Bible Dictionary* 1:138–40. New York.

Kramer, S. N. (1979) *From the Poetry of Sumer: Creation, Glorification, Adoration*. Berkeley.

—— (1983) 'The Sumerian Deluge Myth', *Anatolian Studies* 33: 115–21.

Kramer, S. N. and Maier, J. (1989) *Myths of Enki, the Crafty God*. Oxford.

Lewis, B. (1980) *The Sargon Legend: A Study of the Akkadian Text and the Hero Who Was Exposed at Birth*. American Schools of Oriental Research, diss. series 4. Cambridge, Mass.

Lichtheim, M. (1973–80) *Ancient Egyptian Literature*. vol. 1. Berkeley.

Livingstone, A. (1989) *Court Poetry and Literary Miscellanea*, State Archives of Assyria 3. Helsinki.

Michalowski, P. (1989) *The Lamentation over the Destruction of Sumer and Ur.* Winona Lake.

Pietersma, A. (1994) *The Apocryphon of Jannes and Jambres the Magicians.* Leiden.

Reeves, J. C. (1992) *Jewish Lore in Manichaean Cosmogony: Studies in the Book of Giants Traditions.* Cincinnati.

—— (1993) 'Ut-napishtim in the Book of Giants?' *Journal of Biblical Literature* 112: 110–15.

Shaffer, A. (1963) *Sumerian Sources of Tablet XII of the Epic of Gilgamesh.* Ann Arbor.

Sladek, W. R. (1974) 'Inanna's Descent to the Netherworld.' PhD diss., Pennsylvania.

VanderKam, J. C. (1992) 'AHIKAR', *The Anchor Bible Dictionary* 1:119–20. New York.

Dijk, J. J. van (1983) *Lugal ud me-lám-bi nir-gál: Le récit épique et didactique des Travaux de Ninurta, du Déluge et de la Nouvelle Création.* Leiden.

White Crawford, S. (1996) 'Has *Esther* Been Found at Qumran?' *Revue de Qumran* 17: 307–25.

Wilcke, C. (1969) *Das Lugalbandaepos.* Wiesbaden.

CHAPTER FIVE

HISTORIOGRAPHY IN THE OLD TESTAMENT

———•◆•———

A. D. H. Mayes

GENERAL HISTORIOGRAPHY

That history must be written afresh in each generation (Collingwood 1946: 248) is a basic recognition that provides a framework for understanding both ancient and modern historiography. It presupposes not simply that the production of history is a cumulative process, under continuous revision as new evidence emerges and new methods are applied, but rather also that the past is never objectively there for examination, but is what is mediated through the work of historians. Writing about the past, historiography, is the historian's narrative construction, the result of a process of selection and organization necessarily related to the cultural conditions within which it is formulated and the purposes it is designed to serve. There is a broad field here within which more or less credence can be given to the historian's account as a reliable representation of the past. Frequently, however, the issue is expressed in terms of a principled denial of the possibility of there being anything other than the historian's narrative reconstruction: the past has no independent reality, not in the sense that events did not happen, but in the sense that the narrative rendering of the past, with its connections and explanations, is wholly the imaginative construction of the historian, a creative fiction to be examined and judged by literary criteria rather than by criteria of historical credibility. 'Formerly, when historians invoked the idea of imagination, they meant the exercise of imagination required to transcend the present and immerse oneself in the past. Today, it more often means the opposite: the imagination to create a past in the image of the present and in accord with the judgment of the historian' (Himmelfarb 1992: 14).

The current theoretical discussion in the field of general historiography relates directly to historiography in the Old Testament. It is not simply a question of how Old Testament historiography may be used in the reconstruction of Israelite history, a matter that will be considered briefly at a later stage of this study, but rather in the first instance a question of how that literature is to be understood. In so far as historians in general work within specific cultural conditions, which are the matrix of their narrative constructions, does not the same hold good for those who produced Old Testament historiography? The issue here is to do with understanding the nature of the genre Old Testament historiography, an issue that cannot be divorced from the question of the nature of historiography in general.

An account of the history of thought about the nature of history cannot be the subject of this study (see, e.g., Collingwood 1946; Breisach 1983; Momigliano 1977, 1990), but aspects of current approaches to historiography should be noted, particularly in so far as they find clear resonances within current approaches to Old Testament historiography. At the postmodernist end of the spectrum, the argument that historiography results in texts that are to be approached as literature, without any necessary reference to anything outside itself, carries to its logical extreme the view that narrative history is the historian's construction, in principle no different from a work of fiction as far as the hermeneutical activity of the reader is concerned. Its truth is the reality the 'historian' has constructed, and the same linguistic, stylistic and deconstructionist approaches are appropriate to its expression as are appropriate to any literary work. This may be best exemplified in the work of Hayden White (1973, 1978; though see Barstad 1997: 43), and, for ancient history, Averil Cameron (1989). In neither case is it denied that there is such a thing as a historical event or that a distinction can be drawn between fact and fiction, but in both instances it is clear that, as far as the meaningful relationship of events is concerned, primacy belongs to the text and the text–reader relationship rather than to the objective reality of any referential truth behind the text. This development has arisen in response to White's question 'why do historians persist in failing to consider historical narratives as what they most manifestly are – verbal fictions, the contents of which are as much invented as found and the forms of which have more in common with their counterparts in literature than they have with those in science?' (quoted by Munslow 1997).

On the opposite side, Fustel de Coulanges is frequently held to exemplify the view that the task of the historian is to present the facts, which then speak for themselves: 'it is not I who speak, but history that speaks through me' (see, e.g., Becker 1959: 129f.; Fischer 1971: 4ff.). The objective description of the past as it really was, the simple collection of the facts of the past as discrete, knowable entities, is the historian's function, which may be realized through strict adherence to the historical method. Built on the principles of methodological doubt and analogy, the method involves the critical examination of evidence and the presupposition that events in the past were analogous, in terms of their general nature and their causal relationships, to events in the experience of the historian. Historiography is thus released from the subjective interests of the historian, in that it is concerned with critical enquiry in order to determine the truth about events that actually did occur (Mandelbaum 1977: 7ff.).

A middle path between these two extremes is usually sought: a sequence of events becomes history only when organized by the interpretative human intelligence (Elton 1969: 57). The argument, therefore, can concern only the nature, rather than the fact, of that subjective dimension. The selection of those events in the past that are to be organized and interpreted in historical reconstruction is necessarily a function not simply of the individual historian and his or her purposes and critical insight, but also of the social and cultural context to which the historian belongs. Moreover, the processes involved in the interpretation of data go back to and are dependent upon generalizations concerning human behaviour that are rooted in the contemporary culture (E. H. Carr 1961: 56ff.; Finley 1986: 68f.). Such generalizations are different in principle from the laws of natural science, since they derive from intuitive understanding based on experience rather than from experiments involving empirical observation (see Berlin 1980: 124ff.), and to that extent the idiographic objectives of the historian may still be usefully contrasted with the nomothetic aims of the natural scientist (Mandelbaum 1977: 4ff.). Yet the historian, whether ancient or modern, is writing about the past of the present: whether or not consciously present as a datum for explanation or legitimation, the present of the historian is the reality within the context of which the past is brought to light and interpreted. J. Huizinga's famous definition of history (1963: 9) as 'the intellectual form in which a civilization renders account to itself of its past' may not be wholly adequate to all forms of historiography, but it is peculiarly appropriate as expressing a line of essential continuity between Old Testament and modern historiography.

HISTORIOGRAPHY IN THE OLD TESTAMENT

Historiography

The writing of history is a literary activity that presupposes a historical consciousness. It was until fairly recently widely believed that the rise of a historical consciousness was unique to Israel in the ancient Near East, and that only with the later emergence of Greek historiography did any genuine parallel emerge (Mowinckel 1963: 4ff.). Other nations in the ancient Near East scarcely progressed beyond the keeping of lists and annals, the raw material of history, and their worldview was heavily dependent on an understanding of the actions of the gods in nature rather than in events. In Israel, on the other hand, a real form of historical writing emerged, using sources, and based on a dynamic, linear conception of history as purposive (Porter 1979: 125f.). The sources for historical writing as a literary genre were often the saga and the legend, the differences between them being that while saga and legend were oral and dealt with single topics, historiography was literary and dealt with a sequence of events (Noth 1958: 1498; see the discussion in Van Seters 1983: 209ff.), but the particular impulse that gave rise to that literary form, the emergence of a historical consciousness, was Israel's understanding of Yahweh as the sovereign Lord of history who had entered into a covenant relationship with Israel (Gese 1965). Von Rad's influential study (1966: 166ff.) identified the court history of David (2 Sam. 9–20; 1 Kgs 1–2), deriving from the time of Solomon, as the oldest example of ancient Israelite historical writing. Over against the older hero sagas, such as the Gideon account in Judges 6–8, there are no miraculous divine interventions in this historical writing, but within the chain of cause and effect on the human level the divine hand is at work: it is Yahweh who has brought all to pass, working secretly in the realm of the profane. The predisposing factors that made historical writing of this nature possible in Israel were three: first, Israel's general historical sense, clearly present even in the most primitive manifestations of its consciousness, the tribal aetiological sagas; secondly, Israel's talent for narrative presentation in a simple, limpid style; and, thirdly, Israel's unique conception of the activity of Yahweh in history.

Major weaknesses in this view emerged especially as a result of the work of Albrektson (1967), which demonstrated that in the texts of other ancient Near Eastern nations the gods are depicted as active in the domain of history, historical events being, from very early time, interpreted as divine actions. In neither case is the human chain of cause and effect broken; in both cases the secret divine activity is the effective power at work in human affairs.

Moreover, it had long been recognized (see already Gese 1965: 59f.) that the Hittites in the ancient Near East had 'developed the gift of historical observation to the highest degree'. Particularly in the historical prologue of the Hittite treaty texts, extensive and detailed reviews of past events are provided. The historicity of events, it is argued (Thompson 1992: 206), is here a central concern. In this there is a similarity with Greek historiography, which is characterized by a critical evaluative approach in the interests of ascertaining the truth of events recorded. This has led now to the position that a very different form of contrast may be drawn between Israel on the one hand and ancient Near Eastern and later Greek historiography on the other, in which the suitability of the term historiography for Israelite records may be denied. Historiography, it is argued (Thompson 1992: 207f.; 1996: 26ff.), should be understood as a narrative genre in which reference is made to events of the past understood as true, real and probable in terms of evidence. The distinction between historiography and fiction 'lies within the intentionality of the authors and in their assumptions regarding the reality of the past of which they write'. Historiography thus understood as a critical discipline is rarely to be found in the Old Testament. The biblical tradition, it is argued (Thompson 1992: 209), is marked rather by antiquarianism, a concern to preserve, classify and arrange a cultural heritage. There is only an impression of chronological progression; what is really characteristic is a structuring into a succession of great periods, which is interested more in classifying and cataloguing than it is in historiography.

The attempt to distinguish between historiography and what is not historiography on the basis of an authorial intention to evaluate the historical reliability of the records of past events presupposes a too narrow understanding of the nature of historiography. It may be that critical evaluation of the traditions of the past with respect to their historicity is difficult to find in the Old Testament, but, in Greek historiography, it is not necessarily that, or that alone, which defines it as historiography. Herodotus selected events as worthy of being rescued from oblivion, and he did so on the basis of both the best information available and the intrinsic significance of those events (Momigliano 1977: 190f.). In Greek historiography as in Israelite and other ancient Near Eastern historiography there is the selection and ordering of past events from the perspective of the present. In that Israelite historians did not critically evaluate their sources their historiography may be pre-modern, but its classification as historiography is scarcely to be denied. There are differences between Greek and biblical historiography also in other respects: biblical historiography reaches back to creation; it does not distinguish between a mythical and a historical age (Momigliano 1977: 194ff.), but the fundamental nature of the activity as an interpretative approach to the past from the standpoint of contemporary culture is common. The motivation that leads to its production is, in the most general sense at least, an explanatory purpose: how the past changed into the present, that present offering the conditions from the perspective of which the events of the past are selected and interpreted.

Biblical historiography

Biblical historiography is a term applied mainly to two major sections of the Old Testament, the Deuteronomistic History and the Chronicler's History. The Pentateuch, however, cannot be left out of consideration here, for even though its content may for the most part be dealt with under headings different from this, in its final form it reflects concerns that may properly be viewed as historiographical. In fact, Huizinga's definition of historiography given above may be used in quite a precise way as an interpretative key to the concerns of all three blocks of historiographic material in the Old Testament: the Deuteronomistic History, the Pentateuch and the Chronicler's History. For chronological and other reasons it is appropriate to treat them in that order.

The Deuteronomistic History

The Deuteronomistic History, comprising Deuteronomy to 2 Kings (excluding the book of Ruth, which, in the Hebrew Bible, appears in the final group of Old Testament books known as the 'Writings'), was first fully recognized and described by Martin Noth (1943), who argued for its having originated as a distinct unit on the basis of its consistency of language, structure and ideas. The language, later thoroughly described by Weinfeld (1972: 320ff.) and Hoffmann (1980: 325ff.), was held to be easily recognizable because of its plainness and the repeated use of stock phrases. In structure it is marked by the regular appearance of speeches or narratives composed by the Deuteronomist at critical points to review the history and draw consequences from it (Josh. 1; 12; 23; Judg. 2:11–23; 1 Sam. 12; 1 Kgs 8:14–61; 2 Kgs 17:7–41), the whole being also held together by a consistent chronology maintained throughout the period covered by the history. As far as its ideas and purpose are concerned, Noth noted its lack of interest in the cult, its emphasis on obedience to covenant law as the basis of the relationship between Yahweh and Israel, and its evident purpose to account for the disastrous end to the history of the people as the realization of the curse for disobedience attached to the covenant law.

Noth's work found wide but not universal agreement. Major difficulties emerged in relation to internal consistency in the work, difficulties that could not be resolved by reference to the source material taken up by a single Deuteronomistic author or editor (see Mayes 1983; O'Brien 1989). Neither traditio-historical (Hoffmann 1980) nor literary (Polzin 1980; Van Seters 1983) arguments have proved adequate to maintain the unity of the work: its internal breaks and points of unevenness remain significant indicators of the work's origin and history of construction, even though that origin and history have not yet been convincingly described. Two major approaches, both of which are rooted in dissatisfaction with Noth's understanding of the negative purpose of the history, have developed, one originating with Wolff (1961) and the other with von Rad (1962).

Wolff's argument, which drew attention to the significance of the theme of 'return' in the Deuteronomistic History, assigned responsibility for the work to a Deuteronomistic circle or school, rather than to an individual author; this then provided the possibility of distinguishing between layers of Deuteronomistic editorial work, within which context the work as a whole could be understood as having both negative and positive purposes. Significant contributions to this development have come from Smend, Dietrich and Veijola.

Smend (1971) has argued that Deuteronomistic texts in Joshua (1; 13; 23) and Judges (2) are not unified compositions, but incorporate later supplements to a basic Deuteronomistic text. These supplements, forming a single, secondary layer, are concerned with obedience to the law, and make Israel's success in its conquest of the land conditional on such obedience. Thus, a distinction is drawn between the Deuteronomistic historian, for whom Israel's conquest of the land was complete and successful, and a later ('nomistic') Deuteronomistic editor (DtrN), for whom that conquest has been successful only 'to this day' (Josh. 23:9b).

Dietrich's detailed study of Kings (1972) attempted to distinguish a prophetic stage of redaction of the Deuteronomistic history, preceding the work of DtrN. Noting the regular formal pattern of prophecy and fulfilment, he argued that such prophetic passages are all additions to their contexts, that their form is found with the classical prophets, especially Jeremiah, and that there is influence on their language from both the prophets and the Deuteronomistic History. The general intention of the redactor responsible for them (DtrP) is to unite prophecy with the Deuteronomistic movement, showing history as the arena in which the prophetic word works itself out. The work of the Deuteronomistic historian (DtrH), which reaches its conclusion in 2 Kings 25:21, was carried out shortly after the fall of Jerusalem, DtrN added the conclusion in 2 Kings 25:22–30, shortly after the release of King Jehoiachin; DtrP precedes DtrN, and should be dated to the early part of the exilic period.

Veijola (1975) traced all three layers back into the books of Samuel: DtrH is favourably disposed towards the monarchy and has a positive view of David as the servant of Yahweh; DtrP has subordinated the king to the prophet and presented the king as a source of guilt; DtrN holds up David as an ideal, but only on the basis of his obedience to the commandments, the monarchy in general being seen as an evil institution (Veijola 1977).

Smend later (1978) brought these studies together into a modified synthesis, which, though unable to assign every verse to its appropriate layer, attempted a full account of the development of the Deuteronomistic History: DtrH offered a continuous account, based on different sources, beginning in Deuteronomy 1:1 and ending with 2 Kings 25:30; DtrP introduced prophetic stories into the presentation of the monarchic period, the history of which ran its course according to the scheme prophecy–fulfilment; DtrN introduced an emphasis on the law throughout the work. All three belong closely together, the additions of the later redactors making use of the language of the work being edited. The task of distinguishing them is, therefore, difficult. In time, also, they are not far separated: DtrH, whose account ends with the release of Jehoiachin, cannot be dated before 560 BCE, and the two stages of redaction were completed by the early post-exilic period.

The approach initiated by von Rad involved understanding more radical change in the course of development of the Deuteronomistic History. Von Rad acknowledged that the Deuteronomist wished to explain why the saving history had ended in catastrophe, but argued that for the Deuteronomist the judgment of the law was not the only power active in history; equally effectual was the promise of salvation in the Nathan prophecy (see also McCarthy 1965). The work contains a messianic motif: the description of David, and the measuring of his successors by means of his standard, show that the Deuteronomist 'had a picture of the perfect anointed unremittingly present to his mind' (von Rad 1962: 345).

This tension between judgment and promise has been exploited by Cross (1973), who has argued that there are two themes in the Deuteronomistic History. The first is the sin of Jeroboam and his successors, which reaches its climax in the account of the fall of the northern kingdom and the meditation on that event in 2 Kings 17: 1–23. The second is the promise of grace to David and his house, which reaches its climax in the account of Josiah's reform in 2 Kings 22–3, where Josiah is said to have extirpated the cult of Jeroboam and attempted to restore the kingdom of David. By contrasting these two themes the Deuteronomist created a work that functioned to propagate Josiah's reform: Josiah is the new David, and in him is to be found true faithfulness to Yahweh, as a result of which the restoration of the Davidic kingdom is taking place. The Deuteronomistic History ended with the account of Josiah's reform, and so was a pre-exilic composition. Its extension, to bring the work up to the destruction of Jerusalem and the exile, is the work of a second Deuteronomistic editor, who has turned the history as a whole into an explanation of that catastrophe. This later editor's work can be found in Deuteronomy, Joshua, Samuel and Kings.

Cross's thematic argument was given literary-critical support by Nelson (1981) in his study of the regnal formulae that frame the references to each king in Israel and Judah. The formulae normally display considerable variety, but in the case of the last four kings of Judah they are terse and fixed. Here, they are the work of a later hand extending the work at a secondary stage. Nelson also marked out those parts of Kings that are with all probability to be assigned to the later editor: 1 Kings 8:44–51; 9:6–9; 2 Kings 17:7–20, 34b–40; 21:3bβ–15, all of which prepare for the destruction of Jerusalem and the exile.

Although there are points of contact between this approach and that of Smend, particularly in the anti-monarchic characterization of the later editor and in the passages assigned to him, Cross's approach is distinct in its conception of the significance of the change introduced by editorial work on the original Deuteronomistic History. While for Smend the editors introduced new emphases into a work whose basic nature remained relatively stable, for Cross the original Deuteronomistic History was fundamentally transformed by the later editor: the original work was designed as a paean of praise in support of the reforms of Josiah; the edited version is intended to explain the failure of the Davidic dynasty and the destruction of Jerusalem.

Although the practical possibility of distinguishing redactional layers in the Deuteronomistic History is sometimes rejected (see, e.g., Albertz 1994: 387f.), some useful contributions to the uncovering of that history have come from a variety of directions: for example, major studies of Kings by Weippert (1972) and Provan (1988), of Judges by Richter (1964), of Deuteronomy–Joshua by Lohfink (1981), of Deuteronomy by Seitz (1971) and of the Deuteronomic law by Lohfink (1993) and Braulik (1993, 1995), suggest redactional developments relating to separate parts of the history before it was brought together in a comprehensive form. However uncertain some of these may be, it is still widely accepted that early stages of the emergence of the whole are connected with the royal reform carried out by Josiah in 621 BC in Judah.

This early edition of the Deuteronomistic History, with its focus on divine promises relating to the temple and the Davidic king, had a legitimating function; it was, however, overtaken by the events of 587 BC. The supreme role that had been claimed by the centre, the king and temple, had not justified itself in history, and there emerged an urgent need for a change of perspective that would provide a fresh interpretation of events as they developed in the latter part of the exilic period. The revision of the Deuteronomistic History involved more than an updating; it was an extensive reorientation of the work towards a transformed social, political and religious situation. It involved an extensive supplementation of the Deuteronomic lawbook, particularly through the addition of ethical demands in Deuteronomy 19–25 (see Braulik 1993: 321f., 333f.), and also extensive editing as well as supplementation of what had probably not yet been a complete account of Israel's history in the land.

The transformation of the original pre-exilic Deuteronomistic History was accomplished by a comprehensive redaction that is to be traced from its beginnings in Deuteronomy 4 to its conclusion in 2 Kings 25:27–30. It constitutes a creative retrieval of tradition to meet the needs of an emerging people without statehood, in which Yahweh's relationship is directly with his people and in which the role of the king is little more than that of an exemplary Israelite. The effect of this revision was to release Yahweh from state power, to break the connection between the interests of the state and the interests of Yahweh. However, this was an effect accomplished not as a result simply of sophisticated theological reflection in a generally inimical historical context, but rather within the framework of the end of statehood, when a new legitimation had to be developed for a new way of relating to Yahweh brought about by historical events. The state of Israel had been destroyed, the political institutions formerly legitimated by the pre-exilic Deuteronomist had come to an end, the emerging remnant, in a condition of political and economic dependence on a foreign power, is compelled to establish its religious identity without recourse to political organs of statecraft through which it could be implemented.

The Deuteronomistic understanding of the nature of Israel in its relationship with Yahweh developed in a fundamental way between the first and second editions of the history. While the first edition perceived Israel as a royal state, centred on the capital and the Jerusalem temple, with the king as successor to Moses in the role of lawgiver and mediator between Israel and Yahweh, in the second edition this has greatly changed. The revision of the Deuteronomistic History introduced an emphasis on ethical demand (Deut. 19–25) together with theological commentary such as 2 Kings 17:7–23, 34b–41, as a way of effecting a change in focus from the king to Israel as a whole: it is on the people in the first instance and not on the king that responsibility for the welfare of Israel rests. The monarchy is now (Deut. 17:14–20) one of Israel's institutions rather than the divine foundation on which Israel's welfare rests.

The Pentateuch

Since the book of Deuteronomy both closes the Pentateuch and opens the Deuteronomistic History, the question of the relationship of the Deuteronomistic History with the Pentateuch is an immediate and obvious problem. This is one of a series of fundamental issues in Pentateuchal criticism today, which has led to a situation in which it is difficult to discern anything like consensus on most significant aspects of the topic. In view of the importance of the Pentateuch and its role not only as the 'staging ground for many if not most of the critical questions and methods that later spread to other areas of the biblical literature' (Knight 1985: 263; cf. also Carr 1997: 22), but also indeed as the text on the basis of which Israel's origins have traditionally been discussed and her religious history critically established, the present uncertainty in Pentateuchal criticism has very wide implications. Excellent detailed surveys of the rise and history of the classical critical theories in Pentateuchal criticism are readily accessible (North 1951; Clements 1979; Knight 1985; Nicholson 1998). The delineation of its main trends here is, however, desirable in order to create a general overall context within which the present *status questionis* might be better appreciated.

In so far as the rise of Pentateuchal criticism is to be linked with the questioning of the tradition of its Mosaic authorship, the origins of the critical approach go back to Ibn Ezra in the Middle Ages, but it was not until the mid-eighteenth century that the classical critical theories began to be worked out. On the basis of the use of different divine names, Yahweh and Elohim, in the book of Genesis, Jean Astruc distinguished two independent sources in that book. More detailed studies in the following books by J. G. Eichhorn, G. Ewald, W. M. L. de Wette and others, indicated that the source using Elohim was itself a combination of two sources, one of which had narrative concerns and the other priestly and legal concerns. This led to a distinction between three sources, designated by the sigla P, E and J, while the siglum D was used for Deuteronomy, which was recognized as an independent piece of work. The high point of the development was reached with Ed. Reuss, K. H. Graf and especially J. Wellhausen in the latter part of the nineteenth century. The sources of the Pentateuch had by then been worked out in detail; the contribution of Wellhausen and his associates lay in the absolute and relative dating of these sources. D had long been linked with the reform of Josiah in 621 BC; what now became clear was that P, the priestly and legal source, was later than D, since it presupposed the characteristic D demand for the centralization of worship, while J and E know nothing of D and were to be dated earlier, J being the older of the two and belonging to the time of Solomon. This was a revolutionary development that did not simply result in a stable and comprehensive picture of the process of composition of the Pentateuch, but also had direct implications for the development of an evolutionary view of Israelite religious history.

The first half of the twentieth century saw developments in the position reached by Wellhausen, none of which, at any rate at first, was seen as other than an attempt to refine a position already firmly established. On the one hand, the sources Wellhausen and others had described as the work of individual authors came to be seen as themselves compilations, and so J was divided into J1 and J2 (or J and L, or J and N), with the same being true of P. This approach still continues (Carr 1997: 26ff.), but has perhaps never won the support or interest characteristic of the alternative developments that may be led back to G. von Rad and M. Noth.

Both von Rad and Noth regarded the Pentateuch, and indeed the major sources into which it could be divided, as the final stage in a long process of development. The methods they used to describe that process were, however, different, and their results correspondingly deviated at major points. Von Rad's approach (1966: 1ff.) was form-critical: the Pentateuch, or Hexateuch (since von Rad regarded the Penta-teuchal sources as continuing into Joshua), is an elaborate statement of faith that has the character of a creed. It preserves short credal statements that may properly be regarded as its foundation: examples of these are to be found in Deuteronomy 6:20–4 and Joshua 24:2–13, but especially in Deuteronomy 26:5–9. The short historical creed is the basis of the Hexateuch, but it also provides a point of origin by comparison with which it is possible to mark out the major stages by which the Hexateuch developed. There are three of these: first, the creed makes no reference to the revelation at Sinai, and so a major development stage was the building in of the Sinai tradition between Exodus 19 and Numbers 10; secondly, the creed makes only brief reference to the patriarchs, and so the development of this tradition marks a further significant stage; thirdly, the creed makes no reference to the primeval history, and so Genesis 1–11 must be regarded as having been introduced at a stage in the Hexateuch's evolution. It is the Yahwist (the author of the J source), a major theologian of the Solomonic period, who was responsible for these innovations.

The approach adopted by Noth (1948) is in the first instance a development of Wellhausen's literary criticism and thereafter traditio-historical. The literary-critical developments are twofold. First, against those who argued for the extension of the Pentateuchal sources into Joshua, Noth argued that while indeed the older J and E sources did tell of a conquest of the land, they were in time edited into the framework of the Priestly document (1943: 206ff.). The latter is not to be found in Joshua, and in fact has its focus of interest on the events at Sinai and the figure of Moses. With the death of Moses P, and therewith also the earlier documents edited into the framework of P, came to an end (see further Mayes 1983: 17f.). This has clear relevance to the question of the relationship of the Pentateuch with the Deuteronomistic History, for the conclusion is that the Pentateuch was created through the displacement of the story of the death of Moses from the end of Numbers, where it originally belonged, to the end of Deuteronomy presented as Moses' final speech.

Noth's second literary-critical contribution formed the basis for his traditio-historical study. This was the observation that the two older sources J and E are too similar to be wholly independent of each other. Their similarities can be explained only on the basis that they go back to a common original, to which Noth gave the siglum G ('Grundlage'), a source that may have been either oral or written. This basic source (and in this respect Noth departed in a major way from von Rad) contained all the basic themes of the Pentateuch: patriarchs, exodus, wilderness wandering, Sinai and the conquest of land. The context within which it took its origin was the pre-monarchic Israelite tribal federation, which Noth, making fruitful use of an analogy drawn from later Greek and Roman history, referred to as an 'amphictyony'. At this point Noth's historical understanding worked together with his traditio-historical view to produce a picture of Israel having emerged in the land and having created its identity in the amphictyony through the fusing of the traditions of its constituent groups. On the basis of a detailed analysis of each of the major themes, Noth was able to establish its origin and development in numerous independent traditions fostered by different groups of what later came to comprise amphictyonic Israel.

Although in some respects the work of von Rad and Noth could be seen as complementary, particularly in that von Rad was concerned with the compositional stage of the Hexateuch, whereas Noth was concerned with the pre-compositional stage of the early development of the traditions, there are some major differences between them, particularly in relation to the contribution the Yahwist was understood to have made in the production of the J document. Nevertheless, for several decades their work was considered to point towards the different ways in which future study was to be conducted, and therewith was accepted as effectively confirming the results achieved with the grand synthesis of Graf and Wellhausen.

A number of problems contributed to the breakdown of the programme as determined by von Rad and Noth, and eventually also to the fundamental questioning of the Wellhausen synthesis. As far as von Rad is concerned, the short historical creed came to be recognized as a Deuteronomic composition (Hyatt 1970: 152ff.; Mayes 1979: 332ff.), which could then be seen as a summary coming at the conclusion of a process, rather than a foundational belief statement that initiated it. Noth's proposal of a G source originating in an Israelite amphictyony was doubted for two reasons. On the one hand, the fragmentary character of E, which Noth explained on the basis of its having been preserved only in so far as it differed from J, could rather be understood as the result of E being a redactional level, a stage in the history of development of J (see the review in Knight 1985: 282f.). If this is so, there is no literary-critical argument for a pre-J source. Secondly, the theory of a pre-monarchic Israelite amphictyony as the context of origin of an early G source came under increasing attack (Mayes 1974; 1992): if there was no amphictyony, and Israelite origins were much more fragmented, gradual and unsystematized than that theory suggested, it was difficult to conceive of a context within which such a source, with the identity-creating function that Noth imagined for it, could have emerged. The document P, which Noth argued to have been an independent source used as the final framework for J and E, has also been considered in very different terms. Like E, so P may be seen, particularly in view of the many significant Pentateuchal traditions it does not contain, as a redactional stage rather than a source (Cross 1973: 293ff.). This must then create problems for Noth's argument that the JE conquest story was truncated in favour of the P framework, and so also for his view of the relationship of the Pentateuch and the Deuteronomistic History.

In more recent years, however, the critique has extended beyond this level to bring into question the adequacy of the Wellhausen view in general, with particular attention being directed to the presumed oldest source, J. The critique has come especially from Van Seters (1975, 1992, 1994), Schmid (1976) and Rendtorff (1977). Van Seters (1975: 139ff.) has raised basic questions against the traditio-historical method's claim to be able to trace the oral history of the traditions, and has asserted the primacy of explanations that work with the text as literature. Denying any necessary link between the Genesis story of the patriarchs and non-biblical texts of the second millennium BC, Van Seters has argued for a primary compostion in the exilic or post-exilic periods of those materials traditionally seen as JE. This work, which he assigns to the Yahwist, was later supplemented and revised by a priestly editor.

Schmid provided much of the evidence for Van Seters's later argument (see also Blum 1990) that the non-priestly Pentateuchal texts show clear signs of dependence on Deuteronomistic and prophetic traditions. The story of the call of Moses in Exodus 3f. uses a literary form known from classical prophecy and can be understood only against a prophetic background; the plague stories of J show prophetic and Deuteronomistic forms, while many of the wilderness wandering stories are Deuteronomistic. Other general indications of the late date of pre-priestly material in the Pentateuch are the Deuteronomistic covenant theme of the Sinai pericope, the promise of many descendants in the patriarchal traditions reflecting a late time of decline and threat, the near silence of pre-exilic prophecy on much that is fundamental to the Pentateuch (patriarchs, Moses, exodus, Sinai covenant). The historical theology of J is, therefore, a response to a time of crisis and threat to the national religion of Israel and the very identity and existence of the people.

Rendtorff has contributed significantly to the debate in a number of respects. In the first place, he has questioned the possibility of form criticism and tradition history being seen simply as stages with literary criticism in the single continuum of Pentateuchal criticism. Literary criticism as practised by Wellhausen and most others presupposed that the resulting documents or sources were composed by authors with individual styles and ideas, and it was on this basis that J, E, D and P could be distinguished. Form criticism and tradition history, on the other hand, presuppose not authors but compilers who preserved the essential character of the material they collected. Thus, the distinctive characteristics of this material may point not to diverse compilers but rather simply to diversity in the materials collected by any one compiler. Apart from this, Rendtorff questioned in any case the existence of continuous sources in the Pentateuch. The larger units (patriarchs, exodus, Sinai, wilderness wandering, settlement) are relatively isolated: covenant and promise, so central to the patriarchal traditions, are largely absent from the exodus tradition; the Sinai pericope makes only sporadic reference to the exodus and patriarchal promise; the wilderness wandering tradition makes reference to Egypt but never in such a way as to presuppose the tradition of the exodus as a saving act of Yahweh; the settlement tradition in Numbers makes only slight reference to the exodus and the patriarchs. Such connections between these units as do exist are never central to the narratives but belong to an editorial layer that shows links with the ideas and vocabulary of Deuteronomy. This editing was succeeded by a priestly revision that did not constitute the incorporation of an independent source but rather a further redactional stage in the development of the Pentateuch. It is, however, the earlier Deuteronomic redaction that is of primary significance, since it is this that first brought together the independent larger units within the Pentateuch.

If a connected presentation of the Pentateuchal story is not to be found before the Deuteronomic–deuteronomistic period, and if Deuteronomic–deuteronomistic editing first brought it into existence, then it may follow that the Pentateuch, but in the first instance the Tetrateuch, came to be formed on the basis of the already existing Deuteronomistic History, and indeed as a prologue to that history (Van Seters 1992), and never had independent literary existence. This picture is largely confirmed by Rose's detailed study (1981) of parallel and otherwise related texts in Genesis–Numbers and the Deuteronomistic History, which demonstrated that the general priority is to be assigned to the Deuteronomistic History.

If this is the case, the Tetrateuch is to be seen in the first instance as a creation, within the context of the Deuteronomistic movement, of a prologue to the existing Deuteronomistic History. The later priestly stage of redaction of that material, which covered not only Genesis–Numbers but also the account of the death of Moses in Deuteronomy 34, is to be seen as having had as its overall purpose the separation off of the first five books as a separate entity from the Deuteronomistic History. This development should be set against a background in which the Deuteronomistic History could no longer provide a meaningful foundation for the new community. Although temple and monarchy play a less emphatic role in the second edition of that history, there was little possibility that the work could command the adherence of the diaspora, and therewith a foundation for exilic Judaism. The Pentateuch responds to the inadequacies of the Deuteronomistic History in a number of detailed and general ways: it introduces a greater emphasis on social and ethical demands; through its emphasis on promise and on the law as that which was to be obeyed in the land its orientation is to the future rather than to the past. It has been rightly recognized (Clines 1978) that the theme of the Pentateuch is promise and only partial fulfilment of that promise: the Pentateuch holds out for a scattered Israel a strong and explicit hope to sustain it in its powerlessness.

The Pentateuch in its priestly redaction has a quite distinct understanding of the nature of the community, different from that of the Deuteronomistic History. In terms of the distinction drawn by Eilberg Schwartz (1990: 195ff.), membership of the community in the Deuteronomistic History is achieved: one becomes a member by commitment to belief, membership being open to all those willing to make that commitment; in the Pentateuch, on the other hand, membership is ascribed: one is a member through genealogical descent, and without that relationship membership is not possible (see further Mayes 1996: 505ff.). The Pentateuch has carried through a significant and fundamental shift in the perception of the nature of Israel, marking off the borders of the chosen people much more sharply against the world, and, through Genesis 1–11, setting it in a universalistic context.

Chronicles–Ezra–Nehemiah

In 1943 Noth could write, 'it is generally accepted as certain that in 1 and 2 Chronicles and Ezra and Nehemiah we have but a single work. In this case, therefore, in contrast with the analysis of the Deuteronomistic History, there is no need to start with a demonstration of the work's literary unity' (1943: 110; ET 1987: 29). The date of composition of the work, which is based mainly on canonical but also occasional other independent sources, was about 300 BC or later. Its purpose was to demonstrate the legitimacy of the Davidic dynasty and also of the Jerusalem temple as the cultic centre of the Judean kingdom. The author of the work intended to write history, but, by contrast with the Deuteronomistic historian, was ready to adapt his sources to his own purposes. In this respect the Chronicler was a much more independent narrator than the Deuteronomistic historian.

The three topics that have been the subject of continuing study correspond to this outline of Noth's work: the unity of the Chronicler's history in Chronicles–Ezra–Nehemiah; the sources of that history; and the purpose and theology of the Chronicler.

That Chronicles–Ezra–Nehemiah form a single literary unit composed by the Chronicler is a view based on a number of observations (see summary and bibliography in Klein 1992a: 993; Jones 1993: 86ff., 121): the conclusion of Chronicles in 2 Chronicles 36:22–3 is repeated in Ezra 1:1–3a; 1 Esdras does not make a distinction, bringing together 2 Chronicles 35–36, Ezra 1–10 and Nehemiah 8; the three books share common language and style; there are theological and ideological links between them. None of these arguments, however, has been found compelling. The first point is a deliberate link that could as easily presuppose independent authorship of Chronicles and Ezra–Nehemiah as it could indicate any significant level of common authorship. As far as the second is concerned, Williamson (1977: 5–70) sees 1 Esdras as a secondary compilation which at most shows that a part of the Jewish tradition in the second century associated these works. Likewise the third point has not carried conviction: Japhet (1968) has pointed to linguistic differences, while Williamson has concluded from over a hundred supposed similarities that all but six are either irrelevant or may even indicate diversity in authorship. On the final point it has been argued that there is a common understanding of history, and a common interest in genealogies and lists, in the temple, religious occasions and cultic personnel, to be detected throughout all three books. On the other hand, however, there are differences on highly significant subjects: so Chronicles does not share the exclusiveness of Ezra and Nehemiah, in so far as it understands Israel as all those from the twelve tribes faithful to the Jerusalem temple and its cult, and does not share the rejection of the northerners, which is important to Ezra and Nehemiah (see Ezra 4:2f., 9f.); the significance Chronicles attaches to the Davidic dynasty is not shared by Ezra and Nehemiah; Chronicles does not emphasize the exodus in the manner of Ezra–Nehemiah; the frequent references to prophets in Chronicles disappear in Ezra–Nehemiah.

While the matter is still under discussion, it would seem that the balance of probability is not in favour of a single work or a single author. These are independent works that, at a stage not yet clear, came to be associated. Their time of origin is not certain: on the basis of not only the last events it records, but also some internal clues (Klein 1992a: 994f.; 1992b: 732), the composition of Chronicles may be dated to the late fifth or fourth century; for Ezra–Nehemiah, dates of composition are suggested between c.400 and c.300 BC.

The sources used by the authors/editors of Chronicles, Ezra and Nehemiah include both canonical sources and other possible sources. The genealogies of 1 Chronicles 1–9 have been taken from Genesis, Exodus and Numbers, and the subsequent monarchic history of Chronicles has made extensive use of Samuel and Kings. The genealogies of 1 Chronicles 1–9, which probably have a broadly historiographic purpose (see Hoglund 1997: 21ff.; Braun 1997: 98ff.), find parallels in Greek historiography of the fifth and fourth centuries, and intend to show the organization and interrelationship of the members of the Israelite people, and also the continuity of the people through a time of disruption. The arrangement and focus of the material on Judah, Levi and Benjamin suggest that it is integral to the historiographic presentation of Chronicles.

The Chronicler's use of Samuel and Kings is highly selective. Attempts to show that the Chronicler and the Deuteronomistic historian made independent use of a common source (Auld 1994: 22ff.; Rainey 1997: 43ff.), or that the Chronicler used an earlier redaction of the Deuteronomistic History (McKenzie 1985), are probably not persuasive (see Van Seters 1997: 285ff.) even if it is likely that the particular text tradition of the Deuteronomistic History to which the Chronicler had access was not the Masoretic but rather a Palestinian text attested by the Qumran scrolls (see Klein 1992a: 995f.; also the review of the discussion in Williamson 1987b: 107ff.). Recognition of this will slightly modify the view taken of some of the differences between Chronicles and the Masoretic version of Samuel and Kings, but the overall situation remains the same: the Chronicler made selective use of the Deuteronomistic History, effectively rewriting it to suit his purposes. Saul has been dealt with only as an introduction to David (1 Chr. 10); much of the David tradition is omitted, particularly those parts of it, such as the Bathsheba affair, the murder of Uriah and the rebellion of Absalom, that reflected badly on the king; the history of the northern kingdom, except in so far as it impinged directly on Judah, has been passed over in silence.

As far as non-canonical sources are concerned, it is clear that Ezra and Nehemiah make extensive use of such sources, including official decrees and letters, royal and temple records and lists, together with memoirs deriving from both Ezra and Nehemiah (see Klein 1992b: 732ff.; Williamson 1987a). The editorial arrangement and supplementation of these sources is a matter of considerable complexity and dispute, but the use of autobiographical accounts of contemporary history confers a unique historiographical significance on this material (Momigliano 1977: 27f.).

Chronicles, like the Deuteronomistic History, makes reference to sources, including 'the history of Nathan the prophet', 'the prophecy of Ahijah the Shilonite', 'the vision of Iddo the seer' (2 Chr. 9:29), 'the Commentary on the Books of Kings' (2 Chr. 24:27). That these ever existed as sources under such titles is, however, doubtful: more likely they should be seen as interpretative references to the corresponding sources to which the Deuteronomistic History itself refers (1 Kgs 11:41; 2 Kgs 12:20 [English versions 12:19]), and thus as part of the Chronicler's general interpretative use of the Deuteronomistic History. More difficult, however, is the question of whether or not the Chronicler had available any other pre-exilic sources, outside the canonical texts, for the reconstruction of history. A strongly minimalist view would be that no such sources have been shown (North 1974: 392; see also Wright 1997: 150ff., with reference to those battle accounts in Chronicles without parallels in Samuel and Kings). Others more open to the possibility that the Chronicler did have access to other sources refer to occasional chronological and other references (Barnes 1997: 106ff.; Klein 1992a: 996f.), or more extensive sources including perhaps especially one from which the list of Rehoboam's fortifications (2 Chr. 11:5–12) is derived (see the summary in Jones 1993: 70f.). One particular study (Knoppers 1997: 184ff.) argues that the Chronicler's depiction of the reigns of Uzziah, Jotham and Hezekiah agrees with what archaeology reveals for the eighth century in relation to urban development in the shephelah and the Judaean hill country, and the expansion of Jerusalem. Other aspects of the Chronicles description, however, are complicated by archaeology, especially in relation to the aftermath of Sennacherib's campaign, but it seems, nevertheless, that the unique material in Chronicles, when compared with the Deuteronomistic History, cannot all be dismissed as having no historical relevance.

For the structure and theology of Chronicles, the speeches and prayers of kings and prophets (which have no Deuteronomistic parallels) are of basic importance. These are not to be thought of as belonging to an established genre of levitical sermon as von Rad (1966: 267ff.) believed (see Klein 1992a: 998). They are, rather, compositions by the Chronicler that function as structural markers and vehicles for his views (see Klein 1992a: 998; Throntveit 1997: 225ff.; Balentine 1997: 246ff.). They create strong links between David and Solomon, emphasizing the planning and building of the temple as their joint project, and contributing to the overall presentation of this period as the ideal time in Israel's history. Later prophetic speeches, of which there are ten without parallel in the Deuteronomistic History, are concerned with the theme of retribution, which, in a number of cases (2 Chr. 12:1; 16:7–10; 26:16–21), provides the rationale for events reported in Kings. This theme, absent from Ezra and Nehemiah, is addressed to the post-exilic community. The experience of Manasseh (2 Chr. 33) was to be taken as a paradigm for that of the later community and indeed for individuals in that community: evil brought about deportation to Babylon; repentance and prayer to Yahweh led to restoration and renewal (Schniewind 1997: 223).

The Chronicler's theology of retribution is a warning and call to repentance. Restoration and renewal are a prospect for all who repent and acknowledge the Jerusalem temple, including the people of the former northern kingdom. Even though the Chronicler is generally silent on the north, his description of Hezekiah's Passover (2 Chr. 30), to which all Israel was invited, is an invitation also to the northerners of the Chronicler's own day to acknowledge the place of Jerusalem and its temple as the unique legitimate cult centre for all Israel.

A number of aspects of the Chronicler's theology distinguish that work from Ezra and Nehemiah. There also the importance of the temple is indeed emphasized, but in two respects Ezra and Nehemiah are distinct: on the one hand, the restoration and rebuilding is achieved as a result of the support of the Persian authorities with whom a collaborative attitude is effectively encouraged (Klein 1992b: 739f.); on the other hand, the borders of the community are much more sharply defined through the rejection of foreign wives and the identification of the true community as those who returned from exile. This is a community defined by its strict adherence to the law, and not only by its acknowledgment of the Jerusalem temple as the legitimate cult centre; its hope is for the purging of the community from its imperfections through obedience to the law, rather than for a restoration in which the Davidic dynasty will again receive the steadfast favour of God (2 Chr. 6:42).

OLD TESTAMENT HISTORIOGRAPHY AND HISTORICAL RECONSTRUCTION

It cannot be our task here to discuss the range of problems that confront the historian in reconstructing the history of Israel, still less to attempt any such reconstruction. It is, nevertheless, necessary that brief reference should be made to the implications for the historian of our discussion of the nature of Old Testament historiography.

It is clear that Old Testament historiography is very much concerned with the past of the present: whether or not it aims consciously to justify and legitimise contemporary practice and institutions by showing their rootedness in antiquity, it most certainly does reflect contemporary issues and concerns that have at their heart the identity and self-understanding of the ancient historian's culture. In all three examples of Old Testament historiography the question of national, cultural and religious identity can be understood as the guiding thread that structures and informs the interpretative process that led to their production. As far the Deuteronomistic History is concerned, its first edition, with its focus on Moses, David and Josiah, together with its centralization criterion of judgment, defines Israel in terms of loyalty to the king and the capital city; the second, exilic, edition, on the other hand, has democratized that understanding mainly through relating Yahweh's royal covenant to the people as a whole, and defining Israel in terms of its loyalty to that covenant. The unconditional royal promise of the first edition is in the second made conditional: with obedience Israel will be restored as the people of Yahweh. That conditional element has not disappeared in the Pentateuch, but here is subordinated to two other concerns: first, that Israel is the chosen people as the result of promise to the patriarchs; secondly, that this promise, of land and descendants, is still held out before the dispossessed people. Israel now understands itself in terms of election, covenant and obedience to the law in the land that has been promised them. The future orientation of the Pentateuch is directed towards a diaspora people living without the institutions of national government. There are, as already noted, substantial differences between Chronicles, on the one hand, and Ezra and Nehemiah, on the other. They all, however, share a fundamental interest in the Jerusalem temple, to the extent that Israel may be understood as a worshipping community. In Chronicles that self-understanding is expressed in a remarkable way, not simply through the centrality of the building of the temple in the idealized period of David and Solomon, but in particular through the evident concern of the author to establish the legitimacy of the second temple by establishing its continuity not simply with the first temple but also with the priestly tabernacle of the Mosaic period (see especially Van Seters 1997: 283ff.). The description of the temple building in 2 Chr. 3ff. not only takes over material from Kings but modifies this in the light of both the second temple and the priestly tabernacle. Thus, 2 Chr. 3:14, describing what was probably the veil of the second temple, is not to be found in 1 Kings 6, but is derived from the tabernacle description in Exodus 26:31; 36:35. The temple and its rituals have regained this centrality for defining the people of God.

As far as the sources used by Israelite historiography are concerned, it is true that there is much here to assist in the scholarly reconstruction of Israelite history. This is perhaps particularly true of the decrees, letters, records and lists of Ezra and Nehemiah, together with the accounts of Israelite and Judean kings in the books of Kings, themselves evidently derived from official sources (for an extended discussion of the sources used by the Deuteronomist in Kings see Halpern 1988: 207ff.). Other pre-Deuteronomistic material in the Deuteronomistic History, such as the history of the rise of David in 1 Samuel 16 to 2 Samuel 5 and the succession narrative of 2 Samuel 9–20 and 1 Kings 1–2, has frequently been taken as early historiography that may be used immediately in historical reconstruction. The age of this material is quite uncertain, however, and its clear ideological purpose (on the former see, e.g., Rendtorff 1971: 428ff., and on the latter McCarter 1981: 355ff.) makes its usefulness for historical reconstruction increasingly dubious. A history of Israel is indeed not open to reconstruction without reference to the Old Testament (see the discussion in Miller 1991: 93ff.), but the relevance of Old Testament texts is in the first instance to the time in which they were composed and only after critical evaluation on a case-by-case basis to the times of which they purport to tell.

One must, of course, add to this the point that if ancient historians were motivated, either consciously or unconsciously, by ideological concerns, so also are modern historians. Sasson (1981; see also Oden 1980; Ahlström 1991: 134; 1993: 50) has clearly demonstrated the influence of the contemporary political and cultural context on German and American biblical scholarship, and, in particular, on how the origin and early history of Israel have been portrayed in scholarly reconstruction. The American preference for the 'biblical model', understood in terms of conquest of the new land Israel holds as the gift of God, is not without connection to the national mythology of the origin of the United States; the German preference for a process of peaceful immigration into a cultural and political context that lacked any cohesive national consciousness, leading eventually to the formation of a nation state, may be compared with political developments in the first half of the twentieth century, when Jewish immigration into Palestine led eventually to the establishment of the nation state of Israel; the theory that the ancient Israelite national identity was forged in the creation of a national tradition within the framework of the union of the tribes in an amphictyony expresses also the view of the nature of the nation state and its origins in nineteenth-century German historiography. This uncovering of the hidden influences on biblical scholarship has now been radically extended by those (Whitelam 1996; Davies 1992, 1997) who, while agreeing that there was indeed an 'Israel' of some form or forms in the first half of the first millennium BC, believe that most modern scholarly accounts of the history of Israel are little more than modified versions of the biblical story, which is itself an exilic or post-exilic ideological construction, and in adherence to which modern historians of ancient Israel show their commitment to a particular religious worldview rather than to the requirements of critical historiography.

The sometimes rather strident debate on these issues that characterizes current discussion (see, e.g., the replies to Provan 1995 by Davies 1995; and Thompson 1995) revolves around a number of issues: the ideological nature of biblical texts; the possibly very late date of these texts and also of the sources on which they are based; the relative importance of biblical and non-biblical records, especially the archaeological record; the significance of the interpretative process in the use of sources in historical reconstruction; and the epistemological self-awareness of the historian of today. While the theoretical debate may sometimes seem polarized, on the practical level of actual historical reconstruction it is clear that biblical scholars, while accepting that because of their concern to understand the past certain Old Testament texts may continue to be considered historiographical, are increasingly aware of the significance of the critical use of sources as a basic distinction between biblical and modern historiography, and, consequently, of the necessity in every particular instance to re-evaluate the relative significance of these texts and non-biblical sources for the reconstruction of Israelite history.

BIBLIOGRAPHY

Ahlström, G. W. (1991) 'The Role of Archaeology and Literary Remains in Reconstructing Israel's History', in D. Edelman (ed.) *The Fabric of History: Text, Artifact and Israel's Past*. JSOTSup 127. Sheffield: Sheffield Academic Press, 116–41.

—— (1993) *The History of Ancient Palestine from the Palaeolithic Period to Alexander's Conquest*. JSOTSup 146. Sheffield: Sheffield Academic Press.

Albertz, R. (1994) *A History of Israelite Religion in the Old Testament Period*. London: SCM Press.

Albrektson, B. (1967) *History and the Gods: An Essay on the Idea of Historical Events as Divine Manifestations in the Ancient Near East and in Israel*. Lund: CWK Gleerup.

Auld, A. G. (1994) *Kings without Privilege*. Edinburgh: T & T Clark.

Balentine, S. E. (1997) '"You Can't Pray a Lie": Truth *and* Fiction in the Prayers of Chronicles', in Graham, Hoglund and McKenzie 1997: 246–67.

Barnes, W. H. (1997) 'Non-Synoptic Chronological References in the Books of Chronicles', in Graham, Hoglund and McKenzie 1997: 106–31.

Barstad, H. (1997) 'History and the Hebrew Bible', in L. L. Grabbe (ed.) *Can a 'History of Israel' be Written?* JSOTSup 245. Sheffield: Sheffield Academic Press, 37–64.

Becker, C. L. (1959) 'What Are Historical Facts?' in H. Meyerhoff (ed.) *The Philosophy of History in our Time*. New York: Doubleday, 120–37.

Berlin, I. (1980) 'The Concept of Scientific History', in I. Berlin, *Concepts and Categories*. Oxford: Oxford University Press.

Blum, E. (1990) *Studien zur Komposition des Pentateuch*. BZAW 189. Berlin: de Gruyter.

Braulik, G. (1993) 'The Sequence of the Laws in Deuteronomy 12–26 and in the Decalogue', in D. L. Christensen (ed.) *A Song of Power and the Power of Song: Essays on the Book of Deuteronomy*. Winona Lake: Eisenbrauns, 313–35.

—— (1995) 'Die dekalogische Redaktion der deuteronomischen Gesetze', in G. Braulik (ed.) *Bundesdokument und Gesetz: Studien zum Deuteronomium*. Freiburg: Herder, 1–25.

Braun, R. L. (1997) 'I Chronicles 1–9 and the Reconstruction of the History of Israel: Thoughts on the Use of Genealogical Data in Chronicles in the Reconstruction of the History of Israel', in Graham, Hoglund and McKenzie 1997: 92–105.

Breisach, E. (1983) *Historiography: Ancient, Medieval and Modern*. Chicago: University of Chicago Press.

Cameron, A. (ed.) (1989) *History as Text: The Writing of Ancient History*. London: Gerald Duckworth.

Carr, D. M. (1997) 'Controversy and Convergence in Recent Studies of the Formation of the Pentateuch', *Religious Studies Review* 23/1: 22–31.

Carr, E. H. (1961) *What Is History?* Harmondsworth: Penguin Books.

Clements, R. E. (1979) 'Pentateuchal Problems', in G. W. Anderson (ed.) *Tradition and Interpretation*. Oxford: Clarendon Press, 96–124.

Clines, D. J. A. (1978) *The Theme of the Pentateuch*. JSOTSup 10. Sheffield: Sheffield Academic Press.

Collingwood, R. G. (1946) *The Idea of History*. Oxford: Clarendon Press.

Cross, F. M. (1973) *Canaanite Myth and Hebrew Epic: Essays in the History of the Religion of Israel*. Cambridge, Mass.: Harvard University Press.

Davies, P. R. (1992) *In Search of 'Ancient Israel'*. JSOTSup 148. Sheffield: Sheffield Academic Press.

—— (1995) 'Method and Madness: Some Remarks on Doing History with the Bible', *JBL* 114: 669–705.

—— (1997) 'Whose History? Whose Israel? Whose Bible? Biblical Histories, Ancient and Modern', in L. L. Grabbe (ed.) *Can a 'History of Israel' Be Written?* JSOTSup 245. Sheffield: Sheffield Academic Press, 104–22.

Dietrich, W. (1972) *Prophetie und Geschichte: Eine redactionsgeschichtliche Untersuchung zum deuteronomistischen Geschichtswerk*. FRLANT 108. Göttingen: Vandenhoeck & Ruprecht.

Elton, G. R. (1969) *The Practice of History*. London: Fontana Press.

Finley, M. I. (1986) *The Use and Abuse of History*. London: Hogarth Press.

Fischer, D. H. (1971) *Historians' Fallacies: Towards a Logic of Historical Thought*. London: Routledge & Kegan Paul.

Gese, H. (1965) 'The Idea of History in the Ancient Near East and the Old Testament', in J. M. Robinson et al. (eds) *The Bultmann School of Biblical Interpretation: New Directions?* New York: Harper & Row, 49–64.

Graham, M. P., Hoglund, K. G. and McKenzie, S. L. (eds) (1997) *The Chronicler as Historian*. JSOTSup 238. Sheffield: Sheffield Academic Press.

Halpern, B. (1988) *The First Historians: The Hebrew Bible and History*. New York: Harper & Row.

Himmelfarb, G. (1992) 'Telling it as You Like it: Post-Modernist History and the Flight from Fact', *Times Literary Supplement*, 16 October, 12–15.

Hoffmann, H. D. (1980) *Reform und Reformen: Untersuchungen zu einem Grundthema der deuteronomistischen Geschichtsschreibung*. ATANT 66. Zürich: Theologischer Verlag.

Hoglund, K. G. (1997) 'The Chronicler as Historian: A Comparativist Perspective', in Graham, Hoglund and McKenzie 1997: 19–29.

Huizinga, J. (1963) 'A Definition of the Concept of History', in R. Klibansky and H. J. Patton (eds) *Philosophy and History: Essays Presented to Ernst Cassirer*. New York: Harper & Row, 1–10.

Hyatt, J. P. (1970) 'Were There an Ancient Historical Credo in Israel and an Independent Sinai Tradition?' in H. T. Frank and W. L. Reed (eds) *Translating and Understanding the Old Testament*. Nashville: Abingdon Press, 152–70.

Japhet, S. (1968) 'The Supposed Common Authorship of Chronicles and Ezra–Nehemiah Investigated Anew', *VT* 18: 330–71.

Jones, G. H. (1993) *1 and 2 Chronicles*. Old Testament Guides. Sheffield: Sheffield Academic Press.

Klein, R. W. (1992a) 'Chronicles, Books of 1–2', *ABD* 1: 992–1002.

—— (1992b) 'Ezra–Nehemiah, Books of', *ABD* 2: 731–42.

Knight, D. A. (1985) 'The Pentateuch', in D. A. Knight and G. M. Tucker (eds) *The Hebrew Bible and its Modern Interpreters*. Philadelphia: Fortress Press/Chico: Scholars Press, 263–96.

Knoppers, G. N. (1997) 'History and Historiography: The Royal Reforms', in Graham, Hoglund and McKenzie 1997: 178–203.

Lohfink, N. (1981) 'Kerygmata des deuteronomistischen Geschichtswerks', in J. Jeremias and L. Perlitt (eds) *Die Botschaft und die Boten (FS H. W. Wolff)*. Neukirchen-Vluyn: Neukirchener Verlag, 87–100.

—— (1993) 'Distribution of the Functions of Power: The Laws Concerning Public Offices in Deuteronomy 16:18–18:22', in D. L. Christensen (ed.) *A Song of Power and the Power of Song: Essays on the Book of Deuteronomy*. Winona Lake: Eisenbrauns, 336–52.

Mandelbaum, M. (1977) *The Anatomy of Historical Knowledge,* Baltimore: The Johns Hopkins University Press.

Mayes, A. D. H. (1974) *Israel in the Period of the Judges*. London: SCM Press.

—— (1979) *Deuteronomy*. New Century Bible. London: Oliphants.

—— (1983) *The Story of Israel between Settlement and Exile: A Redactional Study of the Deuteronomistic History*. London: SCM Press.

—— (1992) 'Amphictyony', *ABD* 1: 212–16.

—— (1996) 'De l'idéologie deutéronomiste à la Théologie de l'Ancien Testament', in A. de Pury, T. Romer and J.-D. Maachi (eds) *Israël construit son histoire: l'historiographie déuteronomiste à la lumière des recherches récentes*. Le Monde de la Bible 34. Geneva: Labor et Fides, 477–508.

McCarter, P. K. (1981) '"Plots, True or False": The Succession Narrative as Court Apologetic', *Int* 35: 355–67.

McCarthy, D. J. (1965) 'II Sam. 7 and the Structure of the Deuteronomic History', *JBL* 84: 131–8.

McKenzie, S. L. (1985) *The Chronicler's Use of the Deuteronomistic History*. HSM 33. Atlanta: Scholars Press.

Miller, J. M. (1991) 'Is it Possible to Write a History of Israel without Relying on the Hebrew Bible?' in D. V. Edelman (ed.) *The Fabric of History: Text, Artifact and Israel's Past*. JSOTSup 127. Sheffield: Sheffield Academic Press, 93–102.

Momigliano, A. (1977) *Essays in Ancient and Modern Historiography*. Oxford: Basil Blackwell.

—— (1990) *The Classical Foundations of Modern Historiography*. Berkeley: University of California Press.

Mowinckel, S. (1963) 'Israelite Historiography', *ASTI* 2: 4–26.

Munslow, A. (1997 'The Plot Thickens', *Times Higher Education Supplement* 1272, 21 March.

Nelson, R. D. (1981) *The Double Redaction of the Deuteronomistic History*. JSOTSup 18. Sheffield: Sheffield Academic Press.

Nicholson, E. W. (1998) *The Pentateuch in the Twentieth Century*, Oxford: Clarendon Press.

North, C. R. (1951) 'Pentateuchal Criticism', in H. H. Rowley (ed.) *The Old Testament and Modern Study*. Oxford: Clarendon Press, 48–83.

North, R. S. (1974) 'Does Archaeology Prove Chronicles' Sources?' in H. N. Brean et al. (eds) *A Light unto My Path: Studies in Honor of J. M. Myers*. Gettysburg Theological Studies 4. Philadelphia: Temple University Press, 375–401.

Noth, M. (1943) *Überlieferungsgeschichtliche Studien,* Tübingen: Max Niemeyer Verlag (ET *The Deuteronomistic History*. JSOTSup 15². Sheffield: Sheffield Academic Press, 1991; *The Chronicler's History*, JSOTSup 50. Sheffield: Sheffield Academic Press, 1987).

—— (1948) *Überlieferungsgeschichte des Pentateuch*. Stuttgart: W. Kohlhammer (ET *A History of Pentateuchal Traditions*. Chico: Scholars Press, 1981).

—— (1958) 'Geschichtsschreibung, biblische. I Im AT'. *RGG* 2. Tübingen: J. C. B. Mohr, 1498–1502.

O'Brien, M. A. (1989) *The Deuteronomistic History Hypothesis: A Reassessment*. OBO 92. Freiburg: Universitätsverlag/Göttingen: Vandenhoeck & Ruprecht.

Oden, R. A. (1980) 'Hermeneutics and Historiography: Germany and America'. SBL Seminar Papers, 135–57.

Polzin, R. (1980) *Moses and the Deuteronomist*. New York: Seabury.

Porter, J. R. (1979) 'Old Testament Historiography', in G. W. Anderson (ed.) *Tradition and Interpretation: Essays by Members of the Society for Old Testament Study*. Oxford: Clarendon Press, 125–62.

Provan, I. W. (1988) *Hezekiah and the Books of Kings: A Contribution to the Debate about the Composition of the Deuteronomistic History*. BZAW 172. Berlin: de Gruyter.

—— (1995) 'Ideologies, Literary and Critical: Reflections on Recent Writing on the History of Israel', *JBL* 114: 585–606.

Rad, G. von (1962) *Old Testament Theology*, Vol. I. Edinburgh: Oliver & Boyd.

—— (1966) *The Problem of the Hexateuch and Other Essays*. Edinburgh: Oliver & Boyd.

Rainey, A. F. (1997) 'The Chronicler and His Sources: Historical and Geographical', in Graham, Hoglund and McKenzie (1997), 30–72.

Rendtorff, R. (1971) 'Beobachtungen zur altisraelitischen Geschichtsschreibung anhand der Geschichte vom Aufstieg Davids', in H. W. Wolff (ed.) *Probleme biblischer Theologie (FS G. von Rad)*. Munich: Chr. Kaiser Verlag, 428–39.

—— (1977) *Das überlieferungsgeschichtliche Problem des Pentateuch*. BZAW 147. Berlin: de Gruyter (ET *The Problem of the Process of Transmission in the Pentateuch*. JSOTSup 89. Sheffield: Sheffield Academic Press, 1990).

Richter, W. (1964) *Die Bearbeitungen des 'Retterbuches' in der deuteronomischen Epoche*. BBB21. Bonn: Peter Hanstein Verlag.

Rose, M. (1981) *Deuteronomist und Jahwist*. ATANT 67. Zürich: Theologischer Verlag.

Sasson, J. (1981) 'On Choosing Models for Recreating Israelite Pre-Monarchic History', *JSOT* 21: 3–24.

Schmid, H. H. (1976) *Der sogennante Jahwist: Beobachtungen und Fragen zur Pentateuchforschung*. Zürich: Theologischer Verlag.

Schniewind, W. M. (1997) 'Prophets and Prophecy in the Books of Chronicles', in Graham, Hoglund and McKenzie 1997: 204–24.

Schwartz, H. Eilberg (1990) *The Savage in Judaism: An Anthropology of Israelite Religion and Ancient Judaism*. Bloomington: Indiana University Press.

Seitz, G. (1971) *Redaktionsgeschichtliche Studien zum Deuteronomium*. BWANT 5/13. Stuttgart: W. Kohlhammer.

Smend, R. (1971) 'Das Gesetz und die Völker: Ein Beitrag zur deuteronomistischen Redaktionsgeschichte', in H. W. Wolff (ed.) *Probleme biblischer Theologie (FS G. von Rad)*. Munich: Chr. Kaiser Verlag, 494–509.

—— (1978) *Die Entstehung des Alten Testaments*. Stuttgart: W. Kohlhammer.

Thompson, T. L. (1992) 'Historiography (Israelite)', *ABD* 3: 206–12.

—— (1995) 'A Neo-Albrightian School in History and Biblical Scholarship', *JBL* 114: 683–98.

—— (1996) 'Historiography of Ancient Palestine and Early Jewish Historiography', in V. Fritz and P. R. Davies (eds) *The Origins of the Israelite States*. JSOTSup 228. Sheffield: Sheffield Academic Press, 26–43.

Throntveit, M. A. (1997) 'The Chronicler's Speeches and Historical Reconsruction', in Graham, Hoglund and McKenzie 1997: 225–45.

Van Seters, J. (1975) *Abraham in History and Tradition*. New Haven: Yale University Press.

—— (1983) *In Search of History: Historiography in the Ancient World and the Origins of Biblical History*. New Haven: Yale University Press.

—— (1992) *Prologue to History: The Yahwist as Hisorian in Genesis*. Louisville, Ky: John Knox Press.

—— (1994) *The Life of Moses: The Yahwist as Historian in Exodus–Numbers*. Kampen: Kok Pharos.

—— (1997) 'The Chronicler's Account of Solomon's Temple Building', in Graham, Hoglund and McKenzie 1997: 283–300.

Veijola, T. (1975) *Die ewige Dynastie: David und die Entstehung seines Dynastie nach der deuteronomistischen Darstellung*. Helsinki: Suomalainen Tiedeakatemia.

—— (1977) *Das Königtum in der Beurteilung der deuteronomistischen Historiographie*. Helsinki: Suomalainen Tiedeakatemia.

Weinfeld, M. (1972) *Deuteronomy and the Deuteronomic School*. Oxford: Clarendon Press.

Weippert, H. (1972) 'Die "deuteronomistischen" Beurteilungen der Könige von Israel und Juda und das Problem der Redaktion der Königsbücher', *Bib* 53: 301–39.

—— (1985) 'Das deuteronomistischen Geschichtswerk', *ThR* 50: 213–49.

White, H. (1973) *Metahistory: The Historical Imagination in Nineteenth Century Europe*. Baltimore: The Johns Hopkins University Press.

—— (1978) 'The Historical Text as Literary Artifact', in R. H. Canary and H. Kozicki (eds) *The Writing of History: Literary Form and Historical Understanding*. Madison: University of Wisonsin Press, 41–62.

Whitelam, K. W. (1996) *The Invention of Ancient Israel: The Silencing of Palestinian History*. London: Routledge.

Williamson, H. G. M. (1977) *Israel in the Books of Chronicles*. Cambridge: Cambridge University Press.

—— (1987a) *Ezra and Nehemiah*. Old Testament Guides. Sheffield: Sheffield Academic Press.

—— (1987b) 'Review of S. L. McKenzie, *The Chronicler's Use of the Deuteronomistic History*', *VT* 37: 107–114.

Wolff, H. W. (1961) 'Das Kerygma des deuteronomistischen Geschichtswerks', *ZAW* 73: 171–86 (ET 'The Kerygma of the Deuteronomic Historical Work', in W. Brueggemann and H. W. Wolff (eds) *The Vitality of Old Testament Traditions*. Atlanta: John Knox Press, 83–100.

Wright, J. W. (1997) 'The Fight for Peace: Narrative and History in the Battle Accounts in Chronicles', in Graham, Hoglund and McKenzie 1997: 150–77.

CHAPTER SIX

PROPHECY

——— •◆• ———

Graeme Auld

Nothing connected with biblical prophecy is unproblematic; and that is certainly true of linking the words 'genre' and 'prophecy'. Are we talking about the literary (including oral literary) genres which historical prophets used: about the types of speech or song or memoir or address they adopted or adapted, or even about unique forms only prophets used? Or is our business with the genre(s) or literary characteristic(s) of the whole writings the Bible identifies as prophetic?

The second option seems a safer starting point, and will be followed here. We actually have the prophetic literature as 'a bird in our hand'. Any history of ancient prophecy we would first have to 'catch': to deduce and reconstruct from these same writings. Safer, but not straightforward: there are different Bibles; and different decisions have been made since ancient times about which of their contents are 'prophetic'. A Christian Bible will identify (only) Isaiah, Jeremiah, Ezekiel, and Daniel, along with Hosea, Joel, Amos, Obadiah, Jonah, Micah, Nahum, Habakkuk, Zephaniah, Haggai, Zechariah, and Malachi, as the books of the prophets. And yet writers in New Testament books of that Bible treat David, or the book of Psalms, as prophetic too. A Jewish Bible will not include among its prophetic books Daniel from the list just given. It will group the four 'books' of Isaiah, Jeremiah, Ezekiel, and the Twelve as 'Latter Prophets', alongside four books of 'Former Prophets': Joshua, Judges, Samuel, and Kings.

Questions of genre that start with the literature have to make choices, between one 'canon' and the other, or for neither. It has become commonplace among biblical scholars of prophecy to concentrate their attention on those books common to the two canonical listings: simply Isaiah, Jeremiah, Ezekiel, and the Twelve. In this volume, and convergent with such an approach, the 'Former Prophets' of the Hebrew canon are studied as 'narrative', along with the books of Chronicles to which they are closely related. And Daniel, ranked with the prophets in the Christian canon, is taken as an example of 'apocalyptic' rather than 'prophecy'. These decisions make sense, but only so far: the relevant material spills over the boundaries. Parts of 2 Kings (in chs 18–20 and 24–5) are virtually identical to portions of Isaiah (36–9) and Jeremiah (52). A further portion of Isaiah (24–7) is often called an 'apocalypse'. The stories within 1 Kings 17 – 2 Kings 10 about Elijah and Elisha, and others named and unnamed of similar prophetic ilk, occupy twice as many pages as the longest book of the 'minor prophets' (Hosea), just as the story of the seer Balaam in the Torah or Pentateuch (Numbers 22–4) is twice as long as the book of Jonah. Whether we concentrate on the relevant biblical texts and seek to characterize their genre(s), or whether we try to classify how – keeping or breaking what conventions – historical figures behind these texts may have spoken or written, we must not depart from the canons of the ancients only to become trapped in our own classifications.

'Prophet' translates the Hebrew *nabî'*, and 'prophesy' the related Hebrew verb. The abstract noun corresponding to 'prophecy' is very rare, and found only in the latest texts (Neh. 6:12; 2 Chron. 9:29; 15:8). Yet the much more familiar title and verb bearing the sense we expect may have become common later than is often supposed. 'Prophet' and its associates such as 'seer' and 'man of God' are rare in the writings associated with the earlier figures in the collection; and even these figures are located no earlier than the final 160 years of the monarchy of the house of David in Jerusalem (c.740–587 BCE). When they are mentioned, it is to be criticized: the prophets talked about are not the heroes of the books but their opponents. On the other hand, in the latest books from long after the monarchy, 'prophet' has become a title of honour suitable for their hero. And it has been argued that we can detect the transition in attitude in the growth of two of the long collections, Ezekiel and Jeremiah. In the (earlier) poetry of Jeremiah, for example, prophets prophesy easy lies by a rival god (2:8; 5:31). In the (developed) prose, Jeremiah is a prophet (1:5) and his God is presented as commending an unnamed succession of prophet servants of the past (25:4; 26:5; 29:19; 35:15). Some hold more conservatively that all the characters whom the Bible calls prophets or seers were also so called in their own time. When they read bitter denunciations of prophets in their books, they remind us that the bitterest feuds are often within the same party. I recognize that this can be true, but suspect that 'prophet' is a term that has developed and been used differently within the biblical period as well as after it. What we read in what we call 'the prophets' is more presentation than transcript. Despite the open boundaries of the relevant literature, this must strengthen our hunch that our prime business should be to plot the characteristics of the books. Questions of whether historical 'prophets' modelled their utterances on lament or love-song or liturgy or wisdom-teaching or excited lyric should be held over.

It has already been noted that the books of Samuel–Kings and of Chronicles are closely related. Mention of a series of narratives within the story of David and his successors in Jerusalem that they share may usefully round off this introduction and lead us to the next point. In the first (2 Sam. 7 // 1 Chron. 17), 'the prophet Nathan' was consulted by David about more appropriate housing for 'the divine ark' and gave his own response; but that night he received a vision from the deity and was sent to David to report its contents. Next Gad, who declared the divine options to the king, as a message from Yahweh, after David's sinful census-taking, is described as 'David's seer' (2 Sam. 24 // 1 Chron. 21). Then Jehoshaphat and Ahab, kings of the now separate Judah and Israel, were to make common military cause. They sought divine counsel, first through a large number of (possibly court) prophets, and then of a more independent 'prophet of Yahweh'. Micaiah first said Yahweh would grant success, but then passed on a message in Yahweh's name that the supportive prophets had been made fools of by Yahweh (1 Kgs 22 // 2 Chron. 18). Finally Huldah 'the prophetess', when consulted by courtiers of King Josiah about the import of a book found in the temple, replied in two stages, distinguishing between the man who sent them to her and the king who sent them to inquire of Yahweh (2 Kgs 22 // 2 Chron. 34). In each case the intermediary, though differently designated, has a clearly established role at the outset of the story: each is either consulted by the king or is described as the king's seer. And in three cases (the Gad report is much briefer) clear distinction is made between what the individual says and the divine message with which they are (subsequently) entrusted. In terms of our earlier discussion, these stories may report how things were from David to Josiah; but equally, they may be a projection back to the time of the monarchy of later views about established 'prophets' of Yahweh. Be that as it may, oral formula or literary genre, each of these reports introduces us to the prophet as divine messenger – 'This is what Yahweh has said . . .'.

ELIJAH AND ELISHA

The most extended connected collection of narratives about prophets occupies the central third of the two books of Kings. There is no body of text elsewhere in the Bible with a similar range of interests, yet its concerns intersect with those of many other texts. 1 Kings 17 portrays at the outset an intimate relationship between Elijah and Yahweh ('whom I face standing'), and between what Yahweh and what Elijah say: dew and rain will return only at Elijah's word. Elijah simply instructs King Ahab, without invoking divine authority, having first decided when he will let himself be seen by the king (18:15–19). 1 Kings 17 uses the phrase 'the word of Yahweh' more than any chapter that follows, but in an unusual way. Yahweh's word is not a message to be delivered (at least not until vv. 14, 16), but a private communication to his servant (vv. 2, 5, 8). This feature is reminiscent of the opening chapter of the book of Jeremiah.

These sixteen chapters of Kings are set in the period of Ahab and his immediate successors, and foreground the issue of power. Authority and who bears it – who has 'servants' and sends 'messengers' and whose word counts – is a recurring theme. Ahab, though king of Israel, is effectively belittled between prophet and foreign queen: Elijah and Jezebel instruct him in similar terms (18:41, 42; 19:5, 7, 8). Even where Elijah's role is taken by an anonymous prophet (20:13, 22), the issue remains whether those who have servants and send messengers also have authority. The king himself becomes nameless for long periods (2 Kgs 4–8), as if a cipher rather than a historical personality. Is it because these stories are so critical of Ahab and his house that they can hardly bear to name the royals? Or do the tales issue from a much later period, and simply use as props the names of very wicked kings of the past, for stories in which the details of the civil power are less important than the claims of men of god and prophets. Elisha relates to Elijah as Joshua to Moses: servant to master; lesser to greater; and of course both Elisha and Joshua have 'saving' as an element in their names and cross the Jordan dryshod. There are established structures within prophecy; and Elisha is portrayed as in a leadership role among the prophets (6:1–7; 9:1–3).

Closely related, though subordinate, is the topic of the second story in the opening chapter: the 'man of god' as agent of, or intercessor for, divine healing. The reviving of the son of the widow who had fed Elijah (17:17–24) is the first of several stories in these chapters about healing or non-healing, and is followed by King Ahaziah (2 Kgs 1), Elisha's Shunammite hostess (2 Kgs 4), the Syrian army commander (5), and king of Syria in Damascus (8). The widow's words that end the first of these stories make explicit how they all reinforce the main theme: 'Now I know . . . that Yahweh's word in your mouth is truth.' A further notable element of this story is the role of action alongside words: Elijah stretches himself over the dead child three times as well as calling on God. Sitting with face between knees and sending his servant back and forwards seven times precede the coming of the rain (1 Kgs 18:41–4). Elisha is summoned by Elijah throwing his mantle over him – and Elijah stresses the ambiguity of this action. With the same mantle thrown in the Jordan and Yahweh, God of Elijah, invoked, the waters are divided for Elisha to cross (2 Kgs 2:13–14). And Elisha's last 'action' is posthumous: a corpse dropped in his grave that touches his bones revives and stands up (13:21).

The term 'prophet' is in fact quite sparingly used in 1 Kings 17–2 Kings 10: and most often in plural phrases such as 'one of the prophets', or 'the prophets of Baal'. Elijah is just called 'prophet' twice: once in his own words (18:22), where he notes he only is left 'a prophet for Yahweh', and once where the narrator presents him as 'prophet', precisely where he calls on the God of the ancestors of his people for help in the contest that will settle the allegiance of his nation (18:36). When the king of Syria suspects a traitor among his own people, his courtiers explain the problem as 'Elisha the prophet who is in Israel' (6:12). This nicely picks up the words an Israelite slave in Syria had used to commend 'the prophet who is in Samaria' to the same (?) king of Syria (5:3); and may be a deliberate counter to 'the king who is in Samaria' of 1 Kings 21:18 – prophet rather than king as the real authority in Israel/Samaria

JEREMIAH

Jeremiah is one of three large books in the prophetic collection; and, like the others, it is very varied in its contents. It is also distinctive among all books of the Bible, not so much in being known to us in two different forms, but in the extent to which these two texts differ. The originally Hebrew text translated and preserved in the ancient Greek Bible (Septuagint) is some one-seventh shorter than what became the synagogue text. And it is that longer Hebrew text that is familiar from standard modern translations. Its contents are also differently arranged. The two versions are most alike in the first half (1:1–25:13), which also contains much of the poetry in the book. They are also broadly similar, as far as amount of material is concerned, in the section 'about the nations'. These six chapters are also mostly poetical. However, both the placing of this section and its internal arrangement are different in the two texts. In the shorter version of the book preserved in Greek, it comes at the start of the second half (26–31); in the traditional Hebrew text, it comes at the end (46–51). The order of the nations is also varied: most notably the longest portion, the one on Babylon, comes in the middle of this section in the middle of the Greek version of Jeremiah, but at the end of the nations at the end of the Hebrew version. The Hebrew version is very much longer than the Greek in the remaining twenty chapters; and these are almost entirely narrative prose, but for chapters 30–1 (Masoretic Text).

It is easy enough to state these differences, but harder to explain them. We have to reckon with at least three different sorts of activity. Many of the additions to the prose tradition are simple amplifications, 'dotting the i's and crossing the t's' – such as adding 'the king' or 'the prophet' after someone's name. Others are more substantial 'clarifications', of the sort an official may give after a politician's statement has been challenged: sometimes explaining more clearly what was said; sometimes reusing the original but problematic words to state what 'should have been said'. And the third sort is deliberate rearrangement, as best illustrated in the moving of the chapters 'about the nations' from middle to end or end to middle, and the parallel adjustment within them of the placing of Bablyon. That third sort of activity at least had required a substantial editorial decision. Amplifying and clarifying could have been – and probably were – a more gradual process. McKane has written of poetry generating prose commentary, and prose itself generating further prose; and has helpfully called the developing book of Jeremiah a 'rolling corpus' (1986: l–lxxxiii).

As I attempt to describe the 'genre' of this book, it is vital to include coming to terms with the evidence I have briefly reviewed of a tradition in process. That process is not simply deduced from the differences between two 'snapshots': the Greek and Hebrew texts. The book starts by dating Jeremiah's reception of the divine word up to the month when Jerusalem was taken captive (1:3); and the closing chapter gives the same report of that capture as the end of Kings. Yet the book also reports in extended prose narrative Jeremiah's continuing mediation of that divine word in the years that followed. Granted that the book documents the extension of the tradition and a 'rolling' process of commentary generated by the tradition, is it possible to describe the origins?

For most readers, these beginnings are with Jeremiah in the latter years of the kingdom of Judah and with the poetry of the book. Much of the poetry in the first half of the book is critical of Israel; chapter 2 provides a good sample. It mostly addresses 'you' in the second person, but also talks about 'Israel' in the third (vv. 3, 14, 26). The first example makes clear that this variation occurs within a single unit:

> I remember the loyalty of your youth,
>   your love as a bride,
> how you followed me in the desert,
>   in a land not sown.
> Israel was holy to Yahweh,
>   the first fruits of his harvest.
> All who ate of it were held guilty;
>   disaster came upon them,
>   says Yahweh. (2:2–3 NRSV, adapted)

Translation into the English 'you(r)' masks the much greater variety of the Hebrew: sometimes feminine singular (vv. 2, 16–25, 33–7), once masculine (vv. 26–8), and sometimes plural (vv. 5, 9–10, 29–31). Some readers prefer to see each of these transitions as evidence that several, short, once-separate oral units have been secondarily assembled into a larger structure. For others, the shift from feminine to masculine, from singular to plural, no more signifies distinct origin of short sayings than the shift from you to s/he or they (already a feature of subunits such as 2:2–3, 14–19, 26–8). The shifting differentiation in Hebrew of 'you' simply follows the kaleidoscope of images, from faithless lover (female) to thief (male). The prevailing alternation, between plural and feminine singular, is a natural consequence of the metaphor that controls the whole argument: Yahweh as Israel's aggrieved husband. Marital complaint leads to divorce, and on to the further question of whether – if Israel has remarried (to Baal) – there can be any hope of restoring the first marriage (3:1–5). The rest of that chapter, up to 4:4, explores that question both more and less hopefully, in poetry and prose, and from a number of angles: glimpses of McKane's corpus as it rolls.

Chapters 4–6 comprise some of the most striking, and certainly excited, poetry in the whole book. They conjure up the approach to Jerusalem of a dread, fast-moving, mounted peril from the north; the havoc it will cause; and the double blindness of the population: to the impending disaster, and to the fact that it is their rejection of their God that has brought it close to them. An 'I' speaks poignantly through these poems: sometimes as anguished witness (4:19–22), but more often identifying with the deity. The most nightmarish picture is of creation itself undone, stage by stage:

> I looked on the earth, and lo, it was waste and void;
> and to the heavens, and they had no light. (4:23)

The first half of the largely prose chapter that follows (7:1–8:3) reports a proclamation Jeremiah had to make in the temple of Jerusalem. The rhetoric is similar to much in the books of the Former Prophets; and so, like them, it is often called 'Deuteronomistic'. It restates in more ample prose topics broached more tersely towards the end of the preceding poetry (6:16–21) about the folly of departing from the 'ancient paths' and then supposing that expensive offerings to Yahweh will win back his favour. It is thoroughly plausible to explain this so-called 'temple sermon' as prose generated from the poetry.

The first chapter of the book concerns the divine call of Jeremiah. Verses 4–10 report the commissioning of a spokesman: the deity has known and consecrated him from before he was; has put his words in his mouth; and has appointed him 'prophet to the nations'. The focus on mouth, and word, and ability to speak, resume the immediate introduction: 'Now the word of Yahweh came to me saying'; and also the key terms of the title verses: 'The words of Jeremiah . . . to whom the word of Yahweh came . . .'. The remainder of the chapter starts by reporting briefly two visions, both introduced again by 'Now the word of Yahweh came to me, saying'. For Jeremiah, as we saw for Elijah, this formula was used for a private communication from the deity. The first vision, of an almond rod, is explained as Yahweh watching over the efficacy of his word. The second, of a blown/fanned pot facing away from the north, signifies the disaster that will come from that direction. Readers debate how much of a visionary Jeremiah is depicted as being. Many urge that the rhetoric of this opening chapter, as of the book as a whole, thoroughly subordinates vision to word and message. I would prefer to claim them finely balanced, and to call in support the very visual nature of the poetry we have observed in the immediately following chapters.

Four narratives within chapters 11–20 describe and explain symbolic actions observed, or undertaken, or possibly imagined or play-acted, by Jeremiah: a visit to a potter (18:1–11), breaking a pot (19:1–15), remaining without wife and children (16:1–9), and spoiling a loin-cloth in the Euphrates (13:1–11). A longer set of passages (14:1–15:9) conveys Judah's calamity, her attempts to plead with the deity, and Yahweh's insistence despite his own distress that Jeremiah should not intercede. In and through these reports we read a series of haunting and interlinked poems, most reminiscent of the many laments among the Psalms. Associated prose passages attribute the occasion of some of them to trouble from family and neighbours (11:21–3), unspecified plots (18:18), and official persecution (20:1–6). It is particularly hotly debated whether these prose settings have been extrapolated and developed from the poetry (as was suggested above of 7:1–15 from 6:16–21) or whether they are independent evidence of Jeremiah's actual life. That discussion is more complicated because the more expansive Hebrew tradition maximizes the impression that the laments and protests are individual to Jeremiah, that he is suffering for what he has said; the terser Septuagint suggests that some of these argumentative poems are the response of the community to Jeremiah's hard words.

The oracles about the nations represent some of the finest poetry in the whole book. Most of these nations, disposed so differently in the two versions we possess, are neighbours of Jeremiah's people. The descriptions of Moabites, Philistines, and others, and threats against them, exhibit detailed knowledge of their towns and other geographical features. This is much less true of Babylon, treated at greater length, and placed very deliberately in each version for maximum effect. Chaldea is certainly an occasional alternative, and the god Bel is mentioned once. But it is 'Babel' itself (Babylon is the Greek form) that is constantly intoned, some sixty times in the two chapters: a bell tolling its own doom. What occasioned these poems is much more obscure. There are similar collections in several prophetic books. And, as we know from their own texts, some of Israel's neighbours conducted formal execrations of their enemies. We should at least note that there is a tension between the threat to 'Babel' in these chapters and Babylon's role as Yahweh's agent in Jeremiah 27–9.

The extended narratives (Jeremiah 26–45, or 32–51 [LXX]) are set in the time of the last two kings in Jerusalem and in the aftermath of the city's destruction. They are interrupted by just two largely poetic chapters (30–1): the book of fortunes restored (30:2–3). Similar hopes are found briefly stated here and there in Jeremiah. However, in these chapters the themes of healing and recovery and return and replanting and replenishment are more fully developed: Israel's offspring will cease to be a nation only when the order of heavenly bodies and of tides comes to an end (31:35–7).

Two rather different models suggest themselves for the development of the book of Jeremiah. McKane's 'rolling corpus' helps explain the growth of many smaller clusters or units. Alongside we have to posit some not very intrusive contributions of an ordering, editorial sort. The book as a whole offers an explanation of the ruin of Judah and Jerusalem, and of many of their neighbours. But it looks beyond this to the ruin of the overweening ruiner, Babel; and to restoration after punishment of some of Yahweh's people. No-one can prove that the tradition does not go back to a historical Jeremiah. Equally, it is impossible to deduce with any certainty how much of it might go back, or which elements do. The sorts of material I have sketched have been observed as arranged in a book. Plausibly earlier elements may of course be detached from it; but it is no longer clear how these might be reassembled.

ISAIAH

The notion of poetry that cannot all be attributed to the same original poet, or even collection, provides us with a ready transition to the book of Isaiah. The most obvious point to start a discussion of Isaiah and genre is by noting that it has quite the highest proportion of formal poetry of all the Latter Prophets. While Jeremiah and Ezekiel both start with a commission narrative, the opening chapter of Isaiah samples various themes that are characteristic of the book. Not until Isaiah 6 do we find a narrative at all like Jeremiah 1 or Ezekiel 1–3; and it opens the largely narrative passage Isaiah 6–8 (or 6:1–9:7), which apparently interrupts the progression from the series of 'woe' passages in chapter 5 to the related material in 9:8–10:15. The positioning of Isaiah 6 taken together with its similarity to the vision of Micaiah (in 1 Kgs 22 // 2 Chron. 18, already mentioned above) suggests that the function of Isaiah's vision of the divine king was not to inaugurate his role as seer or prophet. It may have been intended rather to underscore as valid the paradoxical divine commission to render his people blind, deaf, and insensate (6:9–10).

Jeremiah, as we already noted, begins (1:1–3) by envisaging a role for Jeremiah till the fall of Jerusalem; and it ends with a report of that calamity (52). Some of the narratives within the book do in fact carry the story further than that apparent limit. And yet, however much later these may have been written, the story they tell is not itself prolonged beyond the lifetime of Jeremiah. Isaiah is a very different sort of book in this respect too. The title verse locates the contents of the book in the reigns of Uzziah, Jotham, Ahaz, and Hezekiah, kings of Judah. And it is true that the sparse narratives are located mostly in the reigns of Ahaz (7–8) and Hezekiah (36–9). Even the poetry within the first half of Isaiah is hardly explicit about later situations. 'Assyria' may occasionally function (as in 31:8?) as an implicit symbol of a later imperial power; and many have read the promise of a 'shoot from the stock of Jesse' (11:1–9) as implying that the line of David no longer rules in Jerusalem (that the 'stock' intends the stump of a felled tree). And yet all this is true only of the first thirty-nine chapters. From Isaiah 40 a wholly different situation pertains. Imperial Assyria has been displaced by Babylon, which has conquered Jerusalem. The advent of Cyrus some fifty years further on is already in focus (44:28; 45:1) together with the associated fall to his Persian forces of proud Babylon and her gods

(46–7). And the closing eleven chapters (56–66) apparently address a still later period. There is no gainsaying a long period of development. And yet all these judgments about Isaiah 40–66 depend on the internal testimony of their poetic materials: there are no dates; and there is no narrative context, whether accurate or contrived.

The first half of the book is probably the most complex. We have noted that the unity of situation in the period of Assyrian menace is barely challenged openly. Yet we have to note that Babylon's later role is anticipated: it has pride of (first) place (13–14) in the section about the nations (13–23); and an embassy from the distant king of Babylon congratulates Hezekiah on his recovery (39). What in fact contributes to the unity of the whole book is the unspecific future reference of much of it. Nearer the beginning of the book (chs 2–3), 'the Lord of hosts has a day against all that is proud and lofty . . .' (2:12). And the phrase 'on that day' is used to link additional threats (2:20; 3:18; 4:1) to the principal one. Yet after this first insistence that Yahweh's day is 'against', 'that day' becomes a focus of hope: already and most surprisingly in 4:2–6, but see also 11:10, 11–16; 12:1–6; 28:5–6. Expressions of confident hope become much more common throughout Isaiah 40–66, and come to a climax in the radical promise that Yahweh is making a new heavens and new earth (66:22–3).

The first half of the book makes important use of the language of mourning. In 5:8–23 there are six longer or shorter units that begin the same way. It matters little whether we translate their opening words 'Woe to those who . . .' or 'Ah you who . . .'. But we do need to know that the Hebrew *hôy* that starts them all was used in lamentation over the dead. Singing a dirge over the still living people was an eloquent and not so subtle threat that they no longer deserved to live. The theme is continued, with the associated formal introduction, in Isaiah 10 – first rounding off the threat against Jerusalem's establishment (10:1–4); but then mourning (the king of) Assyria (10:5–14), too arrogant to envisage that he too was a disposable agent of Yahweh (10:15). The first group of these ironic laments immediately follows a love-song, or more strictly an aggrieved lover's song, turned entrapment parable (5:1–7). The treacherous vineyard is symbol at the same time of the beloved and of Israel; and Judah and Jerusalem are called to witness Yahweh's case against Israel before it is made plain to them that they had been the choicest plants of his vineyard.

Isaiah 28–33 plays a set of variations on these themes. The ironic *hôy* laments are now set further apart from each other (28:1; 29:1,15; 30:1; 31:1; 33:1). However, not only do they furnish the elements that give these six chapters a shape; but, more importantly, they recapitulate the argument we have just reviewed in chapters 5 and 10. Isaiah 28:1–4 mourns the pride of Ephraim in Israel's heartlands; but talk is subtly turned to Zion in the course of the chapter. Ariel (29:1) is code for Jerusalem; and it is the policy of the court in that city that is lamented in 29:15–16; 30:1–5; and 31:1–3. The last lament of the series hints, in all brevity (33:1), at the fate of disposable Assyria – but mentions no name. Typical of the movement of the book as a whole, this lament over the biter about to be bit retains its rootedness in a real world of the ancient past but is increasingly open to new futures. The rest of the chapter develops rich images of divine graciousness to Zion; and these continue in Isaiah 34–5:

The wilderness and the dry land shall be glad,
  the desert shall rejoice and blossom . . .
And the ransomed of the LORD shall return,
  and come to Zion with singing;
everlasting joy shall be upon their heads;
  they shall obtain joy and gladness,
  and sorrow and sighing shall flee away. (35:1, 10 NRSV)

Much of the intervening material relates to other nations (13–23). We have noted that Babylon occupies a large space at the beginning of this section (13–14), rather than at middle or end as in the two versions of Jeremiah. Moab is also prominent (15–16), as in Jeremiah. Damascus, Ethiopia, and Egypt follow (17–19). A feature of all these chapters is the amount of added prose comment and other secondary material linked by 'in that day'. The contents of Isaiah 20–2 are more varied; but chapter 23 reads as a lament at the fate of Tyre (and Sidon):

Wail, O ships of Tarshish,
  for your fortress is destroyed. (23:1 NRSV)

The following so-called 'apocalypse' opens with desolation on a worldwide scale, even involving shame for sun and moon in the face of Yahweh's glory as he reigns on Zion and in Jerusalem. The dragon in the sea will be killed (27:1); 'death will be swallowed up for ever' (25:8); and a series of threats in other parts of the book is turned to promise, such as the song of the vineyard at the beginning of chapter 5 (27:2–6).

From chapter 40, while the material is still poetic, its character changes substantially. The architecture of Isaiah 40–55 in particular is on an altogether more ample scale. Some points of continuity can be advanced, but there is also a clear change in voice. Those portions within Isaiah 1–39 that most obviously anticipate or may be related to Isaiah 40–55 are in fact those that stand out as most different within the first half (34–5, for example). McKane's description of Jeremiah as a 'rolling corpus' works quite well for Isaiah 1–39 also, although the model itself requires adaptation: most of what can be seen as generated in Isaiah from the earlier poetry is further poetry rather than prose. However, to do some justice to the 'genre' of the book of Isaiah as a whole, to help define how it differs in nature from its neighbours, we require a more explicitly organic image. Two once separate and distinctive organisms have (been) combined to their mutual benefit: much of Isaiah 1–39 provides an excellent setting for Isaiah 40–55; and this vital force now so close to it has influenced the further development of the host.

Tracking how two distinctive divine titles are used in different parts of Isaiah and in the other prophetic books is instructive. The first is 'the Lord of hosts' (Yahweh Sabaoth). It is very common in Jeremiah, and quite absent from Ezekiel. It is also common throughout much of the Book of the Twelve, but absent from Hosea and Joel. Within Isaiah, it is very frequent throughout chapters 1–39; rare in Isaiah 40–55 (six times only); and absent from the final eleven chapters. That suggests that the closing chapters are as distinctive in this respect as Hosea and Ezekiel.

The other expression is the divine title 'the holy one of Israel'. This is relatively common in Isaiah and very rare elsewhere. The report of Isaiah's vision uses the first title, and draws particular attention to the divine holiness (6:3 NRSV):

> Holy, holy, holy is the LORD of hosts;
> the whole earth is full of his glory.

The way they talk about the holy marks off the closing chapters from the rest of the book. 'The holy one of Israel' is mentioned thirteen or fourteen times in Isaiah 1–39, and a similar number in Isaiah 40–55. Yet towards the end of the book the title is found only in Isaiah 60:9, 14; and in these eleven chapters 'holy' refers now to Yahweh's mountain or city, his courts, or house, his people or spirit or day.

It is common to read chapters 56–66 as a series of appendices or responses, and mostly to chapters 40–55. However, if that is true, these closing chapters have escaped the influence of 'the LORD of hosts' and 'the holy one of Israel'. And yet the spirit of these chapters has also influenced the opening half of the book. Isaiah 1 anticipates themes in Isaiah 65–6. 'They shall not hurt or destroy on all my holy mountain' concludes the first of the two promises of 'new heavens and a new earth' (65:17–25 and 66:22–3); and the way it uses 'holy' is more at home in 65:25 than at the end of the promise of new life from Jesse's stock (11:1–9).

That divine promise will be connected with a royal figure related to David, as stated in at least the first part of that passage (11:1–5) is, however, a view found only in the first half of the book. There are just two other relevant passages. Isaiah 9:1–7 follows a puzzling dark passage at the end of chapter 8 with a promise of seeing a great light: a child born, a son given, will have authority on the throne of David and his kingdom. Then Isaiah 32:1–8 conjures a vision of just and right-ruling kings and princes:

> Each will be like a hiding-place from the wind,
>   a covert from the tempest,
> like streams of water in a dry place,
>   like the shade of a great rock in a weary land. (32:2 NRSV)

This latter passage does not mention David or his family. In similar vein, as already noted, the neighbouring Isaiah 33:1 no longer identifies the destroyer as Assyria. In that next chapter, the king whom 'your eyes will see ... in his beauty' (33:17) is almost certainly divine. That is quite explicit in Isaiah 41:21, where 'the king of Jacob' is none other than Yahweh. Corresponding to this development, the 'servant of Yahweh' in Isaiah 42:1–4; 49:1–6; 50:4–9; and 52:13 – 53:12 is described as having some characteristics of the ideal king; but the word 'king' is never used of him – that is a word now suitable only for God.

Isaiah has proved quite the most popular and influential of the prophetic books throughout the centuries – among both Jewish and Christian readers. This reputation rests in part on the innate quality of its sustained poetic rhetoric, which draws on the deep wellsprings of the other and older poetic traditions represented in the Bible: of psalmody and wisdom. It rests also on the prominence throughout, but especially in chapters 40–55, of its promise of divine deliverance or salvation – a theme supported by Isaiah's very name: 'Yahweh is salvation'. Within Christianity it has come to be known as 'the fifth gospel'. The evocative openness of the poetic expression allied with its extended discursiveness have encouraged theological reflection.

THE BOOK OF THE TWELVE

The Book of the Twelve is manifestly a collection of books; and it is useful to deal with it next for reasons negative and positive. On the one side, it is important not to allow our reading of Ezekiel to overinfluence our approach to the other prophetic texts. On the other, the Twelve deserve both comparison and contrast with Isaiah. Like Isaiah, they (at least Hosea, Amos, and Micah among them) are located explicitly in the eighth century BCE by their introductory verses; and, like Isaiah, the later parts of the collection address a situation well into the post-exilic period of restoration. Like Isaiah their material is mostly poetic, though to a lesser extent the last three books, unlike the end of Isaiah, are in prose. Like Isaiah, the Twelve have figured more prominently in commentary since ancient times – our documentation for this is as early as the Dead Sea Scrolls. Perhaps related to the last point, the text of the Twelve and of Isaiah has been more stable than that of Jeremiah and Ezekiel. But all these points of comparison serve only to underscore the one key contrast: the Twelve make the variety of voice and period quite explicit, while all of the voices in the book of Isaiah are anonymous and undated, but one.

It is in fact very hotly debated just in what sense the Twelve are a 'book'. The Wisdom of Ben Sirach, from the second century BCE, mentions them together briefly as the twelve prophets (49:10), but names none of them – suggesting, for this reader, that they have merged into a single entity. Together they fit readily on a single parchment scroll somewhat shorter than any of the big three prophetic books; and there is such a scroll of the Twelve from Qumran, also dated to around 150 BCE. However, fitting on one scroll is a very minimal definition of what it means to be a book, although an acceptable one. The number twelve would imply either deliberate selection and patterning or totality and comprehensiveness, or both.

The most obvious connections linking individual 'books' within the collection are between immediate or at least close neighbours. A good example are the promises at the end of Joel, which we find again at beginning and end of Amos:

> The LORD roars from Zion,
>   and utters his voice from Jerusalem. (Joel 3:16; Amos 1:2 NRSV)

> The mountains shall drip sweet wine,
>   the hills shall flow with milk. (Joel 3:18 NRSV; [Amos 9:13])

It is argued either that the end of Joel provides an envelope for Amos; or, according to the reverse order in the Greek Bible, that the beginning and end of Amos are resumed together at the close of Joel. Joel 2:32 and Obadiah 17 are very closely related – and these books are neighbours in the Greek Bible. At the other end of the collection, Haggai and Zechariah 1–8 share much significant vocabulary; and Malachi opens the same way as the immediately preceding three-chapter units, Zechariah 9–11 and 12–14. It is much harder to decide whether each of these features was original to the short 'book' in question, and such shared features influenced the ordering of the collection; or whether at least some of the links were created by the editors who gave the Twelve its shape.

No answer should be attempted without noting the much wider relationships involved. Isaiah 2:2–4 records the same famous promise of a role for the mountain of the Lord's house in days to come as we read in the first three verses of Micah 4:1–4. Joel 1:15 and Isaiah 13:6 both liken the coming 'day of Yahweh' to destruction (*šd*) coming from the Almighty (*šdy*). Several of the twenty-one verses within Obadiah's 'vision' (quite the shortest 'book' in the Hebrew Bible) are found in a different arrangement in Jeremiah's (not many fewer) words 'about Edom' (49:7–22). The Lord roars and utters his voice in Jeremiah 25:30 as well as in Joel 3:16 and Amos 1:2, but now 'from on high' and 'from his holy habitation'. We noted above that 'the LORD of hosts', so common in Isaiah 1–39, occurs only six times in chapters 40–55, four of these in the statement 'the LORD of hosts is his name'. This formulation is a feature of Jeremiah and of Amos. Are these allusions in one book to another? Or developments from one book to another? Or originally anonymous or traditional material taken up independently into different collections?

There is a historical or chronological aspect to the ordering of the Twelve. This is true first of all in terms of external history. Hosea and Amos deal explicitly with northern Israel (or Ephraim, as Hosea calls the people of the north), which was overrun by Assyria in the final third of the eighth century BCE; and come at the beginning. Micah, dealing with Judah towards the end of the same century, but making no mention of the north, is set in sixth place. Finally, Haggai–Zechariah–Malachi, dealing in different ways with the restoration situation in the Persian period, round off the collection. But there is also (at least some) development from text to text. One obvious example is the way in which Zechariah 13:2–6 reworks part of Amos 7:10–17. That story of Amos's encounter with the 'priest of Bethel' is itself an addition to the book of Amos from a late period, connected with other late prophetic narratives in 1 Kings 13 and 2 Chronicles 25; but the development in Zechariah of the 'I am no prophet' theme must belong to a more advanced period still. Another example of development, though it is less clear in which direction, is where Joel 3:10 (NRSV) urges, in contrast to Isaiah 2:4 // Micah 4:3,

> Beat your ploughshares into swords,
>   and your pruning-hooks into spears;
>   let the weakling say, 'I am a warrior.'

There is considerable variety within many of the books of the Twelve, even the shorter ones. Zephaniah sounds in only three chapters many of the notes heard throughout the whole corpus. And argument for authorship by several hands is quite as energetic in relation to small books of only three chapters such as Zephaniah, or Joel and Habakkuk and Nahum as for the longer Micah, or even Isaiah.

Much the greater part of the material in the Twelve is poetic. In most of these books, narrative is rare and therefore all the more prominent. Hosea in first place opens with three chapters that have proved very difficult to interpret and have tended to draw attention away from the rest of the book. Narrative panels in Hosea 1:1 – 2:1 and 3:1–5 frame mostly poetic material in 2:2–23. In the first, Hosea is commanded by God to take to himself 'a wife of whoredom' and have 'children of whoredom' by her (1:2). In the second, he is to 'love a woman who has a lover and is an adulteress, just as Yahweh loves the people of Israel' (3:1). Yet it is far from clear (1) whether the same woman is intended in the two descriptions, (2) whether we are reading the report of acted parable(s) or theatre, or (3) whether we should suppose the reports are to be read as symbolic or visionary. In fact the questions of genre that these chapters pose should remind us of some of the reports in Jeremiah 11–20. Put in another way, these narratives evoke powerfully the pain and the persistence in the deity's relationship with his people; but they leave tantalizingly obscure whether such painful and persistent love was also symbolically enacted in the life of Hosea to whom the divine word was spoken (1:1–2; 4:1).

One whole 'book' of the Twelve is in its entirety a prophetic narrative, though in fact the whole story of Jonah is not very much longer than the opening three chapters of Hosea. It is very skilfully composed in two almost matching panels (chs 1–2 and 3–4), each inviting reconsideration of how the other should be read. The end of the first panel is a song or psalm of thanksgiving (2:3–10); and the extra degree of openness involved in interpreting that poem artfully complicates the mutuality of the two halves of the story. Jonah appears to be one of the latest books in the Hebrew Bible, not least because for all its brevity it shows good evidence that its author knew many of the others – from Elijah to Joel. In fact, there is some evidence in the second-century scroll from Qumran already mentioned that it appeared as the last of the Twelve. Both its subject and its date encourage us to read it not as a story about a historical Jonah, but as an exploration of the divine nature, and of the phenomenon of prophecy itself.

EZEKIEL

The book of Ezekiel is very different yet again. In more desperate moments, the commentator must wonder whether or in what sense 'prophecy' is *the* 'genre' to which all of these books and collections belong, or whether the attempt to probe and explain that claim simply exposes how disparate they all are. Ezekiel is the most exotic and the most orderly at the same time. The language of the book is remarkably novel within the Bible as a whole. Jeremiah is introduced as being 'of the priests who were at Anathoth' (Jer. 1:1); yet the language of his book is remarkably similar to the language of Kings, or even of the Former Prophets as a whole. But Ezekiel is simply 'the priest' (Ezek. 1:3); and this book uses a host of priestly categories, though in a non-cultic environment. Apparently, language from the Temple in Jerusalem has been not so much desacralized as resacralized. Monarchy and Temple had been the twin institutions through which God had led and been with his people. After the collapse of both, the book of Ezekiel answered the agonized question whether God was still with his people and leading them, whether he could still be met.

The message of the book has twin foci: on the one side, the awful totality of divine judgment; and, on the other, that God meant his people to survive it. The whole book is in fact an elaborate 'theodicy', or justification of the deity: despite the perpetual blackness of Israel's behaviour in the past, God has not given up, nor will he in the future. Themes are developed much more expansively in Ezekiel than in most prophetic books, apart from Isaiah 40–55. Perhaps it is here that we see the beginnings of prophecy as a written phenomenon. The report of Ezekiel's vision (1–3) is much more detailed than what we find in the series of five terse visions in Amos 7:1–9; 8:1–3; 9:1–4; or in the two that are part of Jeremiah's commission (1:11–14); or even Isaiah's dread sight of the Lord on his throne (6). Amos's fifth vision (9:1) is of Yahweh at his altar; and Isaiah 6 is often held to evoke experience of the shrine in Jerusalem. But Ezekiel saw the heavens opened while among the exiles; and attempts to describe the indescribable. The book begins by demonstrating that communication between God and a human being is still possible, even although the house of Israel may be too stubborn to hear. And it ends (40–8) with a vision of very different character: no longer the obscurity of what can barely be uttered, but the clarity of a blueprint for a restored Jerusalem, and a working sanctuary, and priestly arrangements within twelve restored tribes, and a stream issuing from near the holy mountain and strong enough to sweeten the Dead Sea – all of this culminating in the naming of the city in the last words of the book: 'Yahweh will be there' – implying that the deity can still be met.

The shape and structure of the book can be described in two different ways. It is patterned like the Greek book of Jeremiah. Critique of Ezekiel's own people is uppermost in chapters 1–24; the central section is made up of sayings against other nations (Ezekiel 25–32); and more hopeful material relating to his own people is found in chapters 33–48. Then an explicit chronological structure operates in much of the text. An absolute date 'in the fifth year', and tied to external history, is provided at the outset (1:1–2); and then a system of internal dates takes over. Most of the material is located between the sixth year (8:1) and the twelfth (32:1, 17; 33:21). By no means all the material is dated; however, such dates as are provided are presented in chronological order except for some of the sayings about other nations within chapters 25–32, which appear to have been (re-)arranged topically. Two dates in particular stand out. The final vision of restoration is located in the twenty-fifth (40:1), which may intend a half-jubilee. And Ezekiel 29:17 dates to the beginning of the twenty-seventh year the promise of Egypt to Babylon because the Tyre campaign had been so long and hard.

The nations are grouped and weighted quite differently in Ezekiel's sayings. Neighbouring Ammon, Moab, Edom, and the Philistines are despatched first in only seventeen verses of prose (Ezek. 25). Tyre follows in a whole series of poems (26–8); and extended threats to Egypt follow (29–32). Babylon, far from being spoken against (and at prominent length, as in Isaiah and Jeremiah), is mentioned only in the role of divine agent: first against Tyre (26:7), and then (because the king of Babylon had not been sufficiently rewarded by its plunder for his people's very hard work in reducing Tyre) against Egypt (29:18; 30:10; 32:11).

For all the differences between Ezekiel and the other books reviewed, there are interesting links as well; and some of these have to do with the phenomenon of prophecy itself. Ezekiel is never directly addressed as 'prophet' in the book; but some thirty times the deity instructs him using what becomes a stock phrase: 'Son of man, prophesy against . . .'. Yet at two significant points in the book, during the opening vision (2:8) and as the theme turns towards restoration (33:33), he is told that his people 'shall know that a prophet has been among them'. Much the same is said by Elisha to his king (2 Kgs 5:8), distraught that the king of Syria expects healing in Israel for one of his officers: 'Let him come to me, that he may learn that there is a prophet in Israel.' There are other themes common to Elijah/Elisha and Ezekiel: the enabling 'hand of Yahweh' (1 Kgs 18:46; 2 Kgs 3:15; and six times in Ezekiel); and the 'spirit/wind of Yahweh' that might pick up Elijah or Ezekiel and deposit him elsewhere (1 Kgs 18:12; Ezek. 3:14). And I suspect that, in each case, these stories of Elijah and Elisha were influenced by the corresponding themes from Ezekiel.

TAKING LEAVE OF BIBLICAL PROPHECY

The Wisdom of Ben Sirach was mentioned above in our discussion of the Twelve. Ben Sirach is part of the longer Christian biblical canon, though it is not part of the Jewish collection of books that 'defile the hands'. Chapters 48–9 offer us one brief second century BCE overview of prophecy. Elijah receives the fullest treatment of all: a substantial resumé of his career (48:1–9), mention of his coming role 'at the appointed time' (48:10), and a concluding beatitude (48:11). The Elisha chapters in 2 Kings are summarized much more briefly (vv. 12–14), but no less gloriously:

> When Elijah was enveloped in the whirlwind,
> Elisha was filled with his spirit.
> He performed twice as many signs,
> and marvels with every utterance of his mouth.
> Never in his lifetime did he tremble before any ruler,
> not could anyone intimidate him at all.
> Nothing was too hard for him,
> and when he was dead his body prophesied.
> In his life he did wonders,
> and in death his deeds were marvellous. (NRSV)

Isaiah is mentioned in the context of King Hezekiah, who followed in David's footsteps

> as he was commanded by the prophet Isaiah,
> who was great and trustworthy in his visions.
> In Isaiah's days the sun went backwards,
> and he prolonged the life of the king.
> By his dauntless spirit he saw the future,
> and comforted the mourners in Zion.
> He revealed what was to occur to the end of time,
> and the hidden things before they happened. (48:22b–25)

Significantly, it is the role of Elisha's corpse in the restoring of the body thrown on to it that draws the first mention in this chapter of the word 'prophesy'. And, just after 'the prophet' Isaiah is named, there is mention of the sun going backwards.

The others are despatched in a couple of lines each (49:7–10), starting with Jeremiah:

> For they had maltreated him,
>> who even in the womb had been consecrated a prophet,
> To pluck up and ruin and destroy,
>> and likewise to build and to plant.
> It was Ezekiel who saw the vision of glory,
>> which he showed him above the chariot of the cherubim.
> For he also mentioned Job who held fast to all the ways of justice.
> May the bones of the Twelve Prophets
>> send forth new life from where they lie,
> For they comforted the people of Jacob
>> and delivered them with confident hope. (NRSV)

Isaiah, Jeremiah, and the Twelve are all called 'prophets'. New life from the bones of the Twelve, coming just after mention of Ezekiel, reminds us of his prophecy to the dry bones in the valley (Ezek. 37). But it is more likely that the Twelve are being wished *post mortem* success on a par with Elisha. And the mention of Job in connection with Ezekiel is a useful reminder that at Qumran Job and Psalms may have been counted among the Prophets, and that commentators in different ages have found Job, with its persistent critique of accepted wisdom and vision, the most subversively 'prophetic' of all biblical books (memorably, among recent authors, Fishbane 1989: 128–33).

Ben Sirach and many readers since may have overemphasized the role of 'wonders' among the prophets. But judgment, justice, and openness to the future are certainly among their key recurring themes. Wonders do belong to the stories: of Elijah and Elisha, of Isaiah and the deliverance of Jerusalem, of Jonah – and of exotic Ezekiel. And yet we cannot take our leave of the genre of biblical prophecy by simply talking in summary terms about the 'what'; for the 'how' is equally important.

Where prophets speak in the narratives of Samuel–Kings and Chronicles, and equally in the narratives within Jeremiah, Jonah, or Isaiah, they ordinarily speak prose. Yet much of the material in the prophetic books is poetry; and it is also likely that most of the earlier material within the prophetic books is contained in their poetical sections. However, the books themselves provide remarkably little indication of the original historical or social locations of the performance of this poetry. The collection of the poetry in these books has abstracted it from its original contexts. We may be right to discern anti-royal and anti-establishment protest in the pre-exilic kernels of some of these poetic collections. It may be just because this is so that much of the material is carefully ambiguous: 'house of Israel' could refer to court or people as a whole; and the same Hebrew can be translated 'the one enthroned in Jerusalem' or 'the one who inhabits Jerusalem'. (For a fuller discussion, see Auld

1989: 203–26, esp. 210–14.) An unambiguous court critic can quickly become a former critic (2 Chron. 25:14–16).

Ezekiel does draw attention to one aspect of the issue (33:32): 'Don't you see that to them you are a love song – beautiful voice and fine playing? They'll hear your words, but will not be doing them.' His comment seems to regret that the medium, far from being the message, is actually obscuring the message. Certainly, relatively little formal poetry has been preserved in that long book outside the chapters against foreign nations (25–32). The exceptions are found in chapters 7, 15, 17, 19, 21, and 24; and in some of these cases their exceptional status is highlighted. Ezekiel 17:1–10 are the propounding of a 'riddle' or 'parable'; and Ezekiel 19 is a 'lamentation'. The introduction to Ezekiel 24:3b–13 both calls the poem against the 'bloody city' of Jerusalem a 'likeness' (*mashal*) and dates its occasion precisely to the start of the siege by the king of Babylon (24:2–3a).

The three chapters of the book of Numbers (22–4), which report the vain attempt of a king of Moab to curse Israel on its way to its promised land, offer a final perspective on this discussion. The first and longest chapter sets the scene in prose, and includes the well-known episode of the donkey which not only saw Yahweh's angel long before Balaam's eyes were opened to see it, but was able to talk to his master. The next chapters report Balaam's inspired responses that evade Balak's commission. The first is in Numbers 23:7b–10; and its introduction is typical.

> Then God met Balaam; and Balaam said to him, 'I have arranged the seven altars, and have offered a bull and a ram on each altar.' Yahweh put a word in Balaam's mouth, and said, 'Return to Balak, and this is what you must say.' So he returned to Balak, who was standing beside his burnt-offerings with all the officials of Moab. Then Balaam uttered his oracle/'likeness' (*mashal*), saying . . .
>
> (23:4–7a NRSV, adapted)

'*Mashal*' is sometimes used to designate a didactic poem (Ps. 78, for example), a poem that uses appropriate comparisons (and contrasts) to 'tell it how it is' – and, in this case, explain 'How can I curse whom God has not cursed?' (23:8) Each of Balak's three invitations to curse issues in a *mashal* in which Balaam's words become more explicit in promise of blessing for Israel. When Balak then dismisses the 'seer', Balaam promises him future rule by Israel over (Balak's own people of) Moab and over Edom as well. Words hostile to Amalek and the Kenites are attached rather loosely to the end. Assyria will capture the Kenites, but will fall to a seaborne force (24:24).

The stories of Balaam offer an explanatory perspective, and they are a likeness. When Balak requires to curse a neighbouring but foreign people, he hires a 'seer' who performs the task in formal poetry; and we recall Jeremiah, prophet to the nations, and Ezekiel the singer. However, well beyond those comparisons, these chapters in Numbers, taken as a whole, function as something of a *mashal* – a 'likeness-that-explains' – for biblical prophetic literature as a whole. Their poetry is a gift and burden from above, its message unwelcome to the ruler who must tolerate hearing it; its hope for Israel still to be realized, and implying bane for age-old hostile neighbours, not least Moab (cf. Isa. 15–16 and Jer. 48). We might be tempted to add 'only a likeness' and remark that Balaam is not from the people of Israel, until we remember that Ezekiel was regularly addressed by God as 'son of man/ Adam': as a 'human' or 'mortal' with a *mashal* from above to communicate to Israel. That prophetic *mashal*, which both explores and explains 'the ways of God to man', has proved to be a vital stimulus to the whole enterprise of theology.

REFERENCES AND FURTHER READING

Alter, R. (1990) 'Prophecy and Poetry', in *The Art of Biblical Poetry*. Edinburgh: T&T Clark, 137–62.

Auld, A. G. (1989) 'Prophecy and the Prophets', in S. Bigger (ed.) *Creating the Old Testament: The Emergence of the Hebrew Bible*. Oxford: Basil Blackwell, 203–26.

Barton, J. (1986) *Oracles of God: Perceptions of Ancient Prophecy in Israel after the Exile*. London: Darton, Longman & Todd.

Blenkinsopp, J. (1996) *A History of Prophecy in Israel*, 2nd rev. and enlarged edn. Louisville, Ky.: Westminster John Knox.

Davies, P. R. (ed.) (1996) *The Prophets: A Sheffield Reader*. Biblical Seminar 42. Sheffield: Sheffield Academic Press.

Fishbane, M. (1989) *The Garments of Torah*. Indiana Studies in Biblical Literature. Bloomington: Indiana University Press, 128–33.

McKane, W. (1986) *Jeremiah*, Vol. 1. ICC. Edinburgh: T&T Clark.

Sawyer, J. F. A. (1993) *Prophecy and the Biblical Prophets*, rev. edn. Oxford Bible Series. Oxford: Oxford University Press.

The relevant volumes from the series 'Old Testament Guides', published by Sheffield Academic Press.

CHAPTER SEVEN

WISDOM

———·◆·———

Katharine Dell

There is a distinct genre of material in the Bible known as 'wisdom'. This is largely contained in the corpus of Old Testament and Apocryphal literature known as the 'wisdom literature', notably Proverbs, Job, Ecclesiastes, Ecclesiasticus (or Ben Sira) and the Wisdom of Solomon, but extends further than simply these texts. Its influence is felt in the New Testament in the presentation of Jesus both as a wise teacher and as a divine mediator. Any text that contains the genres of wisdom may be seen to be part of a broad wisdom tradition that extends beyond Israel into the ancient Near East. In fact the wisdom tradition is thought to have sprung largely from contact with the wisdom of other nations rather than from within Israelite tradition itself, because it does not mention the saving events of the history of Israel. Rather it is concerned with the human condition in general, with relationships between individuals and between individuals and God. Again, by analogy with the ancient Near East, notably Egypt, the wisdom tradition is thought to have been the product of circles of wise men or sages who perpetuated this material mainly in educational contexts.

PROVERBS

The basic form of wisdom is the proverb and hence our starting point for looking at the wisdom tradition is the book of Proverbs. This book divides into distinct sections and the oldest section of basic maxims is Proverbs 10:1 – 22:16. This section is headed 'The proverbs of Solomon' who has the reputation of being the 'wise man' *par excellence* from whom the wisdom tradition takes its inspiration. We find in this section a succession of proverbs beginning with 'A wise son makes a glad father, but a foolish son is a sorrow to his mother' (Prov. 10:1).[1] This proverb involves a comparison between the wise and the foolish, a theme that pervades the wisdom literature – the study of wisdom has as its goal 'becoming wise' and hence the basic idea is to present a whole series of maxims that will aid the would-be wise person to tread the path of wisdom. The proverbs cover a whole range of themes such as the dangers of laziness and the importance of hard work, the desirability of love rather than hatred, the important place of money and its corresponding dangers, the importance of careful choice of words rather than babbling like a fool, the place of kindness and generosity and the key importance of a good reputation. They speak of fair dealing, the dangers of gossip, humility versus pride, hope rather than despair. The proverbs are full of observations about human nature, 'Anxiety in a man's heart weighs him down, but a good word makes him glad' (Prov. 12:25). Some draw comparisons from the natural world to illuminate human behaviour, 'Let a man meet a she-bear robbed of her cubs, rather than a fool in his folly' (Prov. 17:12); 'Like clouds and wind without rain is a man who boasts of a gift he does not give' (Prov. 25:14, RSV adapted). The proverbs gather data about human nature that eventually form patterns that can be relied upon and built up as a picture of an ordered world that makes sense. However this does not mean that there is no ambiguity in events, even clear contradictions, and the proverbs make allowance for that. An example can be found among the proverbs on speech and communication – one proverb sees silence as a virtue and too much talk as a negative thing – 'He who restrains his words has knowledge, and he who has a cool spirit is a man of understanding.' And in the next breath the proverb goes on to say that 'Even a fool who keeps silent is considered wise; when he closes his lips, he is deemed intelligent' (Prov. 17:27–8), suggesting that the silent can just as well be wise as a fool – one never knows until they open their mouths!

The proverbs are particularly concerned about punishment and reward – to the wicked, the fool, the sluggard or the evildoer punishment will come. Conversely to the wise, the upright, the hard-worker and the diligent, rewards will be great. In this sense there is a simplistic and rather naive attitude to life. It is very simple – you can choose one path or another, the path of wisdom that is smooth and straight and leads to all good things, or the path to folly, full of pitfalls and covered with thorns. There are material rewards attached to these two paths – wealth is the result of wisdom; poverty comes to the unsuspecting fool. For example, 'A man of crooked mind does not prosper, and one with a perverse tongue falls into calamity' (Prov. 17:20). While there is a recognition that the wicked do sometimes prosper, this is seen as a fleeting thing; for example Proverbs 11:18, 'A wicked man earns deceptive wages, but one who sows righteousness gets a sure reward.' The rewards are not only monetary; they are happiness, fulfilment, longevity, family and friends. There is a great confidence in the wisdom quest and in the doctrine of retribution that, as we shall see, was not shared by authors of some of the more questioning wisdom books.

The question is raised, when and where did this proverbial material originate and in what kinds of circles was it transmitted? Those proverbs cited so far are all of a general nature, representing sound common sense and sometimes a profound insight into human nature. These have the character of folk wisdom, of the experience of many generations distilled into pithy sayings. They may be quite old in origin, reflecting a tradition that was once oral and that took place within families and tribes and wherever teaching was needed.[2] It is unlikely that these proverbs originated with Solomon but he may have had an interest in wisdom (as strongly suggested by 1 Kings 4:29–34), which led to clever sayings being associated with him.

There are a number of backgrounds reflected by the proverbs. This section seems to address those for whom slothfulness and poverty are real dangers. The people

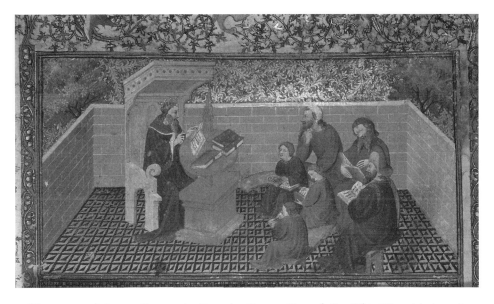

Figure 7.1   Solomon dictates the Proverbs. Roy 15 DIII f.285, Bible Historiale (1357).
British Library. Photo Bridgeman Art Library.

addressed by the proverbs need to work for their living and make their way in a
society made up of both the righteous and evildoers. Making money is seen to be a
good thing, but excessive wealth is criticized, particularly wealth quickly gained,
'Wealth hastily gotten will dwindle, but he who gathers little by little will increase
it' (Prov. 13:11). There are proverbs about the king that have led some to believe
that these proverbs are the work of courtiers or administrators in royal service,[3] for
example, 'Inspired decisions are on the lips of a king; his mouth does not sin in
judgment' (Prov. 16:10). However, these proverbs about the king are of a general
nature that does not preclude a broader context of discussion about the king by
others than those in close contact with him.[4]

We need to distinguish between the origin of the proverbs and when they were
written down. This section of Proverbs, it has been argued, may well have been
intended as a kind of manual for would-be administrators of the Solomonic state.[5]
The actual writing down of wisdom, even if it had a folk origin, would have
been a literary enterprise, only able to be done by intellectuals who could read and
write and had the leisure for reflection of this nature and literary activity of this
kind. So the idea was posited that the writing down of the proverbs could be attributed to a small group of educated sages, such as might have clustered around the
king and his court. At the time of Solomon with the growth of the state, the need
for educated administrators would have been great and these texts may well have
been part of the curriculum of schools specially set up to train such men.[6] This idea
was largely based on the Egyptian model of schools known to have existed for
the training of courtiers. Scholars were convinced of this theory even more strongly
when close parallels were noted between another proverbial section of Proverbs

22:16 – 24:22 and the Egyptian Instruction of Amenemope, which was known to be a school textbook.[7]

On this model of the development of the wisdom enterprise, the character of wisdom is revealed as essentially humanistic, concerned with understanding human nature and society and attempting to impose some kind of moral order on the world. It has been seen as a 'secular' quest by comparison with the rest of the Bible, which starts from divine revelation in history rather than from the human side.[8] However, God is not absent. In Proverbs 10:1 – 22:16 we find odd clusters of proverbs that acknowledge that real understanding is to be found only with God. In chapter 16 for example,

> The plans of the mind belong to man,
>   but the answer of the tongue is from the LORD.
> All the ways of a man are pure in his own eyes,
>   but the LORD weighs the spirit.
> Commit your work to the LORD,
>   and your plans will be established.
> The LORD has made everything for its purpose,
>   even the wicked for the day of trouble. (vv. 1–4)

Even in the earliest wisdom tradition God is at the limits of human understanding and 'The fear of the LORD prolongs life' (Prov. 10:27).

When we move on to consider Proverbs 1–9 we find a more explicitly theological section that is often thought to be later and a development from the more humanistic quest.[9] However, we can also regard it as simply drawing out the theological implications of essentially the same quest. The section contains a number of 'instructions' from father and mother to son, longer exhortations than just the simple maxim, which resemble Egyptian models and again suggest an educational context. However it is unlikely that the references to father, mother and son represent teacher and pupil here; rather they probably indicate a family context (maybe even a scribal/intellectual family) rather than a formal school one.[10] Here the teaching is concerned with trusting God and finding favour with God by pursuing wisdom:

> Trust in the LORD with all your heart,
>   and do not rely on your own insight.
> In all your ways acknowledge him,
>   and he will make straight your paths. (Prov. 3:5–6).

In this section wisdom takes on more profound dimensions. God is seen to have founded the world by wisdom and wisdom, personified as a woman, calls to young men to follow her way. Wisdom has a character of her own and is portrayed as standing beside the city gates trying to win the young to her way (Prov. 1:20–1). Of course there are always the attractions of the foreign or loose woman who also seeks to entice the same innocents along her path (Prov. 7). However, woman wisdom is God's wisdom, created at the beginning of time, the mediator of creation itself:

Figure 7.2 Statue of Sophia at Ephesus. Photo K. J. Dell.

When there were no depths I was brought forth,
   when there were no springs abounding with water.
Before the mountains had been shaped,
   before the hills, I was brought forth;
before he had made the earth with its fields,
   or the first of the dust of the world . . .
   then I was beside him, like a master workman;
and I was daily his delight,
   rejoicing before him always. (Prov. 8:24–6, 30)

In Proverbs 1–9 then we find that wisdom has its own theology – that of creation. The basic societal and human order established by the proverbs and maxims of 10:1–22:16 are brought on to a more profound level in being seen to reflect the order of the world itself. There are Egyptian parallels again with the figure of Ma-at, the principle of order.[11] God stands at the heart of that order – much can be known by humans but ultimately it is God who holds the keys to wisdom. Conversely God mediates wisdom through creation itself and through the figure of wisdom who calls to those who wish to be wise to follow her path (Prov. 8). We might ask about the origin of this more profound theological reflection about wisdom. It certainly does not look like the kind of material used for training administrators; rather it is more religiously orientated and may belong in groups undertaking religious training – in temple schools for example.[12]

There are other smaller collections of material in Proverbs that seem to have originated in different groups of the wise.[13] In Proverbs 25:1 we are told that this collection of proverbs (to ch. 29) was compiled by the 'men of Hezekiah'. This has suggested to some that the writing up of many proverbs may belong to such a group based around the king, but Hezekiah rather than Solomon.[14] It is interesting that these 'men' would have belonged to the eighth century BC, nearly two centuries after Solomon. This might suggest that the actual literary transmission of the proverbs was beginning to take shape at this slightly later time in educated circles rather than at the earlier Solomonic period. The idea of a royal administration and intellectual enlightenment on a large scale at the time of Solomon has in fact largely fallen from favour in scholarly circles in recent years.[15] Rather, it is argued that this was a relatively small state that would have needed its intellectuals who may indeed have gathered together some wisdom from broader contexts and assembled it in literary form, but not on the large scale proposed by those advocating this theory nor as a part of formalized educational activity.[16] We should maybe speak of clusters of literary formulation of proverbs occurring at different times rather than trying to pinpoint specific contexts in which the preservation of wisdom sayings was undertaken.

We have no firm archaeological evidence for the existence of schools along Egyptian lines, but what we do have is a large number of inscriptions and evidence of fairly widespread literacy from the eighth century BC onwards.[17] This might suggest that a once-oral wisdom tradition gradually flowered as a literary activity in narrower, more intellectual circles and found its home ultimately in interaction with the more profound theological reflection of Proverbs 1–9. This theological aspect would have formed part of the concerns of the intellectuals who cast the material in more literary form, individuals who are perhaps to be associated with more religious or priestly circles such as might have existed in a temple school rather than seen as a separate group of sages with concerns isolated from other areas of Israelite life. This theological dimension is what was to be taken up in its later biblical literature, in the books of Job and Ecclesiastes to which we shall now turn.

JOB

The book of Job is generally thought to be later than Proverbs, reflecting a period when the easy answers of the earlier wisdom writers no longer worked for those undergoing more profound experiences of suffering. It is probably to be dated between the sixth and fourth centuries BC – a cross-reference can be found to the person of Job in Ezekiel 14:14, 20, which speaks of a righteous figure who probably existed in folk memory and whose existence no doubt predates the book that may more naturally fit the later date. The reference to 'the Satan' in the prologue of Job is often seen to suggest a date for the whole book in the Persian period, although some argue that these are a later addition.[18] Proverbs was optimistic about the fact that good things come to the wise person and that punishment is inevitable for the wicked. The early maxims encourage one to walk along wisdom's path and all will be well. The more theological approach advocated especially in Proverbs 1–9 is to fear God and trust in his Wisdom and then good things will come to you. The author of the book of Job realized that life was not that simple. Real experience revealed that suffering often came, violently and unexpectedly, to the righteous man who had done all in his power to follow the path of wisdom. How was this to be understood? Did it not simply reveal that the wisdom quest was bankrupt?

The author of the book of Job, who probably lived after the Exile when many earlier certainties had been overturned, is thought to have taken an earlier tale about a righteous man named Job who, despite calamity, held on to his integrity.[19] When all was taken away from him his response was 'Shall we receive good at the hand of God, and shall we not receive evil' (Job 2:10). The first two chapters of the book are in the prose of this tale, and then at chapter 3 we have a lament by Job followed by a long dialogue between Job and three friends who have purportedly come to console him. This debate concerns the question whether or not Job is suffering because he has sinned. Job maintains throughout that he is innocent and so does not deserve the suffering that has come to him. He argues that God has turned against him and 'the arrows of the Almighty' (Job 6:4) are in him, while the friends are convinced that Job has sinned. The dialogue contains three rounds of speeches in chapters 4–14, 15–21 and 22–27 and becomes more and more heated with open criticism on both sides. The third cycle of speeches has been dislocated and characters appear to be saying the wrong things. This is probably the result of scribal error in transmission and many reorderings of the speeches have been suggested.[20]

The dialogue section is thought to be the main composition of the author who used the story of Job to create a more profound response to the problem of innocent suffering and to the issue of how to maintain a relationship with God in the light of such suffering.[21] The folk tale airs the issue of motivation for fearing God. Is it simply a matter of believing in God because of the benefits one can gain (an attitude promoted by the strictly retributive reasoning of proverbs) or is there a more profound relationship than that? It becomes apparent in Job that his relationship with God is more profound and that he is prepared to accept God's punishment if he feels it is deserved. The problem is that he does not feel that it is. The friends act as a foil for the traditional view that the doctrine of retribution does work and that if you are suffering you must have sinned in some way. Job moves beyond such sentiments into a profound questioning of the whole ground of his relationship with God, notably of God's justice. Using legal-type language he tries to force God into the dock to explain himself.[22] The problem is that God is both judge and prosecutor. Job calls for a mediator to judge between himself and God (ch. 19), but of

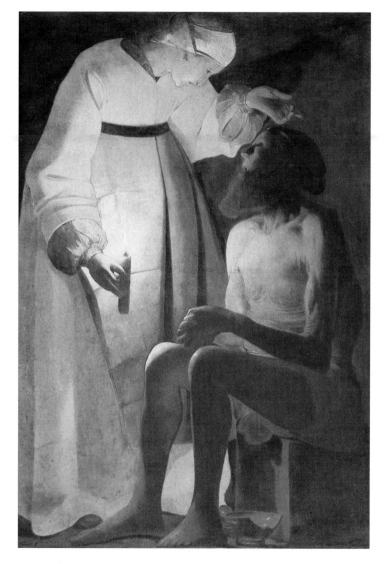

Figure 7.3 Job visited by his wife. Photograph courtesy Musée départemental d'Art ancien et contemporain collection, Epinal, France.

course that is an impossibility. Finally, God does appear (ch. 38), not to answer his questions directly, but rather to point out to him that there are many things in the created world that human beings do not understand. Why does Job presume to understand his own situation or the reasons for God's action? At this point Job repents and confesses to having uttered 'counsel without knowledge' (42:3), a gesture that, for many, spoils the tragic character of the book so far.[23] However in an interesting verse in Job 42:7 God states that the friends were wrong in their words about God and that Job was right – a surprising statement in the light of Job's vehement remarks in his speeches in the dialogue. Job is then asked by God to intercede for the friends by praying on their behalf. Job is thus vindicated by God before his restoration in the epilogue that follows.

The book of Job is very unlike the book of Proverbs in that it contains few maxims and it has its own dialogue genre. At times it more closely resembles the psalms of lament, especially in chapters 3 and 29–31, Job's closing lament, and in fact the book's dialogue section is full of psalmic sentiments turned on their head by the author as he attempts to express Job's anguish and protest at his treatment by God. This represents a parodying of a known tradition, which the author's audience would have understood.[24] There is the same view of God as creator that we find in Proverbs but here it is much expanded. In a section of speeches by God at the end of the book, God reveals himself as the creator who does great things that no one can understand (Job 38–41). As an answer to the problem of suffering, this reply by God seems curiously both to negate and confirm the wisdom quest. The optimism that human beings can understand and to some extent control their own destiny by 'wise' behaviour is overturned, but in its place is an acknowledgement of the greatness and otherness of God whose ways are beyond comprehension. He is indeed at the limits of the wisdom quest and he does things for his own reasons rather than any that human beings can understand. This confirms therefore that trusting in God is all one can do, but it makes the attempt to understand even more frustrating.

The dialogue between Job and the friends reveals a man whose presuppositions have been challenged, a man battling against those who think that they know all the answers. The debate concerns Job's righteousness. Job knows that he has not sinned and that he therefore does not deserve the suffering that has come to him – the destruction of his property, his children and the affliction with a festering disease. The friends generally maintain that he must have sinned or else he would not have received this treatment at the hand of God. At a later stage in the book, in chapters 32–7, a fourth friend appears and confirms these views, while indicating that indeed, as God is about to reveal in his speeches, God's ways are mysterious. These speeches are often thought to be additions to the book[25] as is a hymn to wisdom in chapter 28, which speaks of the impossibility of finding wisdom on earth.[26] The hymn ends with a sentiment that links together divine wisdom and human wisdom, 'Behold, the fear of the Lord, that is wisdom; and to depart from evil is understanding' (Job 28:28). The book of Job closes with the restoration of Job to former prosperity, which seems to contradict all that has gone before in that Job has just disproved the fair working of the doctrine of retribution in his speeches in the dialogue. But here we are back in the folk tale of the original story and in its present position it is best understood as an ironic ending to the book.

It is hard to know what the context of this work might have been. It seems to come from circles concerned to criticize the earlier certainties of wisdom, maybe from a person or group sceptical of earlier wisdom and wishing to express this in literary form.[27] The book of Job belongs less obviously to an educational context, resembling more closely a kind of paradigmatic tale, and it has been questioned whether, on a narrow level of definition that takes its starting point from the character and contexts of the book of Proverbs, it can really be regarded as wisdom at all.[28]

Figure 7.4   Statue of Job from outside Yad Vashem. Photo Nathan Meron.

ECCLESIASTES

The book of Ecclesiastes is often coupled with the book of Job since they both represent wisdom in revolt. However, in many ways Ecclesiastes springs from the same aphoristic style of quest as Proverbs and has more in common with this book. Here we have the musings of an individual, named Qoheleth or 'the Preacher', which belong fairly naturally to an instructional or educational milieu (Eccl. 12:9). The book is thought to date before the Greek period, which began in the third century BC, since it does not demonstrate the influence of Greek ideas (although some have argued for their presence).[29] The author of Ecclesiastes uses a special method of testing maxims and providing commentary upon them.[30] This is interspersed with poems on times and seasons, and one in chapter 12 on old age, and repeated and characteristic phrases such as 'All is vanity and a striving after wind' (1:14). The word *hebel*, 'vanity', is used thirty-eight times in the book and is a kind of keyword in the light of which all things are relativized. The book is generally thought to be pessimistic in tone, although some scholars have stressed its more optimistic aspects.[31] The author certainly advocates enjoying life while we can, 'There is nothing better for a man than that he should eat and drink, and find enjoyment in his toil. This also, I saw, is from the hand of God' (Eccl. 2:24). However this is often tempered by the recognition that all actions are relativized by death, the great leveller (e.g. Eccl. 2:16–18). The book certainly ends on a more optimistic note (that many have seen as a later addition[32]) that the best thing to do is to 'Fear God and keep his commandments' (12:13).

We find in the book a concealed attribution to Solomon – the preacher is described as 'son of David, king in Jerusalem' (1:1), as having 'been king over Israel in Jerusalem' (1:12) and there is a long 'royal testament' section in chapter 2 in which the author seems to take on the persona of Solomon – 'I became great and surpassed all who were before me in Jerusalem; also my wisdom remained with me' (Eccl. 2:9). This attribution can hardly be taken literally knowing what we do about the dating of the book and is probably to be regarded as an attempt to give the book authority. However, it seems odd to conceal the reference to Solomon in this way and some have suggested that it represents clumsy editorial work rather than the work of the main author, Qoheleth.[33] This method maintains the royal link that seems to be a characteristic of much wisdom literature (although not Job, which does not contain an attribution to Solomon or treat royal concerns). This author seeks all means to pleasure but finds it an empty quest. He questions the point of working and of accumulating wealth, for death is all there is to look forward to, 'As he came from his mother's womb he shall go again, naked as he came, and shall take nothing for his toil, which he may carry away in his hand' (Eccl. 5:15). He finds that there is nothing new and that nothing really changes, 'Of making many books there is no end, and much study is a weariness of the flesh' (Eccl. 12:12). He commends enjoyment and sees it as God-given but he questions whether human beings can really understand the mysteries of life. He speaks in his poem in chapter 3 of times and seasons, 'For everything there is a season, and a time for every matter under heaven: a time to be born, and a time to die; a time to plant, and a time to pluck up what it planted' (3:1–2). These are God's times, however, not ours – 'He has made everything beautiful in its time; also he has put eternity into man's mind, yet so that he cannot find out what God has done from the beginning to the end' (3:11).

The author of Ecclesiastes is thus working from within the wisdom tradition, testing its maxims against his experience and finally moving towards an acceptance of the *status quo*. His sentiments are anti-wisdom in the sense that they stress the futility of being able to know anything with certainty, and yet they confirm the God-given aspect of the wisdom quest in that trust in God is seen to be what is of lasting benefit. Human wisdom is ephemeral, but God's wisdom endures. Human beings will never fully understand – all they can do is acknowledge the futility of life but trust in God all the same. There is a pessimism here that contrasts sharply with the optimism of the early wisdom writers but an accompanying realism and a trust in God that the early writings lacked. The author may have belonged to circles of the wise – and this book certainly has a high literary quality – but there is a theological aspect to it that may suggest a broader temple school type context rather than a more secular, educational one.

The consideration of these biblical wisdom books has revealed to us the character of the wisdom literature as starting from human experience but with a profound sense of interaction with the divine. The God of wisdom is the creator who creates the universe and human beings within it, who gives the universe an order human beings can try to discover, who gives human beings the desire to know more and to understand their lives in relation to each other, to the world around them and to God. Yet it is that same God who withholds ultimate understanding from humans, understanding that can come only through communion with the divine that surpasses human reason.

WISDOM PSALMS

There are some psalms in the Psalter generally designated wisdom psalms, of which one is Psalm 73. In this psalm the author is worried about the lack of parity between the expected fate of the righteous and the apparent prosperity of the wicked. But then a profound turning point is reached in verse 17 when the psalmist enters the sanctuary and suddenly sees clearly that in fact the doctrine of retribution is at work after all. Something in the communion with God has made a difference to the psalmist's understanding, which suggests that 'fearing God' might be good advice after all. This psalm resembles the book of Job, the 'turning point' in particular echoing Job's repentance at the end of the book, which many scholars have found incomprehensible after the tirade, found in God's speeches, about God's ways being greater than human understanding. However, it is possible to understand Job's repentance as a moment of understanding as he is at last in contact with the divine, for which he has called during his speeches.[34] The worst torment for Job was feeling that God was not answering him, that he was absent, even hostile. Even though God does not answer his questions, there is something in the appearance of God that seems to satisfy Job. The stage is then set for the happy ending of the epilogue in which Job is restored with twice as many camels and other animals as he had before and a new set of children.

As with Psalm 73, other psalms are likened to wisdom on the basis of parallels with the known wisdom literature; for example Psalm 37 with its interest in the fates of the good and wicked is likened to Proverbs; Psalm 39 is likened to Ecclesiastes in its preoccupation with the vanity of life; and Psalm 49 is likened to Job and is mainly a lament and points to a close relationship between psalmic lament and parts of the wisdom literature. Also psalms concerned with creation, such as Psalm 104, can be ranged alongside the wisdom literature. There are problems however with classifying 'wisdom psalms' within the Psalter as a whole. Many psalms contain a few forms of wisdom or a little of its characteristic content but cannot overall be classified as wisdom; for example Psalm 111, which contains the wisdom motto that the fear of the Lord is the beginning of wisdom in verse 10 but which overall is not of the wisdom genre.[35]

The wisdom psalms, if they are to be designated as a separate group,[36] are generally judged to be literary compositions, belonging to the post-exilic period rather than being liturgical texts used in Israelite worship from early times. Wisdom circles are seen by some scholars to have given the Psalter its final form, the sages being seen as those who shaped much of the literature of the Old Testament in its final stages.[37] The wisdom psalms have often been seen as non-cultic[38] but in fact there is no evidence for this and there may well have been a closer connection between religious observance and instruction than is often maintained (e.g. the writer of

Psalm 119, a long acrostic psalm, prayed to God seven times a day). We shall see this development into the realm of prayer in Ecclesiasticus. It is possible in my opinion that from earliest times the wisdom and worship of Israel found important points of contact, the psalms being in many ways a digest of other Old Testament traditions. Wisdom was part of the self-understanding of the people and thus it legitimately found expression in their cultic life just as all other areas of their life and history did.

WISDOM WITHIN THE OLD TESTAMENT

The wisdom literature has often been divided off from the rest of the Old Testament and given a somewhat poor press.[39] Its theology in particular has been difficult to integrate with the historically based religion of ancient Israel.[40] What is seen to have made Israel distinctive are the great events of Exodus and salvation history culminating in the covenant and the law. This led the Israelites to believe in one God rather than the many gods of other nations and it led them to evolve a distinctive religion that was not cyclical but was linear and temporal. However, this characterization is too simplified. It is clear that the historical revelation was not the full story. There was another mode of revelation through the everyday, through human experience of the world and of God. There was a recognition of God as creator as well as of God as redeemer and this tradition had a separate place in the literature of Israel. We can perhaps see the historical dimension as a horizontal line and the creation/cosmos/wisdom dimension as a vertical line.[41] In cultic life the two lines meet with the praise of God as both creator and redeemer (e.g. Psalm 74). They also meet in prophecy – this link seems to have been of particular significance to the exiles since it is taken up in Deutero-Isaiah where a profound uniting of creation as the first act of the redeeming history is found.[42] It also features in the Pentateuch in the Priestly account of creation in Genesis 1 in which creation stands at the head of the salvation history.

Wisdom then needs to be considered theologically as concerned with creation.[43] However, it is also concerned with justice, retribution, moral concerns, and as such links up with other Old Testament books such as Deuteronomy[44] and some of the prophets, notably Amos, Hosea and Isaiah.[45] We cannot call any of these books wisdom books but we can note an influence from a tradition that was clearly broad in its scope both in terms of its context and its theology. There are also links of wisdom with narratives – the J narrative in the Pentateuch, the Joseph narrative and the Succession Narrative have been particular contenders for having wisdom links.[46] Their high literary quality and their more anthropocentric starting point than other narratives have been seen as pointers in this direction. Some saw them as the product of the Solomonic Enlightenment, while others have been less persuaded by such a view and have simply seen them as the product of intellectual circles with close links with wisdom methods and ideology.[47]

Wisdom then is necessarily seen as a separate genre so that we can identify it properly. However, we have seen that its influence pervades various areas of Israelite thought and that we are wrong to hive it off into its own stylistic and theological ghetto. Biblical wisdom however does retain a separate identity from those books more concerned with relating and understanding historical events. This was set to change. We shall see in considering the two wisdom books of the Apocrypha how the distinctive wisdom tradition was brought into contact with Israelite salvation history, notably with the Torah as the true wisdom of God. However, before that we shall pause for a moment to look at wisdom in its broader ancient Near Eastern context.

WISDOM AND THE ANCIENT NEAR EAST

This is a large topic that cannot be treated in any depth here.[48] However, it is clear that there was a broader tradition of wisdom with which Israel's wisdom links up. The great nations of Egypt and Mesopotamia needed wise men to service the state, to keep archives, and to advise the king. We have seen how many of the suggestions made about the context of Israelite wisdom have sprung from looking at such contextual parallels. The close parallel of Proverbs 22:16 – 24:22 with the Instruction of Amenemope from Egypt occasioned much speculation about a similar school context in Israel in which instructions may have been used.[49] However the precise period of those links are hard to ascertain – it may have been the Solomonic state that had the need for such formal educational processes to train administrators for the state, but current opinion states that this would be an overstatement of the size and nature of the state at that time.[50] Joseph stands out as an Israelite who became a wise man in the court of the Pharaoh, something possible in Egypt but not so likely in Israel. It is possible that under eighth to seventh century kings such as Hezekiah or Josiah there was more literary activity going on in general[51] and hence more need for a trained group of intellectuals. We have evidence of more widespread literacy from the eighth century onwards.[52] However, we have no hard evidence for schools themselves in Israel, only for a common literary tradition.

There are some interesting parallels to the book of Job among the ancient Near Eastern wisdom, notably Ludlul bel Nemeqi and the Babylonian Job.[53] These parallels show that there was a lamenting and questioning tradition in the ancient Near East that plumbed the depths of human experience. Parallels can also be found with Ecclesiastes such as the Dialogue with Pessimism.[54] There are important links between some of the creation imagery used in wisdom and in certain psalms and the ancient Near East, notably links with Canaanite sea monsters[55] and interesting parallels with Canaanite and Babylonian rituals in the cult.[56]

One cannot therefore deny that Israelite wisdom is part of a broader ancient Near Eastern phenomenon. However, some of the parallels have perhaps been overstressed and wisdom too readily seen as the 'foreign element' in Old Testament thought in the light of such links. In fact much Old Testament thought can be related to ancient Near Eastern concepts and myths – wisdom is not a special case.[57] We can perhaps argue that the genre of wisdom forms an important bridge between the ancient Near Eastern world, with its nature/creation faith, and the religion of Israel, with its emphasis on God as creator and with its interest in universal human experience. But it also retains its own distinctive Israelite character as it developed according to the needs of a particular people.

ECCLESIASTICUS OR THE WISDOM OF JESUS, SON OF SIRACH

It is usually maintained that it is Ecclesiasticus or the Wisdom of Jesus, son of Sirach (abbreviated to Sirach in what follows) who first made the link between Wisdom and Torah and this is certainly true of the personified figure of wisdom whose teaching embodies the Torah. However, a suggestion has been made that in fact there were links between legal and wisdom circles before this, found in particular in the book of Deuteronomy, which features a number of wisdom motifs.[58] This might suggest that circles of the wise were found in close contact with other areas of life such as the temple and among those responsible for the literary formulation of texts. It has been argued furthermore that after the Exile we can more readily speak of a broader intellectual tradition in which the borders between groups such as prophets, priests and wise men are becoming more blurred anyway.[59] It is a natural step nevertheless for Sirach in the second century BC to equate following the paths of wisdom with following the Torah. Von Rad remarked that it was rather ironic that wisdom starts on the sidelines of Israelite tradition but, once equated with the Torah, it becomes central in Israelite thought.[60] To express it slightly differently, gradually wisdom traditions are becoming more integrated with more historical traditions, a process that may have started happening after the Exile with the integration of creation into the redemption history in the thought of Deutero-Isaiah.

It is from Sirach that we have a description of the work of the wise man and the need for leisure (Ecclus. 38:24 – 39:11, my trans.) – 'How can a man become wise who guides the plough . . . and talks only about cattle?' (38: 25). He describes the wise man as studying the law, past wisdom and prophecies as well as the sayings of famous men and the intricacies of parables. He is described as mixing with rulers and travelling abroad and is also a man of prayer. There is thus an interesting combination here of many traditions, which suggests that certainly in this period, and maybe earlier too, the wise should not be seen as completely separate from other groups and only as employed in a limited form of education or in the production of wisdom literature. This is probably too narrow an interpretation of their role, which may well have been diverse. Sirach is a named work and has a personal touch that earlier wisdom literature lacks. The author may have been a priest (he shows some interest in cultic life and sacrifice and he praises the High Priest) or some kind of temple scribe. The book suggests an educational function of some kind. It contains proverbial wisdom but usually with an accompanying interpretation in the manner of the author of Ecclesiastes (e.g. Ecclus. 33:14–15; 39:33–4). Sirach uses a style of exhortation that resembles prophecy and uses refrains for emphasis. He also uses poetry, hymn forms (especially hymns to wisdom) and prayers and so there is a real mix of genres in his work that stretches the boundaries of a narrow definition of wisdom.

For Sirach the fear of the Lord is at the centre of the wisdom quest. He is more positive than Ecclesiastes about the possibility of discovering God's order and God's time. There is the same tension that is found in all wisdom between the human quest for wisdom and its limitations and the divine mediation of wisdom. The emphasis in Sirach tends in the latter direction and the message is that the wise man can control his life if he is in a close religious relationship with God. At the centre of the wisdom exercise is the keeping of the Torah. The foolish man is no longer just a sluggard or one who talks too much or one who fritters away his money. The foolish man is the one who defiantly ignores God's commandments, while the wise man follows them in upright manner. True wisdom is hidden in the Mosaic law and in the sacred history as the means of the revelation of that law so that both of these are integrated into the wisdom scheme. The nature of wisdom as a cosmic entity is stressed – wisdom is linked with creation but especially with the creation of the law. This had the effect of losing the universalism that characterized the earlier wisdom enterprise, making it more of a national product, pertinent to Israel alone. However, Sirach is not legalistic and has not lost the breadth of interest in all aspects of human life that characterized earlier proverbial material.

One of Sirach's techniques is to quote and allude to past texts, a technique that characterizes later works in general. For example he quotes from the primeval history in Genesis 1–11, retelling the biblical account of the creation fusing his own interpretation with traditional ideas (17:1–12). In verse 6, for example, he adds a note of wonder at the ability of the human intellect to differentiate between good and evil that is not contained in the Genesis account. Interestingly Sirach did not perceive himself as an innovator; on the contrary he was a preserver of past traditions and saw himself as merely making plain what was already inherent in earlier ideas. He always places the knowledge gained by experience in an explicitly theological context. Thus, for example, the idea of God's time, while seen in a negative light in Ecclesiastes because a person can never know the proper time, is seen as a positive thing since God has a time for everything in his overall purpose for humankind – it is better therefore not to question God but to trust in God. So Ecclesiasticus 39:33 states, 'The works of the Lord are all good and he will supply every need in his hour.' This is where predestination enters his thought, an idea that is in tension with the openness of the human pursuit of wisdom. Related to this idea is another motif in Sirach, his theory of opposites. According to this theory everything comes in pairs and everything has its opposite, and so there is a fixed place for all things. In 33:15 Sirach exclaims, 'Look upon the works of the Most High; they likewise are in pairs, one the opposite of the other.'

Thus with Sirach we find a wisdom that is beginning to change as it fuses with the historical traditions of Israel and as it becomes more overtly pious and God-centred. It is mixing with many other genres from Israelite life and becoming a less distinct phenomenon. This can also be seen to be the case in the Wisdom of Solomon, the final text that we shall look at here.

WISDOM OF SOLOMON

Turning to the Wisdom of Solomon, a first-century work thought to have been influenced by Greek ideas[61] we find a wisdom book of a rather different character that again starts to strain our definition of what wisdom is. There are few proverbs here; rather wisdom has become knowledge of cosmic secrets. The divine revelation dimension has taken over from the human quest for knowledge. There is an emphasis on God – his mercy, his foreknowledge, his forbearance in delaying punishments (which leads some to question whether God is maintaining justice in the world) and his will for humankind. The correct human response is one of piety and virtuous living that includes full faith in God. There can be no rewards for good behaviour without faith in God, a departure from earlier wisdom thought. There are warnings and admonitions in prophetic style in criticism of lifestyles of which the author disapproves (1:16 – 2:24) and there are frightening descriptions of the terrors that await the ungodly. Good and evil are very real forces linked with creative wisdom on the one hand and the frail human spirit on the other. Prayers and psalms feature, as in Sirach, and there are passages of lyrical poetry and pedestrian prose. Historical concerns are merged with wisdom elements and religious concerns, such as the election of the chosen people and polemic against idols, feature prominently. There is a new emphasis on the elect to whom alone full knowledge is available since it is only they who follow the God of Israel. This starts to link up with apocalyptic ideas which stress that the revelation of hidden secrets is reserved for a chosen few. However, there is a tension in this writer's thought in that he wishes to confirm that all the righteous can know God.

The hymn to wisdom forms an important link with earlier wisdom. Here Wisdom is not only personified as a woman; it is hypostatized so that wisdom becomes a manifestation of the divine, an emanation of divine attributes. Wisdom of Solomon 7:22 reads 'for wisdom, the fashioner of all things, taught me. For in her there is a spirit that is intelligent, holy, unique, manifold, subtle, mobile, clear, unpolluted, distinct, invulnerable, loving the good, keen, irresistible'. She is the orderer and creator of all things (8:1, 6) as well as the teacher of virtues such as self-control and justice (8:7) and the supplier of all instruction (7:17–22) including information on branches of the natural sciences, which are enumerated.

This work is attributed to Solomon and yet it is from a period much later than the time of Solomon – probably the first century BC. On grounds of chronology alone it could not therefore have been written by him. It was probably attributed to Solomon, as the symbol of the greatest wisdom thinker, to add more weight to the content of the book. It does however have a wider religious context than just a wisdom one with interests in prophecy in particular, and shows tendencies that indicate that the people of God are now an oppressed minority, a vassal state of succeeding great empires. We can just about include it as wisdom literature but with the awareness that wisdom is becoming less and less of a distinctive phenomenon and is more and more to be seen in conjunction both with influences from other areas of Israelite life and also from outside Israelite culture.

THE NEW TESTAMENT AND WISDOM

Wisdom influence can be found in parts of the New Testament. A number of sayings of Jesus in the gospels can be likened to forms familiar from wisdom literature, notably material traditionally attributed to Q, which may have been a separate sayings source.[62] The question is raised how far Jesus himself spoke in the tradition of wisdom or how far the tradition that preserved what he said modelled the sayings on wisdom genres. It is possible that in the light of the postponement of the second coming or end time a fresh emphasis was placed on leading an ethical life in the present and hence that the ongoing Christian tradition stressed the practical wisdom elements in the Jesus tradition. Jesus' parables resemble the teaching style of the wisdom writers but in fact are subtly different to wisdom genres, suggesting that while he worked within a known tradition he nevertheless branched outside that tradition to express something new. There is also an important relationship between Jesus and personified wisdom, notably in the logos hymn in John's gospel (ch. 1), which can be seen to follow closely the pattern of earlier hymns to wisdom as found in Proverbs 8, Sirach 24 and Wisdom of Solomon 7:22ff. It is interesting that the language of pre-existent wisdom, alongside God at the creation of the world and forming the crucial bridge between God and humankind, was taken up and used to refer to Christ. The effect is to create a profound statement about the complex divinity/humanity question in reference to Christ. There is also debate regarding the influence of wisdom on Paul, instigated by Hans Conzelmann[63] who saw Paul as a teacher of wisdom and then draws conclusions as to Paul's method in dealing with speculative wisdom traditions after studying 1 Corinthians 1:10 – 4:21, the only passage in Paul's letters that deals systematically with the theme of wisdom. We also find hymns about Jesus as pre-existent in Colossians and Philippians. Wisdom influence is commonly found in the epistle of James, which consists of sayings and exhortations and can be likened to Q.[64] The question is raised, is Jesus to be regarded as a sage in any technical sense, or are we better off regarding him as a wise person whose wisdom can be ranked alongside that of any sage but who transcends the category in his cosmological role? It is interesting that he combines in his person the anthropological and the cosmological, the two aspects of wisdom that are seen, particularly in biblical wisdom and most notably in the figure of personified wisdom, to be in tension.[65]

CONCLUSION

Wisdom then is a diverse phenomenon that has a distinctive character of its own and yet forges important links with other Old Testament literature and with the ancient Near East. Its influence extends throughout the biblical period and it changes and develops over time as contexts change and as theological thought develops. One of the main changes is from the universal, human-oriented quest for understanding that characterizes the canonical wisdom books, to the all-pervading theological scheme that it becomes in the work of later writers. Finally, its biblical role culminates in an important contribution to understanding the role and the nature of Jesus as pre-existent wisdom, 'in the beginning with God' (John 1:1).

NOTES

1 Unless stated otherwise, all Bible quotes are from the RSV.
2 See recent discussion of the oral beginnings of wisdom in C. Westermann, *The Roots of Wisdom*, Edinburgh, T. & T. Clark, 1995 (ET of *Wurzeln der Weisheit*, Göttingen, Vandenhoeck & Ruprecht, 1990).
3 Argued for mainly on the strength of Egyptian parallels by W. L. Humphreys, 'The Motif of the Wise Courtier in the Book of Proverbs', in J. Gammie (ed.), *Israelite Wisdom: Theological and Literary Studies in Honor of Samuel Terrien*, Missoula, Scholars Press, 1978, 177–90. See

also more recently M. Fox, 'The Social Location of the Book of Proverbs', in M. Fox et al. (eds), *Texts, Temples and Traditions: A Tribute to Menahem Haran*, Winona Lake, Eisenbrauns, 1996, 227–39.

4 See discussion in K. J. Dell, 'The King in the Wisdom Literature', in J. Day (ed.), *King and Messiah in the Old Testament and Related Literature: Papers from the Oxford Old Testament Seminar*, JSOTSup. Sheffield, 1998. See also R. N. Whybray, *Wealth and Poverty in the Book of Proverbs*, Sheffield, Sheffield Academic Press, 1990, who argues that the majority of royal proverbs do not imply that the speaker was closely associated with the king, and F. W. Golka, *The Leopard's Spots: Biblical and African Wisdom in Proverbs*, Edinburgh, T. & T. Clark, 1993, who reaches a similar conclusion in the light of African parallels.

5 This was propounded most fully by E. W. Heaton, *Solomon's New Men*, London, Pica Press, 1974, who argued for the growth of an administrative class in Israel to service Solomon's state.

6 E.g. A. Lemaire, *Les Écoles et la formation de la Bible dans l'ancien Israel*, Fribourg, Universitäts-verlag; Göttingen, Vandenhoeck & Ruprecht, 1981.

7 A view first put forward by A. Erman, 'Eine ägyptische Quelle der Sprüche Salamos', *Sitzungsberichte der preussischen Akademie der Wissenschaften*, Phil.-hist. Kl. 15, Berlin, 1924, 86–93; and challenged recently by R. N. Whybray, 'The Structure and Composition of Proverbs 22:17–24:22', in S. E. Porter, P. Joyce and D. E. Orton (eds), *Crossing the Boundaries: Essays in Biblical Interpretation in Honour of Michael D. Goulder*, Leiden, E. J. Brill, 1994.

8 An approach taken by, e.g., W. McKane, *Proverbs*, London, SCM Press, 1970.

9 Many scholars have assumed the lateness of Proverbs 1–9, including R. N. Whybray in his early work on Proverbs – see *Wisdom in Proverbs*, London, SCM Press, 1965. In his later work Whybray (in *Proverbs*, Grand Rapids, Eerdmans; London, Marshall Pickering, 1994) modified his opinion that there is a systematic 'Yahwehizing' redaction in Proverbs 1–9, although he still argued for its lateness.

10 Argued, e.g., by C. Westermann, op. cit.

11 See H. Gese, *Lehre und Wirklichkeit in der alten Weisheit*, Tübingen, J. C. B. Mohr, 1958. This idea was developed further by H. H. Schmid, *Gerechtigkeit als Weltordnung*, Beiträge zur historischen Theologie 40, Tübingen, J. C. B. Mohr, 1968.

12 This idea has been expressed by P. Doll, *Menschenschöpfung und Weltschöpfung in der alttesta-mentlichen Weisheit*, Stuttgart: Verlag Katholisches Bibelwerk, 1985, mainly in relation to post-exilic wisdom circles.

13 R. N. Whybray in *The Composition of the Book of Proverbs*, Sheffield, Sheffield Academic Press, 1994, stressed the importance of considering each section of the book of Proverbs separately.

14 R. B. Y. Scott, 'Solomon and the Beginnings of Wisdom in Israel', in M. Noth and D. Winton-Thomas (eds), *Wisdom in Israel and the Ancient Near East*, VTSup 3, Leiden, E. J. Brill, 1955, 262–79 argues that the Solomonic fiction was deliberately played up by Hezekiah and the wisdom that flourished then.

15 S. Weeks, *Early Israelite Wisdom*, Oxford, OUP, 1994.

16 L. L. Grabbe, *Priests, Prophets, Diviners, Sages: Socio-Historical Study of Religious Specialists in Ancient Israel*, Valley Forge, Trinity Press International, 1995.

17 See discussion in G. I. Davies, 'Were There Schools in Ancient Israel?' in J. Day, R. P. Gordon and H. G. M. Williamson (eds), *Wisdom in Ancient Israel: Essays in Honour of J. A. Emerton*, Cambridge, CUP, 1995, 199–211.

18 See L. W. Batten, 'The Epilogue to the Book of Job', *AThR* 15 (1933), 125–128.

19 There is general agreement by scholars over this, although it has been suggested that the dialogue is earlier and that the prose framework was put around it or, of course, that the whole was composed at one sitting. These alternative views however do not, in my opinion, adequately explain the contradictions between prose section and dialogue section.

20 It is a commonly held view that the dislocation of the third cycle is due to scribal error, since there is no third cycle speech by Zophar and only a very truncated one by Bildad; and Job seems to be saying what would belong more naturally in the mouths of these friends. A usual reconstruction would attribute 24:18–25 and 27:13–23 to Zophar, and 26:5–14 to Bildad.

21 The main author may have been drawing on his own experience of suffering here. It is likely that he saw in the prose tale an opportunity for making a more profound statement about human reactions to suffering than the patient response of Job in the prologue allowed.

22 H. Richter, *Studien zu Hiob*, Theologische Arbeiten 11, Berlin, Evangelische Verlagsanstalt 1959, writes, 'The all-pervasive basis of the drama of Job are the genres taken from law' (ET 131)

23 Job has been likened to Greek tragedy by a number of scholars including, J. J. Slotki, 'The Origin of the Book of Job', *ExpTim* 39 (1927–28), 131–5; and W. A. Irwin, 'Job and Prometheus', *JR* 30 (1950), 90–108, who suggests literary dependence between Job and Aeschylus's *Prometheus Bound*. At the other extreme W. Whedbee, 'The Comedy of Job', *Semeia* 7 (*Studies in the Book of Job*, eds R. Polzin and D. Robertson), Missoula, Scholars Press 1977, 1–39, has likened Job to a black comedy. These genre classifications while often shedding light on the content of Job are not generally seen as satisfactory overall and actual literary dependence on a particular Greek tragedy is highly unlikely. Job is generally seen to have failed as a tragic figure because of his repentance, see G. Steiner, 'Tragedy; Remorse and Justice', *Listener* 102 (1979), 508–11.

24 See K. J. Dell, *The Book of Job as Sceptical Literature*, BZAW 197, Berlin and New York, W. de Gruyter, 1991; and B. Zuckerman, *Job the Silent: A Study in Historical Counterpoint*, New York, OUP, 1991. Parody is argued for in Job by both authors but on different grounds.

25 The secondary nature of the Elihu speeches is widely held by scholars, mainly on grounds of structure, since the character is not introduced in the way that the three friends are, and of theme, since there is much repetition of the ideas of others. However there are those who believe that they are part of the original work and even those who see them as the high point of the book.

26 The hymn to wisdom is often regarded as a self-contained poem, added by the author or a redactor at a later stage since it is a misfit in its present context.

27 Argued by K. J. Dell, *The Book of Job as Sceptical Literature*.

28 Argued by K. J. Dell, *The Book of Job as Sceptical Literature*, among others.

29 See, e.g., M. Friedländer, *Griechische Philosophie im Alten Testament: eine Einleitung in die Psalmen und Weisliteratur*, Berlin, 1904.

30 The precise nature of this technique is open to question. See alternatives aired in J. A. Loader, *Polar Structures in the Book of Qoheleth*, BZAW 152, Berlin, W. de Gruyter, 1979; R. Gordis, 'Quotations as a Literary Usage in Biblical, Oriental, and Rabbinic Literature', *Hebrew Union Annual Review* 22 (1949), 157–219.

31 See recently R. N. Whybray, 'Qoheleth, Preacher of Joy', *JSOT* 23 (1982), 87–98.

32 E.g. G. H. Wilson, 'The Words of the Wise: The Intent and Significance of Qoheleth 12:9–14', *JBL* 103 (1984), 175–92.

33 See discussion in K. J. Dell, 'Ecclesiastes as Wisdom: Consulting Early Interpreters', *VT* 44/3 (1994), 301–29.

34 See H. H. Rowley, *Job*, New Century Bible, London, Oliphants, 1970.

35 There is considerable discussion among scholars regarding the boundaries of wisdom psalms. See R. E. Murphy, 'A Consideration of the Classification "Wisdom Psalms"', VTSup 9, Leiden, E. J. Brill, 1962, 160–61; J. K. Kuntz, 'The Canonical Wisdom Psalms of Ancient Israel – their Rhetorical, Thematic and Formal Dimensions', in J. J. Jackson and M. Kessler (eds), *Rhetorical Criticism: Essays in Honor of James Muilenburg*, PTMS 1, Pittsburgh, Pickwick Press, 1974, 186–222.

36 R. N. Whybray, 'The Wisdom Psalms', in J. Day, R. P. Gordon and H. G. M. Williamson (eds), *Wisdom in Ancient Israel: Essays in Honour of J. A. Emerton*, Cambridge, CUP, 1995, 152–60.

37 See G. H. Wilson, *The Editing of the Hebrew Psalter*, SBLDS 76, Chico, Scholars Press, 1985, and 'The Shape of the Book of Psalms', *Int* 46 (1992), 129–42.

38 S. Mowinckel, 'Psalms and Wisdom', in *Wisdom in Israel and the Ancient Near East*, VTSup 3, Leiden, E. J. Brill, 1955, 205–224, and *The Psalms in Israel's Worship*, Vol. 2, trans. D. R. Ap-Thomas, Oxford, Basil Blackwell, 1962, ch. 6.

39 See discussion in ch. 1 of R. E. Clements, *Wisdom in Theology*, Carlisle, Paternoster Press; Grand Rapids, Eerdmans, 1992.

40 E.g. G. E. Wright wrote in 1952, 'It is the wisdom literature which offers the chief difficulty because it does not fit into the type of faith exhibited in the historical and prophetic
literature. In it there is no explicit reference to or development of the doctrines of history,
election or covenant' (*God Who Acts: Biblical Theology as Recital*, London, SCM Press, 1952,
103).

41 Suggested by B. Gemser, 'The Spiritual Structure of Biblical Aphoristic Wisdom', in J. L.
Crenshaw (ed.), *Studies in Ancient Israelite Wisdom*, New York, Ktav, 1976, 208–19.

42 G. von Rad, *Old Testament Theology*, Vol. 1, Edinburgh, Oliver & Boyd, 1965.

43 W. Zimmerli, 'The Place and Limit of Wisdom in the Framework of Old Testament
Theology', *SJT* 17, 1964, 146–58. Also, H. H. Schmid, *Wesen und Geschichte der Weisheit: Eine
Untersuchung zur altorientalischen und israelitischen Weisheitsliteratur*, BZAW 101, Berlin, W. de
Gruyter, 1966.

44 M. Weinfeld, *Deuteronomy and the Deuteronomic School*, Oxford, OUP, 1972, discusses possible
links.

45 See S. Terrien, 'Amos and Wisdom', in B. W. Anderson and W. Harrelson (eds), *Israel's
Prophetic Heritage*, London, SCM Press, 1962, 108–15; J. W. Whedbee, *Isaiah and Wisdom*,
New York, Abingdon Press, 1971.

46 G. von Rad, 'The Joseph Narrative and Ancient Wisdom', in idem, *The Problem of the Hexateuch
and Other Essays*, Edinburgh, Oliver & Boyd, 1966, 292–300; R. N. Whybray, *The Succession
Narrative*, London, SCM Press, 1968.

47 R. N. Whybray, *The Intellectual Tradition in the Old Testament*, BZAW 135, Berlin, W de
Gruyter, 1974.

48 See further R. J. Williams, 'Wisdom in the Ancient Near East', in IDBSup, Nashville,
Abingdon Press, 1976, 949–52.

49 E. W. Heaton, *Solomon's New Men*, London, Pica Press, 1974. See more recently E. W. Heaton,
The School Tradition in Ancient Israel, Oxford, OUP, 1994.

50 S. Weeks, *Early Israelite Wisdom*, Oxford, OUP, 1994; L. L. Grabbe, *Priests, Prophets, Diviners,
Sages: Socio-historical Study of Religious Specialists in Ancient Israel*, Valley Forge, Trinity Press
International, 1995.

51 Deuteronomy is held to be the law book found in the temple at the time of Josiah, as
mentioned in 2 Kings 22:8ff. Furthermore, a section of proverbs, at the very least, was the
work of the 'men of Hezekiah', Prov. 25:1. See R. B. Y. Scott, 'Solomon and the Beginnings
of Wisdom in Israel', VTSup 3, Leiden, E. J. Brill, 1955, 262–79, who argues that Hezekiah's
reign was a time of significant literary activity.

52 Inscriptional and other written evidence is far greater from the eighth century BC onwards.
See D. Jamieson-Drake, *Scribes and Schools in Monarchic Judah: A Socio-archaeological Approach*,
JSOT 109, Sheffield, Sheffield Academic Press, 1991, who argues for the absence of general
knowledge of writing before the eighth century BC.

53 Text in J. B. Pritchard, *Ancient Near Eastern Texts*, Princeton, Princeton University Press,
1950.

54 Text in J. B. Pritchard, op. cit.

55 See J. Day, *God's Conflict with the Dragon and the Sea: Echoes of a Canaanite Myth in the Old
Testament*, Cambridge, CUP, 1985, in reference to the Psalms and Genesis.

56 S. Mowinckel, *The Psalms in Israel's Worship*.

57 Ancient Near Eastern mythology has been found all over the Old Testament in the imagery
used in the Psalms, Pentateuch (notably Genesis 1–11) and prophets.

58 M. Weinfeld, op. cit.

59 R. N. Whybray, *The Intellectual Tradition in the Old Testament*.

60 G. von Rad, *Old Testament Theology*, 449–50.

61 It is a commonly held assumption that Greek ideas have influenced the Wisdom of Solomon.
See J. M. Reese, *Hellenistic Influence on the Book of Wisdom and its Consequence*, AnBib 41, Rome,
Biblical Institute Press, 1970. Hebraic sources may also have influenced the book, although
this is countered strongly by D. Winston, *The Wisdom of Solomon*, AB 43, Garden City, New
York, Doubleday, 1979.

62 See discussion in B. Witherington III, *Jesus the Sage: The Pilgrimage of Wisdom*, Edinburgh, T. & T. Clark, 1994.

63 H. Conzelmann, 'Paulus und die Weisheit', *NTS* 12, 1965–6, 213–44.

64 E.g. P. J. Hartin, *James and the Q Sayings of Jesus*, Sheffield, Sheffield Academic Press, 1991.

65 See discussion of the tension in L. G. Perdue, *Wisdom in Revolt: Metaphorical Theology in the Book of Job*, Sheffield, Sheffield Academic Press, 1991.

CHAPTER EIGHT

APOCALYPTICISM

———·◆·———

Christopher Rowland

INTRODUCTION

The biblical world is an apocalyptic world. By that I mean that the whole of the Bible is suffused with a sense of the revelation of God or access to God's secrets, messengers or redeemer. Even if the Bible is not itself a revelation from God it contains that which was revealed to God's agents: the Torah on Sinai; the dreams or visions to the prophets and seers; the words given to the prophets who spoke the name of God; and in the New Testament the person who embodies the divine glory (Christ). For the writers and readers of the Bible the apocalyptic world was the one they inhabited. Angels were not just temporary visitants but in close touch with their earthly counterparts (as Matt. 18.10 indicates). The study of Scripture was carried out in the expectation that there would be insight as well as the divine presence attending such activity. In this the ancient Jews and Christians differed little from their contemporaries in the pagan world save that their God was superior to all the demons and spirits that existed. Such a plethora of divinities required discernment and the cultivation of rules that would allow one to discern the spirit of truth from the spirit of error, to quote the words of 1 John 4.6. What the Dead Sea Scrolls have demonstrated is the way in which human history can be properly understood only through the eye of vision as a struggle between the forces of light and darkness. In this struggle angelic forces are mingled with their earthly counterparts in a vast cosmic drama that encompasses life in the present and the conflicts leading up to the messianic age to come. When we look closely at all the sources, we see that the world that all Jews inhabited, mainstream and sectarian alike, was an apocalyptic one in which the disclosure was always present. For some it might be only through the reading of Scriptures that there opened up a door through which one might perceive the divine mystery. For others there was the real expectation that they had direct access to more arcane secrets. This is put clearly in the words that conclude *4 Ezra*: 'the Most High said to me, Make public the twenty-four books you wrote first; they are to be read by everyone, whether worthy to do so or not. But the last seventy books are to be kept back, and given to none but the wise among your people; they contain a stream of understanding, a fountain of wisdom, a flood of knowledge' (14.45f.). This is the basis of the thought world of Second

Temple Judaism. It was thoroughly apocalyptic and there was consequently a need to adjudicate between authoritative and spurious claims to the divine mysteries.

As we shall see, apocalyptic ideas are central to New Testament theology. The decisive revelation had come in the gospel of Christ: 'in it the righteousness of God is revealed' (Rom. 1.17).[1] This revelation had ceased to be something just for a learned elite as in *4 Ezra*. It was immediately available to all who could discern the wisdom of God in the crucified Christ (1 Cor. 1.18). A revelatory strand runs right the way through the New Testament writings challenging assumptions about the marginality of the book of Revelation to early Christian experience. That is not to suggest that what we find in the book of Revelation, and indeed the rest of the New Testament, merely replicates the thought world of the apocalyptic literature of contemporary Judaism, for, as the following survey indicates, there are significant differences as well as similarities between the various apocalyptic texts of the Second Temple period.

REVELATION

Revelation (or 'unveiling', the meaning of the word 'apocalypse') was the catalyst in succeeding centuries for a variety of eschatologically inclined movements and readings of history. It is representative of that spirit of early Christianity which allied expectation of historical change with visionary intuition, endowing its message with authenticity.

Traditionally the book's date has been towards the end of the reign of the emperor Domitian (the mid-nineties), who took action against some members of the imperial household for their atheism (a charge that could equally have been levelled at sympathizers of Judaism and at Christians). This may have been part of a much wider attempt to extract a tax from Jews and sympathizers (Christians would have fallen into that category). In this situation there may have been a wave of sporadic persecution, but there is uncertainty whether it was on the empire-wide scope of earlier persecutions. Evidence from Revelation 17 itself suggests that an earlier date is equally likely. If we identify the kings with the first five Roman emperors, that would take us to Nero. After Nero's death in 68, there were four claimants to the office in a year (Galba, Otho, Vitellius and Vespasian who finally became emperor). Revelation 17 points to a date after the fifth king and before the last in the line, who is one of the seven returns. That would seem to exclude the emperor Domitian in whose reign the earliest writers suggested that Revelation was written (e.g. Irenaeus, *Against the Heresies* 5.30.3). The evidence for persecution in Asia Minor at the time of Domitian is non-existent apart from Revelation, though there appears to have been harassment of Jews at the end of Domitian's reign. Domitian claimed for himself the title *dominus ac deus noster*. The external evidence for the book's date is strong for a Domitianic date but the internal evidence of this chapter points in the general direction of a date three decades earlier. Either way the message is unaffected. Contemporary allusions are taken up into the visionary imagination to form part of the prophetic narrative that transcends the particularity of the late first century. Recollections of events, whether in the late sixties at the time of the Jewish Revolt and the chaos after the death of Nero or events in the time of Domitian, have infused the visionary's imagination and become part of the apparatus of the symbolic world and graphic portrayal that confronts us in Revelation. Their original historical significance is transcended and ceases to determine the import they have within the framework of this apocalyptic prophecy.

Revelation is unconcerned with the minute detail of the heavenly ascent (indeed there is a minimum of interest in the paraphernalia of the apocalyptic ascent), nor does it offer details of what is required of the mystic to make a successful entry into the heavenly palaces. We cannot know what led to John's dramatic meeting with the heavenly Son of Man on the isle of Patmos, even if conjectures may be made about the significance of the time (the Lord's Day) and the place (possibly in exile as was the prophet Ezekiel). The book of Revelation is full of mysteries, the content of which is normally hidden from human gaze. Only special insight can see the door opened in heaven and appreciate that which is normally beyond human comprehension.

Revelation is part of a tradition and is a continuation of much of what has gone before. Ezekiel and Daniel have influenced the form and content of the book. The christophany at its opening via the visions of heaven, the dirge over Babylon, the war against Gog and Magog and finally the vision of the new Jerusalem all bear the marks of influence of the written forms of ancient prophetic imagination on the newer prophetic imagination of John of Patmos. Daniel's beasts from the sea become in John's vision a terrible epitome of all that is most oppressive and yet eerily akin to the way of perfection symbolized by the Lamb that was slain, as the similarity to the character of the Lamb of the description of the head of the beast in Revelation 13.3 and 17.8 suggests. So this unique example in the early Christian literature of the apocalyptic genre is profoundly indebted to Jewish apocalyptic ideas.

The vision of Christ marks the very start of John's revelation. After the instruction to write the letters to the seven churches (a scribal role resembling that of Enoch in *1 Enoch* 12–14), John is called to heaven in the spirit and is granted a vision of the divine throne with one seated upon it. There is at the start of this new dimension of John's vision a vision of the throne that owes some of its details to Ezekiel 1 and to the related passage in Isaiah 6. The seer is offered a glimpse of a reality cut off from normal human gaze and opened up only to the privileged seer. There is no mention of a heavenly journey in this text preceding the granting of the vision of God. Indeed, Revelation is singularly lacking in the complex cosmology typical of later Jewish apocalyptic texts and is sparse in the details communicated about the heavenly world.

What is most distinctive about Revelation 4, however, is the vision that immediately follows it, which subtly subverts and reorientates the Ezekelian vision in the direction of the fulfilment of Ezekiel's promise. The scene in heaven is transformed in chapter 5. John sees the scroll with seven seals, which contains the divine will for the inauguration of the eschatological process. The means of the initiation of that process turns out to be the coming of the Messiah, the Lion of Judah. The paradox is that this Messianic Lion turns out to be a Lamb with the marks of death. Superficially, the scene is similar to that described in Daniel 7.9, where there is also a heavenly court. Whereas in the latter a human figure comes to take divine authority, here it is an animal. This parallels the way in which in *1 Enoch* 89–90 animals represent men. Clearly, it was the Lamb's marks of slaughter that qualified it to have this supreme eschatological role and to share the divine throne (Rev. 7.17). At first the Lamb stands as one of the heavenly throng, but wins the right to superiority and the privilege of divine power, as the result of the conquest wrought through death.

The sequence of seals, trumpets and bowls is initiated by the Lamb taking the heavenly book (chs 5, 6, 8–9 and 16). It is the predetermined evolution of the divine purposes in history as the structures of the world give way to the Messianic age (the millennium). Judgement is necessary because there is no sign of repentance. God's righteousness reveals itself in judgement against humanity because of the alienation of human society from the way of God. The reality the Apocalypse shows is that in a disordered world death and destruction are the lot of millions, and the putting right of wrongs demands a seismic shift of cosmic proportions that will happen if humankind does not repent.

The opening of the seals unleashes the Four Horsemen with their destructive potential. This is suddenly interrupted in chapter 7: the sealing of the servants of God with the seal of the living God. There is a contrast here similar to that found in chapters 13 and 14. There the contrast is between bearing the mark of the Beast (13.17; 14.9) and having the name of God written on the forehead (14.1). Here the opening of the seals means judgement for a disobedient world, whereas there is hope for those who are sealed with God's name.

In chapters 10–11 the seer is involved in the unfolding eschatological drama of the apocalypse when he is instructed to eat the scroll and commanded to prophesy. The prophetic commission is followed in chapter 11 by a vision in which the church is offered a paradigm of the true prophetic witness as it sets out to fulfil its vocation to prophesy before the world. Juxtaposed with the vision of the two witnesses, their death and vindication is another vision about persecution. The message is quite a simple one: a pregnant woman is threatened by a dragon. She gives birth to a male child who is precious to God as the Messiah. There is divine protection for both. That is followed immediately by the account of another struggle in which there is war in heaven between Michael and the dragon who had persecuted the woman. Michael and his forces prevail, which means that there is no longer a place in heaven for the dragon. The vision seems to suggest that the picture of a heavenly struggle is closely linked with the earthly struggle of those who seek to be disciples of Jesus to maintain their testimony. The consequence of the defeat of Satan in heaven is that no place was found in heaven, and a particular target of his attack is 'those who keep God's commandments' and maintain their witness to Jesus. The Beast is the incarnation of the fallen Satan, the Devil, and attracts universal admiration for acts that appear to be beneficial. The imagery here is well known in Jewish apocalyptic literature (it is used in Daniel 7) as a way of referring to world governments and in John's day would have applied particularly to Rome.

In the new creation there is a very different cosmological pattern. The celestial city as a whole reflects the proportions of the Holy of Holies from which anything unclean was vigorously excluded (21.27). There is immediate access of the saints to God. The references to the heavenly temple in the book suggest that in a situation where God's will is not done, the Temple in heaven is a sign – unnecessary in the new creation – of the divine dimension to existence.

The throne of God runs like a thread binding the different visions of the Apocalypse together. It is the destiny of the elect and a sign of authority in the universe contrasting with that other locus of power in the cosmos which deludes the world's inhabitants (2.13; 13.2). Worship of the one who sits on the throne marks recognition of true sovereignty and is the basis of true service. In Revelation 21 the tabernacling of God with humankind is fulfilled in the new creation. There is a contrast between the vision of the New Jerusalem in chapter 21 with the initial vision of the heavenly court in chapter 4. In Revelation 4 the seer is granted a glimpse into the environs of God. This contrast between heaven and earth disappears in the new creation where the tabernacle of God is with humanity. God's dwelling is not to be found above the cherubim in heaven; for his throne is set right in the midst of the New Jerusalem where the living waters stream from the throne of God and his servants marked with the mark of God will see him face to face. It is only in the New Jerusalem that there will be the conditions for God and humanity to dwell in that harmony. God is no longer transcendent but immediate. Indeed, those who are his will be his children and carry his name on their heads: they will be identified with the character of God and enjoy the divine presence. Here Revelation comes as near as anywhere to speaking of the transformation of the elect into the divine. So the book's climax speaks of the goal of the mystical ascent to heaven and the immediate presence of God. What is clear is that as far as John is concerned, what is needful are not the ritual preparations of fasting and prayer but lives lived in conformity with the divine holiness, thereby keeping sufficient distance from the contamination of the Beast whose allure in particular can prevent access to the vision of God.

The Apocalypse sets out to reveal things as they really are in both the life of the Christian communities and the world at large. The critique of the present is effected by the use of a contrast between the glories of the future and the inadequacies of the present. John's vision offers the reader a glimpse of reality, so that the distortions of present perception may be understood and action appropriate to the reality now offered in the vision embarked on. The glory the apocalyptic seer enjoyed in his revelation was a matter of living experience here and now for those who confessed Jesus as Messiah and participated in the eschatological spirit. Already those who possessed the spirit of God were sons and daughters of God; already those in Christ were a new creation and a Temple of the divine Spirit. What is more, evidence of divine providence could be discerned with the eye of vision in the death and destruction that was the outworking of the wrath of the Lamb.

DANIEL

The one Old Testament Apocalypse contains a mixture of stories concerning the activity of a Jewish elite in Babylon, chief among whom is Daniel, their activities in discerning the mysterious dreams and signs that confront Babylonian kings, and the limits of compromise that lead to persecution. The second half of the book is a series of visions about the future purposes of God, which, though given in the time of the Exile, relates to the political situation in the middle of the second century BCE. Its scope is international and relates the life of the righteous people to the succession of world empires, and offers promise to the righteous of their eschatological vindication (Dan. 12.2 contains the first explicit doctrine of resurrection in the Bible).

A comparison of Revelation with Daniel reveals differences as well as similarities. In certain visions Revelation is clearly indebted to Daniel (e.g. Dan. 10 in 1:13ff.; Dan. 7 in chs 13 and 17). Both are eschatologically orientated. Unlike Revelation, however, Daniel is pseudonymous (probably written in the second century BCE at the height of the crisis in Jerusalem under the Seleucid king Antiochus IV discussed in 1 Maccabees). John's authority resides primarily in his prophetic call (1:9ff.) rather than any claim to antiquity or apostolicity. The form of the visions differs also. The dream-vision followed by interpretation is almost completely lacking (Rev. 17 is a solitary exception where contemporary historical connections are most explicitly made).

There is in Revelation a more distanced and antagonistic attitude to empire. Although Revelation 18, briefly, reflects on Babylon's fall from the perspective of the kings, the mighty and the merchants, the position is one of vigorous rejection of the power and effects of empire and of satisfaction at the ultimate triumph of God's righteousness (14:11; 19:3). Whereas Daniel presents individuals who are immersed in the life of the pagan court, Revelation countenances no such accommodation. The only strategies are resistance and withdrawal (18.4). Accommodation may be a sign of apostasy (Rev. 2:20ff.). Pagans react with awe (6:15), fear (11:10), and anger at God (6:10; 9:20).

In Daniel a significant part of the book has to do with the royal court in Babylon, and chapter 2 offers an interpretation of Nebuchadnezzar's dream. Here are men who are comfortable, respected Jews who have a good reputation in the land of their exile, though there is nostalgia for Zion (Dan. 6:10) and limits on what the Jews described in these stories are prepared to compromise. As in Revelation, idolatry is the problem (Dan. 3). The fiery furnace and the lions' den are the terrible consequence for those who refuse to conform. Yet there is evidence of admiration on the part of the king (cf. the signs of that in Rev. 11:13) and a reluctance to see these significant courtiers die. Nebuchadnezzar is depicted with a degree of sympathy (unlike Belshazzar in Dan. 4). Those who resist the imperial system are prepared to face suffering but have miraculous escapes. This contrasts somewhat with Revelation where persecution is expected to include suffering and death (2:11; 6:9; 7:14; 11:7; 13:10; 12:11). In Revelation there is promise of vindication (11:7f.) but a clear recognition that there can be no escape from the great tribulation (7:14).

1 *ENOCH*

1 Enoch opens with a statement of the inevitability of divine judgement. Enoch describes himself as a righteous man whose eyes were opened by the Lord and who saw a holy vision in the heavens. This is followed by a more reflective section typical of some strands of the earlier Wisdom tradition of the Bible in which the reader is asked to contemplate the universe, to 'understand how the eternal God made all these things' (5.2). The contemplation of the universe and the human place in it turns abruptly to condemnation. In the following chapters the myth of the angels, the sons of heaven, who desired the daughters of man and woman, parallel Genesis 6. We have in these chapters an alternative account of the corruption of the earth parallel to the opening chapters of Genesis. God's response is to warn the son of Lamech that the whole earth will be destroyed by a deluge, as a preliminary to the restoration of the earth, which the Watchers have ruined. Enoch's position on the boundary between angels and humans gave him access to divine secrets and results in him being asked to intercede on behalf of the fallen angels. This he does, to no avail, following an ascent to heaven. He is then led by the angels to different parts of the cosmos and is shown its secrets as well as the mystery of divine judgement on the Watchers. Enoch eventually reaches Paradise.

At the beginning of the next section of the book, the so-called parables, probably much later than the opening chapters and with many features that distinguish it from the rest of the collection, we have a heterogeneous collection of material that mixes an account of Enoch's activities with God (known as the Lord of the Spirits), in which he describes a figure 'like a son of man' (this section of *1 Enoch* has many connections with the Son of Man sayings in the gospels). In addition to eschatological secrets we have a repeat of the Flood story, in which Enoch enters into dialogue with Noah (parallel to material at the end of this collection in chapters 102–3 and in the fragmentary apocryphal text the *Genesis Apocryphon* from Cave 1 at Qumran). The book of the parables closes with an account of Enoch's ascent to heaven where he is greeted as the son of man.

There is an abrupt transition in chapter 72 to a section dealing with astronomical material, parallels to which have been found among the Dead Sea Scrolls. What is distinctive about this is the peculiar calendar based on solar rather than lunar calculations referred to also in the book of *Jubilees* 6.32–3. This material Enoch reads in the heavenly tablets and in addition Enoch passes on other awesome visions concerning the future of the earth, one of which is a long symbolic vision. This is often called the Animal Apocalypse because it uses animal symbolism to describe the course of the world from creation to eschatological redemption. Another is an account of history partitioned schematically into Ten Weeks of years with a similar kind of historical scope. The book closes with a collection of advice and warning from Enoch to his children with woes for the rich and powerful and vindication for the humble and meek. This advice is grounded in the fact that Enoch has read the divine secrets written on the heavenly tablets, a reflection of which is now contained in the earthly writing that purports to present Enoch's insight.

4 *EZRA, SYRIAC BARUCH* AND THE *APOCALYPSE OF ABRAHAM*

Three apocalypses usually dated to around the end of the first century CE offer contrasting attitudes in their form and content. There is similarity of outlook in the first two, which have led some to suppose some kind of literary relationship between them.

In *4 Ezra* eschatological beliefs make their appearance but there emerges, possibly for the first time in such an explicit form, evidence for a hope for a new age that is transcendent, though it appears, however, alongside the conventional hope for a this-worldly reign of God (7.28f.; cf. 5.45; cf. Rev. 20–1). More prominent is another concern: the apparent inscrutability and mercilessness of God. There is a concern for the majority of humanity whose unrighteousness seems to be about to consign them to perdition. At times it appears that Ezra's concerns are more merciful than the divine reply. Such sentiments, however, are dealt with by urging the righteous to concentrate on the glory that awaits those who are obedient to God. God's patience is not for the sake of humanity but because of faithfulness to the eternal plan laid down before creation. What the righteous need to do is to view all things in the light of the eschatological consummation rather than concentrate exclusively on the apparent injustices of the present. Throughout, the ways of God are vindicated. Just as in the book of Job where the divine answer contrasts human and divine wisdom, so here too the impossibility of understanding the divine purposes in the midst of the old order is stressed.

Ezra longs for the righteousness of the holy to be taken into account when God judges Israel, but the sense of solidarity with the people disappears. The righteous are urged to attend to their destiny and concentrate on obedience to the law of God. The problem with humanity is that it has continued to sin even though God has endowed it with understanding (cf. Rev. 9.20). In the closing chapters of the book there is an eschatological promise for those who endure to the end, and the might of Rome is to be vanquished by God's Messiah.

In *Syriac Baruch* there is a more obvious concern with the destruction of Jerusalem (the setting of the book is the eve of the fall of Solomon's Temple). The reader is left in little doubt that this destruction is not only ordained by God but carried out with God's participation (chs 3 and 80). Israel is culpable and entirely deserves judgement at God's hand. Zion's destruction paves the way for God's eschatological act when the nations are to be judged. As in *4 Ezra* there is questioning of the way the world is: is there any profit in being righteous (ch. 14)? There is assurance that for those like Baruch and Ezra there is the promise of being 'taken up'. In the present what is essential is obedience to the Law. Continual vigilance is necessary as there is nothing left but this one guide to God's purposes and demands. Humanity to which God has given understanding is without excuse and deserves to be punished. Eschatological material serves to remind the reader of the imminent consummation of all things and the present need to use the limited guide available that will enable achievement of Paradise.

The issues raised are what might have been expected of Jews after the traumatic experience of 70 CE. The burning question in both *4 Ezra* and *Syriac Baruch* is not so much 'When will the End be?' but 'How can one make sense of the present and ensure participation in the eschatological Paradise of God?' Eschatology forms a part of the divine answers to the seers' questions that usually concern pressing matters of present concern.

APOCALYPSES: CHARACTER AND ORIGINS

Apocalypses that purport to offer revelations of divine secrets are similar in form and content to the New Testament apocalypse, from which (Rev. 1.1 'apocalypse of Jesus Christ') they derive their generic description. The use of the words *apokalypsis/apokalypto* (reveal or unveil) to describe revelation of God or divine secrets is relatively rare in literature written round about the time of Revelation. In Theodotion's Greek translation of the Old Testament *apokalypto* is introduced in passages where the earlier Greek had other words. The words are more common in the New Testament. In the gospels 'apocalypse' is found at Luke 2:32 and Luke 2.35, of divine secrets (Matt. 11.25/Luke 10.21; Matt. 16.17), and of God in Matthew 11.27, and of the day of the Son of Man in Luke 17.30. An apocalyptic outlook is central to Paul's self-understanding as the autobiographical account of the origin of his apostolic mission in Galatians indicates (Gal. 1:12).

The origins of this literary genre are much disputed but it is clear that in their concerns with the mysteries of God and the divine purposes they have a close affinity with the prophetic literature of the Old Testament. In addition, in some of their concerns, particularly the future hope, the apocalypses draw heavily on prophetic passages. Nevertheless, there have been those who have argued for a link with the Wisdom tradition of Israel, and certainly in the questioning spirit evident in so much of the apocalypses such a connection is not difficult to find.

The fact that there is only one apocalypse included in the canon of the Old Testament, the book of Daniel should not be taken as an indication that the compilers of the canon did not have much interest in the apocalyptic tradition, as it is clear that there was a lively apocalyptic oral tradition in Judaism. Of this the written apocalypses are probably evidence. This tradition has a long history. The discovery of fragments of the Enoch apocalypse at Qumran have pushed the date of this particular text back well before the second century BCE; back, in other words into that obscure period when the prophetic voice began to die out in Israel. The literary evidence of the apocalyptic outlook suggests that it continued to play a vital part within Israelite religion throughout the period of the Second Temple, and even in rabbinic circles persisted as an esoteric tradition that manifested itself in written form in the *Hekaloth* tracts in which rabbinic mystics described their ascents to heaven and the techniques needed to achieve such mystical contemplation.

In the Mishnah (*Hag.* 2.1) brief reference is made to exposition of the first chapters of Genesis and Ezekiel. The cryptic reference there suggests that it is a matter of some concern to the authors and is an anticipation of the central importance mystical and apocalyptic ideas had in the religion of rabbinic Judaism. The Mishnah forbids the use of Ezekiel 1 as a synagogue reading. The *merkabah* (the short-hand way of referring to the call vision of Ezekiel) is linked with apocalyptic-wisdom tradition and is concerned with divine secrets.

Such esoteric traditions associated with Ezekiel 1 were inherited from an apocalyptic milieu. These traditions had both an exegetical component (i.e. they arose as the result of interpretative activity) and also a 'mystical' aspect. Ecstatic-mystical and esoteric exegetical traditions were being developed in circles associated with some rabbinic teachers during the first century CE. By the early second century the esoteric tradition was known to and practised by leading rabbis such as Akiba. Thus some controversy concerning the status and legitimacy of the tradition is likely to have occurred during the first century, probably because of the way in which such traditions were developed in extrarabbinic circles, not least Christianity. We know Paul was influenced by apocalyptic ascent ideas (2 Cor. 12.2ff.) and emphasizes the importance of this visionary element as the basis of his practice (Gal. 1.12 and 1.16; cf. Acts 22.17). Perhaps he should be linked with those other significant figures who became either marginal to rabbinic Judaism or a focus of hostility: Eliezer ben Hyrcanus, Eleazar ben Arak and Elisha ben Abuyah. After all, his apocalyptic outlook enabled him to act on his eschatological convictions, so that his apocalypse of Jesus Christ became the basis for his practice of admitting Gentiles to the Messianic age without the Law of Moses. His relegation of Sinai to the new covenant in the Messiah contrasts with the firm subordination of the apocalyptic spirit of Ezekiel 1 to the Sinai theophany in the rabbinic mystical traditions. The threat posed by apocalyptic may be discerned elsewhere (and indeed could have contributed to the development of christology in early Christianity). It may be that the controversy about two centres of divine power with roots deep within the apocalyptic tradition may lie behind the stories of the confrontation of an early second-century Jewish teacher, Elisha ben Abuyah with Metatron, a mysterious angelic figure who is called 'the little Yahweh' and has several affinities in status with the exalted Christ of early christology.

It is now no longer possible to reconstruct the content of *merkabah* tradition in the late first century with any degree of certainty. The Songs of the Sabbath Sacrifice from Cave 4 at Qumran as well as apocalypses such as *1 Enoch* and Revelation 4 indicate that such mystical interest antedates the fall of the Second Temple. Meditation on passages like Ezekiel 1, set as it is in Exile and in the aftermath of a previous destruction of the Temple, would have been particularly apposite as the rabbis sought to come to terms with the devastation of 70 CE. Of course, if some influential rabbis were hostile to this kind of activity, we should expect the sources to be very reticent about the kinds of activities that went on, especially when the practice was liable to cause theological deviance from the normal practice recommended by the majority of Jewish teachers. This reserve is exactly what is found in the earliest rabbinic sources. There is more evidence available in later sources, however, such as the Talmud and more overtly mystical writings, known as the *Hekaloth* literature because they tell of journeys made to the heavenly palaces. What was later to become the *Hekaloth* visionary tradition was a synthesis of a number of different traditions that employed a variety of texts, pre-eminently Ezekiel 1, Isaiah 6 and the Song of Songs (the latter being particularly important for the *shi'ur qomah* (the speculation based on Ezek. 1.25–8 about the nature of the body of God). The focus of the tradition was the throne-chariot of God and the glorious figure enthroned upon it.

The apocalypses are the most significant group of writings of all the intertestamental literature. Their concerns with the mysteries of God and the divine purposes suggest a close affinity with the prophetic literature and the varied means of apprehending the divine counsel found therein. Indeed, we may suppose that what we find in the apocalypses is the form of the prophetic tradition as it emerged in the Hellenistic age, shot through with elements from the Wisdom books and with its own distinctive revelatory style.

There was a lively apocalyptic oral tradition in Judaism. This tradition has a long history. The discovery of fragments of the Enoch apocalypse at Qumran has pushed the date of this particular text back well before the second century BCE, back, in other words, into that obscure period when the canonical prophecy of Malachi and the latest chapters of Isaiah were written. While the apocalypses are by and large the largest repository of the future hope among the Jewish texts now extant, we have not exhausted their significance once we have recognized the eschatological concerns of this literature. Other matters obtrude: for example, the vision of heaven, angelology, theodicy and astronomy. The fact that several apocalypses have turned up in the gnostic library from Nag Hammadi indicates that the relationship between apocalyptic and gnosticism, which in the past has not been obvious, needs to be reassessed, particularly in the light of the common concern of both the apocalypses and the gnostic texts with knowledge.

In the discussion of apocalyptic since the 1970s or so, there has been a significant difference of opinion about its origins. On the one hand there are those who consider that apocalyptic is the successor to the prophetic movement, and particularly to the future hope of the prophets. On the other hand the Wisdom tradition of the Old Testament with its interest in understanding the cosmos and the ways of the world is a component of apocalyptic. The activities of certain wise men in antiquity were not at all dissimilar from the concerns of the writers of the apocalypses. Traces of this kind of wisdom, concerned as it is with the interpretation of dreams, oracles, astrology and the ability to divine mysteries concerning future events are to be found in the Old Testament; for example in the Joseph stories in Genesis. Most obviously it is present in the stories about Daniel, the Jewish seer who interprets the dreams of Nebuchadnezzar and is regarded as a superior sage to all those in the king's court. Dreams, visions and the like are all typical features of the apocalypses, and it is now recognized that this aspect of the Wisdom tradition may indeed provide an important contribution to our understanding of apocalyptic origins. In addition, *4 Ezra* is preoccupied with theodicy and suffering and has several affinities with the book of Job, and the Enochic literature includes astrology and rudimentary geography.

Apocalypses reveal that which is hidden in order to enable readers to understand their situation from the divine perspective. They seek to offer an understanding that bypasses the conventional means of discerning the divine will by being grounded in the direct disclosure through vision or audition. The apocalypse unmasks the real significance of past, present and future.

There has been much confusion in the discussion of apocalyptic, in particular its relationship to eschatology. In discussions of both subjects the two are closely related and can often be used interchangeably. It is probably better to reserve eschatology for the various beliefs found in ancient Jewish and Christian texts concerned with the divine purposes for the future. Despite the widespread view which asserts that there existed in Judaism two types of future hope (a national eschatology and an other-worldly eschatology found principally in the apocalypses), the evidence indicates that such a dichotomy cannot be easily substantiated. The doctrine of the future hope as it is found in the apocalypses is on the whole consistent with the expectation found in other Jewish sources. We should then use apocalyptic as a way of describing an epistemology, which characterized an expectation that the divine could inform and indeed invade what passes for normal attempts to discern the divine will through study and interpretation of Scripture. So that dream, angelic pronouncement or even ecstatic vision can supplement, or on rare occasions even countermand, that which has been received or worked out by means of painstaking interpretation.

THE SOCIAL SETTING

Apocalypses are often seen as a body of protest literature of a marginalized minority. Post-exilic Judaism was characterized by a polarization between a powerful hierarchy and groups whose views are represented in the writings of the apocalypses. Such marginality is sometimes linked with a despair of political change and a consequent retreat from hope in the fulfilment of the divine promises in history No neat division can be made between the dominant and the marginal, for all used apocalyptic ideas and all expected hope to be fulfilled on this earth. Indeed, the Dead Sea Scrolls with their hostility towards the Temple suggest an expectation of a day when the cult was organized on the right lines.

When apocalyptic ideas are linked with sectarian traditions in the early modern and the modern periods, it is easy to see why commentators suppose that the apocalypses must be the particular product of the religious and political aspirations of the marginalized and disinherited. Study of the apocalypses reveals that they contain a vast array of different subjects (the future purposes of God; astronomical mysteries; descriptions of heaven; angels; and theodicy topics), which were of just as much concern to the learned groups within Second Temple Judaism.

Writing apocalypses was not a task for the uneducated. Certainly it may have been carried out by the marginalized as the Dead Sea Scrolls indicate. All the evidence suggests that we have in the extant literature the views of those who were sophisticated enough to write down their beliefs and practices. In the Dead Sea Scrolls it is apparent that we have the ideology of a group whose origin at least was among some of the most self-consciously elite members of Israelite society: the priests. Nowhere more than in the case of the priesthood was there a concern to make sure that the power was kept in the hands of that elite.

In its emphasis on revelation apocalyptic can seem to offer an easy solution whereby divine intervention offering insight to unfathomable human problems can cut the knot of intractable problems. It can be an antidote to a radical pessimism whose exponents despair of ever being able to make sense of the contradictions of human existence by means of the revelation of God. The kinds of answers offered by the apocalypses are by no means uniform, however. There are apocalypses (or at least parts of them) that use the concept of revelation to offer a definitive solution to human problems. So we find particularly in a work like the book of *Jubilees* an angelic revelation to Moses on Sinai in which there is a retelling of biblical history following the sequence of what is found in Scripture. There are divergences, the significance of which is nowhere greater than when halakic questions emerge. The fact that the book is a revelation to Moses functions to vindicate one side in contentious moral matters in Second Temple Judaism and to anathematize opponents. In this situation the text's meaning is transparent and is promulgated as the final, authoritative, pronouncement.

Not all apocalypses offer unambiguous and exclusive answers that seem to brook no dispute, however. They certainly offer revelation, much of which is in effect what was traditionally believed already. The horizon of hope is reaffirmed by revelation and the historical perspective of salvation supported. But sometimes the form of the revelation is such that it can produce as much mystification as enlightenment. There is frequently need for angelic interpretation of enigmatic dreams and visions (this happens occasionally in Revelation; e.g. at 7.14; 17.15). Even these angelic interpretations are not without their problems. It proved necessary for revelations coined in one era to be the basis of 'updating' and application in the different political circumstances of another. Thus the symbolism of the fourth beast of Daniel 7 is given new meaning in the Roman period when it ceases to refer to Greece but instead is applied to Rome (a process that continued, as the history of the interpretation of Dan. 7 shows). Examples of this may be found in both Revelation 13 and in *4 Ezra* 12. So some apocalypses do not provide 'answers' through revelation and offer nothing more than the refusal of a complete answer as being something beyond the human mind to grasp. Instead, there is a plethora of imagery or enigmatic pronouncement that leaves the reader either with no possibility of ever knowing the mind of God, or gives tantalizing glimpses in the enigmatic symbols of dreams and visions. In *4 Ezra* the seer wishes to know why Israel has been allowed to suffer and why God seems content to allow the bulk of humanity to perish. The revelation, akin to God's answer in the final chapters of the book of Job, is to stress the puny nature of human understanding in the face of the transcendence of God, to stress the ultimate victory of God's righteousness and to urge the need for those committed to the ways of God to continue in the narrow way that leads to eschatological salvation. There is no solution to the problem posed by the human seer, at least in terms that the seer could understand.

The problem with humanity is that even though God has endowed it with understanding (a theme reminiscent of that found in Rev. 9.20) there is incomprehension and unwillingness to change. Evil permeates the human mind and makes it difficult for men and women either to fulfil the divine command or to glimpse the totality of reality *sub specie aeternitatis*. *Fourth Ezra* purges the mind of any presumption to be able to fathom the wisdom of God because of the error of the assumptions that a corrupted mind engenders. Those who, like Ezra, continue in obedience, a way of life that seems so pointless, receive reassurance that faithful endurance will pay off ultimately. That is the only kind of answer on offer in this tantalizing apocalypse.

The persistent concern throughout the earlier part of the dialogue between Ezra and the angel is the exploration of the conditions for understanding the ways of God. It is a theme that forms a central concern of John 3. In the dialogue of Jesus with Nicodemus Jesus' response, which hardly begins to engage with the substance of Nicodemus's discourse, cannot begin to engage with the wisdom of the world, which remains, in the person of Nicodemus, dull and uncomprehending. For Nicodemus to see the Kingdom of God there is need for a complete transformation, epistemological and social, a move from a position of power as a leader to share the lot of Jesus and those who followed the one whom they considered the emissary from heaven. When persons come to baptism, they enter the realm of light and their perspective on reality changes. They then see that their deeds were evil and that in the past they loved darkness rather than light.

APOCALYPTIC IN THE NEW TESTAMENT

It should come as no surprise that all parts of the New Testament are permeated with this outlook. Early Christians emphasized access to the divine power, and this may have been an important element of its appeal. Paul, for example, in several of his letters made much of the dramatic, charismatic and experiential as bases for his arguments for his particular understanding of religion. The conviction about the access to privileged knowledge of the divine purposes was in certain cases linked to decisive action. The Scriptures are now read in the light of the conviction that the age of the Spirit has come. Christians in Corinth, for example, are told that they were fortunate to be alive when the decisive moment in history came about (1 Cor. 10.11). So the present has become the moment to which all the Scriptures have been pointing, though their meaning can only be fully understood with that divinely inspired intuition which flows from acceptance of the Messiah.

Paul speaks about the centrality of the divine revelation (Gal. 1.12 and 16). In the early Christian story other decisive moments have at their centre visionary insight (Mark 1.10; Acts 10–11). In the case of Peter in Acts 10 the vision is used, in part at least, as the basis of the new turn in Christian practice: the admission of the Gentiles into the people of God. Similarly, while Scripture may be used to support a divine mystery, it is that which is the basis of Paul's conviction about the future salvation of Israel (e.g. Rom. 11.25). Significant shifts in opinion might be the subject of intense wrangling and discussion but are offered as the result of some kind of supernatural validation. Such an appeal to visions might not matter if the subject matter was itself uncontroversial. When it becomes the basis for a significant new departure it becomes problematic.

The central role that prophecy played within early Christianity indicates the problems posed by claims to divine inspiration. When these involved controversial items of behaviour, they would have been very much to the fore in debates between adherents of Messianism and those who dissented from these convictions. All this could have been lived with if there had not been a substantial difference of opinion over an area of halakah. Religious authority claimed as a result of experience of God was something that had a continuing history within early Christianity. The Nag Hammadi texts indicate the extent of the influence of the apocalypticism, both in the use of the genre of the apocalypse and in the persistence of typical apocalyptic themes, albeit in a gnostic guise. Threats from individuals or groups who claimed divine support by means of visions and revelations seem to have been quite a pressing problem (*Didache* 11.3ff. and 16.3; cf. 1 Tim, 4.1; cf. Jude 4ff.). If Paul could claim authority on the basis of a vision as also did John of Patmos, what was to distinguish them from those visionaries who came to be regarded with suspicion by later Christians? After all, their esoteric teaching too was communicated with all the marks of divine authority? The heart of early Christian self-understanding was its realized Messianism authenticated by the apocalyptic insight. Eschatological conviction is the content of the message, but the means whereby individuals came to apprehend its meaning came through claims to visions from God. What we find in earliest Christianity is apocalyptic functioning as the basis of its Messianic convictions.

The application of apocalyptic imagery to contemporary institutions came naturally to most early Christians. It was not just an optional mode of discourse that one could either take or leave. Antichrist was no remote, supernatural, figure. The solitary New Testament appearance of Antichrist refers not to supernatural figures but to the heretical and immoral opponents of the writer of 1 John: 'Children, it is the last hour; and as you have heard that antichrist is coming, so now many antichrists have come ... They went out from us ... that it might be plain that they all are not of us' (1 John 2.18–19). The present is permeated with a critical character.

Significant strands within the New Testament exhibit an outlook that invests present persons and events with a decisive role in the fulfilment of the Last Things. In various texts of the New Testament there are signs that the present becomes a moment of opportunity for transforming the imperfect into the perfect; history and eschatology become inextricably intertwined, and the elect stand on the brink of the Messianic age itself. Of course, the event of Jesus' life in due course became hallowed as the irruption of the divine into history. Nevertheless, in many of the stories told about him he is presented as proclaiming the present as decisive in God's purposes and himself as the Messianic agent for change. But not as some dreamer awaiting the apocalyptic miracle wrought by God alone. It has been wrongly assumed that Jesus' and the early Christians' *eschatological* expectation was for an act of God brought in by God alone without any human agency, humankind being merely passive spectators of a vast divine drama with the cosmos as its stage. The foundation documents of Christianity suggest a different story. For many of their writers history is illuminated by apocalypse; vision opens ultimate possibilities, and responsibilities that others could only dream of. Thereby they are equipped with insight hidden to others and privileged to enjoy a role in history denied even to the greatest figures of the past. I Peter 1.11–12 speaks for the outlook of many other New Testament documents in its emphasis on the privilege of the writer's time: 'It was revealed to [the prophets] that they were serving not themselves but you, in the things which have now been announced to you ... things into which angels long to look'. For Paul the apostolic task is not a parochial affair, for the apostles themselves are engaged in an enterprise on a truly cosmic scale (1 Cor. 4.10) as God's fellow-workers (3.9). The apostle sees himself as an architect working according to a divine master-plan, parallel to Moses himself. Indeed, that to which the apostles are bearing witness is itself an apocalyptic event and they are stewards of the divine mysteries (1 Cor. 4.1).

Despite the lack of apocalyptic terminology in the gospel, John is concerned with the revelation of divine mysteries. The quest for the highest wisdom of all, the knowledge of God, comes not through the information disclosed in visions and revelations but through the Word become flesh, Jesus of Nazareth, and through the activity of the Spirit/Paraclete who is ultimately dependent on the Son. John's gospel is permeated with a major theme of the apocalypses: revelation. Jesus proclaims himself as the revelation of the hidden God. He tells Philip, 'He who has seen me has seen the Father' (14:9) and, at the conclusion of the Prologue, the Evangelist speaks of the Son in the following way: 'No one has ever seen God; the only Son, who is in the bosom of the Father, he has made him known' (1:18). The vision of God is related in the Fourth Gospel to the revelation of God in Jesus. No one has seen God except the one who is from God; he has seen the Father (6:46). The vision of God reserved in the book of Revelation for the fortunate seer (4.1) and for the inhabitants of the 'new Jerusalem' who will see God face to face (22.4) is found, according to the Fourth Evangelist, in the person of Jesus of Nazareth.

An interesting thing about Luke's account of visions is that it gives an insight into the problems posed by resort to visions. In Acts 10 there is no angelic inter-pretation of the meaning of the vision. Peter may initially be left at a loss as he is confronted with the need to make sense of what has appeared to him. In Acts 10.28 Peter has drawn the conclusion that if he is allowed to eat anything without discrim-ination he is also obliged to regard all human persons in the same way.

The problematic character of resort to visions and dreams as a way of settling ethical disputes, so important in Deuteronomy 13, 18.20, is hinted at only in the reserve expressed by the elders in Jerusalem. The fact that a dreamer of dreams might lead Israel astray (Deut. 13) is not contemplated by an author who has every confi-dence that the voice of God is to be heard in the experience of those heroes of Christian origins. This is not surprising, not only because the writer can with the benefit of hindsight have confidence that the movement is of God (cf. Acts 5.39) but also because his record of the significant role of the heavenly vision is used with discrimination. These are no ordinary people who receive visions. Even the radical Stephen is subtly woven into the fabric of the early Christian authority structure by his role as one who served at tables but ended up being an early protagonist for a radically disjunctive form of Judaism.

Acts is a story primarily about apostles who are duly commissioned (and that even includes Paul who just manages to make the grade). As such they can be safely entrusted with visions because they would be no false prophets. There is no sense that *anyone* could come along with an 'apocalypse' as contemplated by 1 Corinthians 14.26 (though here too in 1 Cor. 14.30 discrimination is needed) or claim to be an authori-tative prophet as the Montanists were to do in the mid-second century and claim the inspiration of the Spirit–Paraclete. Joel may have prophesied that the Spirit would fall on all flesh and 'your sons and daughters would prophesy' but it is only chosen 'sons' whose stories are allowed to be recorded in Acts even if the daughters' prophetic powers may be alluded to in passing (21.9). Agabus, it is true, emerges as a signifi-cant figure (mentioned in 11.28) but his intervention later in the narrative predict-ing Paul's capture, which leads to fellow-Christians seeking to dissuade Paul from his chosen strategy, is not allowed to interfere with the working out of 'the Lord's will' (21.14; cf. 11.18) as Paul goes up to Jerusalem. The account is a paradigm for an understanding of God's activity, which remains in part faithful to the ecumenical spirit of the Joel quotation in Acts 2.17ff. Nevertheless, it is no ordinary person who is converted. Luke makes it quite clear in his description of Cornelius that he is just the sort of person with whom God might be expected to be happy.

Luke's narrative is imbued with a sense of inevitability and conformity with the manifest purposes of God. Just as Josephus had introduced his description of the climax of the Jewish War (*War* 6.289) in 70 CE when Titus's legionaries raised their standards in the Temple by reporting the plain warnings of God in the form of prodigies and prophecies, so Luke's narrative is peppered with visions and angelic appearances that point in the direction of the veracity of the Christian claims for those with eyes to see them. Gamaliel perhaps voices the author's desire to persuade his readers that there can be no brooking the divine purposes (5.39; cf. 11.17f. and 21.14). Just as Josephus used the divine oracles of old to validate Roman imperial claims, the frequent insertion into the narrative of the visionary and angelic pronouncement serves to remind the reader that this is no ordinary story, however insignificant and unremarkable the participants.

Revelation's purpose is to reveal that which is hidden in order to enable readers to understand their situation from the divine perspective. Like the apocalypses of Judaism it seeks to offer an understanding that bypasses human reason by being grounded in direct disclosure through vision or audition. The book of Revelation offers a basis for hope in a world where God's way seems difficult to discern. It does this by unmasking the real significance of past, present and future. In addition, Revelation is described as prophecy. This is probably in line with the conviction that appears to have been widespread in early Christianity that the spirit of God had returned, a sign that the last day had arrived (a point stressed by the author of the Acts of the Apostles when he describes the events of the Day of Pentecost as a sign of the Last Days in Acts 2.17).

The visions of hope should be viewed not as some kind of aberration but as an authentic outworking of the central traditions of the biblical tradition. At the heart of its record of its self-understanding in the canon of the New Testament, Christianity chose in Jesus and Paul to recall instances of individuals with an understanding of the ultimate significance of their historical actions expressed to or linked with the apocalyptic tradition. Christian theology has been in part an attempt to articulate that basic apocalyptic datum. In the New Testament we have documents saturated with hope and the conviction that an apocalyptic insight of ultimate significance has been vouchsafed, which relativizes all other claims and also breathes the spirit of accommodation, domestication and stability. Apocalyptic has expressed a critical response to the injustices of the world, and opened eyes closed to realities that all too often have become accepted as the norm.

Apocalypses frequently include explanations of their imagery by means of an authoritative angelic interpreter. The book of Daniel functions in this way as also do parts of *4 Ezra* 11–13. Revelation by contrast differs from these in not having such a pattern of symbolic vision followed by prose interpretation. It is not an angelic monologue but a thoroughly symbolic vision (or series of visions) whose meaning is to be found in the words and symbols themselves rather than in an accompanying authoritative exposition of their true meaning. The revealed mystery comes through something that is in fact ambiguous and opaque. Just as in *4 Ezra* where the apocalyptic seer has revealed to him that he cannot understand the divine inscrutability, the means of knowing is couched consistently in Revelation in language and discourse whose syntax and vocabulary taxes the conventions of normality. John writes as an outsider, an insignificant person in the face of the might of Rome. Yet he is the one who glimpses the mystery of God's purposes. The very strangeness of the imagery reminds the reader of the fact that God's ways are not humankind's ways and God's thoughts not their thoughts (Isaiah 40ff. and Job 40f.). Human wisdom, to paraphrase Paul, is stretched to its limit as 'normal' language seeks to bear witness to the mystery of God. With the book of Revelation we are brought into the world of apocalyptic mystery. Despite attempts over the years to play down the importance of this book the indications suggest that its thought-forms and outlook were more typical of early Christianity than is often allowed. The fact that we possess no visionary material elsewhere in the New Testament accounts for some of the differences, but they are superficial. Beneath the surface we have here convictions about God, Christ and the world that are not far removed from the so-called mainstream Christianity of the rest of the New Testament. In the earliest period of Christianity resort to the apocalyptic language and genre enabled the New Testament writers to have access to the privilege of understanding the significance of events and persons from the divine perspective. Apocalyptic, therefore, was the vehicle whereby the first Christians were able to articulate their deepest convictions about the ultimate significance of Jesus Christ in the divine economy.

NOTE

1   Unless stated otherwise, all Bible quotes are from the RSV.

BIBLIOGRAPHY

General

Charlesworth, J. H. (1983) *The Old Testament Pseudepigrapha*, Vol. 1. New York: Doubleday.
Cohn, N. (1957) *The Pursuit of the Millennium*. London: Paladin.
Collins, J. J. (1984) *The Apocalyptic Imagination: An Introduction to the Jewish Matrix of Christianity*. New York: Eerdmans.
—— (1998) *The Encyclopedia of Apocalypticism*. Vol. 1: *The Origins of Apocalypticism in Judaism and Christianity*. New York: Cassell and Continuum.
Emmerson, R. and McGinn, B. (1992) *The Apocalypse in the Middle Ages*. Ithaca: Cornell University Press.
Hellholm, D. (1989) *Apocalypticism in the Mediterranean World and the Near East*. 2nd edn. Tübingen: J. C. B. Mohr.
Kvanvig, H. S. (1974) *Roots of Apocalyptic: The Mesopotamian Background of the Enoch Figure and the Son of Man*. Neukirchen-Vluyn: Neukirchener Verlag.
McGinn, B. (1998) *The Encyclopedia of Apocalypticism*. Vol. 2: *Apocalypticism in Western History and Culture*. New York: Cassell and Continuum.
Rowland, C. (1982) *The Open Heaven*. London: SPCK.
Schäfer, P. (1992) *The Hidden and Manifest God*. New York: State University of New York.
Scholem, G. (1955) *Major Trends in Jewish Mysticism*. London: Thames & Hudson.
—— (1965) *Jewish Gnosticism, Merkabah Mysticism and Talmudic Tradition*. New York: Jewish Theological Seminary.
Stone, M. E. (1984) 'Apocalyptic Literature', in idem, *Jewish Writings of the Second Temple Period*. Philadelphia: Fortress Press, 383–441.

Revelation

Aune, D. (1997) *Revelation*. Word Biblical Commentary. Waco: Word Books.
Bauckham, R. (1992) *The Climax of Prophecy*. Edinburgh: T&T Clark.
—— (1993) *The Theology of the Book of Revelation*. Cambridge: Cambridge University Press.
Rowland, C. (1998) *Revelation*. New Interpreter's Bible 12. Nashville: Abingdon Press.
Schüssler Fiorenza, E. (1993) *Revelation: Vision of a Just World*. Edinburgh: T&T Clark.
Thompson, L. (1990) *The Book of Revelation: Apocalypse and Empire*. Oxford: Oxford University Press.

Daniel

Collins, J. J. (1993) *Daniel*. Hermeneia. Minneapolis: Fortress Press.
—— (1998) 'From Prophecy to Apocalypticism: The Expectation of the End', in idem 1998, 1: 129–61.

1 Enoch, 4 Ezra, Syriac Baruch and the *Apocalypse of Abraham*

Nickelsburg, G. (forthcoming) *1 Enoch*. Hermeneia. Minneapolis: Fortress Press.
Rowland, C. (1995) 'Enoch', in K. van der Toorn, B. Becking and P. W. van der Horst (eds) *Dictionary of Deities and Demons in the Bible*. Leiden: E. J. Brill, cols 576–81.
Stone, M. E. (1980) *Scriptures, Sects and Visions*. London: Collins.
—— (1984).
—— (1990) *Fourth Ezra*. Hermeneia. Philadelphia: Fortress Press.
VanderKam, J. C. (1984) *Enoch and the Growth of an Apocalyptic Tradition*. CBQMS 16. Washington: Catholic Biblical Association of America.
VanderKam, J. C. and Adler, William (1996) *The Jewish Apocalyptic Heritage in Early Christianity*. Assen: Van Gorcum.

Character and origins

Barker, M. (1987) *The Older Testament*. London: SPCK.
J. Barton (1986) *Oracles of God: Perceptions of Ancient Prophecy in Israel after the Exile*. London: Darton, Longman & Todd.
Cohn, N. (1993) *Cosmos, Chaos and the World to Come*. New Haven: Yale University Press.
Cook, S. L. (1995) *Prophecy and Apocalypticism: The Post-Exilic Social Setting*. Minneapolis: Fortress Press.
Davies, P. R. (1989) 'The Social World of the Apocalyptic Writings', in R. E. Clements (ed.) *The World of Ancient Israel*. Cambridge: Cambridge University Press, 349–70.
Grabbe, L. (1989) 'The Social Setting of Early Jewish Apocalypticism', *JSP*, 4: 27–47.
Gruenwald, I. (1978) *Apocalyptic and Merkavah Mysticism*. AGJU 14. Leiden: E. J. Brill.
Halperin, D. (1988) *The Faces of the Chariot*. Texte und Studien zum antiken Judentum. Tübingen: J. C. B. Mohr.
Hanson, P. D. (1975) *The Dawn of Apocalyptic*. Philadelphia: Fortress Press.
Hengel, M. (1974) *Judaism and Hellenism*. London: SCM Press.
Himmelfarb, M. (1993) *Ascent to Heaven in Jewish and Christian Apocalypses*. Oxford: Oxford University Press.
Mach, M. 'From Apocalypticism to Early Jewish Mysticism?' in Collins 1998, Vol. 1: 229–66.

Stroumsa, G. (1996) *Hidden Wisdom Esoteric Traditions and the Roots of Christian Mysticism*. Leiden: E. J. Brill.

Apocalyptic in the New Testament

Ashton, J. (1991) *Understanding the Fourth Gospel*. Oxford: Oxford University Press.

Aune, D. (1983) *Prophecy in Early Christianity and the Ancient Mediterranean World*. Grand Rapids: Eerdmans.

Bockmuehl, M. N. A. (1990) *Revelation and Mystery*. WUNT 2/36 Tübingen: J. C. B. Mohr.

Boer, M. de 'Paul and Apocalyptic Eschatology', in Collins 1998, 1: 345–83.

Danièlou, J. (1964) *The Theology of Jewish Christianity*. London: Darton, Longman & Todd.

Fossum, J. (1985) *The Name of God and the Angel of the Lord*. WUNT 36. Tübingen: J. C. B. Mohr.

—— (1995) *The Image of the Invisible God: Essays on the Influence of Jewish Mysticism on Early Christology*. NTOA 30. Göttingen: Vandenhoeck & Ruprecht.

Hurtado, L. W. (1990) *One God, One Lord*. London: SCM Press.

Kanagaraj, J. J. (1998) *'Mysticism' in the Gospel of John: An Inquiry into the Background of John in Jewish Mysticism*. JSNTSup 158. Sheffield: Sheffield Academic Press.

Kim, S. (1981) *The Origin of Paul's Gospel*. Tübingen; J. C. B. Mohr.

Lane Fox, R. (1986) *Pagans and Christians*. Harmondsworth: Penguin Books.

Lincoln, A. T. (1981) *Paradise Now and Not Yet*. SNTSMS 43. Cambridge: Cambridge University Press.

Rowland, C. & Morray-Jones, C. (2003) *The Mystery of God*. Compendia Rerum Judaicarum ad Novum Testamentum 4/2 Assen: Gorcum/Minneapolis: Fortress Press.

Segal, A. (1990) *Paul the Convert: The Apostolate and Apostasy of Saul the Pharisee*. New Haven: Yale University Press.

Trevett, C. (1995) *Montanism*. Cambridge: Cambridge University Press.

CHAPTER NINE

THE JEWISH NOVEL

———•◆•———

Lawrence M. Wills

Although once neglected in biblical scholarship, the Jewish literature composed between the time of the Hebrew Bible and the New Testament (including the Old Testament Apocrypha) has in recent decades come into its own.[1] From about 200 BCE on, there is a rich flowering of Jewish literature in genres that were greatly altered from their older counterparts: histories (1 and 2 Maccabees), apocalypses (*1 Enoch*; *Jubilees*), and wisdom (Wisdom of Jesus ben Sira; Wisdom of Solomon). However, one important group of texts constitutes a completely new genre: Jewish novels. The texts that we may include here among Jewish novels are Esther and Daniel – not in their form in the Hebrew Bible, but as they appear in the Apocrypha – Tobit and Judith (also found in the Apocrypha), and the later novel *Joseph and Aseneth*. Even where they make use of older motifs or allude to earlier biblical texts, they reflect new literary themes and techniques. Although there was no genre in ancient Judaism labeled 'novel' as such – nor was there such a label in use for the Greek and Roman novels – it is clear that throughout the Greek-controlled world, which by this time included most Jews, many ethnic groups were writing and reading entertaining narratives. From the texts themselves we may ascertain which group we would include in this category and why.

First, we must define what we mean by 'novel.' A novel is an entertaining prose narrative, written as opposed to oral (though the narrative may have begun as an oral tradition), which attains enough length to allow for the development of plot and subplot, description, dialogue, characterization, and the examination of thoughts and motives. Realism in description is often considered part of the essence of the modern novel, but in the ancient world it is present only in small amounts. More to the point is the inclusion of a strong emotional component, emotion that is reflected both in the storm and stress of the characters, and likely in the reading experience of the ancient audience as well.[2]

Contemporary also with the Jewish novels are writings that may be considered 'novelistic,' even if they are related to other genres or are simply not sufficiently developed to be considered novels in their own right. Artapanus in about 200 BCE wrote highly embellished accounts of Abraham, Joseph, and Moses, which glorify the exploits of these early heroes of Jewish history. We may call these texts 'national hero romances.' Several historical works also created a more dramatic atmosphere in addressing the recent past of Jewish history: 2 Maccabees, 3 Maccabees, and the so-called *Tobiad Romance* and *Royal Family of Adiabene* contained in Josephus's *Antiquities*, books 12 and 20. Although they have generally been regarded simply as bad history, they were perhaps intended as more engaging, even entertaining versions of important historical topics, and in this respect they are more novelistic than, say, 1 Maccabees. For instance, in 2 Maccabees 2:19–32 the author of that work states that the goals are different from documentary history, and tend more toward instructive entertainment. This understanding of the subgenre was likely carried on in the other Jewish historical novels as well, and also in the Christian Acts and apocryphal acts. In addition, other texts of the same period, which are not novels on the surface, have certain recognizable novelistic elements, such as *Testaments of the Twelve Patriarchs*, *Testament of Abraham*, and *Testament of Job*.[3]

The existence of these related genres or subgenres gives the impression of a morass of interrelated texts, in the midst of which it would be impossible to distinguish a single genre 'novel.' Indeed, the unclear boundaries of the ancient Jewish novels is both a blessing and a curse. On the one hand, unlike the ancient Greek and Roman novels or the modern European novels, where we have a more clearly defined corpus, in the case of the Jewish novels the boundaries between the novel and other genres are not clear. Instead we find a number of texts that reflect experimentation with novelistic techniques and only a *gradual* approximation to what we would think of as the fully formed novel. The novel seems to come about slowly, as a result of innovations in the new medium of written entertainments intended for a class of wealthier Jews at home in the brave new world of Greek and Roman domination. However, this also represents a tremendous opportunity for the scholar to witness the origins and evolution of the novel at every stage of development, an opportunity that is not available in the case of the Greek and Roman novels.

The Jewish novels take their plot elements and motifs in some cases from older Hebrew Bible narratives, in some cases from legends and oral narrative traditions, and in other cases from Persian narrative traditions (Bickerman 1967, 1988; Wills 1990, 1995). They can also, like the ancient Greek novels, include fragments of other genres, whether pre-existing or artificially created to suit the particular literary context: Daniel and Esther are derived from court legends, Apocryphal Esther includes artificial apocalyptic visions and royal decrees, Judith begins with a dating formula typical of the biblical historical books, and *Joseph and Aseneth* begins and ends in a way similar to the Jewish national history romances of Artapanus. Still, it is the new 'package' of the novel that indicates the transformation of old motifs in a new genre.

As these novels took shape and grew and evolved, it is clear that they were not considered fixed narratives or sacred history. Although the canonization and the fixing of the texts of the Hebrew Bible proceeded slowly – Jeremiah, Proverbs, and Psalms, for example, were not transmitted in a fixed text until fairly late in the canonization process – the discrepancies in the texts and versions of the novels were even greater. All of the novels except Judith existed in multiple versions in the ancient world, suggesting that they were popular enough to be copied and altered often. These stories were evidently viewed as malleable entertainments that could be expanded and altered at every turn to address a new audience. Fragments found

Figure 9.1   Fragment of an unidentified novelistic work from Qumran (4Q550d).
Copyright Israel Antiquities Authority.

at Qumran even suggest that novelistic literature was copied on shorter scrolls with
fewer lines (see Figure 9.1). J. T. Milik (1992: 363–5) refers to these novelistic
scrolls as the 'pocket editions of the ancient world.' However, when they became
part of sacred scripture, they were likely read in a different way, as edifying histories
of important episodes of Jewish life.

The rise of the novel in the Greco-Roman world and in the Jewish world came
about as a result of similar social changes.[4] The conquests of Alexander the Great
in 332 BCE had resulted in a new world order, and in time Greek education became
standard for advancement in all the cities of the Near East. The advances in trade
and economic interdependence in the eastern Mediterranean allowed for a new,
ethnically mixed, entrepreneurial class, and Jews were well represented in this group.
There are thus many similarities between the Jewish and Greco-Roman novels: the
threat of chaos and destruction and the dramatic deliverance of the protagonists,
the melodramatic tone and play upon the readers' emotions, and the use of dialogue
to explore the interior states of the characters. Still, the differences are equally
important. Jewish novels apparently arose before the earliest Greek novelistic work.[5]
They are also shorter, more varied in their plot structures, and more primitive in
their literary attainments. The Jewish novels do not generally involve the element
of travel – although exotic foreign courts are featured – and the erotic attachments
and the separation of lovers do not propel the plot forward. In the Greek novels,
the breakdown of the older city-state social structures based on tribe, class, and
extended family lay just beneath the surface, and as a result, the Greek novel focused
on the conjugal couple, reunited at the end of the novel, as the newer model of the
nuclear family. The Jewish novel, on the other hand, focused on the protagonists in
relation to their *extended* family. The audience of the Jewish novel evidently felt
very keenly the attractions of living in the Hellenistic diaspora, at the same time
that fears of persecution or assimilation could be projected as threats to the safety
of all Jews.

We may now turn to a brief consideration of each of the Jewish novels.

DANIEL

Daniel, as we have received it in the Jewish and Protestant canons, consists of narratives told in the third person about the wise courtier Daniel and his three companions, Shadrach, Meshach, and Abednego (Daniel 1–6), combined with apocalyptic visions of Daniel, recounted in the first person (Daniel 7–12). Because the latter chapters make reference to events of the Maccabean Revolt (167–64 BCE), they are dated to that period, but the narratives of Daniel 1–6 do not refer to these hostilities, and seem to reflect the period prior to the Maccabean Revolt (Collins 1977: 33–59; Wills 1990: 75–152; Humphreys 1973). The book of Daniel probably originated, then, as a collection of originally independent oral narratives from about the fourth – third centuries BCE, which were collected and committed to writing. The earliest collection may have been limited to Daniel 4–6, but at any rate Daniel 1–6 probably also circulated as a collection from the period before the Maccabean Revolt. Although the individual narratives, which contained elements of danger, escape, and humor, already contained the seeds of novelistic interest, they were by themselves not novelistic. However, the mere collection of the stories signals a move in a new direction, placing all the stories of Daniel into one 'book.'

Figure 9.2 *Susanna and the Elders*, Rembrandt (1647), Berlin, Staatliche Museen.
Copyright Fotomarburg/Art Resource, New York.

The addition of the apocalyptic visions of Daniel 7–12 constitutes a development that was not novelistic – it was an application of the Daniel tradition to the specific issues of the crisis of the Maccabean Revolt – but soon thereafter other chapters were added that explore various novelistic motifs. Susanna depicts a threat to the virtue of a beautiful young woman by unscrupulous elders, the Prayer of Azariah and the Song of the Three Jews gives voice to an inner, psychologizing penance of pious Jews, and Bel and The Dragon extends the theme of piety and danger begun already in Daniel 1–6. Here we see another important step toward expanding the book to create a new art form, and it is the addition of Susanna that is most instructive. A woman character, placed in danger and contemplating her own moral position, whose experience and point of view are rendered for the audience, is at the center of this story, and it is equally important that the social setting is no longer the royal court, and the worldwide body of Jews is not the issue. The new setting is a local, domestic setting, where an individual person faces problems that are played out within the family. This is the essence of the novel. The novelistic – and erotic – interest in the depiction of Susanna has been followed by many visual representations of her throughout history (see Figure 9.2; Miles 1989: 121–25).

ESTHER

Like Daniel, Esther may have evolved from an oral court legend influenced by Persian tradition (Bickerman 1967: 182–4). The version found in the Hebrew Bible is already somewhat novelistic, but it is perhaps best to consider it transitional to the novels that follow. At the core is a plot that focuses on the two Jews Esther and Mordecai, and the drama that surrounds them (and by extension, all the Jews of Persia), played out in the court of the great Persian king Ahasuerus (Xerxes). But already this court legend reflects the experimentation characteristic of novels: the plot and subplot of Esther and Mordecai – which is plot and which subplot? – the grandiose descriptions of the court settings, and especially the dialogue and examination of Esther's inner turmoil in chapter 4 as she must decide at Mordecai's behest whether to identify as a Jew and try to save her people. This last element is intriguing because Esther seems to change and develop as a character, moving beyond the self-centered complacency of one who is comfortable and in denial to the more self-actualized status of one who recognizes her responsibility to her fellow-Jews and decides to act upon it, even at the risk of her own life (Berg 1979: 173–87; Fox 1991). Although it is often said that character change and development were only discovered in the modern novel, it seems that they are met with here as well, perhaps for the first time.

The version of Esther in the Hebrew Bible may already show signs of having been composed of several older narrative traditions, but when we turn to the later versions – two Greek, two Latin, and two Aramaic – we witness what must have been typical of novelistic literature: free and experimental change and development of novelistic motifs. We shall focus here on the Greek version that became semi-canonical as part of the Old Testament Apocrypha. There Esther is embellished by the addition of six significant expansions that add excitement (visions of the coming conflict placed at the beginning), exploration of interiorizing emotions (Mordecai's and Esther's prayers and inner turmoil), and dramatic detail (the text of the king's two decrees,

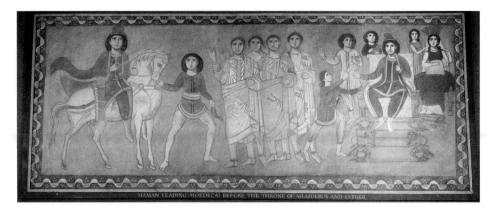

Figure 9.3 Haman leading Mordecai before the throne of Ahasuerus and Esther.
Copyright Yale University Art Gallery, Dura-Europos Collection.

lacking in the earlier version of Esther). Although the additions sometimes mimic earlier literary forms, they are here thoroughly 'novelized'; that is, they are written to be dramatic within the narrative context and to advance the plot. Mordecai's dream, for instance, is meant to sound like an apocalyptic vision, but it is concerned only with the upcoming events of the story and not with the events at the end of time; it merely heightens the sense that an ominous conflict is about to take place. (Greek novels, it should be noted, also feature premonitory dreams and oracles.) Likewise Esther's prayer and the two royal decrees explain important psychological issues and motivations, and add a much richer texture to the story. Perhaps nowhere are the novelistic changes more in evidence than in the entrance of Esther into the king's court:

> When she had gone through all the doors, she stood before the king. He was seated on his royal throne, clothed in the full array of his majesty, all covered with gold and precious stones. He was most terrifying. Lifting his face, flushed with splendor, he looked at her in fierce anger. The queen faltered, turned pale and faint, and collapsed on the head of the maid who went in front of her.
>
> (15:6–7 NRSV)

Hebrew Esther has been transformed here into a romance, with description quite similar to the Greek novels.

The synagogue painting of Esther and Mordecai found at Dura Europos (dated about 250 CE; see Figure 9.3) indicates the importance this story had achieved, and as in the various renditions of the narrative, Mordecai and Esther vie for the position of greater importance. In the painting, Mordecai commands the central position, and Esther remains a 'power behind the throne.'

TOBIT

The book of Tobit is a charming and spirited tale that recounts the intertwined experiences of two protagonists: Tobit, a pious Jew who is 'rewarded' by God with blindness, and Sarah, his distant cousin, whose seven fiancés have been slain on their wedding nights by the evil demon Asmodaeus. Tobit and Sarah, though unknown to each other and separated by many miles, pray at the same time for God to end their misery by taking their lives. The goodness and piety of these central characters are emphasized, and God has a secret means of delivering them from their problems: the angel Raphael is dispatched to resolve their difficulties, and by doing so draws the two plotlines together. Preparing for death, Tobit sends his son Tobias to a distant city to retrieve a huge sum of money placed on deposit there many years earlier. The angel Raphael appears in the guise of a mortal to act as a guide, and on the journey gives Tobias the means to bind Asmodaeus and take Sarah in marriage. Tobias returns to Tobit with both bride and money, and also produces another healing agent that Raphael had given him to cure Tobit's blindness. There is much rejoicing at the end, as the main characters celebrate their good fortune and Raphael reveals his identity to them.

The magical tone in Tobit may seem somewhat at odds with its status as a semi-canonical biblical book. It has been read as a pious and uplifting account of God's protection of virtuous people, but it may have been originally composed with a deliberate whimsy, to entertain a well-to-do Jewish audience with marriage on its mind. At any rate, unlike Daniel and Esther, the source of the story does not lie in the court legend tradition, but in common folktale motifs – the spirit that rewards a person for burying the dead, the magical healing agents that are found in a fish, the binding of the evil demon, even the dog that accompanies Tobias on his journey – all of these motifs are found in folktales from around the world (Zimmermann 1958: 5–12; Wills 1995: 73–6). Still, the parallels to oral tales do not preclude a novelistic composition, and that is evidently what we find in Tobit. It is interesting that here as well several different versions of Tobit circulated in the ancient world.

JUDITH

The book of Judith is in many ways different from the Jewish novels described so far, and these differences are in part explained by the fact that Judith was probably composed from the first as a novel, and not derived from an older narrative. Judith is longer that Daniel, Esther, and Tobit, but surprisingly, is much less dependent upon a complicated plot and subplot. It is more of an artful and elongated development of a single literary movement: the evil general Holofernes arises on the horizon to threaten the Jews, and is cut down in a moment of weakness by the beautiful Jewish widow Judith. Despite the simplicity of this plotline, *how* all this comes about, and *what* it means occupy the interest of the author and audience. The rising action, denouement, and falling action are more clearly developed in this novel than in any of the others, through a clever structuring of the dramatic scenes (Craven 1983). Judith consists of two main acts, the rising threat of Holofernes (chs 1–7), and the response of the Jews (8–16). In each half phrases and motifs are found that are paralleled or reversed in the other half, giving rise to two countervaling propositions: Holofernes is the servant of his lord Nebuchadnezzar, and Judith is the servant of her Lord God. The battle is a struggle to see which lord, working through his servant, will prevail, and by what means.

There is a certain literary pleasure that is evident in both halves. The buildup of Holofernes's forces and the alliances that are formed create a vivid picture of a world at war. The geographical sweep (1:7–10; 2:21–7) impresses the reader with the

Figure 9.4 Two views of Judith and Holofernes. (a) *above* Statue by Donatello (c. 1386–1466), Piazza della Signoria, Florence. Copyright Alinari/Art Resource, New York. (b) *opposite* Painting by Caravaggio. Copyright Nimatallah/Art Resource, New York.

tremendous stakes and the might of the advancing Assyrian army. Formerly neutral parties take sides (3:7–8), and the fully marshalled troops of Holofernes strike fear into the Jews when they are all amassed at the foot of the pass where Bethulia lies (7:1–5). Just before Holofernes reaches that point, however, there is a pause in the narrative as a new character is introduced: Achior the Ammonite. He describes to General Holofernes just who the Jews are, and in doing so presents the side of God in this morality play (ch. 6). Holofernes is incensed, and has Achior bound and dumped at the edge of Bethulia, there to die with the Jews Achior has just described so positively. The first half thus ends with Achior left in the same uncertain state as the Jews of Bethulia. When the second half begins, the male leaders of Bethulia are on the verge of capitulating to Holofernes's demands. It is only Judith, the beautiful, pious, and wealthy widow of Manasseh, who steps forward to upbraid the weak-willed citizens. She argues that God will not abandon the Jews, and then sets out on a plan to deliver them. Accompanied only by her maidservant, she proceeds down the mountainside to the Assyrian camp, and when at night Holofernes invites her into his tent, she leads him on until he becomes drunk, and then decapitates him, places his head in her food pouch, and sneaks back to her village. The next day, the Jews, with the head of Holofernes displayed before them, attack and rout the Assyrians in fear.

The story is told with a deft touch of irony throughout. When Holofernes orders that Achior be exiled to Bethulia, he tells him, 'You shall not see my face again until I take revenge on this race' (6:5, my trans.). The audience will later find that

Achior does see Holofernes's face again, when Judith pulls it from her pouch. When Judith is before Holofernes, she also engages in a banter that is very humorous. She promises Holofernes, 'If you follow the words of your servant, God will accomplish something through you, and my lord will not fail to achieve his purpose' (11:6, my trans.). The audience, of course, knows that when Judith mentions 'my lord,' she is secretly intending a reference to God, while Holofernes assumes it is a reference to him. This ironic humor, together with the careful balancing of both halves of the story, indicate a more assured novelistic technique than in the other Jewish novels, a technique that will allow the extension of the narrative in a way more sophisticated than the mere insertion of unintegrated episodes and subplots, as was the case in Daniel, Esther, and Tobit.

It is also interesting that the ancient text does not reveal any ambivalence about Judith's actions – her lying, her sexual provocativeness, her nerveless decapitation of Holofernes – even though she is viewed with great suspicion in the modern world, beginning with paintings of the seventeenth century, where she is often depicted with strong psychological undertones. For example, the 'classical' triumphant Judith by Donatello (c.1455; see Figure 9.4a) can be contrasted with the intensely troubling painting by Michelangelo Caravaggio (1599; see Figure 9.4b; Jacobus 1986: 110–36).

JOSEPH AND ASENETH

Joseph and Aseneth is the longest of the novels considered here. It combines danger and adventure with an evolving romance (often understood in an ascetic manner), and emphasizes the inner psychological turmoil of the vulnerable heroine. Taking its inspiration from a verse in Genesis (41:45) that states that Joseph was given Aseneth, daughter of Potiphera, priest of On, in marriage, this novel fills in the gaps of that story. It begins by describing how the haughty Egyptian Aseneth is so struck by Joseph's appearance that she renounces the attentions of the Pharaoh's son and falls hopelessly in love with Joseph. She has never slept with a man – in fact, she has never even been seen by a man! – but immediately upon catching a glimpse of Joseph, falls madly in love. She is smitten with the same lovesickness that is so typical of the Greek novels, but Joseph will have none of her advances. He had been badly treated in his encounter with Potiphar's wife, and chooses not to take up with a Gentile woman. He departs temporarily, allowing for Aseneth's wrenching self-examination and conversion. She repents of the sins of idols and luxury, and purifying herself through an ascetic practice of fasting and penance, renounces her pagan past and becomes Jewish through a mystical encounter with a 'man from heaven.' Afterward, however, Joseph's half-brothers (sons of the maidservants Bilhah and Zilpah) conspire with the jilted son of the Pharaoh to try to kill Joseph, and it is up to Aseneth to intercede. With the aid of Joseph's brothers Levi and Benjamin, Aseneth foils the plot, and Pharaoh's son is accidentally killed in the process. The Pharaoh also dies of grief, but Joseph comes to rule Egypt in his stead.

In some ways, *Joseph and Aseneth* represents the culmination of the process of novelistic development in ancient Judaism. The emphasis on the female protagonist, present to some extent in all the other Jewish novels, here reaches its apex. Joseph is important at the beginning, but soon the audience's entire interest is focused on the inner turmoil of Aseneth. Whether this text addresses the actual concerns of people who converted to Judaism (Chesnutt 1995; Kee 1983) or simply uses the conversion subplot as a metaphor for other issues is not clear. In addition, it is sometimes suggested that Christian motifs can be found in the novel, and that it may have been written several centuries after the other novels (Kraemer 1992: 110–12). It would, in that case, still be useful as a comparison point, but not as a window into the Jewish social world of the period of the Bible.

CONCLUSION

Having described each of the five known Jewish novels, we may now turn to a fascinating and controversial question. Granting that the novels utilized novelistic techniques, were they, like other novels, also read as fictions, that is, were they understood by both author and audience as an experiment in narration that does not recount actual events? The answer is not clear. Each of the novels contains a historical blunder that seems to signal an intentional abandonment of anything resembling history: Daniel 5:31 refers to 'Darius the Mede' (Darius was king of Persia), Esther describes a Jewish queen of Persia (there was never a Jewish queen of Persia), Tobit 14:15 refers to 'Ahasuerus of Media' (Ahasuerus, or Xerxes, was king of Persia), Judith takes place during the reign of 'Nebuchadnezzar, king of the Assyrians' (Nebuchadnezzar was king of the Babylonians), and *Joseph and Aseneth* concludes with Joseph as viceregent of Egypt (Joseph, according to the biblical text, was never viceregent of Egypt). These are all historical inaccuracies so egregious that it is scarcely possible that the audience would have believed them. On the other hand, the pious nature of the writings indicates that the characters were at least seen as moral exemplars for the readers, and it appears that soon after their composition some of the texts were treated as factual accounts by historians such as Josephus. What seems more to the point, however, is the experimentation with unreal worlds and unreal figures found in these novels, and the playful way in which 'history' can be rewritten in a triumphant way. The audience may not have been making a clear distinction between fact and fiction, but were perhaps inhabiting the gray world of experimentation. The same may have been true in the case of the Greek literature that paved the way for the novels in that culture, such as Xenophon's *Cyropaedia* or Pseudo-Callisthenes's *Alexander Romance*. It is not always easy to determine what is *fiction* and what is understood as 'bad history.' Fiction was evidently scorned by some intellectuals in the ancient world because it seemed like an affront to 'truth-telling,' but the Jewish novels discussed here seem to begin by experimenting with the idea of fictitious characters and events, and grow more novelistic by exploiting the techniques outlined above.

The Jewish novels hold a very important place in the religious life of a wealthy class of Jews, and provide us with a window into the world of their values and ideas. The romantic interest is sometimes present, but always tied to the demands of the extended family and to the body of Jews in general, and these remain as demands upon the reader from beginning to end. The penitential aspect of the texts is also inescapable, revealing an interiorizing psychology that is often quite intense. Penance had become a strongly emphasized aspect of Jewish spirituality in the ancient world (Nehemiah 9; Baruch 1), and here we find this spirituality 'narrativized.' Although it is the woman character who lives through the most intense penitential self-examination, it is likely both the male and female members of the audience who see themselves in her purification. This process in the narrative seems closely akin to asceticism, and may be a transitional stage to the asceticism that was practiced in early Christianity, and which is reflected in the historical novels known as the Christian apocryphal acts.

NOTES

1 Two recent works that introduce most of these texts are Nickelsburg 1981 and Collins 1982. In addition to the Apocrypha, which are now printed in most study Bibles, the English translations of the other Jewish texts are readily available in Charlesworth 1985.

2 The definition of the novel used here, and the discussion in general, was first presented in Wills 1995.

3 On *Testaments of the Twelve Patriarchs*, see Bickerman 1988: 210; on *Testament of Abraham*, Wills 1995: 245–56; and on *Testament of Job*, Levine 1997: 351.

4 See Wills 1995: 1–39 on the Jewish novel; and on the Greek novel, Perry 1967; Reardon 1991; and Holzberg 1995.

5 The earliest known fragment of a Greek novel has been dated to the first century BCE. To be sure, the Jewish novels probably did not influence the Greek novels directly; they are instead similar to the popular prose narratives that were appearing among different ethnic groups in the Greco-Roman world. The *Ninus Romance* was probably read by native Syrians, *Sesonchosis* and *Petubastis* among Egyptians, the *Alexander Romance* among Hellenized Egyptians, and so on. These are similar to the Jewish 'national hero romance' by Artapanus.

BIBLIOGRAPHY

Berg, Sandra Beth (1979) *The Book of Esther: Motifs, Themes, and Structure.* Missoula: Scholars Press.

Bickerman, Elias (1967) *Four Strange Books of the Bible.* New York: Schocken Books.

—— (1988) *The Jews in the Greek Age.* Cambridge, Mass.: Harvard University Press.

Charlesworth, James H. (ed.) (1985) *The Old Testament Pseudepigrapha*, 2 vols. Garden City, N.Y.: Doubleday.

—— (1988) *The Jews in the Greek Age.* Cambridge, Mass.: Harvard University Press.

Chesnutt, Randall D. (1995) *From Death to Life: Conversion in Joseph and Aseneth.* Sheffield: Sheffield Academic Press.

Collins, John J. (1977) *The Apocalyptic Vision of the Book of Daniel.* Missoula: Scholars Press.

—— (1982) *Between Athens and Jerusalem: Jewish Identity in the Hellenistic Diaspora.* New York: Crossroad.

Craven, Toni (1983) *Artistry and Faith in the Book of Judith.* Chico: Scholars Press.

Fox, Michael V. (1991) *Character and Ideology in the Book of Esther.* Columbia: University of South Carolina Press.

Holzberg, Niklas (1995) *The Ancient Novel: An Introduction.* London: Routledge.

Humphreys, W. Lee (1973) 'A Life-Style for Diaspora: A Study of Esther and Daniel,' *Journal of Biblical Literature* 92: 211–23.

Jacobus, Mary (1986) *Reading Woman: Essays in Feminist Criticism.* New York: Columbia University Press.

Kee, Howard Clark (1983) 'The Socio-Cultural Setting of Joseph and Asenath,' *New Testament Studies* 29: 394–413.

Kraemer, Ross (1992) *Her Share of the Blessings: Women's Religion Among Pagans, Jews, and Christians.* New York: Oxford University Press.

Levine, Amy-Jill (1997) Review of Wills, *The Jewish Novel in the Ancient World, Journal of Religion* 77: 350–52.

Miles, Margaret (1989) *Carnal Knowing: Female Nakedness and Religious Meaning in the Christian West.* Boston: Beacon Press.

Milik, J. T. (1992) 'Les modèles araméens du livre d'Esther dans la grotte 4 de Qumrân,' *Revue de Qumraân* 15: 321–406.

Nickelsburg, George W. E. (1981) *Jewish Literature Between the Bible and the Mishnah.* Philadelphia: Fortress Press.

Perry, Ben E. (1967) *The Ancient Romances.* Berkeley: University of California Press.

Reardon, Bryan (1991) *The Form of the Greek Romance.* Princeton: Princeton University Press.

Wills, Lawrence M. (1990) *The Jew in the Court of the Foreign King: Ancient Jewish Court Legends.* Minneapolis: Fortress Press.

—— (1995) *The Jewish Novel in the Ancient World.* Ithaca: Cornell University Press.

Zimmermann, Frank (1958) *The Book of Tobit.* New York: Harper & Brothers.

CHAPTER TEN

THE GOSPELS

——————·◆·——————

John Muddiman

THE GOSPEL MESSAGE AND THE GOSPELS

In the biblical world itself, in contrast to the post-biblical world of later inter-pretation, the word 'gospel' (Greek *euangelion*) does not denote a type of literature, namely the four texts that make up the first half of the New Testament, but the proclamation of salvation through faith in Jesus Christ.

In classical Greek the singular noun is rare and is used technically in reference to the payment made to someone who brings glad tidings; the more normal term to refer to the content of the message is, as in English, the plural, 'good news' (*euan-gelia*). This typically denotes the announcement of some cause for *public* rejoicing, like a victory in battle or the birth of an heir to the throne. The impoverished under-classes of the Roman Empire probably did not greet such announcements of 'good news' with any great enthusiasm, for they would have served only to reinforce the old world order. In a lively linguistic innovation, Paul or some other early Christian used 'gospel' in the singular to refer to the contents of the only genuinely good news. Building on the use of the verb in the Old Testament (e.g. Isa. 40.9; 52.7; 61.1), he coined this semi-technical term to sum up the heart of a world-changing and subversive message of salvation through the death and resurrection of Jesus of Nazareth, a Jewish prophet believed to be Messiah and Son of God, and expected to return soon to raise the dead and establish a reign of justice for the poor.

The cross of Jesus was good news because it was not what it appeared to be, the torture and humiliation of yet another victim of Roman state terrorism. It was rather the sacrifice that paid the price of sin, ordained of God and fulfilling scriptural prophecy. It was good news because believers could enter into this event by a leap of spiritual and ethical imagination, made visible and concrete in the sacraments of baptism and Eucharist, and die to their old selves (or even be 'crucified with' Christ, Gal. 2.19). Above all, it was good news because it was the moment when a dramatic shift in the timetable of universal history had occurred, for on the third day God raised him from the dead. Similarly, the resurrection of Jesus was not what it at first appeared to be, a freak phenomenon of physical resuscitation or wish-fulfilment on the part of his demoralized followers; it was good news because the end-time hope of a new world had been anticipated and guaranteed in one representative instance, and the risen Christ who had thus been designated to come again soon to judge the world was also the one who, as the Wisdom of God, created the world in the first place, and is the explanation of all that happens in salvation-history between the beginning and the end. All of this is what 'gospel' meant for Paul and arguably it is still what the word means for the writers of what we call the Synoptic Gospels, when they occasionally use it (e.g. Matt. 26.13; Mark 1.15; Luke 9.6).

In New Testament scholarship, the early Christian message of salvation outlined in the previous paragraph is normally referred to as the *kerygma* (the Greek word for 'proclamation'), in order to avoid any confusion with the literary category of 'gospel'. It is a matter of continuing scholarly dispute whether and to what extent a distinction needs to be made between the Pauline *kerygma* and other early *kerygmata*. We are entirely dependent for direct knowledge of the first three decades of Christian history on the authentic letters of Paul, and so we do not know whether his way of presenting the gospel to mainly Gentile audiences, with hardly any use of the sayings of Jesus (only certainly 1 Cor. 11.23–5) and no reference to any incident prior to his passion, was typical of the movement as a whole. If it was, interest in the life-story of Jesus as a medium through which to proclaim the good news may have developed only in the second, post-Pauline, generation. But it is perhaps more likely that other early missionaries would have appealed more often to Jesus' life and teaching than Paul does in his letters, although, as Paul himself says (see Gal. 2.7), all agreed on the basic content of the gospel. There is no evidence (*pace* Crossan 1999: 239–56, and others, e.g. Koester 1990) that a very different kind of early *kerygma*, which focused exclusively on Jesus' preaching of the Kingdom, existed alongside and in competition with the gospel of the cross and resurrection. The hypothetical Q sayings source presupposes (see the lament over Jerusalem, Luke 13.34–5 and par.) the rejection, and indeed vindication, of Jesus in the line of Israel's prophets. Only by a highly tendentious process of selection and isolation of certain Q traditions and by equally speculative claims about the antiquity and significance of the so-called *Gospel of Thomas* can such a dichotomy between two types of early Christianity be sustained.

How, then, are we to explain the development from Paul's gospel to what the New Testament Gospels contain? There is clearly a move away from the existential and universal and towards the historical and particular, and thus towards the very *Jewish* detail of the life of Jesus. Various explanations of this move are possible: the influx of non-Jews into the Church may have made it necessary to be more explicit about the Jewish matrix of Christian belief in Jesus as God's Messiah; delay in the expected Parousia may have led to a greater consciousness of the movement's continuing existence over time and the consequent need to establish its identity by a recovery of origins; devotion to the heavenly Saviour may have become so strong in Christian spirituality that doubts were beginning to be raised (cf. 1 John 4.2) about his identification with the one who was 'born of a woman' and 'suffered under Pontius Pilate'. In addition to such general stimuli towards the writing of the Gospels, each of them is probably also responding to particular needs and circumstances.

The construction of life-stories of Jesus creates at first an epistemological distance between reader and the central figure in the narrative; the lordship of Christ as the object of faith is no longer being apprehended directly, but indirectly through the medium of authoritative tradition. The four evangelists seem to be aware of this danger and adopt different strategies to cope with it. But the common purpose of the New Testament Gospels is to express through the form of a selective story about Jesus, dealing mainly with his public career and its final week, an urgent summons to believe in him as Christ and Son of God. The focus on the person and life of Jesus arises, then, not so much from biographical curiosity, as from the basic religious commitment of early Christians that 'in Christ God was reconciling the world to himself' (2 Cor. 5.19).

The four Gospels were produced by Greek-speaking Christians probably in the eastern Mediterranean during the last third of the first century. Attempts to claim that Matthew and John are translations of underlying Aramaic texts or that Mark was first composed in Latin are generally now considered unconvincing. While some still argue for a western provenance for Mark or Luke (i.e. Rome), the trend in recent scholarship has been to locate them all in Christian communities in Syria, Asia Minor or Greece, such as Antioch, Ephesus or Corinth, which were the historic centres of the Pauline mission field. The surprising neglect of the Jesus tradition in Paul's own letters, noted above, implies that the Gospels themselves, if not their narrative style of proclaiming the good news, appeared only after his day, and the allusions in each to the destruction of Jerusalem in 70 CE (Mark 13.2; Matt. 22.7; Luke 19.13; John 2.19) confirm a dating near or sometime after that event.

The literary relations between the Gospels provides some information about their relative chronology: Mark was probably the first and was used as the basis for Matthew and Luke. John's Gospel, preserving a largely independent stream of tradition, may reflect knowledge of the Synoptics at the latest stage of its editing, for it appears to have been re-edited after the death of its original author (21.24). The earliest patristic citations and manuscript evidence on papyrus put the *terminus ante quem* for the gospels at around 110 CE.

The titles of the Gospels, 'According to Mark', and so on, distinguishing them by named apostles or co-workers of apostles, are almost certainly later additions and not to be relied on (*pace* Hengel 2000). They could not have been added before the word 'gospel' had come to denote a type of literature, and that did not happen before the mid-second century, when it became clear that the Church needed to authenticate its traditional books, over against more recent products, by attaching to them explicit claims to apostolic authorship. The original works we know as the New Testament Gospels are themselves anonymous and deliberately so: for their authors to have identified themselves would have been an inappropriate claim to 'copyright' over what was essentially the common property of Christian communities.

WHAT IS A GOSPEL?

An answer to this question has been implied above, in terms of the contents and function of the books so designated in the New Testament. Many scholars would consider this to be a sufficient answer. The more precise question of their literary type or *genre* seems to be irrelevant, for it implies too high an estimate of the literary pretensions of their authors and the literary competence of their audiences. The New Testament Gospels are not 'high literature', so we should not expect them to fit into the conventional classifications familiar to the leisured and cultured élite of Graeco-Roman society.

If we define genre less strictly as a certain set of expectations that readers bring to any particular text based on their previous acquaintance with literature of a similar type, then the generic problem as regards the Gospels can be summed up in the following way. There is nothing to show that the intended readers of the Gospels were acquainted with any literature other than the Jewish scriptures (and this is probably true of their authors too, with the possible exception of Luke, see Acts 17.28), and there is very little in Jewish scripture that is sufficiently similar to the Gospels to explain how their first readers would have received them. The Old Testament contains no proper example of biography. The tales of Abraham, Moses, David and Elijah in Jewish scripture are not told continuously or for their own sakes; the episodes that are selected are subordinated to a larger plot, telling the life-story of God with his people, Israel; there is no attempt to analyse character as the key to the events in the story. There are some partial parallels between the Gospels and prophetic histories like the Elijah–Elisha cycle in Kings (1 Kgs 17–2 Kgs 13), with apocalyptic history, like the book of Daniel, or with a novel like Tobit, but they are insufficient to explain the large-scale structures, tone or purpose of the Christian texts.

One broad description of the Gospels as 'passion narratives with extended introductions' has often been quoted since it was formulated by the neo-Lutheran systematician, Martin Kähler, in 1882 (1964: 80 n.). It was endorsed, in particular, by the form-critics who understood the Gospels to have developed backwards from their passion narratives, where their similarity to each other is most pronounced. The 'remembering of the Lord's death until he comes' (1 Cor. 11.23) or the graphic portrayal of Christ crucified (Gal. 3.1; 1 Cor. 1.23) was the centre of the *kerygma*, and other material was added simply to explain how and why the story ends the way it does. There is still much to be said in favour of this view, especially in regard to Mark and John. For in both cases, the coming passion overshadows the story from the beginning. At John 1.29 already Jesus is announced as the 'Lamb of God who takes away the sins of the world' and, after a series of minor clashes with opponents, already at Mark 3.6 they are plotting Jesus' death. However, this definition fails to do justice to the movement in the other direction, not simply from the passion backwards but also from salvation-history forwards towards its fulfilment. The latter emphasis is clearest in Matthew and Luke, but it is not absent from the other two. Furthermore, the messages about the Kingdom in the Synoptics or, in the Fourth Gospel, about eternal life through faith in the Word incarnate, are not properly understood as introductory elements but are separate themes and can in a certain sense be appreciated apart from the passion narrative.

Recent investigations into the Hellenistic background of the New Testament have revived the attempt to classify the Gospels as 'ancient popular biography' (see Talbert 1977; Burridge 1991). As a descriptive category there can be no objection to calling the Gospels biography; modern literary historians are free to group similar writings together as they see fit. But as a prescriptive category there are several problems with this classification. Ancient works that have 'life' (*bios*) in their title are usually about some great figure from the past and they pretend (at least) to be objective

(Plutarch; Diogenes Laertius). But works about contemporaries or near contemporaries that are really eulogies in narrative form are not normally called 'lives'. Furthermore, the Gospel-writers pass over in silence the 'formative years' of their subject and apart from the incident in the Temple when Jesus was twelve (Luke 2.41–51) include no premonitions of greatness to come. The teaching of Jesus in the Synoptics is not principally intended to illustrate the character of the teacher but the character of the Kingdom whose coming he announces. The sharp contrast between the miraculous acts of power in the ministry and the utter powerlessess of the passion is left unresolved even by the resurrection stories. Certainly the Gospels aim to achieve the strong personal attachment of the audience to their central figure, but it is an attachment that is wider and deeper than the admiration evoked by biography. Some of their more educated readers no doubt recognized certain similarities between the Church's Gospels and the biographies they knew, but the evangelists and the audience for whom they initially wrote would probably not have made any connection.

When Justin Martyr in the mid-second century (Apology 106) wanted a literary classification in which to place the Gospels he called them the 'memorabilia' of the apostles (Greek *apomnēmoneumata*, like Xenophon's classic of that title), a term that emphasizes the privileged vantage point of the authors as witnesses, rather than the nature of their subject matter.

Several other attempts have been made to connect the Gospels with types of hellenistic literature in pure or mixed forms: memorabilia mixed with elements of Jewish prophecy (so Robbins 1984), aretalogy (so Hadas and Smith 1965) and tragedy (so Bilezikian 1992). These throw some light on certain aspects of the Gospels but leave others unexplained. More recently, Mary Ann Tolbert (1989: 44) has proposed that we should look for parallels to Mark's Gospel lower down the aesthetic scale of Hellenistic literature and she points to several similarities between Mark and popular romantic novels (ibid. 75). Self-evidently, the Gospels are not themselves romances, but their odd mixture of historiographical form with epic and dramatic substance, their loose episodic plots with summaries and fore-shadowings and stock characters, point to a *subliterary* oral genre, which has, unusually in the case of the Gospels, been preserved in writing, while most other examples of it, naturally enough, have disappeared.

In short, there is no simple answer to the question of genre. Just as Paul developed the letter-form to become a vehicle for preaching and moral exhortation, so also the writers of the Gospels used storytelling for their own kerygmatic and didactic purposes. It would be too much to say that they invented a wholly new genre: or at least it was not apparent that they had done so, until the four books were put together with a standard title in the Church's canon of scripture. Before then, it is more appropriate to look at each of the books separately and ask about the structure, contents, mood and purpose of each. Attentive listeners, acquainted with the discourse of early Christian groups, would not need to know what type of literature this was; they could pick up the thread as they went along.

MARK

Mark's Gospel is generally reckoned to be the earliest of the four. Since it is almost entirely reproduced in one or both of the other Synoptics, there would be little point in its composition if it came later. Its supposed priority has made it the object of intense scholarly interest and debate over the last 150 years.

At first, it was hoped that Mark, as the earliest Gospel, would provide a 'royal road' to the historical Jesus, what lawyers would call a good witness: accurate, detailed, and none too bright. This is implied in the earliest patristic testimony about the origins of the Gospels. Papias, writing about 125 CE (his remarks are preserved by Eusebius, *Ecclesiastical History* 3.39.15), retails the opinion of the 'presbyter' that 'Mark, indeed, who became the interpreter of Peter, wrote accurately, as far as he remembered them, the things said or done by the Lord, but not however in order'. Papias goes on to explain that the lack of order (presumably in comparison with Matthew's tidy rearrangement) was due to Peter's practice of adapting his preaching 'to suit the needs of the moment'; but he insists that Mark's book was, nevertheless, a full and accurate record of what Peter used to say.

This defence of the apostolicity and accuracy of Mark does not stand up to closer scrutiny. Already, at the turn of the twentieth century, William Wrede argued that one of Mark's most typical features, the so-called messianic secret, was not the result of historical reminiscence – that is to say, it did not reflect a policy on the part of Jesus during his lifetime to keep his messiahship a secret – but was a secondary theological motif, which showed that this Gospel was no less a product of post-Easter Christian beliefs than the others. The secrecy theme comprises all or some of the following: the command to disciples not to reveal Jesus' identity (8.30) until after his resurrection (9.9), the silencing of demons who have supernatural knowledge of Jesus as Son of God (3.12), the ban placed on the disclosure of (some of) Jesus' miracles (e.g. 5.43), the allegorical form of Jesus' parables understood as a deliberate attempt to prevent the crowds from understanding the secret (Mark 4.10–12). Putting all this material together, the conclusion seemed unavoidable: the secrecy theme was a way of accommodating the (Pauline) understanding of the gospel of the death and resurrection within the framework of a story about Jesus, in other words of delaying the climactic moment of revelation till the end of the book. For Christ cannot truly be known simply 'after the flesh' (cf. 2 Cor. 5.21): one can only know him truly as the crucified and risen one.

Mark figured prominently in the next most important development in gospel study, the rise of form-criticism (see esp. Bultmann 1921; Dibelius 1933). The lack of order in his account of the ministry of Jesus, already noticed by Papias's presbyter, the general absence of indications of time and place, the breathless haste and the compression of the narrative, with a brief Galilean ministry, one journey to Jerusalem, and then the trial and passion, were due to the writer's imposition of a rather simplified storyline upon a diverse stock of separate, independently circulating oral traditions. Close inspection of these revealed that they fall into a limited number of stereotypes – miracles, conflict dialogues, sayings, parables, and so forth. Mark's Gospel was dismantled, like the Jerusalem Temple, so that no stone was left standing on another. Apart from the messianic secret, the evangelist was viewed as a mere scribe and compiler of community traditions, hardly worthy to be called an author in the true sense. Of course while dismembering the author, this approach also 're-membered' the lived experience in all its variety of early Christian communities: it seemed a small price to pay.

Doubts about the ability of form-criticism to explain the total phenomenon of Mark were already being expressed by R. H. Lightfoot when he introduced the English-speaking public to the method in his Bampton Lectures of 1934. The order of paragraphs in the account of the ministry was not as haphazard or arbitrary as it might appear. The writer had juxtaposed incidents or enfolded one within another in such a way that they interpret each other (see e.g. the cleansing of the Temple, sandwiched between the cursing and withering of the fig tree, Mark 11.12–21). There was clearly an individual mind at work, even if he was constrained to stay within the limits of the traditional way of recounting the 'things concerning Jesus'. It was almost inevitable that, as scholars ran out of things to say about the history of traditions before Mark, their attention should be drawn back to the editing or 'redaction' of them. But what started as a supplement to the earlier approach soon became its competitor, disputing the origins of much of the contents of the Gospel. Eventually, this rivalry would lead to the erosion of the very distinction between tradition and redaction on which the competing methods both depended.

Early redaction-criticism was no less a 'sociological' method than form-criticism. It agreed that the Gospels were not *belles-lettres* to entertain and inform an educated audience but expressions of the living faith of a community. It differed in its determination to throw light on Mark's own community and its concerns as the controlling factors in the composition of the Gospel. For example the Little Apocalypse (chapter 13) had formerly been treated as a kind of 'fossil' representing an earlier crisis of persecution and expectation for imminent rescue by the coming of the Son of Man. But redaction-criticism saw it instead as a 'window' into the contemporary experience of Mark's church. The genre of Mark as a whole (and not just ch. 13) could be described as 'apocalypse mediated through narrative': its focus was still on the imminent future. In other words, Mark was not historicizing the *kerygma* by writing down a story about the past: he was kerygmatizing history in the light of its fast-approaching end. The Markan community was attempting to make sense of its external situation of persecution and suffering, whether in Rome under Nero – the traditional setting – or in Palestine during the Revolt of 66–70 CE (Marxsen 1956), by appeal to the Jewish model of the eschatological tribulation of the saints as a sign that the cosmic struggle between good and evil was about to reach its climax (Robinson 1957).

As redaction-criticism developed, however, it began to concentrate more on what might have been happening within the community. The change in perspective from external to internal factors as determinative for the selection and editing of the Church's traditions about Jesus is noteworthy. It arises from the observation, largely correct, that early Christian groups, as evidenced by Paul's epistles, seem to have been oblivious to the politics of the time in which they lived (Rom. 13.1–7 was, for instance, written when Nero sat on the imperial throne!), and obsessed with inner-church controversy. The starting point for the new approach was the peculiarly negative portrayal of the disciples in Mark (Tyson 1961), taken as indicating an internal theological conflict within his community (Weeden 1971). For, the disciples in the text represent not model Christians, as one might have expected, but increasingly blind and arrogant opponents of Jesus' (and thus the evangelist's) teaching on the necessity of suffering. The conflict between Jesus and the disciples is understood as an inner-church theological conflict between miracle-working power and the way of the cross. Paul's argument with false apostles, especially in 2 Corinthians 10–13, provides the template for this reconstruction. The Gospel of Mark is a thinly veiled reflection of a similar dispute within the Church, and its genre is, in effect, that of 'a controversial treatise on Christology', and, when competently decoded, everything can be seen to be directly relevant to it.

But is this at all plausible? Why does Mark include so many miracle stories, and summaries of others, if they contribute nothing to a proper understanding of Christ, and lead only to misunderstanding? And why does Mark attribute deviant views to Peter, James and John, whose authority it would be surely impossible, by the time he was writing, to contradict, and not to someone like Judas who would deserve any calumny heaped upon him? One of the methodological consequences of the redaction-critical determination to provide a total explanation of the Gospel by reference to the theological outlook and contemporary setting of the evangelist is that it becomes unnecessary to make any distinction between tradition and redaction.

This has given rise in more recent scholarship to 'holistic' readings of the Gospel of two rather different kinds. Narrative criticism (see Rhoads and Michie 1982; Fowler 1991) has insisted upon the significance of story as the generic category that most obviously fits the Gospel, and applied to it the literary-critical techniques that are appropriate to this genre: synchronic attention to the narrative as a whole; the narrator's 'point of view' and persuasive strategies; the development of plot and characters within the text and the involvement of the implied readers in the construction of its overall meaning. Many new insights have been gained by this method, but its neglect of factors external to the narrative leads also to the extreme position of Mark as novelistic fiction (Kermode 1979) or myth of origins (Mack 1988).

Socio-political readings (see Waetjen 1989; Myers 1990) draw upon insights from the sociology of literature and liberation exegesis for their own holistic approach to Mark. They ask questions about the ideological stance of the author and his readers particularly with regard to the economic conditions of their contemporary social context, the ownership of land, taxation, vagrancy and class solidarity. Again, many new insights have been gained, but Mark's Gospel is too concerned with religious faith and an otherworldly, eschatological conception of salvation from sin and death for its genre to be described as that of 'political manifesto'.

I have given above a brief survey of scholarly disputes about method and conflicting proposals about genre that arise not from comparison with other texts but from the examination of the contents and likely purposes of this one. The question of Mark's genre is, in this sense, subject to constant revision and reappraisal, and there is always room for new proposals. In the last part of this section I shall offer some observations on the likely format, style and actual content of Mark's Gospel that point towards a rather different conclusion to those mentioned so far.

Critics have rarely asked what Mark's book looked like, physically. It is notice-ably *much shorter* than the other three, which are all the length of a standard ancient scroll. Although this is disputed, the Gospel seems to have lost its final sentences or paragraph. The certainly authentic text finishes at 16.8, and two alternative endings, both very different in style to Mark's, have been added in the manuscript tradition to make up the deficiency. A scroll is unlikely to lose its end (it is the best protected part): but the risk is much greater with a codex (there are many examples of incomplete codices among the papyri). And the length of a codex is not, as in the case of a scroll, more or less predetermined. If Mark was written in codex form, what would that imply? The scroll was the proper format for Jewish religious text and serious Graeco-Roman literature. In the pre-Christian period, the codex was mostly used for business purposes. Especially in the case of Mark, which is so short, the codex has a singular advantage over the scroll: it can be easily carried about. It is unlikely that such a book would be reproduced in multiple copies for sale. It would rather have been read aloud to assembled companies of adherents or interested enquirers. Mark's Gospel is not an attempt to record the story of Jesus for posterity, that is, for preservation over time, but to spread the good news to other contemporaries, that is, for transportation over distances. As with the Pauline letter-form, so also with the Marcan Gospel-form, geographical necessity was the mother of literary invention.

The style of Mark is that of the spoken word. This widely acknowledged fact has usually been taken as an indication of its *origin* in the Church's oral tradition; but it may also throw light on Mark's *purpose*, that is, that the book was intended to be performed in popular oral contexts. Mark then would have been an oral story-teller who decided at some stage to write down one particular performance of his tale: the tradition is, in other words, just as Marcan as the redaction.

The book starts with a verbless sentence that may be its title. 'The beginning of the gospel of Jesus Christ, the Son of God.' It would be anachronistic to interpret this as 'Here begins the gospel . . .', because, as we have seen, 'gospel' is not used in the literary sense in the New Testament. Although the 'beginning' (*archē*) usually has a temporal meaning, it may also imply priority in importance (see Heb. 6.1) and, if so, the book's title might be rendered, 'Basic Preaching about Jesus'. The opening scenes of the Gospel suggest that one of Mark's main interests is missionary preaching. The first character to appear is John the itinerant preacher of a baptism of repentance. Jesus, after his own baptism and anointing as Spirit-filled Son of God, continues the mission to preach the gospel (1.15) and his first public act is to call others to join him as 'fishers of men' (1.16–20). The theme of mission is strongly emphasized in the first half-chapter and continues through later scenes where the gospel is proclaimed in acts of healing and exorcism, by debates with opponents and implicitly through parables and the two feeding miracles, which disclose the secret plan of God to open the gospel to all.

Despite all the scholarly discussion about a *messianic* secret in Mark, the noun 'secret' (*mysterion*) only occurs once, in reference to the parables (4.10–12) and there it has nothing to do with Jesus' messiahship and everything to do with mission, the mystery of why some people respond to the word and others for various reasons do not (4.13–20). The quotation from Isaiah 6.9f. is used also by Paul (Rom. 11.7) in

his attempt to explain the 'mystery' of missionary failure and success (see Rom.
11.25).

After the mission charge (6.6–12), delayed to enhance its dramatic contrast with
the rejection of Jesus by his own townsfolk (6.1–6), there is a section that begins
and ends with miraculous feedings (6.30–44 and 8.1–10). They form a bracket
around a private conversation with a Gentile woman (7.27–9), which offers the clue
to their puzzling significance. The emphasis in the feeding stories is not on the
miracle itself or on Jesus as miracle-worker, but on the unused leftovers (see 8.17–20),
and this is explained by the words of Jesus: 'Let the children first be fed. It is not
right to take the children's bread and throw it to the dogs' and the Syro-Phoenician
woman's quick-witted response: 'Yes, Lord, but even the dogs beneath the table eat
the children's leftovers.' The mission to Israel has priority, as it did for Paul (Rom.
1.17), but Israel's decline into hardness of heart and rejection of the gospel require
extraordinary means, if it is to be turned to good purpose (again see Rom.11.11–12).

The suffering Messiah is a stumbling-block even to his closest followers (see 8.33)
and the second half of Mark's Gospel dwells on this theme, and includes disciples
themselves in various kinds of 'suffering' for the sake of the gospel (8.35), poverty,
homelessness, apostolic care for all the churches (10.30) and humble service (9.35;
10.43) as well as the threat of violence and literal martyrdom (13.9, 11f.). But the
time between the resurrection and Parousia of the Son of Man will be filled not just
with suffering but with the proclamation of the gospel to all nations (13.10.) Already,
at the moment of his death, the first Gentile convert is won over to the new faith
(15.39). And the promise (14.28; 16.7) that Jesus will go before his disciples into
Galilee, the threshold of the Gentile world, is among other things a promise of the
power of the risen Christ in the missionary work of the Church.

Thus, the whole content of Mark's Gospel continually focuses on mission, in
particular towards non-Jews. It hints also at a profound theology of mission:
Mark is attempting to explain the riddle of Christianity, that faith in Jesus as the
Jewish Messiah should be increasingly rejected by Jews and yet accepted more and
more by Gentiles. In this context, his practice of using the 'things concerning Jesus'
as the medium for preaching was itself somewhat problematic. Should the Church
not rather play down its Jewish roots? But without them Jesus of Nazareth would
not remain the centre of Christian worship and life. So Mark resolves this dilemma
by showing that Jesus anticipated and endorsed the preaching of the gospel to the
Gentiles. He presents Jesus' teaching and miracles, as well as his crucifixion, as possible occasions of misunderstanding and rejection. For 'signs' and 'wisdom' are not
sufficient to elicit saving faith – as Paul also asserts (1 Cor. 1.22f); the stumbling-
block of the cross is the true power and wisdom of God. By portraying even the
Jewish disciples as temporarily blind to this truth, Mark offers hope even for the
final conversion of Israel.

Recent scholarship has been reluctant to follow this line of reasoning, and has
sought to contain Mark's Gospel within the inner life of one particular community,
claiming that it was written 'from faith to faith'. It is true that the Gospel presupposes
some acquaintance with, and even acceptance of, certain Christian presuppositions,
about the rites of baptism and Eucharist, for example, or the meaning of the titles
applied to Jesus. However, in dramatic performance it would have been able not only

to reinforce the faith of adherents, but also to attract those on the edge of the movement, who might be drawn further in. Mark's Gospel does not merely reflect community; it also has the power to create community (see further, Bauckham 1998). It is a handbook for itinerant storytelling and mission preaching.

MATTHEW

Matthew's Gospel quickly gained pre-eminence in the early Church; it is the one most frequently quoted by second-century fathers from Ignatius of Antioch (115 CE) onwards; it appears at the head of the emerging canon; it is credited (unlike Mark and Luke) with direct authorship by an apostle. According to Papias in the same passage as that quoted above, 'Matthew made an ordered arrangement of the sayings (or oracles, *logia*) in the Hebrew language, and each translated them as he was able.' While some scholars would still want to lend some credence to this testimony, referring it to possible Matthean authorship of a pre-Marcan Aramaic gospel or of Q, most believe that it is mistaken. Matthew's Gospel, at any rate, was not written by the tax-collector apostle (so named at Matt. 9.9, but contrast Mark 2.14) who was an eyewitness of Jesus' ministry, for it was composed originally in Greek and is closely based on Mark (using 95 per cent of it, with many close verbal parallels). In effect, Matthew is a second edition of Mark, amplifying it with a fuller account of Jesus' birth and his teaching in parables and aphorisms, along with multiple quotations, allusions and typological patterns drawn from Jewish scripture. At the same time as presenting a more Jewish portrait of Christ as Son of David, New Moses (see Allison 1993) and Teacher of true righteousness, this Gospel also contains a strain of anti-Jewish polemic so virulent that it has even been doubted whether its author could himself have been a Jew (cf. e.g. Meier 1976: 14–21). This is the most puzzling aspect of Matthew, to which we shall return: its anti-Jewish, Christian Judaism.

The evangelist was almost certainly a Jewish Christian (Luz 1989: 79f.): he was able to translate Jewish scripture directly from the Hebrew to suit his own purposes (e.g. 8.17) and to organize the genealogy with which the book begins (1.2–17) into three series of 14, creating a subtle allusion to David (the sum of the Hebrew letters of whose name have that numerical value – the technique is known as *gematria*). From his orderly arrangement (Papias was correct in this observation, at least) of the teaching of Jesus into five substantial sermons, each ending with the same formula (see e.g. 7.28), it is possible that he was himself a Jewish teacher, who had become, as he says at 13.52, 'a scribe discipled to the Kingdom of Heaven', and that one of his purposes in writing was pedagogical. Yet it would be a mistake to conclude that Matthew has reduced the story of Jesus to exegesis and moral exhortation; the narrative framework – even if it is largely taken over from Mark – is still important to him, for it provides the context of forgiveness and grace in which the Gospel's severe ethical demands are to be situated.

Nevertheless, the theme of right conduct is almost as important for Matthew as that of right belief, and reveals his peculiar purpose in writing. There are repeated references to 'righteousness' and 'doing the will' of the Heavenly Father, some of which are probably editorial (e.g. 6.33; 7.21). On the one hand, Matthew constantly attacks the scribes and Pharisees for failing to keep the Law. On the other hand, he warns members of his community that their salvation is in doubt unless they produce fruits worthy of repentance. There are therefore two sides to Matthew's rhetoric: an externally directed polemic and an internally directed exhortation. And these are closely interrelated – the moral superiority of Christians is to be the practical proof of their claim to have replaced Israel as the people of God.

In a pioneering redaction-critical study of Matthew (Bornkamm et al. 1963) Gerhard Barth argued that the internal threat was decisive for understanding the Gospel, and that those (7.22f.) who prophesy and work miracles 'in the name' but whose deeds are lawlessness (*anomia*) were antinomian libertine gnostics within the community (of the sort Paul may have confronted at Corinth). But 'lawlessness' is a practical and heedless (see 25.44) failure to act charitably; it is not a theoretical rejection of the rule of law. Even the Pharisees can be charged with the same fault (23.28). Furthermore, spiritual enthusiasts would be more likely to be rigorist in ethics (this is probably the case in Corinth) than libertine. Whatever its precise cause, the internal threat is real enough; and it gives rise to a whole series of 'division parables' separating wise from foolish (e.g. 7.24–7), faithful from unfaithful (e.g. 25.21, 26), rotten from productive disciples (e.g. 7.18).

If lawlessness has to be avoided, how much law is positively to be obeyed? Does Matthew's community insist on strict observance of Torah even for its Gentile members? This is a difficult question to answer. On the one hand, Matthew has taken over from Mark incidents where certain strict applications of sabbath law (12.1–13) are rejected, and yet, on the other, he implies that, even in a situation of life or death (24.20), it will still be rigidly observed. A key passage on this issue is 5.17–18: 'Think not that I have come to abolish the law and the prophets; I have not come to abolish them but to fulfil them. For truly I say to you, till heaven and earth pass away, not an iota, not a dot will pass from the law until all is accomplished.' The introduction (v. 17) is probably redactional and indicates that what follows is intended as a response to the accusation that Christians fail to observe Torah. This is firmly denied; rather, Jesus came to 'fulfil' the law and the prophets in the minutest detail. But there is a deliberate ambiguity in this statement. For prophecy is 'fulfilled' (cf. the frequent fulfilment quotations) by enactment in messianic history (see 'until all things be accomplished', v. 18), while the Law is fulfilled by observance of its commands. For Matthew what is not 'fulfilled' in one way is 'fulfilled' in the other. Paul argues in a not dissimilar fashion when he says that outward circumcision is just a symbol of inward circumcision (Rom. 2.29), which is achieved through a 'circumcision not made with hands', namely baptism and new life in Christ (Col. 2.11). While Jewish Christians in Matthew's community probably continued with the practice, circumcision was not to be imposed on Gentile converts, for baptism was sufficient. It is surely no accident that this Gospel, unlike Luke's, passes over in silence the circumcision of Jesus in the birth story. The allegorization of obsolete laws was not of course peculiar to Matthew: post-70 CE Judaism had to do the same with the laws of sacrifice. And his apologetic against the accusation of law-breaking quickly turns into polemic against the accusers. The scribes and Pharisees are berated for hypocrisy, evasive casuistry, and superficial conformity disguising inward corruption.

Jewish Christian as it no doubt was, Matthew's church was nevertheless open to the mission to the Gentiles. The evidence on this issue is also admittedly somewhat confusing. Matthew has edited the Mission Charge to exclude explicitly from its scope Gentiles and Samaritans (10.5), and even seems to allow no time for more extensive mission before the coming of the Son of Man (10.23). Jesus was sent only to the 'lost sheep of the House of Israel' (10.6, cf. 15.24). Furthermore, Gentiles are attacked for their wordiness in prayer (6.7), and worldiness of life (6.32), in a way that implies that none belongs to the Church (cf. 18.17). However, greatly outweighing this evidence is the emphatic commission at the end of the book (28.16–20) to baptize and teach all the Gentile nations, and many earlier passages imply a similar openness (e.g. 12.18–21 – a Matthean fulfilment quotation, drawn from Isa. 42.1–4); indeed Gentiles are to replace the unbelieving Jews in the Kingdom (see 8.11–12; 21.43). Assuming that Matthew has not merely conflated conflicting traditions, his intention may have been to grant Israel the prerogative of an initially exclusive mission in order to highlight the grave consequences of her failure to respond to it, for the future judgement of the Son of Man had been exemplified historically in the fall of Jerusalem. Since 'true Jews' of whatever race are those who believe in Jesus as Christ, those who reject him become 'Gentiles' even if they are Jews. (For a similar polemical inversion of terms, see Phil. 3.2 where Paul calls Jewish opponents '[uncircumcised] dogs' and claims the title 'true circumcision' for Gentile Christians.)

Clearly, then, Matthew is not so much of a hardline Jewish Christian (if ever such existed in the early Church) as to exclude the possibility of salvation for Gentiles. But to determine more precisely what kind of Christian Judaism he advocated requires an investigation into the kind of Judaism he opposed.

The discovery of the Dead Sea Scrolls in 1947 stimulated renewed interest in the Jewish background of Matthew's Gospel (Stendahl 1968). The Qumran community was a perfectionist and ascetic group who studied scripture in a scholastic way for its clues into the meaning of the last days; they were in dispute both with the Jerusalem priesthood and with those they called 'speakers of smooth things', possibly in reference to the Pharisees. In several respects, then, the similarities with this Gospel are striking: and it might be tempting to call Matthew's Judaism a Christian Essenism. But, though ascetic (cf. Matt. 19.12, on celibacy), there is no evidence that Matthew's community has withdrawn into monastic isolation, or that the book is the product of a school.

In his classic study of the setting of the Sermon on the Mount, W. D. Davies (1964) pointed to the parallels between Matthew's Gospel and early rabbinic Judaism as it attempted to reconstitute itself after the Jewish War, as a way of explaining the extreme tension between them. Like the Jewish Christians who had escaped Jerusalem before it fell (24.16) the scribal schools under the leadership of Rabbi Johannan ben Zakkai gained safe passage out of the besieged city from Vespasian, the Roman general, soon to be emperor. Neither group was ready to stay and die in defence of Jerusalem. No doubt each afterwards accused the other of bringing upon the nation that unmitigated disaster. For Matthew it was the rejection of the Messiah by the Jewish leadership that was the root cause (24.38–41; cf. 27.25) of this punishment from God. For rabbinic Judaism it was those who failed to observe

Torah correctly, such as the followers of the Nazarene, who were responsible for destroying the Temple, this time round just as before (Jer. 7.3f.).

In post-70 Judaism, the vacuum left by the cessation of the sacrificial cult in Jerusalem was filled by Torah and in particular by the 'acts of loving-kindness', namely, almsgiving, fasting and prayer. The proof-text favoured by Johannan to justify this transfer was Hosea 6.6, 'I desire mercy and not sacrifice' – a text that is one of Matthew's favourites too (9.13; 12.17); but whereas reconstituted Judaism tried to use public prayers, fasts and almsgiving to inculcate Jewish solidarity, Matthew's church stood apart from this movement, rejecting such display as hypocritical and insisting on an inward piety that would not be visibly divisive between its Jewish and Gentile members (6.1–18).

Observance of Torah in accordance with its interpretation by the scribes became the main identity marker for Jews in this period, and Matthew by no means dismisses the importance of scribal *halakah* (oral law). In chapter 23 Jesus begins a long tirade against the scribes and Pharisees by conceding that they 'sit on Moses' seat' (23.2) and possess the key of knowledge (cf. 21.13), though they fail to practise what they preach. It has sometimes been deduced from such statements that Matthean Jewish Christians were still 'within the fold' and able to benefit from scribal teaching by attendance at synagogue. But Stanton (1992) and others have argued cogently that they had decisively broken with the Jewish synagogues (called '*your* synagogues', e.g. 23.34). Matthew was aware that conditions that applied at the time Jesus was presumed to be delivering this speech no longer applied. His purpose in including the qualified endorsement of scribal authority is to provide an analogy for the Jewish Christian leadership in his mixed community, who like Peter held the power of the 'keys' and were entitled to legislate ('bind and loose', 16.19) for the true Israel, the Church (16.18). This is the only Gospel that uses the term church (*ekklēsia*) and in slightly different senses in its two occurrences. At 16.18 it has a universal reference, of the whole company of believers looking back to their apostolic foundations ('on this rock I will build my Church') and forward to its eschatological victory ('the powers of death will not prevail against it'). In the other instance (18.17) it refers to the local gathering of Christians, exercising their corporate responsibility for church discipline. It would be a mistake to exaggerate this difference; for universal and local concepts of the church coexist in Paul's letters (Phil.3.6; cf. 4.15) and the authority of the community does not detract from the apostolic office (1 Cor. 5.4b), although the use of grand titles, like those of contemporary Judaism, 'Rabbi' and 'Abba', is frowned on (23.8–10).

Matthew's legitimation of Christ-centred Judaism as the true heir to God's promises to Israel produces a distinctive emphasis in his Christology, namely Jesus as Wisdom and Torah embodied. This is already implied in the birth narrative where Emmanuel is taken as a title for Jesus, 'God with us' (1.23). In the antitheses of the Sermon on the Mount (5.21ff.), the only one who could on his own authority ('I say unto you . . .') intensify and interiorize the Law of Moses must represent the eternal Torah of God. In a pivotal passage, 11.25–30, which momentarily reaches the lofty heights of Johannine Christology, Matthew represents Christ as the unique plenipotentiary and revealer of the Father, who like Wisdom (Ecclus 24.19–24 and ch. 51) summons those who feel burdened by legal obligation to come and learn obedience through the attractive beauty of righteousness. In a similar vein at 18.20 Matthew appears to adapt a Jewish proverb (Mishnah *Aboth* 3.2): 'If two sit together to discuss the Law, the Glory (*Shekhinah*) rests between them.' If so, it has been thoroughly christologized: it is meeting 'in the name of Christ', not studying Torah in the synagogue, that guarantees the presence of the true 'Glory' of God (which is Jesus himself). The invisible spiritual presence represented by these 'I' sayings is not so much the Jesus of history as the Risen Christ whose words conclude the Gospel (28.20): 'Lo, I am with you always.'

As we should have expected from a Gospel written more than a generation later than Jesus, there is evidence of the problem caused by the delay of the Parousia (see 25.5, 'the bridegroom is delayed'). And yet Matthew underscores the importance of continuing to believe in the imminence of judgement by ending each of his discourses on this note. The last, chapters 24–5, is particularly striking in this respect. Matthew takes over from Mark with little change the apocalyptic prophecy of Jerusalem's fall and the coming of the Son of Man, but then adds the parables of the Ten Maidens, the Talents and the vision of the last assize, commonly called the parable of the Sheep and the Goats. In each case the emphasis is on producing a store of good works in this life. For Matthew the End may no longer be temporally so near, and since Christ is always present (28.20) there need be no anxiety in the wait for his return; but it is still morally pressing and inevitable. Eschatology has ceased to be a way of discerning the hand of God in the final stages of human history; it has become instead the ultimate sanction for ethical exhortation.

As an expanded second edition of Mark, Matthew inevitably shares some of the purposes of his main source. Its undiminished emphasis on mission implies that this book also is meant in some way to serve that end. But there is, at the same time, a heavier emphasis on the needs of the Christian community. The Gospel legitimates the Church's claim, against contemporary Jewish opponents, to be the true Israel, defined, not by Temple, land or Law, but by allegiance to God's Anointed; it also informs its audiences of their own responsibility to live up to that claim in practice. In other words, Matthew adds polemical and didactic elements to his kerygmatic narrative.

The exclusion of Jewish Christians from the synagogue would naturally have led to an increase in the use of Old Testament scripture in meetings of the Christian *ekklēsia*. Its worship would no longer be supplementary to that of the synagogue but a rival replacement of it. That Matthew's Gospel is well suited to the liturgical needs of the Church has long been recognized (Kilpatrick 1946). While it is difficult to correlate precisely the sequence of themes in the Gospel with Jewish lectionary cycles of readings from the Law and Prophets (*pace* Goulder 1974), it is in general more than likely that Matthew's scroll was the first attempt we know of to meet the need for specifically Christian scripture.

LUKE

Luke's Gospel poses something of a problem in terms of genre, because of its second volume, the Acts of the Apostles. The interconnecting prefaces (Luke 1.1–4; Acts 1.1–2) show that the two books were meant in their final form to be read as one.

But it is possible that they were originally separate, and even that Acts was the first to be composed.

The Gospel follows closely the now familiar pattern of a kerygmatic, didactic and apologetic story about Jesus. But the Acts of the Apostles is unique in the New Testament, although it stimulated a number of imitations to be found among the later New Testament apocrypha (Schneemelcher 1991: 1). Its added title is misleading. According to the writer's own definition of an apostle (Acts 1.21f.), as an associate of Jesus' public ministry and eyewitness of his resurrection, several of the main characters, Stephen, Philip, Barnabas and Paul, are excluded from that category, and many of the twelve full apostles play no part in the story. Acts is more fittingly described as the Acts of the Holy Spirit guiding the progress of the gospel from Jerusalem to Rome and in terms of genre as a kind of *travellers' tales*, satisfying the thirst for a good adventure story, new places and strange happenings.

Both volumes are clearly written from the perspective of Christian faith, but unusually the author can also view the 'Way' more objectively, as from the outside, as 'the sect of the Nazarenes' with Paul as its 'pestilent ring-leader' (Acts 24.5). Luke–Acts would perhaps not be altogether incomprehensible to sympathetic outsiders and, from the cosmopolitan scope of the story, the primarily intended Christian readership is unlikely to have been confined to a single location.

The preface to the Gospel is a rare example of an evangelist appearing momentarily 'in front of his text' and offering to explain its sources and purpose. It has for that reason attracted much scholarly attention and debate (see Alexander 1993). The preface is written in an elegant literary Greek, unmatched by anything that follows in the Gospel (though passages in the last part of Acts come close). The 'Septuagintal' style of the infancy narrative and the Synoptic style of the account of Jesus' ministry must be concessions by the author to Christian convention. He claims that 'many' have written before him – a permissible exaggeration in context, but apart from Mark we cannot be sure how many other texts he had to hand. It partly depends on the date we ascribe to this work. It must have been written after the capture of Jerusalem (21.20) and probably some time afterwards because it envisages a subsequent period, called 'the times of the Gentiles', during which Jerusalem will be trampled down (21.24). No certain quotation from the Gospel can be identified before Justin Martyr (c.150 CE) and nothing from Acts until even later. There are parallels between Luke and Matthew (the Q material) and also between Luke and John (especially in the resurrection appearances). The later the Gospel is dated the greater the likelihood that the evangelist knew Matthew's Gospel and used it, whether by direct consultation or from memory, along with other overlapping Synoptic-type traditions; and he may even have known the Gospel of John perhaps in an earlier version to the one we know. Its major themes like the revision of eschatology, the continuity but separation between Judaism and Christianity, and the relation between Church and State (see below) might be particularly apposite to conditions prevailing under Trajan (98–117 CE: see esp. Pliny, *Letters* 10.96, 97). The dating of Luke–Acts remains, however, an unsolved problem.

While the preface claims that the following work is based on the author's own exhaustive research, it admits that he was not himself an eyewitness of the events he reports. That is clearly so from his extensive use of sources in the Gospel. Is it also true of Acts? Four passages in the second half of Acts are phrased in the first-person plural (16.10–17; 20:5–15; 21.1–18 and 27.1 – 28.16) as though the author was present with Paul on those occasions. Church tradition eventually (Irenaeus c.180) came to identify Paul's companion as 'Luke, the beloved physician' (Col. 4.14). But if this were so, it would be hard to explain the numerous errors of fact and interpretation in his portrait of Paul (Lentz 1993). Other explanations might be that the author was drawing on information from an eyewitness in these sections, or that the first-person plural is a literary fiction (it is used frequently in the Acts of John, see Schneemelcher 1991: 2). The fact that a minority of manuscripts have yet a fifth 'we' passage (at Acts 11.28) may even indicate that this phenomenon is secondary and has arisen early in the process of scribal transmission. To record personal reminiscences is unlikely to be one of Luke's main motives for writing: to understand these better, we need to look at the way the evangelist edits the sources available to him, and try to detect his theological and ideological stance.

On source-critical grounds, the basic motivation for the production of Luke's Gospel and the explanation of its resulting genre would be largely the same as those for Matthew's, the desire to expand Mark's narrative with more extensive use of the sayings of Jesus. The distinctive features of Luke, for example parables, birth story and resurrection appearances would be due to a Lukan special source, either already combined with Q (the Proto-Luke theory) or a peculiar stream of tradition to which the evangelist alone had access.

As redaction-criticism moved the focus of attention from sources to their editing, a different sort of answer to the question of genre began to emerge: Luke's Gospel as a theological schematization, under the form of storytelling, that provides a solution to the problem of the delay of the Parousia (Conzelmann 1960). According to this analysis, the expected End has been relegated to the distant, indefinite future. Its place has been filled with a salvation-historical scheme in three distinct periods: the time of the Old Testament prophets culminating and ending with John the Baptist: the 'middle of time' when the transcendent Kingdom of God comes near in the ministry and person of Jesus; and finally, decisively separated from it by the Ascension, the age of the Church, in which the Spirit functions as a substitute and compensation for the loss of Parousia hope. This theory is clearer and more cogent than Luke's actual text. There, imminent and delay strands are found side by side (Wilson 1973: 67–77). John the Baptist is both the end of the old age, but also – most obviously in the parallel infancy stories – the child of promise heralding the new. The Ascension is explicitly a pattern for what will happen (in reverse) at the Parousia (Acts 1.11) and the Spirit (given, according to Acts 2.17, 'in the last days') still retains its eschatological forward-looking function.

A more holistic reading of Luke that rejects too sharp a distinction between tradition and redaction (since the author by choosing to include traditions endorses them and makes them effectively redactional) may somewhat blur the contours of the theology, but it provides an even more interesting Lukan answer to the problem of Parousia delay. The evangelist was undoubtedly aware that, beginning with the twelve apostles themselves, there had been a false expectation of a speedy arrival of the Kingdom (19.11). He suggests that if they had paid closer attention to the Lord's teaching, they would have realized that first the gospel would have to be preached to the ends of the earth and that would take some time (24.47). However, once Paul had preached in Rome, the outline of Acts implies, the essential programme of missionary expansion was completed. What happened afterwards is theologically less significant and is not to be recounted as part of sacred history.

Luke has subdivided the age of the Church into the recordable apostolic age and the subapostolic age, which is not worthy of inclusion in his record. The first, initial, period of delay for the sake of salvation was foreseen and intended; the second, post-apostolic, period of patient waiting and quiet perseverance in hope (18.1–8) could end any time now, for it would not interrupt the divine plan. Luke's concern is to demonstrate that the apostles faithfully imitated Christ, in mission and martyrdom, and authentically expounded the faith. He is not interested in setting up institutional structures for the long-term survival of the Church, like the authorization of successors to the apostles or the regularization of the rites of baptism and laying on of hands. The characteristic twofold shape of his work set the pattern of a twofold historical criterion for Christian truth, reflected in the New Testament canon itself: Christ *and* Apostle – Gospel *and* Epistle.

A further subsidiary answer to the problem is offered in a series of special Lukan passages, the Rich Fool (12.16–21), the Rich Man and Lazarus (16.19–31) and the Penitent Thief (23.40–3). While the end of history may or may not be in sight – we just do not know – the end of any individual's history (death, judgement, hell or paradise) is always in imminent prospect. These Lukan insights, the separation of apostolic from subapostolic history and the individualization of eschatology, were eventually to become the Church's official answer to the problem.

Luke's attitude towards political power may reveal another of his purposes. As in the earlier Gospels, the Jewish authorities are regularly portrayed as unscrupulous and hostile towards Jesus and as the instigators of persecution against his followers. But there are some odd exceptions: at 13.31, for example, some Pharisees attempt to warn Jesus of Herod's murderous intentions, and Rabbi Gamaliel (Acts 5.34) pleads for tolerance (5.38f.) towards the movement. The Jerusalem populace at the crucifixion retains a touching sympathy for him (23.48) which is entirely lacking in the other Gospels. In the trial before Pilate, the Roman governor three times affirms the innocence of the defendant and pleads for him to be released (23.16). But his pusillanimity is already an indictment of him, from a Roman administrative perspective, and the picture is confused further by the fact that Luke alone recalls the outrage of Pilate's slaughter of Galilean pilgrims (13.1). The evangelist may have muddled the incident with Pilate's notorious massacre of Samaritan worshippers that led to his downfall, but, uniquely in the Gospels, he here comes closer to the negative and probably more accurate portrait of Pilate that appears in Josephus (e.g. *Antiquities* 18.85). In Acts, Paul's status as a Roman citizen, once known, is respected by the authorities (Acts 16.37–9; 22.25–9) and is his means of escaping the clutches of Jewish opponents. But again, more ambiguous notes are sounded: for example, the procrastination of the governor Felix in dealing with Paul's case is explained by the suggestion that he was hoping for a bribe (24.26).

The once popular theory that Luke–Acts was intended as an 'apologia' addressed to a Roman governor, seeking to demonstrate the innocence, nobility and loyalty to the State of Jesus and his followers, in order to gain for Christianity the special privileges enjoyed by the Jewish religion, has been increasingly questioned by recent scholarship (see e.g. Esler 1987: 201–19). 'Political legitimation', rather than direct apologetic, is no doubt a more accurate description of Luke's purpose. Faith gives one the courage to challenge corruption and stand up to oppression, but, for the time being at any rate, some way of living at peace with the pagan world is necessary.

If Luke is politically quietist, socially his message appears at first sight to be more radical. Warnings against the wealthy and the preference for voluntary poverty (see Johnson 1977) are pervasive themes in the Gospel, starting already in the infancy story (1.52f.). In the programmatic Nazareth sermon (4.18–21) Isaiah's prophecy of good news 'for the poor' is at last fulfilled. The Lukan beatitudes offer an unqualified blessing on the poor and plain woe to the rich (6.20, 24). The theme is especially prominent in two sections of the travel narrative (12.13–34; 16.1–31). The account of the early Jerusalem church sharing its possessions and having 'everything in common' (Acts 2.45; 4.34–7) is probably an idealization, but, whether practicable or not, the ideal is still cherished.

Yet, for all its emphasis on poverty, Luke's is not a Gospel directed only at the poor. Wealthy converts are welcome (Acts 17.4; 18.8). The rich may retain their capital, as long as they do so honestly (cf. Acts 5.3), and, imitating the good Samaritan (10.35), distribute alms (11.41; 12.33; 16.9) to those in need. The urban Christian congregations of Luke's day attracted converts not least by offering a security safety-net for the sick, the unemployed and widows (on the latter see 2.37; Acts 6.1). His warnings to rich and callous outsiders function as congratulations to the rich and generous insiders. Luke is anxious, like the writer of the Pastoral Epistles, to help those who may be poor but are at least respectable (1 Tim. 5.3–16). Luke's portrait of Paul in Acts is illuminating on the topic of social class. On his Jewish side, Paul is a distinguished graduate of Gamaliel's school, fluent in Hebrew and learned in the scriptures; on the Roman side, he is a citizen by birth, socially a match for those who presume to interrogate him. The Christian Way is one of voluntary poverty and charitable giving, but it is not uncivilized or uncouth!

The themes I have selected for particular comment, the timing of the End, politics and poverty, illuminate some of the extra motives behind a complex and multifaceted work. I might have discussed others – the apparent understatement, in order to avoid undue complexity and controversy, of Christology (Christ as Prophet, 7.16; 24.19) and Atonement (Christ as martyr 23:46; contrast Mark 15.34); the emphasis on the joy and power of the Spirit, the very positive characterization of women throughout. Each of these in its own way contributes to the attractiveness of Luke's presentation.

To return finally to the preface, Luke dedicates his work to a high-ranking Roman official who we can assume was already sympathetic to the movement. His name, as literary patron of the work, is used to commend it to other readers. The Gospel and Acts were evidently written in the format of two scrolls. Whether the author saw his second volume through to actual publication has been questioned (so Strange 1992: 178–85) but 'publication' was definitely intended. With Luke–Acts we reach a new stage in the sophistication of early Christian literature, that is books produced in multiple copies and sold for use in the homes of middle-class Christians who, reading them, will be assured that their new faith is intellectually and socially respectable.

JOHN

At first sight, the Gospel according to John looks like the same kind of work as the Synoptics. It recounts Jesus' public career from his baptism onwards, as a mixture of teaching and healings, and it concentrates particularly on his final week in Jerusalem. But within this similarity of structure there are even more striking differences. Instead of a birth story, the book starts with a prose-poem on the Word of God in creation and redemption. The teaching takes a very different form from the pithy aphorisms and vivid parables of the Synoptic tradition; instead we find long drawn-out monologues and dialogues that circle around images and abstract concepts of universal application. The miracle stories bear closer comparison with Synoptic parallels (esp. 6.1–21), but they have been subordinated to Christology, as manifestations of the divine glory of Jesus (2.12) or as pegs on which to hang teaching or debates about his person. In place of the Synoptic parables of the Kingdom, we find christological allegories, Christ as living Bread, good Shepherd and true Vine. The Passion narrative begins already at chapter 12, midway through the book and is proportionately longer even than Mark's, but much of it is devoted to two farewell discourses (13–14 and 15–17) that are the Johannine equivalent of the Synoptic Apocalypse (Mark 13 and par.) and replace expectation of the future coming of the Son of Man with the presence of the Paraclete–Advocate to strengthen the disciples' faith as they undergo persecution in the world.

At certain points of difference, for example the three-year public career, or the Sanhedrin trial of Jesus in his absence (11.47–53) and the crucifixion the day before Passover (18.28), it is plausible to argue for John's superior historicity, but at most others the Synoptic account may be preferable. This leaves us with the problem of explaining how such a divergent tradition arose. Bultmann (1941) argued that the Fourth Gospel is a combination of three different genres: the Signs source, that is, a numbered collection of miracle stories (or *aretalogy*) portraying Jesus as a Hellenistic wonder-worker, which the evangelist is seeking to correct; a set of proto-gnostic revelation *discourses*, which the evangelist has Christianized to convey his understanding of eternal life available through Christ; and finally a more or less conventional *Passion narrative*, which counterbalances the idea of the divine revealer with an insistence on his mortality and therefore full humanity.

Although the reuse of sources probably does help to explain the present form of the Gospel (see Fortna 1988), Bultmann's theory, which involves accidental displacement at a later stage of composition, is not widely accepted today. Certainly a later editor, different from the main author, has made some minor corrections (e.g. 4.2) and at least one major addition (ch. 21), but how many other changes are due to him is difficult to say. The homogeneity of the style makes it likely that the Gospel grew out of the preaching activity of one remarkable early Christian prophet (Lindars 1972: 51–4). The stylistic similarity between the Gospel and the so-called First Epistle of John (which is not a letter but 'a written sermon') supports this suggestion. The same kind of summary statements about life, light, truth and love appear in both, though in the Gospel these meditations are attached to sayings or deeds of Jesus, unlike the First Eepistle, which ignores them. The warrant for this free development of the Jesus tradition is given in the Gospel itself in passages that speak of the Holy Spirit as Paraclete or Advocate. The eschatological promise of the Spirit's assistance to Christians on trial (see Mark 13.11) has been extended to include the present functions of remembering, expounding and defending the truths of faith (cf. e.g. 16.4–15, and see further Harvey 1976).

The identity of the prophet whose inspired words were accorded such authority is unknown. But the final editor, writing after his death, believed – perhaps mistakenly – that he had been an eyewitness of Jesus' ministry. At several points in the Gospel, a disciple is referred to as the 'one whom Jesus loved' or 'the other disciple'. He occupies the place closest to Jesus at the Last Supper (13.23; in the same relation with Jesus as he has with the Father, 1.18) and unlike the rest stands by him during his trial and crucifixion (19.26f.). He is the first to believe in the resurrection (20.8). At each of these points he is sharply contrasted with Peter. It may be that the negative portrait of the latter in the Synoptics has created an idealized 'true disciple'; or that the Johannine community is here projecting on to the narrative a representative of its own claim to have a more profound understanding of Christ than other Christian groups; or that a genuine historical figure (such as the apostle John, who is otherwise not mentioned in the Gospel) lies at the root of the Johannine tradition. Indeed, all three of these explanations may be partly correct.

The Fourth Gospel has often been interpreted in the same way as Paul's epistles, as a work of constructive theology: the main concern of this approach was to lay bare the essential structure of thought and the intellectual influences on the mind of the writer (Dodd 1953). If the Synoptics were all much earlier than John it would be possible to claim that they provided him with the raw material for his Gospel as a kind of meditation on the inner meaning of the Christ event in the full light of Easter faith. For a while in the mid-twentieth century this view was widely questioned (Dodd 1963) but it is coming back into popularity.

Certainly one of the main purposes of the Fourth Gospel is to expound the doctrine of Christ. The death and resurrection of Jesus, still affirmed as central to the *kerygma* (*pace* Käsemann 1968), are set against a wider backdrop of the incarnation of the unique and pre-existent Son of God. It has often been assumed that such a lofty Christology must be a late development and could only have arisen after the Church had abandoned its Jewish roots and shaken off the constraints of monotheism. But the development is not that late: Paul's Christology, after all, is earlier and just as exalted (see Phil. 2.6–11). And there was much speculation about mediatorial figures in Jewish apocalyptic texts that veered close to the wind on the issue of a strict monotheism. It is not necessary to posit a Hellenistic background to account for John's theology.

Arguably, Christology is the only doctrine in the Fourth Gospel, since everything else is drawn within its ambit. Thus, salvation consists in replicating the Father–Son relationship in the mutual indwelling of Christ and believers. Creation and future redemption are brought together in the present, timeless moment of communion with Christ through faith and knowledge. The Church is made up of those who are rooted in Christ as true Vine or gathered around him as the good Shepherd. Morality is reduced to his own new commandment to 'love each other as I have loved you' (13.34).

John's Gospel well illustrates the difficulty of using the story of the pre-Easter Jesus as the means of promoting faith in the post-Easter Christ. The evangelist is torn between fidelity to his storyline and full commitment to its central character. If the Gospel contains within it discrete homilies, then the message had to be included in each: it could not be reserved to the denouement of the plot as a whole. An unintended side-effect of this is that it gives the impression of docetism: intellectually at least, Jesus only 'appears' to be genuinely human; his head is in the clouds, communing with his Father.

However, a Gospel is not a treatise on Christology, even though John's encouraged a second-century development in that direction (see section 'Non-canonical Gospels and So-Called Gospels' below). And recent scholarship, in two rather different ways, has attempted to recover the importance of the narrative, in spite of the overpowering edifice of Johannine theology.

The literary artistry of the Fourth Evangelist is most apparent in his use of irony, misunderstanding and symbolism (Culpepper 1983). The dialogue with the Samaritan woman is a good example. The audience, who already know that Jesus is the true source of living water, appreciate the privilege of that knowledge in the face of the woman's literal-minded insistence that the well is deep and the water is stagnant. While the dialogue partners in the text remain at cross-purposes, the evangelist and his audience are drawn ever closer into a relationship of confidentiality and revelation.

The technique of double meaning is apparent also in the larger structures of the Gospel. To take one example, John places the cleansing of the Temple at the beginning of the ministry (2.13–22) and the raising of Lazarus in its place at the end (11.1–53). The earlier scene is then related to the Passion by the double meaning of the Psalm text: 'Zeal for thy house will consume me' (69.9). The disciples will only understand this later, we are told (2.22) when they realize that the assault on the money changers will result in Jesus' being 'consumed' in his trial and passion. But in John's rearrangement, the Lazarus episode becomes the immediate antecedent, within the narrative, of those events, and the revised chronology creates a deliberate irony: Jesus will be crucified because of the resurrection! (For further discussion of the narrative-criticism of John, see Stibbe 1992.) In terms of genre, the free use of the imagination brings this Gospel at certain points into the category of fiction, but it is fiction put to the service of theological insight.

The other approach to John's Gospel that has reassessed its significance as narrative was pioneered by J. L. Martyn (1979) in his study of chapter 9, the man born blind, as a dramatization of Johannine community history. The hostility of 'the Jews' in general towards Jesus, which is fully reciprocated (cf. 8.44), is even more emphatic than it is in Matthew. At 9.22 we are told that the Jews had already decided that anyone confessing Jesus as the Christ should be expelled from the synagogue: the motif recurs again at 12.42 and 16.2 – it was obviously important to the evangelist. The Jews try to manoeuvre the man, and even his parents, into confessing Christ, until finally, in frustration and offence at his cheek (v. 34), they excommunicate him anyway. The man born blind is one of the few secondary characters in John who has his wits about him! Martyn proposed that this incident represents the retrojection into the ministry of Jesus of a recent bitter memory on the part of the Johannine Jewish Christians.

This approach was developed even further by Raymond Brown (1979) who found a whole sequence of events in community history dramatized through the narrative. The founding group in Palestine accepted Jesus as Davidic Messiah and attracted some of the followers of John the Baptist (1.35–7): the latter's role in the Gospel is to encourage others to join. The missionary work of this group among the Samaritans (ch. 4) catalysed the development of a higher Christology of Jesus as a heavenly 'prophet like Moses' (Deut. 18.15). The higher Christology led to contro-versy and finally breach with the synagogue and a move by Johannine Christians probably into Asia. There they were in competition with other forms of Christianity (represented by Peter in the text). On this showing, the Fourth Gospel tells two stories at the same time: that of Jesus and that of the community. In terms of genre, John would be a Gospel and an Acts, run together. Not all the elements of this comprehensive theory are equally plausible, but its central explanation of the vein of polemic against Judaism, amid the evidence that points to a strongly Jewish dimension in Johannine Christianity, is thoroughly convincing.

At the beginning and end of its evolution as a text, that is, its underlying keryg-matic story and its final editing, John is closer to the form of the Synoptics than it is in the middle of that process, during which explicit and powerful defences of Christological faith, against all detractors, have been incorporated into the Gospel itself: John is both text and interpretation in one. The 'layers' in the book are the result not only of its peculiar prehistory, but also of a deliberate layering technique: characters like the woman of Samaria and the man born blind function at three different levels, that of reported event, that of rhetorical foil and that of collective symbol of the community's history.

NON-CANONICAL GOSPELS AND SO-CALLED GOSPELS

Apart from the four Gospels that made it into the canon, there were several others that are lost to us except for odd citations in the early Church fathers. Origen and Jerome preserve, for example, half a dozen fragments of the *Gospel of the Hebrews*, and a dozen or so from the *Gospel of the Nazaraeans* (Schneemelcher, 1991, 1: 154–78.). These Gospels, though plundered for the odd insight, were excluded as being too 'Jewish Christian' by a Christianity that was increasingly defining itself over against Judaism, and removing that middle category. There were also partial 'Gospels', especially legendary accounts of Jesus' birth, building on those of Matthew and Luke, and ascribed to James and Thomas (ibid., 1: 421–52); and the Passion narrative attributed to Peter (ibid., 1: 216–27). The discovery in 1945 of a Coptic gnostic library (see Robinson 1988) brought many more texts into discussion of the Gospel genre, but with little justification. What are called Gospels by the scribes who produced these translations are actually quite different in form. 'The Secret Sayings of the Living Jesus', which we know as the *Gospel of Thomas*, has no narra-tive to speak of: it is an amorphous collection of sayings, though quite early in its original Greek form and may contain, among the dross, some valuable variations on Synoptic material. The *Gospel of Truth* and the *Gospel of Philip* are theological treatises; the *Gospel of the Egyptians* is an imaginative cosmogony; and the fragmentary *Gospel of Mary* (known from earlier papyrus discoveries) is a dialogue between Mary Magdalene and Peter on the gnostic claim to esoteric knowledge. While each is fascinating in itself, none of these texts can throw any light on the Gospel genre in the Bible.

CONCLUSION

The survey above of some of the more distinctive features of the individual Gospels has led us to question further the assumption that there is a generic similarity between them, as though their authors were all consciously engaged in the same activity of 'Gospel-writing'. Only retrospectively, when the four were collected together, did the word 'Gospel' take on that sense. Genre is as much a matter of purpose as of form, and the evangelists' purposes only partially overlap.

Mark's Gospel arose naturally out of oral storytelling as the means of evoking and confirming faith in Christ. It was intended for dramatic performance by itinerant preachers and it contains, for those with ears to hear, an answer to the problem of Christian mission, how to account for the temporary blindness and apparent rejection of the crucified and risen Messiah by his own people.

Matthew was not writing another Gospel of the same type as Mark. Its exhaustive use of his main source implies that this expanded edition was intended to replace it. The evangelist draws on more of the oral tradition of Jesus' teaching than Mark, and sharpens it in two directions, with attacks on Jewish opponents and warnings against backsliding Christians. While Mark, like Paul, still hoped that Israel would finally accept the good news, Matthew's community, violently excluded from the synagogue and constructing its own parallel but separate institutional structures, no longer envisages that possibility. The Gospel may itself be one such institution, the first example of Christian scripture.

Luke's two-volume work is different again. The Gospel is content to coexist with others that the author knows and from which he selects the choicest elements. His main theological purpose is to provide an answer to the problem of continuing history and the disappointment, so far, of hopes for the imminent return of Christ. Luke legitimates a Christ-centred form of Judaism but on different criteria from those used by Matthew, not with arguments about scripture and righteousness, but with the criteria, more familiar in the Graeco-Roman world, of honour, citizenship and compassion towards social inferiors. His work constitutes perhaps the first foray of the Christian movement into the world of publishing and book production.

John's Gospel in its present form is an amalgam of different elements. Its base is a kerygmatic narrative like Mark's but independent, into which have been woven some sermons and meditations in a mystical, poetic style and some sharp passages of polemic against the world and the Jews. These additions are, I suggest, the result of an exceptional kind of inspiration to which the main author of the book lays claim: the spirit of advocacy and prophecy that testifies to Jesus (cf. Rev. 19.10) in the continuing trial of faith. This was finally edited by someone who wanted to preserve and promote the distinctive insights of the 'beloved disciple' in a Christian world that was starting to fill with books (21.25).

BIBLIOGRAPHY

Alexander, L. C. (1993) *The Preface to Luke's Gospel.* (SNTSMS 78) Cambridge: CUP.

Allison, D. C. (1993) *The New Moses: A Matthean Typology.* Edinburgh: T & T Clark.

Ashton, J. (1991) *Understanding the Fourth Gospel.* Oxford: Clarendon.

Bauckham, R. (1998) *The Gospels for All Christians: Rethinking the Gospel Audiences.* Grand Rapids: Eerdmans.

Bilezikian, C. (1992) *The Liberated Gospel: A Comparison of the Gospel and Greek Tragedy.* Grand Rapids: Baker.

Bornkamm, G., Barth, G. and Held, H. J. (1963) ET *Tradition and Interpretation in Matthew.* London: SCM.

Brown, R. E. (1979) *The Community of the Beloved Disciple.* New York: Paulist.

Bultmann, R. (1921) ET (1968) *The History of the Synoptic Tradition.* Oxford: Basil Blackwell.

—— (1941) ET (1961) *The Gospel of John.* Oxford: Basil Blackwell.

Burridge, R. (1991) *What Are the Gospels?* Cambridge: CUP.

Conzelmann, H. (1960) ET *The Theology of St Luke.* London: Faber & Faber.

Crossan, J. D. (1999) *The Birth of Christianity.* Edinburgh: T & T Clark.

Culpepper, R. A. (1983) *Anatomy of the Fourth Gospel: A Study in Literary Design.* Philadelphia: Fortress.

Davies, W. D. (1964) *The Setting of the Sermon on the Mount.* Cambridge: CUP.

—— (1989) *The Setting of the Sermon on the Mount.* Atlanta: Scholars Press.

Dibelius, M. (1933²) ET (1934) *From Tradition to Gospel.* London: Ivor Nicholson & Watson.

Dodd, C. H. (1953) *The Interpretation of the Fourth Gospel.* Cambridge: CUP.

—— (1963) *Historical Tradition in the Fourth Gospel.* Cambridge: CUP.

Esler, P. (1987) *Community and Gospel in Luke–Acts.* (SNTSMS 57) Cambridge: CUP.

Fortna, R. T. (1988) *The Fourth Gospel and its Predecessor: From Narrative Source to Present Gospel.* Edinburgh: T & T Clark.

Fowler, R. (1991) *Let the Reader Understand.* Philadelphia: Fortress.

Goulder, M. D. (1974) *Midrash and Lection in Matthew.* London: SPCK.

Hadas, M. and Smith, M. (1965) *Heroes and Gods: Spiritual Biographies in Antiquity.* New York: Harper & Row.

Harvey, A. E. (1976) *Jesus on Trial: A Study in the Fourth Gospel.* London: SPCK.

Hengel, M. (2000) *The Four Gospels and the One Gospel of Jesus Christ.* London: SCM.

Johnson, L. T. (1977) *The Literary Function of Possessions in Luke–Acts.* Missoula: Scholars Press.

Kähler, M. (1964) ET *The So-called Historical Jesus and the Historic Biblical Christ.* Philadelphia: Fortress.

Käsemann, E. (1968) *The Testament of Jesus.* London: SCM.

Kermode, F. (1979) *The Genesis of Secrecy: On the Interpretation of Narrative.* Cambridge, Mass.: Harvard University Press.

Kilpatrick, G. D. (1946) *The Origins of the Gospel according to St Matthew.* Oxford: OUP.

Koester, H. (1990) *Ancient Christian Gospels.* London: SCM.

Lentz, J. C. (1993) *Luke's Portrait of Paul.* (SNTSMS 77) Cambridge: CUP.

Lindars, B. (1972) *The Gospel of John.* London: Oliphants.

Lightfoot, R. H. (1935) *History and Interpretation in the Gospels.* London: Hodder & Stoughton.

Luz, U. (1989) ET *Matthew I–VII: A Commentary.* Minneapolis: Augsburg.

Mack, B. L. (1988) *A Myth of Innocence: Mark and Christian Origins.* Philadelphia: Fortress.

Martyn, J. L. (1979²) *History and Theology in the Fourth Gospel.* Nashville: Abingdon.

Marxsen, W. (1956) ET (1969) *Mark the Evangelist.* Nashville: Abingdon.

Meier, J. P. (1976) *Law and History in Matthew's Gospel* (AnBib 74). Rome: Pontifical Biblical Institute.

Myers, C. (1990) *Binding the Strong Man.* New York: Orbis.

Rhoads, D. M. and Michie, D. (1982) *Mark as Story.* Philadelphia: Fortress.

Robbins, V. (1984) *Jesus the Teacher.* Philadelphia: Fortress.

Robinson, J. M. (1957) *The Problem of History in Mark.* Nashville: Abingdon.

Robinson, J. M. ed. (1988). *The Nag Hammadi Library.* New York: Harper & Row.

Schneemelcher, W. (1991). *New Testament Apocrypha*, 2 vols. Cambridge: James Clarke.

Stanton, G. N. (1992) *A Gospel for a New People.* Edinburgh: T & T Clark.

Stendahl, K. (1968²) *The School of St Matthew and its Use of the Old Testament.* Philadelphia: Fortress.

Stibbe, M. (1992) *John as Storyteller: Narrative Criticism and the Fourth Gospel.* (SNTSMS 73) Cambridge: CUP.

Strange, W. A. (1992) *The Problem of the Text of Acts* (SNTSMS 71). Cambridge: CUP.

Talbert, C. H. (1977) *What Is a Gospel?* Philadelphia: Fortress.

Tolbert, M. A. (1989) *Sowing the Gospel.* Philadelphia: Fortress.

Tyson, J. B. (1961) 'The Blindness of the Disciples in Mark', *Journal of Biblical Literature* 80: 261–8.

Waetjen, H. C. (1989) *A Reordering of Power: A Socio-political Reading of Mark's Gospel.* Philadelphia: Fortress.

Weeden, T. J. (1971) *Mark: Traditions in Conflict.* Philadelphia: Fortress.

Wilson, S. G. (1973) *The Gentiles and the Gentile Mission in Luke–Acts.* (SNTSMS 23) Cambridge: CUP.

Wrede, W. (1901) E.Tr. 1971 *The Messianic Secret.* Cambridge: James Clarke.

CHAPTER ELEVEN

LETTERS IN THE NEW TESTAMENT AND IN THE GRECO-ROMAN WORLD

———·◆·———

Harry Gamble

It is a striking feature of Christian scripture that it consists mainly of letters, espe-cially when we consider that no document of Jewish scripture is a letter. Of the twenty-seven documents belonging to the New Testament, no fewer than twenty-one are letters, or at least have traditionally been regarded as letters. The Apocalypse may legitimately be added for, although it has a distinctive form, it is framed and apparently was disseminated as a letter. Thus of the canonical literature only the four Gospels and Acts do not belong to the epistolary genre. Moreover, within the literature of the New Testament we hear of still other letters – several letters of Paul that have not been preserved (1 Cor. 5:9; 2 Cor. 2:2–4; Col. 4:16), letters of recom-mendation (2 Cor. 3:1–3), letters from churches to Paul (1 Cor. 7:1), letters announcing decisions of general interest (Acts 15:22–9), and even forged letters (2 Thess. 2:2). The contents of the New Testament suggest that the letter was not merely a prominent form but the most characteristic medium of early Christian writing. This observation is confirmed by a persistent reliance on the letter during the second and third centuries by such Christians writers as Clement of Rome, Ignatius of Antioch, Polycarp of Smyrna, Dionysius of Corinth and Cyprian of Carthage. Christian letters were, if anything, still more abundantly written in the fourth and fifth centuries, as shown, for example, by the prolific correspondence of Basil, Gregory, Augustine, and Jerome, among others.

The ubiquity of letters in early Christian literature should not, however, be surprising, for there are good reasons why Christians exploited this medium. Christianity from its earliest days was a vigorously missionary faith, and rapidly planted new communities of converts across a broad area: by the end of the first century small Christian conventicles were to be found throughout the eastern Mediterranean world – in Egypt and Syria, across Asia Minor, in Macedonia and the Greek peninsula, and in Italy. Despite their number and wide dispersion, these communities retained a common identity as outposts of the one church, the *ekklesia katholike*, and this identity was both expressed and cultivated by their frequent communications through letters and messengers. Yet the popularity of letters in the early church was not merely situational, but owed much to the larger tradition of letter-writing in the Greco-Roman world.

LETTERS IN THE GRECO-ROMAN WORLD

Until modern times, the epistolary form of so many of the documents of the New Testament was little remarked and had no great consequence for their interpretation. To be sure, other letters from antiquity had been preserved as part of the larger classical literary tradition. The letters of Cicero (106–43 BCE), Horace (65–8 BCE), Seneca (4 BCE – 65 CE), Pliny the Younger (61–112 CE), and Fronto (100–166 CE), for example, had long been known, but seemed to have only limited relevance to the letters of the New Testament. Thus it was a watershed in the study of early Christian letters when, in the late nineteenth and early twentieth centuries, archeologists unearthed thousands of papyrus letters in the trash heaps of ancient Egypt. Besides adding enormously to the quantity of extant ancient letters, these discoveries have revealed that there was a lively traffic in letters in the Greco-Roman world. The vitality of the genre owed a good deal to the growth of international commerce, to the large scale displacements of population groups, and to the increasing mobility of individuals around the Mediterranean world. In addition, these discoveries display the great variety of ancient letters: familiar letters (to friends or family), business letters, letters of recommendation, letters of request and petition, and official letters are all well represented. These letters have furnished a new basis for studying the forms, functions and conventions of letter-writing in the ancient world, and have provided a rich context in which to appraise anew early Christian letters. As a result, scholarship in the twentieth century has been in a uniquely privileged position to assess ancient epistolography in general and early Christian letters in particular.

Types of ancient letters

The large number and rich diversity of ancient letters now available has prompted efforts to classify them into types. Many taxonomies have been proposed. A simple but widely influential division was made early in the twentieth century by Adolf Deissmann, the first to undertake a comparative study of ancient letters in light of the papyrus discoveries (Deissmann 1910: 290–301). Deissmann distinguished between 'letters' (*Briefe*) and 'epistles' (*Episteln*). Letters he defined as actual pieces of correspondence, artless in form and practical in purpose, written for principally private purposes and dealing with ordinary matters of daily life. Epistles, on the other hand, he defined as artistic literary compositions that treat more elevated subjects and are intended for a literary public and posterity. Although this is a necessary and serviceable distinction, it cannot do justice to the immense variety of ancient letters, which requires more elaborate and nuanced typologies. Among more recent efforts to analyze and classify ancient letters, several approaches have been taken. One of these attends mainly to content and on this basis distinguishes eight basic types of letters: public affairs, character sketches, patronage, admonition, domestic affairs, literary issues, geographic and scenic interest, and social courtesy (Sherwin-White 1966). Another approach considers the social functions of ancient letters, and discovers the following types: the personal letter, the business letter, the official letter, the public letter, the nonreal (i.e., fictive or pseudonymous) letter, and the discursive letter (or letter-essay) (Doty 1973: 4–8). Still another, taking a cue from ancient epistolary theorists, offers a typology based on the rhetorical functions of letters, and proposes the categories of friendship, family, praise, blame, exhortation or advice, meditation, and apology (Stowers 1986). A simpler scheme of three broad categories – private letters, official letters, and literary letters – is basically adequate, though each of these may be subdivided, and though the distinctions are not always hard and fast (Aune 1987: 162–6).

Efforts to classify letters into specific types were made even in the ancient world, principally as an aid to letter-writers (Malherbe 1988). The handbook entitled *Epistolary Types* (falsely ascribed to Demetrius of Phaleron and probably dating from the second or first century BCE) enumerates, describes, and provides examples of no fewer than twenty-one types of letters. Another handbook, *Epistolary Styles* (wrongly attributed to Libanius or Proclus, but belonging to the fourth–sixth centuries CE), works with an even larger scheme of forty-one types. A more general ancient treatise, *On Style* (also wrongly attributed to Demetrius of Phaleron), discusses literary style generally, but devotes a lengthy section to epistolary style in particular (223–35).

Letters are perhaps most usefully distinguished according to their purposes. Broadly speaking most letters have one of the following purposes: to sustain or nurture personal relationships (the familiar letter), to communicate orders or instructions (the official letter and, to some extent, the business letter), to make requests (the letter of petition or recommendation), or merely to convey information. Correspondingly, the major types of letters were the familiar letter (written to a friend or family member), the official letter (and to some extent the business letter), and the letter of request (petition or recommendation). To these must be added the literary letter, which employed the letter for the exposition of intellectual topics in high style and with a view to a broad readership.

The ancient epistolary handbooks, along with passing comments of some ancient letter-writers, are valuable for the insights they give into the prevailing theory and practice of letters and letter-writing, especially letters of the private, familiar type. They assume that the personal and private letter from one friend to another is the original and normative form of correspondence. Because a letter in its nature presupposes the separation of the writer and recipient and stands as a surrogate for their presence to each other, its principal purpose is to mitigate their separation by the expression and cultivation of friendly relations (*philophrosune*), by the eager anticipation of renewed presence (*parousia*), and by providing (written) conversation (*homilia*) in the interim (Koskenniemi 1956: 34–47; cf. Thraede 1970). The handbooks advise that, because it is a substitute for familiar conversation between friends, a letter should resemble an actual conversation as closely as possible, being immediate and natural in tone. Moreover, a letter should bring into play the personalities and dispositions of writer and recipient, so that as far as possible the writer might convey to the reader something of his personal presence (Seneca, *Ad Lucilium epistulae morales* 1: 263–4).

Of course, not all ancient letters had this familiar character or aimed to nurture friendship. Many official letters have been preserved from antiquity. Whether administrative, diplomatic or military, their purpose was to convey rulings, orders, instructions, admonitions or simply information from persons in authority to their distant responsible agents or subjects. Naturally, being written by persons of authority, letters of this sort are characterized by a more formal, elevated, and precise style of writing. Likewise business letters, being devoted to practical matters of commercial transaction, tended to be direct and precise, with little attention to personal details or effort to cultivate personal relationships.

The letter of request did not necessarily presuppose a direct acquaintance between the writer and addressee. The statement of request is normally accompanied by an explanation of its motivating circumstances or occasion, and is followed by an expression of appreciation or benefit, and sometimes (depending on the status of the one making the request), by an offer to return the favor. Letters of petition, in which ordinarily the writer is inferior to the recipient, tend to formal rather than familiar expression, whereas letters of recommendation, in which writer and recipient have more or less equal status, are composed in more familiar reciprocal terms.

The literary letter represents the adaptation of the letter form for broader purposes. Literary letters were themselves of the most various sorts (Aune 1987: 165–69). Some were real letters written to a specific individual, with or without having a wider readership also in view. Many examples are offered by Cicero, Seneca, Pliny, and Fronto, among others. Other literary letters were of an ideal type, written in an elevated style and intended for publication, the epistolary genre being artificially used as a literary vehicle. The poets Horace, Ovid, and Statius composed such letters. Still others were fictive letters, contrived for use within extended historical or fictional narratives. And many literary letters were letter-essays, in which the epistolary form is used for topical expositions of technical, literary, political, or philosophical questions. Such letter-essays were also composed by Seneca, Plutarch, and Fronto, among others. Of particular interest here are philosophical letter-essays which adopted the epistolary format as a medium of instruction in philosophical subjects and came into vogue in the first century CE. Such literary letters were typically much longer than ordinary letters of other types. The composition of literary letters shows the adaptation of the epistolary medium to broader purposes than the situational concerns that governed private or official letters.

The forms and conventions of ancient letters

Despite their variety of purpose and type, all ancient letters had a fundamental structure delineated by formulaic elements that were largely conventional and stereotypical (Exler 1922; White 1984: 1733–738; 1986: 198–212). Indeed one of the remarkable features of ancient letters is to be seen in the stability of their basic form and the regularity of their formulae. Letters had three fundamental parts: opening, body, and closing. The opening and closing portions both contributed mainly to the affirmation and cultivation of the interpersonal relations between the writer and recipient, while the letter body contains the particular information, request or instruction that prompts the writing of the letter. The principal purpose of any letter can usually be gauged by how these several parts of a letter are developed: elaboration of the opening and closing portions, with only brief attention to the body of the letter, shows that the letter's aim is mainly to sustain and nurture the relationship, whereas perfunctory opening and closing sections and a more detailed letter-body indicates that the aim is practical rather than personal (White 1986: 198).

At its simplest, the opening consisted of an efficient prescript (*praescriptio*) in the form 'A to B, greetings (*chairein*).' Thus both the writer and intended recipient were immediately identified (hence ancient letters typically lacked signature at the end). Each element of this formula was susceptible of elaboration, according to situation or inclination: the names of the writer or addressee could be supplied with titles, terms of relationship, or expressions of endearment, and the statement of greeting could be heightened by modifiers. The prescript was often followed by a wish for the health and well-being of the recipient (the *formula valetudinis*): 'if you are well, that would be excellent. I also am well'), and this often connected to a prayer formula (*proskynema*) stating a supplication made by the writer on behalf of the recipient ('I make supplication for you always to the gods,' etc.).

These opening conventions gave way to the body of the letter, which provided the substance of the communication. The body of the letter was its most variable component: it might comprise information, instruction, request, or admonition, according to the letter's circumstance and purpose. Yet there are stock phrases that routinely recur in the bodies of ancient letters, depending upon a letter's aim. For example, information is often adduced with such phrases as 'I want you to know' or 'just as you instructed me,' while requests or instructions are commonly conveyed with the phrase 'you will do well to . . .' usually preceded by a brief statement of the background. Other conventional phrases mark transitions to the conclusion of the body: 'I wrote so that you may know . . .'; 'Write (back) in order that I may know . . .'; 'Take care in order that . . .'

Although letters sometimes concluded abruptly, they were customarily rounded off with various concluding formulae (Weima 1994: 28–56). The simplest and most common closing was a final wish, normally merely 'farewell' (*erroso*) or 'may you prosper' (*eutuchei*). But like the prescript, the final wish was open to various elaborations that expressed respect or affection, extended the scope of the wish to include others beyond the recipient, or heightened its force. Although a health-wish seems to have belonged mainly to the letter-opening, such wishes can also appear in conclusion, just before the final wish, and they typically take the form 'Take care of yourself so that you may be healthy.' Near the end of the first century CE there appeared the formula 'I pray that you may be healthy,' which did duty as a combined health wish and final wish. From the first century BCE on, greetings were increasingly added (either before or after the final wish). These greetings could be those of the writer to family members, or to friends or associates of the recipient, or they could be greetings from family members, friends or associates of the writer, which the writer conveyed to the recipient or to others associated with the recipient (Exler 1922: 116; Koskenniemi 1956: 148–50).

While letters normally ended with the final wish, many of them also carried postscripts. Lying outside the formal structure of the letter, such additional matter is usually brief, either adding information unintentionally omitted from the body of the letter, or appending a conventional element (a greeting or a health-wish) that would normally belong to the closing. But occasionally postscripts are more substantial, supplying information that has only lately come to hand, or even summarizing the main points of the letter as a whole.

The writing and delivery of ancient letters

There was no mass literacy in the ancient world: throughout the Greek, Hellenistic and Roman imperial periods, only about 10 percent of the population was literate (Harris 1989). Further, reading and writing were separate skills, and those who could write were fewer still. Hence ancient letter-writers, the illiterate by necessity and the literate for convenience, routinely relied on scribes or secretaries (Richards 1991: 15–127). A secretary possessed the accomplished skill of writing legibly on papyrus, but was also familiar with the types of letters, the appropriate styles, and the standard conventions. The sender might either dictate, syllable by syllable, to the secretary, or provide merely the gist of what was to be communicated, but in either case the letter was actually penned by the secretary. The use of secretaries clarifies two features that frequently appear in ancient letters, namely the autographic conclusion and the illiteracy formula.

In a considerable number of papyrus letters we find an autographic conclusion, that is, a visible change of hands at the end: after the secretary had penned the letter, the sender added some matter in his or her own handwriting. Sometimes this is only a repetition of the final wish, sometimes it adds a greeting, and sometimes it constitutes postscriptive remarks of substance. The motives for such autographic subscriptions were various. Authentication was certainly one of them, although this is rarely stated. Another motive, especially in certain business letters, petitions, or other official letters, was to make a letter legally binding. Still another may have been confidentiality. Such motives do not, however, suffice to explain autographic conclusions in private, familiar letters. In those cases the force of the autograph can only have been to overcome the intervention of the secretary by furnishing the letter with a more personal and intimate touch, thus acknowledging and affirming the friendly relationship of the sender and the recipient.

In this connection it should also be noted that a large number of ancient letters contain at the end an illiteracy formula, which explains that a secretary has written the letter at the commission of an illiterate person. It takes the usual form 'X wrote for Y because Y did not know how to write' (Exler 1922: 124–27).

The popularity of letter-writing in antiquity and the abundance of ancient letters are even more remarkable when we consider that there was no structured system for the transmission and delivery of private letters. The only organized postal systems in the ancient world were those devised by governments for purposes of official, diplomatic, and military communications. Of these the most highly developed and efficient was the Roman *cursus publicus* established by Augustus. This transport system, consisting of a network of well-maintained highways with milestones and relay stations, enabled the efficient movement of military forces, the transport of governmental officials, and the rapid transmission of administrative, diplomatic and military dispatches carried by mounted couriers (Westerman, 1938). This system was limited, however, to governmental use. Private letters had to be delivered by private means. While the wealthy could enlist their slaves or employees as couriers (*tabellarii*) for their letters, the ordinary person had to seek out traveling people, of whom there were many (Casson 1974) – business persons, friends, acquaintances or even strangers – whose itineraries included the destination of the letters (Epp 1991;

Llewelyn 1994). This haphazard, *ad hoc* procedure seems to have worked well enough: though mischance, delay and nondelivery were common, private letters apparently moved with relative ease and surprising speed around the Empire. Sometimes the mere availability of a carrier provided the occasion for a letter to be written, and when the identity of the carrier was known as the letter was being written, the carrier might be mentioned in the letter and commended to the recipient. When the carrier of a letter was known to be reliable, he was sometimes entrusted also with information, whether supplementary or confidential, to be communicated orally to the letter's recipient. Ancient letters were not routinely dated, since the carrier was usually able to indicate to the recipient when the letter had been dispatched.

EARLY CHRISTIAN LETTERS

As noted earlier, the New Testament presents us with an abundance of epistolary literature. But early Christian letters, like those of their Greco-Roman environment, are of diverse types, ranging from actual and occasional pieces of correspondence to more formal letter-essays of a literary sort. Thus we must view early Christian letters not only in comparison to non-Christian letters but also in comparison to each other.

The earliest extant Christian letters are those of the apostle Paul, which belong roughly to the decade 50–60 CE. Paul may or may not have been the first Christian to write letters, but his forcefully established the letter in Christian usage, and in large measure provided both the impetus and the model for later Christian letter-writers. Hence his letters deserve special attention.

The letters of Paul

Paul's authentic letters, far from being the abstract theological essays for which they have sometimes been mistaken, are actual pieces of correspondence. They are all occasional: they are (with the exception of Romans) addressed to individual communities that Paul himself had established, deal with specific issues that had subsequently arisen in those communities after Paul's departure, and aim to achieve particular results. That Paul's letters are actual letters was most fully and forcefully shown by Adolf Deissmann, who closely compared them with the many recently discovered papyrus letters of antiquity. On the basis of this comparison, he regarded Paul's letters as having a similarly nonliterary character, and as corresponding in the main to ancient private letters (Deissmann 1910: 146–251). In this, however, Deissmann clearly went too far (Richards 1991: 211–16). Despite some resemblances, Paul's letters are distinguished from private letters in several important ways. They have an official character, for Paul addresses his churches as a person of authority, always calling attention in the prescripts to his status as an apostle, and presuming on that authority throughout. Moreover, he addresses not individuals but communities, which he undertakes to instruct and admonish on matters of their corporate life (the letter to Philemon is not a real exception). Further, in their considerable length, argumentative development, and rhetorical features, Paul's letters more closely resemble the literary and philosophical letters of antiquity than any merely private correspondence. These features of Paul's letters must have been plain to his sophisticated opponents in Corinth, who regarded his letters as 'weighty and strong' (2 Cor. 10:10). If Deissmann succeeded in emphasizing that Paul's letters were actual letters and in showing their resemblance to nonliterary letters, we are better able to see today that they also have strong resemblances to letters of the official and the literary types. Hence the letters of Paul fall on a continuum between the familiar and the official, and between the literary and the nonliterary (Doty 1973: 26; Stowers 1986: 25; Richards 1991: 215).

The forms and conventions of Paul's letters

Paul was naturally dependent upon the epistolary practices of his day. This is easily recognized in the structure of his letters and in the conventions he employed. In his letters Paul conforms to the basic structure of all ancient letters (opening, body, and closing), and follows but also consistently adapts the formulaic elements of ancient letters. The prescripts of Paul's letters correspond to the common pattern 'A to B, greeting,' but Paul variously elaborates each of these elements with descriptive characterizations of himself and of the church addressed, and in place of the common statement of greeting he consistently declares upon his readers the specifically Christian blessing 'Grace (*charis*) and peace (*eirene*) from God our father and the Lord Jesus Christ.' This double-wish seems to combine the common Greek epistolary greeting (*chairein*) and the standard greeting of 'peace' in Jewish letters.

The prescript, which is sometimes lengthy (e.g. Rom. 1:1–7), is commonly followed by another formal element, the thanksgiving (replaced by the formula of blessing in 2 Cor. 1:3–7; cf. Eph. 1:3–10) (Schubert 1939). The thanksgiving is effectively a prayer that takes the place of the prayer-wish for the health of the recipient (the *formula valetudinis*) in ordinary letters (although a few papyrus letters incorporate also a formula of thanksgiving, 'I give thanks to the gods . . .' [Schubert 1939: 158–79]). Here Paul expresses gratitude for the community, its well-being, faithfulness and growth. (Only in Galatians is this element omitted, and understandably, since Paul finds nothing in that community for which to be grateful.) Functionally the thanksgivings affirm the relationship between Paul and the community and engender the goodwill and receptivity of the readers toward the writer and his message.

The thanksgiving leads to the body of the letter, the beginning of which is customarily signaled by a formula of disclosure ('I want you to know . . .' [Phil. 1:12], 'we do not want you to be ignorant . . .' [2 Cor. 1:8], 'You yourselves know . . .' [1 Thess. 2:1]), but occasionally by a formula of appeal ('I appeal to you . . .' [1 Cor. 1:10; Phlm. 8–9], though Paul can also proceed directly to a strong statement of his theme (Rom. 1:16–17; Gal. 1:6). The body of the letter is its most important and longest part, for here Paul conveys or requests information, and deploys instruction and argument. But in substance the body of the Pauline letter is also its most variable part, since the letters are occasional and each responds to a different set of circumstances or issues. A sense of the possible range and character of the letter body can be gained by comparing Romans and 1 Corinthians. In the former we find an almost seamless argument that develops on a grand scale the theme of the revelation and outworking of God's righteousness, while in the latter we have a somewhat disjunctive series of smaller instructions and arguments on a variety of particular topical issues that the Corinthian community has brought to Paul's attention.

By way of conveying his thought Paul employs in the body of his letters not only a variety of typical epistolary formulae and themes, but incorporates citations of and arguments from scripture, and draws upon early Christian confessional, paraenetic, and liturgical traditions (credal and hymnic elements, virtue and vice lists, benedictions, doxologies). Beyond these, however, recent research has usefully shown that the argumentative and dialogical portions of the letter-body are also shaped under the influence of the rhetorical traditions of Greco-Roman antiquity, and reflect different types of oral argumentation (Kennedy 1984; Stowers 1981; Murphy-O'Conner 1995: 65–95). Given that Paul's letters, like all letters, are surrogates for personal presence and oral delivery, it is only to be expected that the forms and the techniques of oral communication cultivated in the practice of ancient rhetoric should be present in Paul's letters, whether or not Paul had been formally trained in rhetoric. Yet Paul's argumentation does not consistently conform to any one of the main types of rhetorical argument; rather he uses them variously in contexts where they are specially servicable to his purpose.

The body of the Pauline letter is often rounded off with moral exhortations and appeals (Rom. 12:1 – 15:13; Gal. 5:1 – 6:10; 1 Thess. 4:1 – 5:22), and often also with a statement of his reasons for writing and/or of his intention either to send an emissary or to make a personal visit to the recipients (Rom. 15:14–33; 1 Cor. 16:1–11; 2 Cor. 12:14 – 13:13; Phlm 21–2). These last elements refer, in order of ascending importance, to the three modes of Paul's apostolic *parousia* or presence to his congregations: the letter, the emissary, and Paul himself (Funk 1967: 258–61). Here Paul's personal presence and authority come explicitly to the fore, and he thus induces his readers to attend to his instruction. At the same time, Paul, like other ancient letter-writers, reveals his awareness of the letter as a substitute for personal presence and conversation.

The closing of the Pauline letter, like the prescript, consists largely of formulaic elements, though here too Paul distinctively Christianizes such elements and adapts them to his own purposes (Weima 1994: 77–155). The most typical and uniform features of Paul's letter-conclusions are the grace benediction ('The grace of the [our] Lord Jesus [Christ] be with you [all]'), which consistently occupies the final position, and the wish of peace ('The God of peace be with you,' with elaborative variations), which stands earlier in the closing. Between these two elements other elements frequently appear. The most frequent of these are final greetings, including the request that the addressees also greet each other with an exchange of the 'holy kiss.' The conclusions of Paul's letters sometimes also include a greeting or other statement in Paul's own hand (1 Cor. 16:21–4; Gal. 6:11–18; Phlm. 19; cf. Col. 4:18; 2 Thess. 3:17–18). Such explicit references to his own hand point to Paul's frequent, and probably habitual, use of a secretary for the inscription of his letters (Richards 1991: 169–201; Rom. 16:22 preserves the name of one of Paul's secretaries, Tertius). Paul himself then penned some part of the conclusion. For the motive of these autographic interventions we need look no further than common practice, since papyrus letters frequently reveal similar autographs. The appearance of the author's own hand reemphasized the personal character of the letter, though we should not discount such additional aims as authentication (cf. esp. 2 Thess. 2:2), accountability (Phlm 19), or strong emphasis (Gal. 6:11).

The writing and delivery of Paul's letters

It is noteworthy that in the prescripts of his letters Paul customarily names another (or others) as co-senders with himself (among the authentic letters only Romans lacks a co-sender). This is apparently no mere formality, but indicates that these co-senders participated in the conception and perhaps even the composition of Paul's letters. As the letters themselves make clear, these persons (Timothy, Silvanus, Sosthenes, among others) belonged to Paul's missionary entourage and were his fellow-workers, assisting him in organizing and overseeing his congregations, often traveling as envoys between Paul and his churches, and sometimes, no doubt, carrying his letters as well as oral instructions (Ellis 1971; Ollrog 1979). This group structure of the Pauline mission has encouraged some scholars to speak of a Pauline 'school,' whose work under Paul's leadership probably included not only administrative and ambassadorial tasks, but also the study of scripture and interpretive reflection upon the gospel message (Schenke 1975; Conzelmann 1965, 1979). The substance of Paul's thought as we meet it in his letters, while it bears the unmistakeable impress of Paul's own mind, must also have owed much to these co-workers.

Paul's reliance upon his fellow-workers and his use of secretaries opens up the possibility that his letters may have been composed and inscribed in various ways. Some letters may have been dictated to a secretary skilled in shorthand. At the other extreme, Paul may have entrusted the rough drafting of a letter to his associates or a secretary. The former method could account for the vividly oral style of Romans or of 1 Corinthians 10–13. Appeal is sometimes made to the latter method to explain why some Pauline letters vary so widely from others in language, style, or thought. Yet the basic consistency of style and substance among the undisputed letters of Paul argues for his own close control over the content and formulation of his letters, however much assistance he may have gained from members of his entourage.

Paul's letters were delivered by private letter-carriers, and these are frequently named and commended in the letters themselves: Phoebe (Rom. 16:1–2), Epaphroditus (Phil. 2:25–9), Onesimus (Phlm. 12), Timothy (1 Cor. 4:17; 16:10) Titus and another unnamed (2 Cor. 8:16–24), among others (cf. Col. 4:7–9; Eph. 6:21–2). If not all of these were among Paul's closest associates, they were all surely trusted Christians, and it must have been rare for messages between Christians to be transmitted by non-Christians. With Christian as well as non-Christian letters, the letter-carrier was often entrusted with additional information (Col. 4:7–9; Eph. 6:21–2), and sometimes was in a position to assist in the interpretation of the letter (1 Cor. 4:17).

It was Paul's intention and expectation that upon reaching their destinations his letters would be read aloud to the congregations addressed (1 Thess. 5:27; cf. Col. 4:16). This was the common mode of reading in antiquity, and would have been necessary in any event since the large majority of Christians, like the majority of non-Christians, were illiterate. Correspondingly, Paul's letters, like all ancient literature, were composed not so much to be read as to be heard, that is, recited or performed (Achtemeier 1990; Botha 1993), which accounts for their oral style and rhetorical features.

The role of Paul's letters and their later influence

All of Paul's letters are occasional in nature: they are directed to individual communities that Paul himself had established, and they address specific issues that had arisen in those communities after Paul had departed to work elsewhere. (The letter to the Roman church, which Paul did not establish, is also occasional, though its occasion lay with Paul.) But if his letters were occasional, they were by no means casual. They were important and practical instruments of his itinerant missionary activity, and were carefully thought out and composed to be effective means by which he might instruct, guide, and regulate his congregations when he was absent from them.

We cannot easily judge whether Paul's letters achieved their intended purposes. Paul clearly thought them useful, and undoubtedly they conveyed his ideas and intentions. Yet they were not always successful: one of Paul's missives to the Corinthians was clearly misunderstood (1 Cor. 5:9–13), and another caused painful reaction (2 Cor. 2:3–9; 7:8–12) which led to further difficulties. For most of his letters it is simply impossible to know if they had the results that Paul hoped for when he wrote them – whether, for example, the Galatians were dissuaded from their judaizing inclinations, or whether the Romans were prepared to welcome Paul and support the western mission he projected. It is, however, a more general measure of success that, despite their specific addresses and occasional character, most of Paul's letters came to be valued and preserved, and were soon widely disseminated among other churches both within and beyond Paul's own mission field. It was in consequence of this that Paul's letters had their greatest influence. At the same time, Paul's practice served to inaugurate the long and broad tradition of letter-writing in Christianity. The availablility and usefulness of Paul's letters fostered the idea that the appropriate and even expected medium of written Christian teaching was the letter. More particularly still, Paul's letters effectively created the genre of the apostolic letter, and this genre quickly took hold within early Christianity (White 1983).

Pseudo-Pauline letters

The effect of this is first to be seen, not surprisingly, within the Pauline mission field. Among the letters traditionally ascribed to Paul, some are clearly pseudonymous, written by others but in Paul's name. Those widely agreed to be pseudomymous are Ephesians and the Pastoral epistles (1 and 2 Timothy, and Titus), but many also consider Colossians and/or 2 Thessalonians not to be genuine. These letters may be variously differentiated from the apostle's authentic letters on the grounds of vocabulary and style, characteristic religious ideas, and situation, though in varying degrees they are all indebted to the tradition of Paul's thought. But whereas all of Paul's letters were addressed to individual local communities and had specific relevance to them, this is not the case with all of the pseudo-Pauline letters. Ephesians appears not to have had a particular original address, and thus had an encyclical character, envisioning a very broad readership, and the general character of its contents corresponds with this. The Pastoral epistles, on the other hand, are unique among the Pauline letters in being addressed only to individuals, ostensibly to Paul's associates, Timothy and Titus (Philemon, an authentic letter, was addressed not only to the individual, Philemon, but also to the community that met in his house). But in spite of their individual addressees, the Pastoral epistles were probably intended for a broad readership, since they aim to encourage fidelity to Pauline teaching and its transmission to others, to strengthen resistance to false teaching, and to sponsor a structured form of church organization and authority. Colossians and 2 Thessalonians, on the other hand, both have particular circumstances in view, and were probably written to specific communities rather than for an entirely general readership. In these documents we have early examples of pseudonymous apostolic letters.

The composition of pseudonymous letters (among other sorts of pseudonymous works) was a familiar practice in Greco-Roman antiquity generally (Speyer 1971; Brox 1975) and was sometimes followed both in Judaism (Smith 1971; Alexander 1984) and in early Christianity (Brox 1975; Meade 1986). Within Christianity this occurs first in connection with the name of Paul. The motives of fictive authorship were various. The production of pseudonymous letters in Paul's name and after his time may perhaps be understood against the background of the corporate character of Paul's missionary efforts, noted previously. Some of his close associates certainly survived him, and after his death no doubt sought to continue his work. It is probably to this group, and their successors, that we should look for the origins of the pseudo-Pauline letters. The various authors of these letters were clearly acquainted with Paul's thought, presumed upon Paul's authority, and under his mantle aimed both to perpetuate his teaching and adapt it to new circumstances after the apostle's demise. The production of these letters not only takes for granted the importance of Paul's thought and the weight of his authority, but shows also that the letter had early become the acknowledged, expected, and effective medium of Pauline teaching.

Despite the curious failure of Acts to represent Paul as a writer of letters, allusion to that role was entirely commonplace in reminiscences of Paul in the late first and early second centuries (2 Peter 3:15–16; *1 Clement* 47:1–3; Ignatius, *Eph.* 12:2; Polycarp, *Phil.* 3:2). The knowledge of Paul as a letter-writer and the early and apparently broad influence of his letters had a still larger consequence: it fostered a close association in early Christian thought and practice between the letter and apostolic teaching, such that the letter became the expected vehicle of authoritative instruction. This provides a perspective from which to examine other early Christian letters.

Hebrews and the catholic epistles

The so-called Epistle to the Hebrews, which has traditionally been associated with the Pauline corpus, is something of a literary enigma: although it has a clearly letter-like conclusion (13:22–5), it has no epistolary introduction at all, so that there is some ambiguity about its genre and no indication of its ostensible author or intended recipients. Beginning with a formal prologue (1:1–4), this document reads much more like a carefully composed, highly rhetorical homily than a letter proper, and indeed it is self-described as a 'word of exhortation' (13:22). While it is conceivable that an original epistolary introduction has been accidentally lost or deliberately eliminated, it is more likely that the epistolary conclusion was added, either by the author of the whole or someone else, possibly to suggest Pauline authorship or at least a connection with Paul's circle (note the reference to 'our brother Timothy' in 13:22). Thus, although Hebrews was certainly not written by Paul and is not to be considered a letter in any compositional sense, we nevertheless see even here, as in the pseudo-Pauline letters, an interest in associating the substance of this document with the Pauline epistolary tradition. Hebrews would appear, then, to have been written not as a letter but as a hortatory address for a particular group of Christians. This does not, however, preclude its subsequent adaptation and broader distribution, perhaps by the author himself, in letterlike form. Similar peculiarities attach to some other New Testament letters.

The four letters appearing under the names of Peter, James, and Jude, together with three other letters that are traditionally associated with the name of John, but are actually anonymous, have been known at least since the fourth century as the catholic (that is, universal) epistles, and prior to that time two individual letters among these (1 Peter; 1 John) had been described as catholic. The designation was apparently employed because it was thought that these letters were written not to local congregations but to a wider, more general readership. The addresses of most of these letters are indeed quite general: 1 Peter is directed to 'the exiles of the dispersion in Pontus, Galatia, Cappodocia, Asia, and Bythinia' (1:1) – which is to say, to Christians in the Anatolian regions of Asia Minor; still more general are the addresses of 2 Peter ('to those who have obtained faith,' 1:1), James ('to the twelve tribes of the dispersion,' 1:1), and Jude ('to those who are called, beloved in God and kept for Jesus Christ,' 1:1). The three Johannine letters present a more varied picture: 1 John lacks any address at all, while 2 John is addressed to an unnamed local church ('the elect lady,' 1:1), and 3 John to an individual (Gaius, 1:1). With the exception of 2 and 3 John, then, the catholic epistles are characterized by general addresses and appear to envision broad readerships, which contrasts sharply with Paul's practice of writing to particular, local congregations, though some of the pseudo-Pauline letters (e.g. Ephesians) are much more generally conceived. It corresponds to their broad addresses that most of the catholic epistles communicate teaching of a general type that seems to take little or no account of the local circumstances of any particular community, although even teaching of general relevance may also have been addressed to an individual church (Bauckham 1988: 488).

Like Hebrews, not all of the catholic epistles were self-evidently composed as letters. One of them, 1 John, has neither an epistolary address nor an epistolary conclusion and thus lacks most of the formal features that would mark it as a proper letter. The rest of these letters all begin with relatively standard epistolary conventions, and thus immediately create the impression that they are letters, yet a regular epistolary conclusion is lacking not only in 1 John but also in 2 Peter, James, and Jude. Of all the catholic epistles, 1 Peter has the most vividly letterlike quality, and by its full use of epistolary conventions leaves no real doubt that it was composed as a letter. At the other extreme is 1 John, which lacks all the recognizable marks of a letter. Yet the author of 1 John repeatedly uses the formula 'I am writing' (1:4;

2:1, 7, 12, 21, 26; 5:13), and thus conceives of his work as a written communication rather than an oral address. Hence, whether or not some of these documents (or parts of them) may originally have been composed as sermons, or ever had a nonepistolary form, it would be a mistake to conclude from their general character that they were not actually dispatched as letters and meant to be widely read.

The catholic epistles as a group have no explicit relationship to the tradition of Pauline thought (although 1 Peter and James are occasionally resonant of Pauline teaching), nor do they follow the style, form or conventions of the authentic Pauline letters. Lacking the personal dimension and situational specificity of Paul's letters, some of the catholic epistles (especially James, 2 Peter, 1 John, and Jude) bear a closer comparison with some Greco-Roman literary or philosophical letters, which have a similarly didactic quality without reference to particular circumstances. Yet in one respect we should probably see in the catholic epistles an important after-effect of Paul's letter-writing practice. Apart from the three letters associated with the name John (which, however, are actually anonymous), the catholic epistles are associated with the names of apostolic figures (Peter, James, and Jude). There are good reasons in each case to think that these are all pseudonymous writings. If so, these letters attest an established expectation that authoritative apostolic teaching should be found in letter-form, an expectation that must have rested mainly upon a wide knowledge and use of Paul's own letters in the early church (White 1983).

Later, in the second century, a Christian writer named Apollonius claimed that a heterodox Christian named Themiso 'dared to write a catholic epistle in imitation of the apostle' (Eusebius, *Ecclesiastical History* 5.18.5). This charge indicates that the catholic epistle had become a recognized literary genre in the ancient church and, even though the apostle who was imitated is not named, shows how closely the early Christian mind had come to correlate apostolic authority and catholic address. By this time, to write as an apostle meant to address the church at large, and, correspondingly, to address the whole church meant to write as an apostle. It is very likely that the apostle intended by Apollonius was none other than Paul, for even though, strictly speaking, none of Paul's authentic letters had a general or catholic address, they had come to be valued and used by the whole church, despite their original particularity (Dahl 1962). Indeed, this view seems already to be presupposed in the pseudonymous catholic epistles, and becomes explicit in 2 Peter 3:15–16.

Revelation

It is not immediately evident that the Apocalypse of John should be regarded as a letter. The author himself refers to his work as a prophecy (1:3), a book (1:11) or, more frequently, a book of prophecy (22:7, 10, 18–19), never simply as a letter. It commences not with epistolary formulae but with a title, a warranting explanation of the book's origin, and a blessing (1:1–3). Yet immediately thereafter we come upon an epistolary prescript of common form, 'John to the seven churches that are in Asia,' and a typically Christian (indeed, Pauline) epistolary greeting, 'grace to you and peace . . .' (1:4–5). Correspondingly, at the conclusion of the book we find a benediction of the type that regularly concludes early Christian letters (22:21). Thus, even though in its larger substance the Apocalypse is a revelatory narrative, it is cast in the form of a letter. In this respect the Apocalpyse of John is unique among Jewish and Christian apocalyptic writings.

But the Apocalypse is also peculiar as a letter, for like no other letter it aims at once to address both a specific and a general readership. It is directed to a circle of seven specific churches in Western Asia Minor – Ephesus, Smyrna, Pergamum, Thyatira, Sardis, Phildelphia, and Laodicea – and thus is a circular letter aimed in the first place at all of them equally. Within this framework, however, the author also undertakes to address these congregations individually, and so incorporates into the general letter specific messages for each (2:1 – 3:21). Yet the intended readership was probably broader than even these seven churches: the number seven was taken in Judaism and Christianity as a symbol of perfection and completeness, so that seven individual churches might signify also the whole church. In a document as given to number-symbolism as the Apocalypse, it seems probable that the author intended his work to address Christians at large.

This strange conflation of an apocalypse into a letter that is both general and specific finds its explanation in the instruction to the seer to 'write what you see in a book and send it to the seven churches' (1:11). The revelation is provided to John in order that he should 'bear witness' to it (1:2), that is, make it widely known. Until and unless the revelation is communicated, the revelatory process remains incomplete and ineffective: only dissemination – writing and sending – brings it to completion. 'Writing and sending' most naturally indicates a letter. In this sense, the epistolary form is by no means incidental or irrelevant, but belongs to the fundamental conception and purpose of the work. The whole of the book should therefore be considered a circular letter addressed to seven specific churches, yet not only to them.

Early Christian letters display a rich diversity of form, substance and function. Our understanding of them is much enriched by comparisons with other letters of Greco-Roman antiquity – literary and nonliterary, familiar and official, occasional and general – yet they do not correspond precisely to any non-Christian types of letters, but represent mixtures of standard types and draw upon diverse models. Not only are Christian letters as a rule much longer than ordinary letters, a feature undoubtedly related to their instructional purposes (White 1986: 19). They also reflect in notably vivid ways the unique socioreligious setting of the early church by which they were shaped, but which they also helped to shape: small religious communities separated geographically but bound together by a means of written communication that sustained their common faith, their mutual affection, and their social solidarity as one universal Church.

BIBLIOGRAPHY

Achtemeier, P. (1990) '*Omne verbum sonat*: The New Testament and the Oral Environment of Late Western Antiquity,' *JBL* 109: 3–27.

Alexander, P. S. (1984) 'Epistolary Literature,' in M. E. Stone (ed.) *Jewish Writings of the Second Temple Period*. Philadelphia: Fortress, 579–96.

Aune, D. E. (1987) *The New Testament in its Literary Environment*. Philadelphia: Westminster.

Bahr, G. H. (1966) 'Paul and Letter Writing in the First Century,' *CBQ* 28: 465–77.

Bauckham, R. (1988) 'Pseudo-Apostolic Letters,' *JBL* 107: 469–94.

Bjerkelund, C. J. (1967) *Parakalo: Form, Funktion und Sinn der Parakalo-Sätze in den paulinischen Briefen*. Oslo: Universitetsforlaget.

Botha, P. J. J. (1992) 'Letter Writing and Oral Communication in Antiquity,' *Scriptura* 42: 17–34.

—— (1993) 'The Verbal Art of the Pauline Letters: Rhetoric, Performance and Presence,' in S. E. Porter and T. H. Olbricht (eds.) *Rhetoric and the New Testament*. Sheffield: JSOT Press, 401–28.

Brox, N. (1975) *Falsche Verfasserangaben: Zur Erklärung frühchristlichen Pseudepigraphie*. Stuttgart: K. B. W. Verlag.

Casson, L. (1974) *Travel in the Ancient World*. London: Allen & Unwin.

Conzelmann, H. (1965) 'Paulus und die Weisheit,' *NTS* 12: 231–44.

—— (1979), 'Die Schule des Paulus,' in C. Andresen and G. Klein (eds.) *Theologia Crucis – Signum Crucis: Festschrift für E. Dinkler*. Tübingen: Mohr, 85–96.

Dahl, N. A. (1962) 'The Particularity of the Pauline Epistles as a Problem in the Ancient Church,' *Neotestamentica et Patristica*. NovTSup 6. Leiden: Brill, 261–71.

Deissmann, A. (1901) *Bible Studies*. Edinburgh: T & T Clark.

—— (1910) *Light From the Ancient East: The New Testament Illustrated by Recently Discovered Texts of the Graeco-Roman World*, trans. L. R. M. Strachan. London: Hodder & Stoughton.

Dormeyer, D. (1993) *Das Neue Testament im Rahmen der antiken Literaturgeschichte: Eine Einführung*. Darmstadt: Wissenschaftliche Buchgesellschaft.

Doty, W. G. (1973) *Letters in Primitive Christianity*. Philadelphia: Fortress.

Ellis, E. E. (1971) 'Paul and His Co-Workers,' *NTS* 17: 437–52.

Epp, E. J. (1991) 'New Testament Papyrus Manuscripts and Letter Carrying in Greco-Roman Times,' in B. A. Pearson (ed.) *The Future of Early Christianity: Essays in Honor of Helmut Koester*. Minneapolis: Fortress, 35–56.

Exler, F. X. J. (1922) *The Form of the Ancient Greek Letter: A Study in Greek Epistolography*. Washington, DC: Catholic University of America.

Funk, R. W. (1966) *Language, Hermeneutic, and Word of God*. New York: Harper & Row.

—— (1967) 'The Apostolic Parousia,' in W. R. Farmer (ed.) *Christian History and Interpretation*. Cambridge: Cambridge University Press, 249–68.

Harris, W. V. (1989) *Ancient Literacy*. Cambridge, Mass.: Harvard University Press.

Kennedy, G. A. (1984) *New Testament Interpretation through Rhetorical Criticism*. Chapel Hill: University of North Carolina.

Koskenniemi, H. (1956) *Studien zur Idee und Phraseologie des griechischen Briefes bis 400 n. Chr.* Helsinki: University of Helsinki Press.

Llewelyn, S. R. (1994) *New Documents Illustrating Early Christianity*. Sydney: Ancient History Documentary Research Center.

Malherbe, A. J. (1988) *Ancient Epistolary Theorists*. Atlanta: Scholars Press.

Meade, D. G. (1986) *Pseudonymity and Canon*. WUNT 39. Tübingen: Mohr.

Murphy-O'Conner, J. (1995) *Paul the Letter-Writer: His World, His Options, His Skills*. Collegeville, Minn.: The Liturgical Press.

Ollrog, W. (1979) *Paulus und seine Mitarbeiter*. WMANT 50. Neukirchen-Vluyn: Neukirchener Verlag.

Richards, E. R. (1991) *The Secretary in the Letters of Paul*. WUNT 42. Tübingen: Mohr.

Schenke, H.-M. (1975) 'Die Weiterwirken des Paulus und die Pflege seines Erbes durch die Paulusschule,' *NTS* 21: 505–18.

Schubert, P. (1939) *Form and Function of the Pauline Thanksgivings*. BZNW 20. Berlin: Töpelmann.

Sherwin-White, A. N. (1966) *The Letters of Pliny: A Historical and Social Commentary*. Oxford: Clarendon.

Smith, M. (1971) 'Pseudepigraphy in the Israelite Literary Tradition,' in K. von Fritz (ed.) *Pseudepigrapha I: Pseudopythagorica – Lettres de Platon – Litterature pseudepigraphique juive.* Vandevres-Geneve: Fondation Hardt.

Speyer, W. (1971) *Die literarische Falschung im Altertum.* Munich: Beck.

Stowers, S. K. (1981) *The Diatribe and Paul's Letter to the Romans.* Chico: Scholars Press.

—— (1986) *Letter-Writing in Greco-Roman Antiquity.* Philadelphia: Westminster.

Thraede, K. (1970) *Grundzüge griechish-römischer Brieftopik.* Munich: Beck.

Weima, J. A. D. (1994) *Neglected Endings: The Significance of the Pauline Letter Closings.* JSNTSup 101. Sheffield: Sheffield Academic Press.

Westerman, W. L. (1937–8) 'On Inland Transportation and Communication in Antiquity,' *Political Science Quarterly* 43: 270–87.

White, J. L. (1983) 'Paul and the Apostolic Letter Tradition,' *CBQ* 45: 433–44.

—— (1984) 'New Testament Epistolary Literature in the Framework of Ancient Epistolography,' *ANRW* 2.25.2. Berlin: de Gruyter, 1730–756.

—— (1986) *Light from Ancient Letters.* Foundations and Facets: New Testament. Philadelphia: Fortress.

PART III

DOCUMENTS

TEXT AND VERSIONS
The Old Testament

———•◆•———

Carmel McCarthy

INTRODUCTION

Various factors in modern times have deepened our understanding of how biblical books were created and compiled, preserved and transmitted. The more significant of these include the Dead Sea Scrolls (from 1947 onwards), and further textual discoveries in the Judean desert. Also important are the Genizah manuscripts uncovered in Cairo at the end of the nineteenth century. Analysis of their contents has stimulated fresh insights in relation to already existing textual sources, while also expanding our understanding of biblical languages.

To these unexpected discoveries of ancient texts, and their impact on contemporary theory and practice in the field of textual criticism of the Bible, must be added the various advances of modern technology. These permit greater accuracy both in the reproduction of manuscripts and in the compilation of critical editions, while developments in computer software have produced invaluable tools that facilitate research in the textual data themselves. Also significant in furthering our understanding of biblical texts are the more refined methodologies in Old Testament textual criticism, which are constantly being updated and tested in light of the new data. When all of these factors are taken into account the modern biblical student is better positioned to appreciate more fully the importance of a solid textual basis for interpreting the great wealth and wisdom contained in these time-hallowed texts.

Furthermore, an understanding of the history of the biblical text's transmission highlights the care with which the believing communities, both Jewish and Christian, preserved their sacred heritage. A study of textual origins also helps to illuminate the processes whereby certain 'books' were recognized as 'canonical' or authoritative for a particular community, while others, for one reason or another, were excluded from the normative lists. Finally, the variety and complexity of the textual material heightens the challenges facing both editors of critical editions of the biblical texts and those who seek to translate them authentically into a vast range of vernacular languages for modern readers.

THE HEBREW TEXT OF THE OLD TESTAMENT

The pre-textual situation

The Hebrew text that forms the basis of contemporary critical editions and translations of the Bible reached its final stage in medieval times after many centuries of careful transmission. Usually referred to as the Masoretic Text (hereinafter MT), from a Hebrew word, *masorah*, meaning tradition, and linked with a body of medieval Jewish scholars called Masoretes, its prehistory reaches back into ancient times – its beginnings shrouded in mystery. Therefore, rather than speak of the 'original' text of the Hebrew Bible, it might be more helpful to view the coming into being of the biblical text that we possess today as having occurred in approximately four main phases, the first of which is least accessible (Barthélemy 1982: *68–9).

This earliest phase could be described as consisting of oral or written units in forms as close as possible to those that would have formed the 'original' literary production of the different books of the Bible in their final form, the circumstances and length of time for the coming into being of these units varying considerably from book to book. In some instances it might even be argued that there may have existed more than one 'original' form for a given book or biblical unit. Literary analysis of the existing text may help to disclose some of these units and give some clues regarding their preliterary history, but such reconstructions remain tentative in the absence of adequate evidence concerning 'original' compositions.

The earliest attested text

A second phase in the development of the Hebrew text that forms the basis of contemporary critical editions is more tangible and consists of the earliest form or forms of the text that can be determined by the application of the techniques of textual analysis to the existing textual evidence. This can be called the 'earliest attested text'. While for the most part there would not have been major discrepancies between the content of phases one and two, this distinction between the 'earliest attested text' and so-called 'original' texts is both useful and necessary for the task of the textual critic. As will be explored in greater detail below, one of the objects of biblical textual criticism is to try to establish, on the basis of existing textual evidence, what is most likely to have been the form or forms of this second phase of the textual development of the MT. To reach back further and, without supporting textual evidence, reconstruct 'original' readings for those sections of the biblical text that appear to be corrupt or inadequately preserved belongs to the realm of hypothesis and conjecture.

The Proto-MT and the MT

The third phase consists of the consonantal text as authorized by influential circles in Judaism shortly after 70 CE. This phase is often referred to retrospectively as the Proto-MT, since it was this form of the text that was subsequently adopted by Jewish communities from the second century CE onwards, and in due course brought to its final form by the Masoretes in the ninth and tenth centuries CE, through the addition of vowel pointing, accentuation and certain paratextual elements.

This fourth and final phase constitutes the MT properly so-called, and, while it is more or less identical with the text that exists in the principal manuscripts associated with the Masoretes of Tiberias in Galilee, it must be remembered that no manuscript of the Bible presents an entirely unified Masoretic tradition, and that no one textual source in itself fully represents the MT. Rather, what exists in the medieval manuscripts is a group of Masoretic Texts, each representing varying attempts to provide the Bible with a *Masorah* and a consistent vocalic system. The selection of the particular textual form destined to become the MT is linked with socio-religious and historical factors relating to the first century CE, and that it was chosen at that time by a central stream in Judaism in preference to other extant texts does not necessarily imply that it thereby contains the best text of the Bible in every respect (Tov 1992a: 24). Indeed, there are certain instances where the Septuagint or some of the Qumran texts reflect a textual reading superior to that of the MT. But, because of the meticulous attention given by the Masoretes to preserving this particular form of the text in all its detail over the centuries, it can be said to represent the most accessible, reliable and commonly used form of the Hebrew Bible.

The contribution of the Masoretes

In giving a brief overview of the unique role of the Masoretes in the stabilization and transmission of the Hebrew text a distinction must be made between the consonantal text attested in Second Temple sources (mainly between 250 BCE and 70 CE) – the principal component of the MT – and all the other elements that the Masoretes progressively added to it (collectively known as the *Masorah*). Thus, while the medieval form of the MT is relatively late, its consonantal base reflects a very ancient textual tradition, in existence for over a thousand years, and strikingly well preserved. The closeness of the better-quality medieval manuscripts to the earliest attestation of the consonantal form of the MT (in many but not all Qumran texts) illustrates just how carefully the MT was transmitted through the ages. By any standards this is a remarkable achievement, reflecting a concentrated effort to transmit the texts with the utmost precision over the centuries, and reaching its zenith in the ninth and tenth-century Tiberian families of ben-Asher and ben-Naphtali.

Apart from these two illustrious Tiberian families, who were among the most skilled and famous towards the end of the Masoretic period, little else is known about the Masoretes in any great detail. Active in the centuries preceding 1000 CE, this body of scholars was responsible for both the faithful transmission of the consonantal text and for the construction of the *Masorah*, a detailed system of vocalization and accentuation of the biblical text, together with specific rules for copying and counting letters, words and verses of the text.

According as Hebrew ceased to be a spoken language a reliable vocalization system became increasingly necessary, its main function being to eliminate uncertainty regarding the reading of the text, especially where passages or words were susceptible to more than one interpretation. Since this included an interpretative element, the vocalization in the Masoretic manuscripts not only reflects ancient exegetical traditions, but at times incorporates the views of the Masoretes themselves.

It took a number of centuries to perfect the vocalization system and for the eventual supremacy of the Tiberian system as refined by Aaron ben-Asher in the eleventh century. Three main systems were developed for the MT, all of them so respecting the integrity of the consonantal text that vowel signs and accents were only added either above or below the consonants. With time, according as the Tiberian system became authoritative, it slowly replaced the other systems (Babylonian and South-Palestinian).

In addition to creating and perfecting the vocalization system, the Masoretes were also responsible for certain paratextual elements and the *Masorah* proper. The paratextual elements included traditions concerning paragraphing, verses divisions, and a number of other scribal signs, the original functions of which are sometimes unclear. Their aim was to preserve the MT in all its details, including its special characteristics, its inconsistent orthography and even its errors!

The word *Masorah* in the narrow and technical sense of the word refers to an apparatus of instructions for the writing of the biblical text and its reading. This apparatus consists of two main parts, the *Masorah parva* (Mp) and the *Masorah magna* (Mm), as well as an appendix at the end of each book or discrete section, called the *Masorah finalis* (Mf). The Mp consists of an extended set of notes written in Aramaic on the side margins and is concerned with specific occurrences of spellings or vocalizations, certain paratextual elements, and special or peculiar features such as the middle verse of a book, or words that occur in pairs, and such like. In a large number of instances – ranging from 848 to 1,566 according to the different traditions – the Mp indicates that one should disregard the written form of the text (*ketiv*, what is written) and read instead a different word or words (*qere*, what is read) supplied in the margin. In the majority of these instances the actual meaning of the text in question was not affected, but the device illustrates the degree to which the Masoretes were unwilling to change or correct the consonantal text, even when they disagreed with it.

The Mm is written on the upper and lower margins of the biblical manuscripts, and, closely linked to the Mp, its function is to elaborate in greater detail what the marginal Mp notes allude to. The Mf contains various lists, such as lists of the number of verses, letters, or words in the different biblical books.

Although the details of the Mp and Mm differ slightly from one manuscript to the next, and even though there are some inconsistencies in the notes within a single manuscript, the overall accuracy of content and cross-referencing contained in the *Masorah* is simply astounding. Created and developed long before chapter and verse numbering was introduced into the Bible in the thirteenth century via the manuscript tradition of the Vulgate, the *Masorah* could be called a kind of computerized database centuries before such concepts were to become part of today's vocabulary.

Manuscripts of the Hebrew text

Sometimes designated as 'crown' (*keter* in Hebrew), certain manuscripts enjoyed the status of 'model' codices for the study of the text and *Masorah* as developed by the ben-Asher family. A number of these have survived to the present day and are foundational for critical editions of the printed Hebrew Bible. Of these the oldest is the Cairo Codex of the Prophets. Written and provided with vowel points by Moses ben-Asher in 896 CE, it is the oldest dated Hebrew Old Testament manuscript now extant. Containing both Former and Latter Prophets, its text and *Masorah* have been edited in a series at Madrid under the direction of F. Pérez Castro (1979–).

The Aleppo Codex was originally a complete Hebrew manuscript of the Old Testament, provided with vowel points and accents by Aaron ben-Moses ben-Asher (c. 930 CE). Given first to the Karaite community in Jerusalem, its fame is largely due to the fact that Maimonides (d. 1240) declared it to be the authoritative text of the Bible. Its presence in Aleppo is attested from 1478, but anti-Jewish rioting there in 1947 resulted in its being badly damaged, and for a time it was thought to be irretrievably lost. It reached Israel in 1957 in a less than complete form (lacking the Pentateuch up to Deut. 28:17, as well as certain other sections). It has been chosen as the base text for the *Hebrew University Bible* (*HUB*) and for the new edition of the *Mikra'ot Gedolot 'Haketer'* (Cohen 1992).

The Leningrad Codex (dated 1009 CE) is recognized as the best complete manuscript of the Hebrew Bible, and continues to be used as the basis for successive critical editions to the present day. Brought from the Crimea by A. Firkowitsch in 1839, it contains a scribal note indicating that it was written, vocalized and equipped with *Masorah* by Shemuel ben-Jacob from manuscripts corrected and annotated by Aaron ben-Moses ben-Asher. Other important manuscripts of high quality include Codex Or. 4445 of the British Library, dated by some scholars to the end of the ninth century, and by others to the first half of the tenth century, and Codex Sassoon 507, also known as the Damascus Pentateuch, likewise dated between the ninth and tenth centuries.

Printed editions of the Hebrew Bible

The earliest printed complete edition of the Bible can be traced back to the Soncino edition of 1488, while an edition of the Psalms with Qimhi's commentary is earlier still (Bologna 1477). Editions up to 1525 were based on a limited choice of manuscripts, and since some of these latter are no longer extant, it is not possible to evaluate the textual reliability of these early editions. After the appearance of the first Rabbinic Bible in Venice in 1518 (the Hebrew text with *Masorah*, Targum and a selection of Jewish medieval commentators combined on folio pages), a second Rabbinic Bible was published by D. Bomberg in 1524–5. The editor of this edition, Jacob ben-Hayyim, was a careful student of the *Masorah*, but was handicapped by the modifications and refinements introduced into the tradition during the six centuries between Aaron ben-Asher and his own day. The text of ben-Hayyim became, for better or worse, the norm for nearly all printed Hebrew Bibles until recent years. Its four-hundred-year dominance has earned it the status of a type of *Textus Receptus*.

Up until 1975, with the publication in Jerusalem of the first volume of the *HUB* (the *Book of Isaiah*), the monopoly in the production of critical editions of the Hebrew text lay with the tradition associated with R. Kittel. The *Biblia Hebraica* (*BH*), which he first published in 1906, is the most widely used – and still the only complete – critical edition of the Bible. This edition (Leipzig 1906) was based on the second Rabbinic Bible, and called *Biblia Hebraica Kittel* (*BHK*1). A revision of this edition (Leipzig 1913) soon followed (*BHK*2). The further revision of 1929–37 marked a new departure in that it was now based on the Leningrad codex and edited in conjunction with P. Kahle (*BHK*3). From 1951 onwards variants from the Qumran material available were included in its critical apparatus. The next revision of *BH*, usually referred to as *BHS*, under the editorship of W. Rudolph and K. Elliger, was also based on L (Stuttgart 1967–77) and has been reprinted and revised in 1984, 1987, 1990 and 1997 (and reproduced electronically in 1994). A completely new critical edition, on the initiative of the United Bible Societies and with the sponsorship of the German Bible Society, is currently underway (*Biblia Hebraica Quinta*). It continues the *BH* tradition of using L as its base and will incorporate a full Masoretic apparatus in addition to a comprehensive text-critical apparatus which, together with the versional textual evidence, will also include all the Qumran data. It is projected that this new edition will be completed in the early years of the twenty-first century.

The *HUB*, which published its first volumes in 1975 (the *Book of Isaiah*, Vols 1–2, Jerusalem 1975, 1981) and in 1998 (the *Book of Jeremiah*), has opted for the Aleppo Codex as its basic text, together with its abbreviated Masoretic notes on the right margin, and variants in the vowel and accent marks (from a small group of early manuscripts) on the left. The lower part of the page also contains three other apparatuses, the first of which cites the evidence of the versions, the second gives variants from the Qumran scrolls and from rabbinic literature, and the third lists readings from important medieval Hebrew manuscripts on a selective basis.

The British and Foreign Bible Society's edition by N. Snaith (London 1958), while not a critical edition, is based on a Lisbon manuscript of 1483. It also takes into account a small group of manuscripts principally of Spanish origin, and the resultant text is quite close to that of *BHK*.

The Samaritan (and pre-Samaritan) Pentateuch

The Samaritan Pentateuch (SP), as its name implies, contains the text of the Torah only, and constitutes normative sacred scripture for the Samaritan community, a distinctive group of people whose exact origins are unclear. Some scholars consider them to be the descendants of the people of Samaria who separated from the people of Judah in the Persian period (cf. Ezra 4:1–5), while others, on the basis of Josephus, ascribe the origin of the community as well as the building of the temple in Shechem to the period of Alexander the Great. Whatever the ambiguity regarding the dating and origins of the community itself, this does not necessarily have implications for their Torah, since the non-Samaritan (or pre-SP) substratum could well have been created prior to the establishment of the community, or alternatively the SP text could have been formalized much later.

Critical investigation of the SP tradition by European scholars dates back to 1616, the year Pietro della Valle obtained an SP manuscript in Damascus and brought it back to Europe. Copies in European libraries range in age from the twelfth to the twentieth century CE. The 'Abisha Scroll' is the oldest known exemplar (secondarily reassembled from sections of varying date – the oldest from the eleventh century CE), and is kept by the Samaritan community at Nablus. In more recent times the Dead Sea discoveries have helped considerably in reconstructing more clearly the distinctive nature and origin of this particular text tradition.

The SP is a consonantal text written in a special version of the 'early' Hebrew script as preserved for centuries by the Samaritan community. Its reading tradition is an oral one, with only a few manuscripts in recent years having been provided with a full vocalization. Its major significance for critical text studies lies in the fact that it is a Hebrew text not subject to the standardization effected by the late first century CE Jewish scholars. Its nature can be best described by a comparison with the MT from which it often deviates. The first critical classification of these differences was prepared in 1815 by Gesenius. Investigation of texts from the Judean Desert representing a Samaritan-type text has led to a better understanding of the various components of the SP. Recent scholars are of the view that it consists of two strata, a pre-SP substratum and a second layer that is relatively thin and mainly ideological in nature (Tov 1992a: 85–97).

Characteristic of the pre-SP texts are harmonizing alterations and certain linguistic and orthographic differences, while the second layer can be recognized through the presence of typical aspects of the Samaritan religion, literature and language, particularly its ideological changes concerning the place of worship (wherever Jerusalem is referred to in the MT as the central place of worship, the SP text reads Mt Gerizim in its stead).

Scholars are divided on the date of the SP, but it seems likely that it was based on an early pre-SP text similar to those found in Qumran. A palaeographical analysis of the specific version of the Hebrew script used by the Samaritans shows that the preserved texts reflect a form of the script from the Hasmonean era in the second century BCE. As already indicated above, the value of the SP text tradition lies in the fact that, often in accord with the Septuagint, it preserves ancient Palestinian readings of words or phrases that differ from the MT. Where such variants do not just simplify the MT reading or make it more explicit, they need to be evaluated individually. The Samaritan tradition therefore provides a useful and critical point of entry into the textual situation prior to the stabilization of the Proto-MT.

THE GREEK TEXT OF THE OLD TESTAMENT

LXX beginnings and theories of origins

The term Septuagint (LXX), from the Latin word for seventy (*septuaginta*), reflects a legendary story that the Torah was originally translated into Greek by seventy-two elders in seventy-two days. Although the story is recognized as fictitious, the name 'Septuagint' continues to be used and covers a variety of meanings. In its original and most specific usage it refers to the Greek translation of the Torah.

By extension it can denote the entire Jewish–Greek Scriptures. It can also cover the Christian Greek Bible, which includes six deuterocanonical (or apocryphal) books and some additions to other books. The deuterocanonical writings were excluded from the Hebrew canon at the end of the first century CE and placed in the category of books 'which do not defile the hands' (*y. Sanh* 28a). Finally, accepting that the translation of the Hebrew Scriptures into Greek took place in several stages from the third to the first centuries BCE, the term LXX can refer, in a technical sense, to the printed text of editions that carefully and critically seek to establish from the extant witnesses the earliest attainable texts of the Greek translations for the various books of the Hebrew Scriptures, as well as the text of the deuterocanonical books.

In seeking to uncover LXX origins it may be useful to begin by distinguishing between its legendary origin as recounted in the fictitious *Letter of Aristeas to Philocrates*, and whatever may have been the actual circumstances underlying the earliest initiatives to provide a trustworthy Greek translation of the Torah for the sizeable Jewish community in Alexandria in the third and second centuries BCE. The *Letter of Aristeas* relates how a certain King Ptolemy, probably Ptolemy II Philadelphus (285–247), having set out to equip his royal library with all the books in the world, was informed by his librarian that they lacked a copy of the Laws of the Jews. The king thereupon dispatched a letter to Eleazar, the high priest in Jerusalem, requesting that seventy-two learned elders, six from each tribe, be selected to provide a suitable translation of these Laws. On arrival in Egypt the translators were put to work on the island of Pharos near Alexandria. There, in a secluded and pleasant environment, and in the space of seventy-two days, they accomplished their task. The quality of their translation was highly praised by the Alexandrian Jewish community, and its status considered to be so final that a curse was to be pronounced on any who would seek in any way whatsoever to change any part of it.

While scholarly consensus accepts that the letter itself is a literary fiction, its dating and the historical circumstances underlying its composition have given rise to much debate. Views on its date range from 200 BCE to 50 CE, depending on how its purpose is understood. Some scholars argue that the letter is an apologia intended to promote and support an official Greek translation of the Torah. Others view it as propaganda directed at Greeks to show them the superiority of the Jewish religion and law. Others see it as a work intended to defend the literary activities of Alexandrian Jews against the attacks of other Jews in Palestine or elsewhere in Egypt; and, finally, others understand it, not in relation to the first official initiative to translate the Torah, but rather as propaganda against any contemporary attempts to revise an already existing translation.

In spite of this considerable variety of approaches to the *Letter of Aristeas*, there is broad consensus on the following: the events described in it relate only to the Pentateuch, which was the first part of the Jewish Scriptures to be translated into Greek; the translation was an official undertaking supported by Jewish authorities possibly for synagogue and instructional use, and done in Egypt probably in the middle of the third century or earlier; and thirdly, while the number of translators is not certain, it is highly unlikely that there were seventy-two (Peters 1992: 1096).

The LXX Pentateuch therefore bears the hallmark of having been an officially initiated and officially approved translation, made for a very specific community in

Alexandria. As a translation it is generally faithful, competent, and idiomatic, and reflects the work of about six distinct translators. For Genesis the differences between MT and LXX are relatively limited, but for Exodus through to Deuteronomy the variations are greater. The other LXX books came into being over a span of at least two centuries, their translations varying considerably in accuracy and style from one book to the next, and sometimes even within a single book. A case in point are the longer (MT, 4QJer[a,c]) and shorter forms (LXX, 4QJer[b,d]) of the book of Jeremiah and the pluses and minuses in 1–2 Samuel (Pisano 1984: 283–5). A study of the individual relationship between the LXX books and the MT and, more recently, with Qumran biblical texts, has led to varying theories of origin for the LXX as a whole.

Given this complexity, it is not surprising that there have been various attempts over the centuries to unravel LXX origins. In more recent times P. Kahle questioned whether what is preserved in our LXX manuscripts is a single pre-Christian translation or an arbitrary, almost random, selection from many oral renderings, analogous to the early Palestinian Targums. Because of the diversity of witnesses to the LXX text he maintained that there never was one original translation but rather several, designed to meet the needs of specific communities. The Aristeas story, he held, was propaganda for an official revision of earlier translations, not the description of a new one (Kahle 1959).

By contrast the approach of P. de Lagarde maintained that all LXX manuscripts could be traced back to one prototype (or *Urtext*) for each of the LXX books and that variations in the manuscript traditions were due to subsequent interventions and revisions. This position is more representative of the mainstream of contemporary scholarship, notwithstanding various reservations and qualifications, and forms the working hypothesis for the Göttingen *Septuaginta-Unternehmen*, the only institute currently involved in critical LXX editions.

Earliest revisions

Traditionally the earliest identifiable or official revisions of the LXX have been associated with the names of three second-century CE Jewish scholars, Aquila, Symmachus and Theodotion (whose work Origen sought to record in his Hexapla a century later). Analysis of discoveries in the Judean desert, however, has led scholars in more recent years to believe that the work of revising the LXX began much earlier than this, and that these three were merely heirs to a process already well in motion (Barthélemy 1963). It seems likely in fact that revision of the LXX translations began almost as soon as they were copied for the first time. While it is difficult to document this process satisfactorily in its earliest stages, what seems probable is, that by the second century, in reaction to the widespread (and often polemical) use of the LXX by Christians, this work of revision came to particular fruition with the production of editions intended to correct mistranslations and eliminate Christian additions. Their overall aim was to have the LXX text conform to the Hebrew text that had by then become normative in Palestine (the Proto-M).

The best known of these scholars was Aquila, a Jewish proselyte of Pontus and disciple of Rabbi Akiba. His revision took place about 128 CE and, based on strict principles of Jewish interpretation, was extremely literal with regard to the Hebrew text, even to the extent of representing untranslatable elements such as the Hebrew object-marker. Aquila had a good knowledge of Greek, and his literalism and precision made his work particularly attractive to his Jewish contemporaries. His version was respected for many years, and impressed both Origen and Jerome, the latter even borrowing from it in the case of a few rare words. In the past, attempts were made to identify Aquila with Onqelos, the compiler of the most important of the Pentateuchal Targums, but there is no compelling evidence to support this identification.

A second revision is identified with Symmachus, and dated towards the end of the second century CE. Distinguished for its literal accuracy and use of good Greek idiom, the revision is very precise in some places, while in others it translates in keeping with the sense. Some sources (Eusebius) identify Symmachus as an Ebionite, and thus a Christian; others (Epiphanius) contend that he was a Samaritan convert to Judaism. Since there are no traces of Ebionite belief in his Pentateuch translation, it would seem that the view that he was originally a Samaritan is more reliable. He may even have been a disciple of R. Meir, since some aspects of their exegetical techniques coincide, and his revision of the Pentateuch displays a thorough knowledge of rabbinic exegesis of the time (Salvesen 1991: 297).

Theodotion, the third reviser, presents one of the more intriguing problems in modern LXX studies. According to early Christian writers, there was a historical Theodotion variously identified as an Ephesian proselyte to Judaism (Irenaeus), and an Ebionite (Jerome) who worked towards the end of the second century CE. The text on which he worked as a reviser seems, however, to have been different from the standard LXX and to have been in existence since the early part of the first century BCE. In the case of the book of Daniel, Theodotion has replaced the LXX in all but two manuscripts. This situation has led some scholars to postulate a proto-Theodotion in order to explain the presence of Theodotionic readings before the time of Theodotion.

The discovery in 1953 of a Greek Scroll of the Minor Prophets at Nahal Hever led to a rethinking in some circles of the Theodotion problem (Barthélemy 1963). Following Barthélemy, some scholars argue that a second century CE Theodotion is no longer necessary. They suggest that proto-Theodotion (or *kaige*-Theodotion)[1] was all there was, and that this reviser flourished towards the end of the first century BCE, his work being the basis for that of both Aquila and Symmachus in the light of all three being similar in so many instances.

Other scholars, recognizing that Barthélemy's thesis raised as many problems as it solved, have been more cautious and maintain that the historical Theodotion may have worked as a reviser within the tradition reflected by the earlier so-called proto-Theodotion. Questions have also been raised as to whether or not the so-called Theodotion text in Daniel is to be attributed to Theodotion, or whether the sixth column of Origen's Hexapla, traditionally considered to be Theodotion, is indeed what it has claimed to be. While there is agreement on the main characteristics of the revision as identified by Barthélemy, scholars continue to propose further refinements as the work of textual analysis continues.

Later recensions and the Hexaplaric initiative

Next to the story of Aristeas, that of Origen and the Hexapla is perhaps the best known in the history of the LXX text. A native of Egypt, and a Christian, Origen was endowed with an enormous capacity for detailed and hard work. He had the benefit of a wealthy benefactor who provided the means to facilitate his publications. The Hexapla, a massive six-columned work estimated to have numbered about 6,500 pages, was completed between 230 and 240 CE. Origen's chief purpose was to equip Christians for their discussions with Jews, who frequently appealed to the original Hebrew. Accordingly he arranged in parallel columns the following texts:

1	2	3	4	5	6
Hebrew of his day	Hebrew transliterated into Greek	Aquila	Symmachus	LXX	Theodotion

In some books it is reported that he added yet more columns, which he called Quinta, Sexta and Septima. Origen's main concern was the fifth column, LXX, which he hoped to link with the Hebrew text of his day. To achieve this he borrowed from Aristarchus (217–145 BCE) certain sigla, well known and used in Alexandrian philological studies, and incorporated them into his work. Words in his LXX without Hebrew counterparts were placed between an obelus [÷] and a metobelus [◀]. Words and passages in Hebrew without LXX equivalents were copied from another version (most often Theodotion) and inserted into the LXX column between an asterisk [✳] and a metobelus [◀].

That would have been somewhat acceptable had the Hexapla been retained in its original form, or if Origen did only what he claimed to have done. However the situation is more complex because Origen seems to have made other adjustments without indicating them, and, in the subsequent process of copying, some of the signs were omitted, thereby sabotaging the main purpose of the endeavour.

The modern text critic seeks to get behind Origen, to identify pre-Hexaplaric readings, in order to approach in some reasonable way what might have been original LXX. Because Origen mistakenly believed that the Hebrew text available to him was identical with that from which the Greek translators worked, he unwittingly perpetuated the very confusion he tried to remove.

The Hexapla was not easily duplicated, but its fifth column containing the LXX was copied and widely circulated during the fourth century. A new recension was thereby created consisting of a mixture of Origen's Septuagint with random readings from Theodotion and Aquila. In addition, the word order of this Hexaplaric Septuagint differed in places from that of the Greek on which Origen worked, because he, believing in the primacy of the Hebrew, deliberately changed the Greek word order to conform to the Hebrew. The copying of the fifth column in isolation from the Hebrew resulted in a gradual misunderstanding of the Hexaplaric symbols, and a tendency of scribes to omit them. Consequently, many extant manuscripts show the influence of Origen's work but do not retain the Hexaplaric signs. The fifth column was translated into Syriac by Paul, Bishop of Tella, in a monastery not far from Alexandria between 615 and 617, and is known as the Syro-Hexapla. While opinions vary as to how accurately the Hexaplaric signs and the marginal readings from Aquila, Symmachus and Theodotion were copied, few question the importance of the Syro-Hexapla.

Whereas the Hexapla was copied in Caesarea for use in Palestine, two other revisions, according to Jerome, were in circulation, one for use in Egypt and the other in Antioch. Identified with Hesychius and Lucian respectively, practically nothing is known about the Hesychian recension. The more important revision is identified with Lucian, a martyr who died in 312 CE, but the ancient sources, while referring to his life and activity, give no clear indication of either the range or nature of his revision.

Seminal work in isolating traces of the text of Lucian was carried out by Ceriani, Field and de Lagarde, thereby initiating a detailed investigation into the so-called Lucianic recension. Rahlfs refined and extended this work in relation to the books of Kings, and, while several attempts were made by other scholars to identify Lucian outside Samuel–Kings, none of these has proved conclusive. Indeed for much of the Pentateuch there is no evidence of Lucian at all.

What has attracted even greater interest in more recent decades is the so-called proto-Lucian debate. Many have observed the similarity of certain texts, known to have existed before the time of the historic Lucian, to what were determined to be 'Lucianic' readings.[2] The debate on Lucian and proto-Lucian has continued into the modern period with varying positions being upheld by Rahlfs, Barthélemy, Cross and Tov (Tov 1988: 186–87).

LXX manuscripts

The earliest and most important witnesses to the LXX consist of a number of papyri containing sections of the Pentateuch for the most part, dating from the second century BCE to the first century CE. More precise data relating to their extent and dates may be obtained from the Göttingen editions where they are cited (according to Rahlfs's numeration). Also important are the Qumran LXX fragments (Skehan et al. 1992). Among the more important later papyri are the Chester Beatty IV and V (Rahlfs 961 and 962) from the fourth and third centuries CE respectively, containing Genesis 8–46 with some lacunae, as well as Chester Beatty VI (Rahlfs 963) containing Numbers and Deuteronomy with lacunae and dating from the second or early third century CE (Pietersma 1977). Chester Beatty IX (Rahlfs 967) from about 200 CE is particularly significant because it contains the LXX for Daniel (and not the Theodotion text found in all early witnesses).

The uncial (or majuscule) manuscripts date from the fourth to the tenth centuries CE and are so called because in antiquity only majuscules or capital letters, written in sequence and without ligatures, were used for books. The uncials are the main source for our knowledge of the LXX, and the three most important of them contain all or almost all the LXX books. Codex Vaticanus (B), the best complete manuscript, dates from the fourth century and is relatively free of corruptions and influences from the revisions of LXX. Sinaiticus (S, also named א) is likewise fourth century and usually agrees with the text of B, but it is also influenced by the later revisions of the LXX. It was brought to Russia in the nineteenth century from St Catherine's monastery in Sinai, hence its name. Codex Alexandrinus (A) dates from the fifth century, is greatly influenced by the Hexaplaric tradition, and in several books represents it faithfully.

The tradition of joining the letters in a cursive hand gained ground from the eighth century onwards, so that hundreds of minuscule or cursive manuscripts have survived from the ninth to the sixteenth centuries. Although the minuscules are relatively late, they often preserve ancient traditions, particularly if copied from lost uncials containing a good text. Up to the eighth century, texts were written in continuous sequence, without word division, accents, breathing, or punctuation.

Printed editions of LXX

The first printed text of the complete LXX was included in the Complutensian Polyglot prepared in Spain in 1514–17. The Greek text of this Bible then formed the basis for the LXX columns of four other great polyglots (the Antwerp in 1569–72, the Heidelberg in 1586–7, the Hamburg in 1596, and the Paris in 1645). In more recent times almost all the uncials have been published in diplomatic editions, of which the two most important are those of R. Holmes and J. Parsons (Oxford 1798–1827) and A. E. Brooke, N. McLean and J. St.J. Thackeray (Cambridge 1906–40).[3]

The Göttingen *Septuaginta-Unternehmen*, based on the principles of de Lagarde, and incorporating the work of A. Rahlfs, was established in March 1908. This series presents the reconstructed 'original' text, selected from elements found in all known sources. The idea underlying the production of this type of 'eclectic' text derives from the assumption that there once existed an original text of the LXX, but any such reconstructed text can be based only on the data known prior to the preparation of the edition (new data may require adjustments and re-evaluation of existing evidence). The first critical editions to appear in the Göttingen series were Ruth in 1922, Genesis in 1926 and Psalms in 1931, and work continues with some twenty editions available at present. Rahlfs's popular edition of the LXX based on the three major uncials was edited just before his death in 1935 and is perhaps still the most widely used edition of the LXX today. The Göttingen *Septuaginta-Unternehmen* has produced the most reliable critical editions of the Septuagint to date.

The significance of the LXX

Among the early Old Testament versions the LXX holds a unique position. Being the first authoritative attempt to translate the Hebrew Bible in a different cultural milieu, it provides insight into the art of translation and the variety of subtle and not-too-subtle ways in which texts can be reinterpreted in the process of translation. It thereby provides an understanding of how the Hebrew Bible was interpreted by Jews in antiquity. It is particularly important for uncovering the textual history of the Hebrew Bible, since any reconstruction of the Hebrew text underlying the LXX will pre-date by several hundred years the earliest complete manuscript on which our Hebrew Bible can be edited.

For the early Christians the LXX was not secondary to any other scripture – it was Scripture. It was the form in which the Old Testament was most widely circulated in apostolic times, and is the text underlying most New Testament citations of the Old Testament. It provides the context in which many of the lexical and theological concepts of the New Testament can best be understood. As well as having been the literary vehicle for the preaching of earliest Christianity to the Gentile world, the LXX has been and continues to be the liturgical Old Testament text used by Eastern Christians down through the centuries. It also contains the original text of some of the deuterocanonical books (Wisdom, 2 Maccabees) and the basic form (in whole or in part) underlying some of the others.

OTHER ANCIENT VERSIONS

The Old Latin

Since the vernacular language in the first centuries of Christian expansion in the Mediterranean world was mainly Greek, the earliest translations of the Bible into Latin were from Greek, with the exception of Jerome's Old Testament rendering from the Hebrew. Towards the end of the second century Tertullian (c. 160–220) was already using a Latin version, and, according to Jerome (d. 420), by the early fifth century it appears that there were 'as many forms of the text for Latin readers as there are manuscripts' (*Praef. in Josue*). As it appears from patristic quotations and from manuscripts, the Old Latin (OL) is not constant and contains many divergencies. We no longer possess a complete OL version, and its history might be described in terms of successive revisions according to various Greek models, together with alterations in Latin vocabulary and style deriving from the evolution of the language itself. The five books best known in the OL form are those excluded from Jerome's undertaking because he judged them non-canonical. Since these deuterocanonical books were preserved by the church in any event and became part of the Vulgate, we possess a relatively intact text for them, the product of a single translator.

The OL form of other Old Testament books, however, has survived more by way of accident than anything else, apart from the book of Psalms, which has a particularly complicated textual history. While the Pentateuch, along with Joshua and Judges, is recognizable as the work of a single translator, much of the rest has to be pieced together from various sources. These sources fall into five main categories: patristic citations; biblical manuscripts written in the period when the OL was still in use; Carolingian and medieval Bibles; glosses or additions to the translations of Jerome; and finally, biblical lessons, canticles and antiphons in early and medieval liturgical books.

The Vetus Latina Institute at Beuron (Germany) published a comprehensive inventory of extant OL manuscripts and editions of the Old Testament and OL patristic citations in 1949, and is currently engaged in providing critical editions of the biblical books. Already published are Genesis (1951–4) and Wisdom (1977–85), while Isaiah, Sirach and Song of Songs are in preparation, with some fascicules already published. Meanwhile P. Sabatier's *Bibliorum sacrorum Latinae versionis antiquae* (3 vols, Rheims, 1739–49) continues to maintain its usefulness.

The contribution of OL studies is twofold. The OL, not the Vulgate, was the Bible used and commented on by the Fathers. The earlier forms of some OL readings are older witnesses to the Greek than the preserved Greek manuscripts, and in some cases attest the Old Greek. Thus its principal value lies in its relationship with the Greek rather than with the Hebrew text of the Bible.

The Vulgate

The term Vulgate means 'common', referring to a text generally accepted as standard (cf. *koinē* in Greek), and as such was used by the Latin Fathers (including Jerome) for the non-revised text of the Greek Bible, as well as for its Latin version. It is only since the sixteenth century that the term was applied to Jerome's Latin Bible. Because of the diversity of OL texts, in 382/3 Pope Damasus commissioned Jerome (c. 342–420) to produce an authoritative Latin Bible. Jerome began with the New Testament, and after initial work on a revision of the OL form of the Old Testament, particularly in the Psalter (for which he produced two revisions, one of the OL called *Psalterium Romanum*, and one of the Hexaplaric Psalter, called the *Psalterium Gallicanum*), he then began to turn to the Hebrew as crucial for the completion of his task. To abandon the LXX as the basis for his translation was a courageous step since the Greek Bible at that time held a higher status in the Western church than did the Hebrew.

Between 390 and 405 the Latin version of the *Hebraica veritas* began to appear, beginning most likely with the Psalter (Jerome's third version, the *Psalterium iuxta Hebraicum*), then Samuel and Kings, the Prophets and Job being completed by 392. The progress of his work can be traced by his own prefaces to the various groups of books, so that he probably completed his task by about 405. His knowledge of Hebrew was good, of Aramaic slightly less so. In some respects his new translations simply increased the multiplicity and diversity he fought to eliminate.

It is important to distinguish between the work of Jerome as a translator and the subsequent creation of the Vulgate itself. Although Jerome's name is inextricably linked with the Vulgate, the latter term covers a more complex reality, including those parts of Scripture that Jerome seems not to have touched, as well as the later and multifaceted development of the Vulgate in medieval times to the present day.

Jerome's Old Testament from the Hebrew is based almost entirely on the received consonantal Hebrew text; its value in relation to the original is therefore primarily exegetical. By contrast, the various OL renderings from the Greek represent a stage in the transmission of their prototypes that often cannot be attained directly through any extant Greek manuscripts.

The Old Testament Vulgate has been critically edited by the Benedictines of San Girolamo in Rome (1889–1954) with only 1–2 Maccabees not yet published. An edition in one volume with an abridged apparatus was prepared by R. Weber (*Biblia Sacra Vulgata* 1969), its fourth revision appearing in 1994.

THE TARGUMS

According as Hebrew declined as the spoken language of the Jews in post-exilic centuries, it became necessary in synagogue liturgy to provide oral renderings in Aramaic to accompany the public reading in Hebrew of the Law and the Prophets. To preserve their distinction from the sacred texts themselves it seems that these renderings could only be made orally during the service, and not read from a scroll. The same person could not publicly read the Hebrew and recite the Targum. Targum belonged to the oral Torah, whereas the reader had to be seen to read the Hebrew from the scroll. But the Targum was not a free-standing translation to be used on its own; it was always to be heard and studied in conjunction with the original Hebrew.

Since the writing down of these Aramaic renderings was not forbidden, written Targums (*targumim*) gradually came into being. Because of this transition from oral to written transmission, and because the Targums contain paraphrase and midrashic expansions reflecting their practical purpose, it is understandable that their wording varies from place to place, with considerable variation among the different types of Targums. In no other versions of the Bible is the interpretative element as pronounced as in the Targums, a fact that reduces their value as textual witnesses.

The word 'Targum' comes from a quadriliteral root *trgm* that occurs early in Semitic languages and is attested in the world of trade and diplomacy where translation from one language to another was essential. In its one biblical occurrence (Ezra 4:7) it also means 'translate' (from Aramaic to Persian). In later rabbinic Hebrew the root was used in a restricted sense of translating the Bible from Hebrew into another language, usually Aramaic, but sometimes also Greek. Since the verb in rabbinic Hebrew could also mean simply 'to explain' a biblical verse, the term 'Targum' in some situations came to be understood as including more than translation.

Although tradition ascribes the first Targum to Ezra, it is not clear when the first Targums were actually produced. Apart from the Targum fragments from Qumran, which can be dated to the first century CE, the Targums that have been printed and studied in modern times come mostly from late manuscripts. Written Targums of Esther and of other books alluded to in the Mishnah (*Meg.* 2.1; *Yad.* 4:15) most likely antedate 200 CE, and some elements of the Palestinian Targums may reflect a second century BCE date. But the final forms of the Targumic tradition as a whole lie well into the fifth century CE onwards. Targums are extant for all books of the Hebrew Bible except Ezra, Nehemiah and Daniel.

Babylonian Targums

While the basis for all extant Targums most likely originated in Palestine, two principal compilations, Targum Onqelos to the Pentateuch and Targum Jonathan to the Prophets, were reworked extensively in the Jewish schools of Babylonia around the fifth century CE. Targum Onqelos was the only Targum officially approved by the scholars of the talmudic period (before c. 650 CE). In a reworking that adapted it to the details of the standard Hebrew consonantal text, it would have lost whatever midrashic expansions and clues to variant textual readings that it may have had in earlier times. The same may be said for Targum Jonathan to the Prophets, which has a similar history. And yet, despite this reworking, the enormous textual fluidity of the extant Targums (reflecting regional variation and a largely oral transmission over long periods) proves that official uniformity was never achieved. Both Targums have been published in new editions (Sperber 1959–62) that include variants from several extant manuscripts and from a number of early printed editions.

Palestinian Targums

Targum materials directly Palestinian in origin, while less easy to come by, are of greater significance for textual, literary and exegetical purposes. As its medieval designation ('Targum Yerusalmi') suggests, Targum Pseudo-Jonathan (Ps-J) is essentially a Palestinian Targum. The most expansive of the Pentateuchal Targums (roughly twice the length of the original Hebrew text), it is a complex document combining traditions from widely different periods. Although containing elements that appear to be 'early' (before the redaction of the Mishnah and the Jerusalem Talmud), Ps-J as it now stands cannot have been redacted before the seventh/eighth century CE.

Incorrectly catalogued in the Vatican Library in 1892 as 'Targum Onqelos', Targum Neofiti (N) was identified in 1956 by Díez Macho as a recension of the Palestinian Targum to the Pentateuch. N contains a colophon dating it to 1054 CE, and its language has been classified as a form of Palestinian Jewish Aramaic close to the Galilean dialect of the Jerusalem Talmud (Alexander 1992: 323). Though not as expansive as Ps-J, it nonetheless contains many midrashic additions and marginal glosses, and appears to have evolved over a long period of time. There are many views as to its date, ranging from pre-Christian times (Díez Macho 1959) to the Renaissance (Goshen-Gottstein 1975). Accepting that a base text, annotated and expanded over a considerable period of time, lies beneath N, there seems to be no solid basis for dating anything in it later than the third/fourth century CE.

The Fragmentary Targum contains a variety of texts that fall into at least five groups, all containing a distinct type of Palestinian Targum in western Aramaic, and showing certain characteristics which suggest that they are interrelated (Klein 1980). Their incompleteness seems deliberate, rather than the result of accidental fragmentation.

Though aimed primarily at a popular audience, the Targums were the work of scholars well-versed in Hebrew, Aramaic, and biblical exegesis, and should not be taken as spontaneous renderings of untutored translators. Despite their present textual fluidity, the content of the Targums was to a large extent both predetermined and traditional.

Just how directly the extant written texts go back to the Targums of Talmudic times is a matter of dispute. It would be incorrect to assume that they all represent direct transcripts of the oral Targum delivered in the early synagogue. Some of the texts were recited in synagogue. However, there are others (such as Ps-J and N) whose liturgical role, at least in their present form, must be seriously questioned. They more accurately represent scholarly editions of genuine Targumic traditions put together in early medieval times as serviceable collections of early biblical exegesis.

THE SYRIAC VERSION: THE PESHITTA

The earliest translation initiatives for rendering the Old Testament into Syriac lie hidden in antiquity. With roots most likely in the Targumic tradition already in existence for western Aramaic, both their date and place of origin remain uncertain. Syriac, the literary dialect of eastern Aramaic, has been preserved in an abundant Christian literature that came into being towards the end of the second century and flourished until the fourteenth. On the analogy of Targumic origins it is possible that first/second century Jewish and Christian preachers from Palestine initiated translation processes in the district of Adiabene (near Irbil in modern Iraq), especially in Edessa (Urfa in modern Turkey). Like the LXX, the Peshitta Old Testament was not translated as a whole, but book by book, with most books possibly originating in the first/second century CE, since the Old Syriac Gospels adapt certain Old Testament quotations to the Peshitta Old Testament text.

Representing a compilation and careful reworking of these early materials, the Peshitta Old Testament was firmly established by the fifth century, an initiative linked with the name of Bishop Rabbula. There are varying views on the precise meaning of the term Peshitta, the more commonly accepted one being 'simple'. As a term it was not attested until the ninth century, when it was used to distinguish this version from the Syro-Hexapla, the other main Syriac translation in existence for the Old Testament (of seventh-century origin). Though basically a translation from a Hebrew text more or less identical with the MT, the Peshitta occasionally exhibits secondary influences from the LXX in those books most used in the liturgy (Isaiah, Psalms). Apart from Sirach, the deuterocanonical books were translated from the LXX. The Peshitta rendering of the various books of the Old Testament is uneven in quality, ranging from fairly accurate to paraphrastic. Certain books, especially the Pentateuchal ones, occasionally reflect loose connections with the Targum tradition.

Compared with the LXX, the textual history of the Peshitta Old Testament is relatively stable, and variations of any real importance are infrequent (Brock 1992: 794). Recent studies in the extant manuscripts have revealed three slightly different text forms in many of the books. The earliest stage, closest to the Hebrew, is partially represented in the rare fifth-century manuscripts. The second stage, represented by sixth to eighth-century manuscripts, is well preserved and aims for a more smoothly flowing text. This process reached a further stage in the medieval manuscripts that form the *Received Text*. The older editions contained in the Paris (1645) and London (1657) Polyglots are based on late manuscripts, and are not critical editions. The oldest complete Peshitta Old Testament manuscript (Codex Ambrosianus of the sixth/seventh century, edited by A. Ceriani in 1876) is more useful for text-critical purposes, and has been adopted as the basis for the Leiden Peshitta Institute critical editions. A number of volumes in this series have already been published, each accompanied by a detailed apparatus containing other early manuscript readings.

OTHER EARLY VERSIONS

From the point of view of the transmission of the biblical heritage the other early Old Testament versions of interest include the incomplete Coptic versions in the

Sahidic and the Bohairic dialects, and the Ethiopic, Armenian, Georgian and Arabic versions. Since these represent translations from the Greek, vary in the quality of translation, and are relatively late in origin, their interest lies more in the sphere of LXX transmission-history rather than being of direct relevance for the textual history of the Hebrew Bible.

TEXTUAL CRITICISM AND THE OLD TESTAMENT

Nature and aims

Before embarking on a discussion of the procedures and practical methods of Old Testament textual criticism, one should first form an opinion on whether there once existed *one* original textual form (*Urtext*) or *several forms* of biblical books, and, secondly, what it is one seeks to achieve in attempting to determine the nature of this text or texts. The majority opinion supports the *Urtext* view, although some of the implications of this assumption have not been adequately tested (Tov 1992b). But how realistic is it to speak of the 'original' text, and how feasible is it to hope to attain it? The transmission history of the Old Testament text as outlined above shows clearly that all the witnesses stand somewhat removed from such an 'original' text, however one understands this term. A detailed comparative study of the content of the textual witnesses reveals that they not only contain a great variety of scribal errors, such as occur inevitably in any form of manuscript transmission, but also a number of variant readings that show actual transformations and changes of meaning, both accidental and deliberate.

A crucial question in investigating how the biblical text was created, how it was copied and transmitted, and how variant readings came into being is to distinguish between differences created in the course of the textual transmission, and those that derive from an earlier stage, that is, during the literary growth of a book. The work of textual criticism is properly focused only on those created during the textual trans-mission, while those belonging to earlier stages must remain in the domain of literary criticism (even though occasionally some traces of these may remain in the textual witnesses). As already indicated at the outset, the prehistory of our present Old Testament text lies beyond the province of textual criticism. Reconstructing the exact words of the prophets for example in their presumed 'original' form, separating the various layers of Pentateuchal traditions, investigating questions of literary integrity and the like, are among the tasks properly entrusted to literary criticism and exegesis. Perhaps a more modest goal for the text critic would lie in establishing 'the earliest attested text'. This does not mean attempting to recover the original wording of the sentences as they were first conceived, but the textual form of the Old Testament books when they attained their present shape and content and became canonical writings, the finished literary product that stood at the beginning of the textual transmission stage. It is with such a goal in view that the remainder of this section will unfold, keeping in mind that it will not always be easy to determine the precise stage in the development of a given biblical book that can be called either the *Urtext* or 'the earliest attested' text.

Since textual criticism strictly speaking deals only with attested textual evidence, the critical editions of the Hebrew Old Testament are not eclectic, but 'diplomatic', that is, they reproduce a particular form of the received text as the base text (L for the *BH* tradition, or A for that of the *HUB*), while recording divergent readings or variants from Hebrew and non-Hebrew sources in accompanying critical apparatuses. For theoretical as well as practical reasons this has to be the case, because, as indicated above, not all scholars agree that initially there existed only one 'original' text of a biblical book. By contrast, most modern translations of the Old Testament are eclectic: while basically following the MT, they replace certain MT readings with alternative ones from the versions.

Methods and procedures

Old Testament textual criticism can be divided into two sections: analysis of the biblical text as attested in Hebrew manuscripts and as reflected in the ancient versions on the one hand, and the identification, characterization and evaluation of the variant readings that emerge in relation to the MT. When all the variants are assembled from the Hebrew sources, and reconstructed from the versional evidence, they need to be evaluated. This is done through comparison with the MT without implying that the MT is automatically the best text in all instances. The aim of this comparison is to determine which, if any, of the variant readings has a better chance of representing the 'earliest attested' text than the others. The fact that it is not possible to decide in all instances does not invalidate the correctness of the procedure as a whole (Tov 1992b).

The evaluation of variant readings is based on a number of considerations, some of which are less objective than others. When all the different forms of a particular text are carefully compared, it becomes evident that various types of factor come into play in determining which form of the text is likely to have been more 'original', and which form or forms are more typically secondary. A first set of factors pertains to the *structural relationship* between the texts. Rather than *count* text traditions, one should *weigh* them. For example, if a textual variant occurs in only one tradition, the significance of this fact must be explored. On the other hand, a textual variant may appear to have a broad basis of support, in that it is represented by a number of different textual traditions; but closer examination, however, may reveal that these have all followed the same interpretative tendency (such as attempting to make an obvious improvement on some obscurity in the original text). In situations where there is dependence of a variety of text forms upon one earlier form it may be helpful to look for a 'key' to explain how the diverse forms have arisen. Analysis of these structural factors on their own is insufficient, and must be supplemented by one or more of the causal factors that follow below.

This second set of factors are termed *causal* in that they attempt to explain the reasons for certain alterations in the text, and cover both conscious and unconscious aspects. The conscious factors include processes such as *simplification* of the text (a natural tendency for ancient scribes and translators), and *assimilation* of the text of one passage to that of a similar or proximate passage, usually with the apparent purpose of attaining greater consistency. Both of these tendencies have given rise to rules of thumb that, in certain situations, more difficult or shorter passages are to be preferred.[4]

Translational adjustments to the linguistic requirements of the ancient receptor languages, as well as misunderstanding of linguistic or historical data, are also ways in which a text may be consciously (or even subconsciously) altered. In other instances a particular form can be essentially interpretative, reflecting specific initiatives of ancient editors, scribes or translators to have the underlying text changed or amplified to conform to certain views, often theological in nature (McCarthy 1981). Unconscious alterations include mechanical errors such as accidental omissions of similar letters, words, or sentences, repetitions of identical sequences, and the occurrences of conflate readings and doublets.

While the foregoing is a brief attempt to indicate some of the chief considerations and guidelines that textual critics use in making textual evaluations or characterizations of variant readings, it is also true that to some extent textual evaluation cannot be bound by any fixed rules. The main task of the text critic is one of choosing 'the contextually most appropriate reading', a task that of necessity involves a subjective element (Tov 1992a: 309–10). A judicious mixture of careful analysis, intuition, and common sense in the application of the considerations described above should be the main guide. In the last analysis textual criticism is an art in the full sense of the word, a faculty that can be developed, guided by intuition based on wide experience. It is the art of defining the problems and finding arguments for and against the originality of the readings. And in that process there can sometimes be room for more than one view.

NOTES

1   This recensional activity was called *kaige* from the fact that this was an unusual Greek form characteristically used to render a particular Hebrew combination (*and also*).
2   Among these 'pre-Lucianic' readings are parts of the Old Latin version dating from the second century CE, the Peshitta version of the OT, a papyrus fragment of Ps 77:1–18 dating from the third/second century CE, certain New Testament quotations, and second-century papyrus fragments of Deuteronomy.
3   Based on the *Sixtina Romana* edition of 1587, which in turn is based on Codex B, the former records variants from 164 manuscripts, the early translations of LXX, and the first editions of LXX. The latter, also according to Codex B, has been supplemented by A or S where B is lacking.
4   *Lectio difficilior potior* and *lectio brevior potior*.

BIBLIOGRAPHY

Alexander, P. S. (1988) 'Jewish Aramaic Translations of Hebrew Scriptures', in M. J. Mulder (ed.) *Mikra*. CRINT 3. Assen: van Gorcum; Philadelphia: Fortress.
—— (1992) 'Targum, Targumim', in D. N. Freedman (ed.) *The Anchor Bible Dictionary*, Vol. 6. New York: Doubleday.
Barthélemy, D. (1963) *Les devanciers d'Aquila*. VTSup 10. Leiden: Brill.
—— (1982, 1986, 1992) *Critique textuelle de l'Ancien Testament*. OBO 50/1, 50/2, 50/3. Göttingen: Vandenhoeck & Ruprecht.
Bogaert, M.-P. (1992) 'Latin Versions', in D. N. Freedman (ed.) *The Anchor Bible Dictionary*, Vol. 6. New York: Doubleday.

Brock, S. P. (1992) 'Syriac Versions', in D. N. Freedman (ed.) *The Anchor Bible Dictionary*, Vol. 6. New York: Doubleday.

Cohen, M. (1992–) *Mikra'ot Gedolot 'Haketer'*. Ramat Gan: Bar Ilan University.

Díez Macho, A. (1959) 'The Recently Discovered Palestinian Targum: Its Antiquity and Relationship with the Other Targums', VTSup 7: 222–79.

Dirksen, P. B. (1988) 'The Old Testament Peshitta', in M. J. Mulder (ed.) *Mikra*. CRINT 2/2. Assen: van Gorcum; Philadelphia Fortress.

—— (1989) *An Annotated Bibliography of the Peshitta of the Old Testament*. MPI 5. Leiden: Brill.

Dirksen, P. B. and Mulder, M. J. (eds) (1988) *The Peshitta*. MPI 4. Leiden: Brill.

Goshen-Gottstein, M. H. (1963) 'Theory and Practice of Textual Criticism – The Text-Critical Use of the Septuagint', *Textus* 3:130–58.

—— (1975) 'The "Third Targum" on Esther and MS Neofiti 1', *Bib* 56: 301–29.

—— (1983) 'The Textual Criticism of the Old Testament: Rise, Decline, Rebirth', *JBL* 102: 365–99.

Kahle, P. (1959) *The Cairo Geniza*, 2nd edn. Oxford: OUP.

Klein, M. L. (1980) *The Fragment Targums of the Pentateuch*. AnBib 76. Rome: Biblical Institute Press.

McCarthy, C. (1974) 'Emendations of the Scribes', in *The Interpreter's Dictionary of the Bible, Supplementary Volume*. Nashville: Abingdon.

—— (1981) *The Tiqqune Sopherim and Other Theological Corrections in the Masoretic Text of the Old Testament*. OBO 36. Göttingen: Vandenhoeck & Ruprecht.

Pérez Castro, F. (1979) El Códice de profetas de el Cairo. Madrid: Instituto Aras Montano.

Peters, M. K. H. (1992) 'Septuagint', in D. N. Freedman (ed.) *The Anchor Bible Dictionary*, Vol. 5. New York: Doubleday.

Pietersma, A. (1977) *Chester Beatty Biblical Papyri IV and V*. Toronto: Samuel Stevens Hakkert.

Pisano, S. (1984) *Additions or Omissions in the Books of Samuel*. OBO 57. Göttingen: Vandenhoeck & Ruprecht.

Salvesen, A. G. (1991) *Symmachus in the Pentateuch*. Manchester: Manchester University Press.

Skehan, P., Ulrich, E. C., Sanderson, J. E. and Parsons, P. J. (1992) *Qumran Cave 4 IV, Palaeo-Hebrew and Greek Biblical Manuscripts* (DJD 9). Oxford: OUP.

Sperber, A. (1959–62) *The Bible in Aramaic*, Vols. 1–4. Leiden: Brill.

Tov, E. (1988) 'Septuagint', in M. J. Mulder (ed.) *Mikra*. CRINT 2/2. Assen: van Gorcum; Philadelphia: Fortress.

—— (1992a) *Textual Criticism of the Hebrew Bible*. Minneapolis: Fortress.

—— (1992b) 'Textual Criticism (Old Testament)', in D. N. Freedman (ed.) *The Anchor Bible Dictionary*, Vol. 6. New York: Doubleday.

Weil, G. (1971) *Massorah Gedolah iuxta codicem Leningradensem B 19a*, Vol. 1. Rome: Pontifical Biblical Institute Press.

Würtwein, E. (1995) *The Text of the Old Testament*, trans. E. F. Rhodes, rev. and enlarged edn. Grand Rapids: Eerdmans.

Yeivin, I. (1980) *Introduction to the Tiberian Masorah*. Missoula: Scholars Press.

TEXT AND VERSIONS
The New Testament

——— •◆• ———

David Parker

Although the authors of the New Testament writings were part of the biblical world, the story of the passing down of these writings steps in and out of many different worlds, including our own. This introduction will attempt to concentrate on the world of late antiquity in which they were written and first copied, referring less frequently to the subsequent medieval and Byzantine eras, and hardly at all to any more recent times.

The study of the texts and versions of early Christianity is a study of oral traditions and of manuscript copies. It begins with the Aramaic sayings of Jesus, and passes through Greek to Syriac, Latin, Coptic, Armenian, and eventually to our modern languages – in fact to more tongues and dialects than those listed in Luke's account of the gift of the Spirit at Pentecost. The texts include gospels, epistles, apocalypses and acts of apostles.[1] Some of these today comprise the collection called the New Testament. We should not forget that to their early compilers and users, these New Testament texts were only a part of that wider body of early Christian writings. These groups of texts (the Gospels, Epistles, Apocalypse and Acts) require somewhat different treatment, according to the nature of their origins and their character. But before this treatment can be attempted, a general description of the transmission of texts in the ancient world must be offered.

In the days before computers, before recording and before printing, the transmission of texts was very different from that known today. The most obvious difference is that the production of handwritten copies was far more laborious: one typesetting can be the source of a thousand copies; but a thousand manuscripts are the product of a thousand copyings. The second point is that each of those copyings will be unique, containing its own characteristics and its own errors. While it is possible to copy a text very accurately if one is determined enough, it is clear that the early Christians were not particularly determined in this respect. It is as though copyists took rather literally Paul's statement that he and his colleagues were 'ministers of a new covenant, not in a written code but in the Spirit' (2 Cor. 3.6). But Christianity did espouse the book quite enthusiastically. And in doing so it happened to have a significant effect on book production.

Books in the ancient Mediterranean world had traditionally taken two forms: the skin roll and the papyrus roll. Usually, the skin was parchment – animal skin (most often of sheep or goat) treated so as to produce a fine-textured, thin material. Sometimes leather (tanned skin) was used. Papyrus was a kind of reed, grown almost solely in Egypt. Two layers of the thin-sliced stems would be laid at right angles to each other, glued and pressed together to make a sheet. A roll was formed by gluing skins or papyrus sheets together. Skin was generally used by Jews for producing the Torah and other books, while papyrus was used by Greeks and Romans for book production.[2] In addition to these materials, wax tablets were used for notes. These were formed by tying a number of blocks together. Papyrus notebooks of a similar format were used for similar purposes. These were the traditional ways of making books. It is a striking contrast that very few copies of New Testament texts were written on a roll. Instead, they took the format of the tablet or notebook, and enlarged it into the papyrus codex, the book that we know today. Whether they invented the format is still not clear. But it is abundantly clear that they were the first to use it regularly.[3]

The codex came to the church early, and became a central part of its activity. The importance accorded it continues to be seen today. Whether in magnificent volumes or in cheap pocket copies, the books of the New Testament enjoyed a wide circulation. This breadth and variety is attested today in the way in which the surviving Greek manuscripts are catalogued. The vast majority are from the Byzantine period, produced between the tenth and sixteenth centuries. They were copied in a hand called minuscule, and they are listed by a simple number, such as 1 or 565. Most manuscripts of the first millennium are divided according to the material on which they were written. Papyrus copies are given a number prefixed by an upper-case 'P', as P45 or P66. This number is generally written as a superscript (P^{45}, P^{66}). Parchment manuscripts are classified in several ways. Because they have been recognized since the sixteenth century to be older and often more significant than minuscule copies, they have often been given names, reflecting their provenance (such as Codex Vaticanus) or some particular characteristic. When this became difficult to record succinctly when providing variant readings from them, upper-case letters were used, first of the Roman, then of the Greek and finally of the Hebrew alphabet (such as A, Π, or א). Then, numbers prefixed by a zero were adopted, such as 01, 0289. But the name and the letter are still often used for the first forty-five of them. Finally, there are lectionaries. These are manuscripts that contain the passages as prescribed in the lectionary, in the order in which they are to be read. They are indicated with a number preceded by an italic lower-case l, as *l*184.[4]

In reading the Gospels, and in considering their copying in early and medieval times, we should bear in mind the process of copying. The scribe had the task of preparing his materials. If he was writing on parchment, then he needed to cut it to the size he needed, and to complete the smoothing down of the surface for writing. He then needed to mark the margins and lines for writing. This was usually done with a dry point, after first marking the place for each line with a sharp point (pricking). Different writing centres had different customs, and it is often possible to ascribe a medieval manuscript to a particular area or even centre, on the basis of such details as whether the parchment leaves were laid out flat and all the leaves of a gathering pricked and ruled at once, or separately, and according to the placing of hair and flesh sides in a gathering. The two sides of a sheet of parchment are slightly different in colour and character: the hair is darker and absorbs the ink more readily, while the paler flesh side is oilier and sometimes repels the ink. The two sides are obvious at a glance. It was the custom for the facing leaves of a codex to show the same side of the skin.

With papyrus, the scribe had again to cut the sheets to the size that he wanted, and to prepare the surface. But, as far as we can tell, the sheets were not ruled for the lines of writing. At any rate, no papyrus has yet been found on which any traces of pricking or ruling may be discerned. Either the scribe wrote without them, or they were provided by a means no longer visible.

The sheets ready, the scribe then prepared the pen, made in antiquity from a length of reed. This was held, not like a modern pen but between the first, second and third fingers, with the thumb free and the little finger supporting the hand. The cut of the pen and the angle at which it was held were two key factors in the scribe's producing a desired script. The ink also had to be prepared. For papyri, a vegetable ink was generally used. Parchment manuscripts, on the other hand, were generally written on with a metallic-based ink. This gives off an acid, which has seriously damaged some copies. A small number of de luxe manuscripts were produced, in which the parchment was dyed purple, and silver and even some gold ink was used. But this was exceptional. The illuminated manuscripts and fine miniatures that attract many people are the product of the medieval world. Any kind of extensive adornment was unusual in early Christianity. Perhaps a simple rope pattern at the end of a book was all that a scribe supplied, or maybe even that was lacking. Later there came more adornment. But most books were functional. Clarity of writing was paramount, and after that beauty of script.[5]

The scribe is now ready to begin. There were no desks, tables or chairs in antiquity. The scribe sat cross-legged, with the blank writing material on his knee, perhaps with a flat board under it, and with the manuscript to be copied beside him on the floor. In the Byzantine period, he will have had a kind of lectern. Dictation, in which one person read while a number produced copies, was certainly practised in the medieval monastic tradition. Its use in the early period is far less certain, and there is no incontrovertible evidence for it. It is more likely that individual scribes copied, looking at their copy, remembering the word or phrase, speaking it out loud to themselves as they wrote it down. And thus the wearisome process went on, until the book was done, the sheets could be bound into gatherings and the gatherings into a codex, and the finished article delivered to the customer. Before that could be done, it was desirable that the copy be checked. Some New Testament manuscripts were thus corrected; many were not. Even where they were, the modern reader will be puzzled to note how much imperfection the corrector allowed to stand. It may be asked how long it would take to copy the entire New Testament. There are variables here, and no categorical answer can be given. But one medieval Latin copy, the Stavelot Bible, contains a note telling us that the whole work, writing, illumination and binding, took two scribes 'the best part of four years'.

The question of dates brings us to the issue of dating manuscripts. Byzantine manuscripts were frequently dated. But the custom did not exist in antiquity; the oldest dated New Testament manuscript is a copy finished on 7 May 835. We depend for the earlier period almost wholly on palaeography, the comparative study of hands.

It is possible to place hands in a sequence of development, since formal literary hands were carefully taught and imitated, and developed in observable ways. One should consider any date as accurate within half a century, the approximate working life of an individual scribe.

The purpose for which books were produced must also be considered. Some were written by a scholar for private use. While these are harder to identify from antiquity, many examples are known from the Byzantine world. A sufficiently wealthy book-collector might send a slave to copy a particular text that he wished to acquire. But we should probably assume that the majority of copies of New Testament texts were produced for church use. The corollary of this is that for most people the texts were heard, not read. Ancient books had virtually no punctuation, and were written without spaces between words. The lector's task was not an easy one, and there is evidence that church copies would be taken home for preparation. In the course of time, various aids were added, especially from the third century on. These consisted of divisions into sections, into short chapters, and eventually the provision of lists of contents, and tables for finding parallel passages between Gospels. Before that, the barest of titles at the beginning and end of a book was all that the reader had. Even running titles and page numbers were a considerable rarity in Greek books in late antiquity.

The use of the New Testament texts in early Christianity has still to be fully explored. Besides the formal literary copies I have described are other, possibly more influential texts. A substantial number of papyri of John's Gospel contain a passage of text, perhaps a verse or more, and beneath a fortune-telling sentence. Copies of the Lord's Prayer or of other texts on tiny scraps of writing material, or even on shards of pottery (ostraka) perhaps served as spells to ward off evil spirits. Many such artefacts have been recovered in the course of excavations of Egyptian sites. They may have been the closest that many or even most people got to written Christian texts.

To return to the literary end of the spectrum: The ways in which a text came into circulation were quite different from the process of publication familiar today. A writer might circulate a few copies among his circle of friends. If they liked the work and talked about it, then other people might send one of their scribes to make them a copy, and so on. There were booksellers, but their shops did not contain rows of pristine volumes waiting to be sold. Production would have been on commission. Thus, we must reckon with quite a slow beginning to the circulation of most texts, including those of early Christianity. But we shall have to reckon with different circumstances for different books. This is because they circulated separately, not only initially, but for the most part down to the invention of printing. Only four complete Greek Bibles survive from antiquity (they are of the fourth and fifth centuries), and a further five from the tenth to the fifteenth. While the idea of a New Testament canon emerged in the course of events from the second century on, the idea of a single codex containing them does not seem to have become common until much later. We should consider the New Testament to have been to early Christianity a small library rather than a single volume.

The books circulated in small collections: the Gospels, Paul's Epistles, Acts and the Catholic Epistles and, in different associations or on its own, Revelation. We shall study them beginning with the first to be written.

PAUL'S LETTERS

The writings of Paul are the earliest collection of Christian books to have come down to us. Produced in the 40s and 50s, they consist of thirteen letters, nine of them to congregations, and four to individuals. While doubts have arisen as to the authenticity of some (Ephesians, Colossians, 2 Thessalonians, 1 and 2 Timothy, and Titus), and to the literary integrity of others (1 and 2 Corinthians), we still have a collection of at least seven of Paul's letters. They have in common that they were written in one place and sent to another. They were produced in response to specific events (Gal. 1.6), sometimes at least partly in reply to another letter (1 Cor. 7.1), or to reports (1 Cor. 1.11). They were dictated by Paul to an amanuensis (Rom. 16.22) sometimes with a final greeting in Paul's own hand (1 Cor. 16.21; Gal. 6.11). They were taken to their destination, and then read aloud in the congregation (1 Thess. 5.27). These individual letters would have been written on small rolls; Philemon perhaps on a single sheet.

The situation with regard to the recipients of Romans and Ephesians is somewhat uncertain. As to the latter, several of the most important manuscripts omit the words 'in Ephesus' in 1.1. It is conceivable that this is a circular letter (see also Col. 4.16). The circumstances surrounding the Epistle to the Romans are even more complicated. It circulated in antiquity in a fourteen-, fifteen- and sixteen-chapter form, with 16.25–7 standing at the end in each. That is to say, in some copies the letter ended at the end of chapter 14, in others at the end of 15, and in others at the end of 16. In addition, a few copies omit the words 'in Rome' at 1.7. It has been suggested that the final chapter of personal greetings (strange to a church Paul had never visited – 1.10–11!) is a later addition, supplied to revise the letter for sending to the Ephesians. Whatever the truth of the matter, it is certain that this letter circulated in three different forms in the early church.[6]

What happened to these letters next? We only know that they were evidently kept safely, presumably by their recipients. The care with which this was done may have varied, for it is clear that Paul wrote at least one other letter to the Corinthians (1 Cor. 5.9). The vital point for the later preservation of the letters is the one at which the separate letters were brought together into a single collection. Some theories propound a date around the year 100. Here the fact that some of the letters, notably the pastorals, are best explained as dating from the subapostolic age, must be borne in mind. For if the earliest collection was of all the Pauline letters in the New Testament, then a suitable lapse of time after his death in the mid-60s must be included in the reckoning. One may conjecture that copies were taken from those in the local archives, and these in turn copied into a single volume. Whether this was a roll or a codex, we simply do not know. The theory that this collection was the first codex has recently been advanced. Previously it had been argued and accepted that the first codex was a Gospel book. The matter remains under consideration.

Whatever the format, it is with this event that the copying process of the collected Pauline letters begins. It is this collected text that it is the primary goal of the critic to recover. The task of establishing the text that Paul originally sent will follow from this. The situation with regard to Romans is less simple. Whichever of the three forms of the text was included in the collection, it may be that the problems are the result of the continuing influence of another form, perhaps one sent to a separate destination.

We know very little about the text of the collection in the second century, except for the fact that it was subjected to a revision by Marcion. Marcion held the view that the creating god of the Old Testament was not the god of the New, and that this fact had been obscured by a 're-Judaizing' of Christianity. He set out to rid the early Christian writings of these interpolations. He accepted ten Pauline epistles (apparently he did not know of the Pastorals). Ironically, given his status as a heresiarch, his prologues to these ten letters later became part of the standard ancillary material in the Vulgate Latin Bible.

It is with the transition from the second to the third century that our knowledge of the collection becomes secure. For it is from around the year 200 (perhaps a hundred years after the formation of the collection and fifty after Marcion) that the oldest extensive manuscript may be dated. Now in the Chester Beatty collection in Dublin since its discovery in Egyptian sands in the early 1930s, this remarkable survival is a papyrus codex. It contains portions (it has suffered considerable damage) of Romans, 1 and 2 Corinthians, Galatians, Ephesians, Philippians, Colossians, 1 Thessalonians and Hebrews. We therefore learn at once that Hebrews, anonymous though it is, had by now been included in the collection. On the other hand, the codex did not contain the Pastorals. We know this by a simple computation. It is a single-quire codex, made by folding a pile of sheets in half. We can calculate the number of sheets missing at the beginning, and thus at the end also. The letters are in descending order of length, and the missing portion was not sufficient to contain the Pastorals.

The oldest complete copy of the letters is another century and a half younger. The accession of Constantine brought the church both peace and prosperity. With these came more money and more time for producing books. The lasting result was a transition from papyrus to parchment for the production of books. Thus the parchment codex became for over a thousand years the medium of Christian book production. The immediate result was a number of extensive collections of Christian texts (Septuagint, New Testament and other early writings) provided in three or four matching codices. Two of these survive from the fourth century (Codex Vaticanus and Codex Sinaiticus), and two from the fifth (Codex Alexandrinus and Codex Ephraemi Rescriptus). Vaticanus, preserved in the Vatican Library since at least the fifteenth century, is the product of the most careful tradition of copying. Alexandrinus is of similar quality. Ephraemi Rescriptus is a palimpsest, a manuscript whose parchment has been scraped clean and reused (making it very hard to read the older text).

One other Greek manuscript deserves mention as a key witness to the Pauline text. Produced in the middle of the tenth century in Byzantium, this manuscript is written in the minuscule hand that had by the previous century become the normal script for writing manuscripts. According to the custom for designating manuscripts in this script, it is given a simple number: in this case, 1739. Although so comparatively recent, it preserves ancient materials: according to various notes, it is a copy of a manuscript that itself had been copied from a manuscript compared with a copy

Figure 13.1 A page of one of the oldest Bibles of the Old and New Testaments, the monumental Codex Sinaiticus, showing John 1.1–38. The four-column format is unique. Among the many corrections, note at the bottom of Column 3 the alteration of Bethania to Bathabara in John 1.28. Add. Ms. 43725. Copyright British Library.

annotated by the early third-century scholar Origen, by Pamphilus, martyred in 309. It is important to note that the Chester Beatty papyrus and this manuscript often agree together. Such agreements against other witnesses are an important pointer to the text of the late second and early third century.

A few examples of textual variation in Paul's letters must suffice.[7] General is the problem that in Hellenistic Greek the first- and second-person plural personal pronouns were pronounced identically. Since scribes wrote words speaking them out loud to themselves, there is considerable confusion in many places. Does Paul mean 'us' or 'you', does he include himself in the statement? A similar problem arises at Romans 6.1. Did Paul write, 'We have peace', or, 'Let us have peace'? The difference is between a long and a short 'o', pronounced identically in the Hellenistic period. The more familiar wording of Romans 8.28 is 'all things work together for good to them that love God'. More likely and more profound is the reading of Codex Vaticanus, now supported by P[46]: 'For those who love God, God works everything for good.' At Hebrews 2.9 (Pauline to our early scribes, though not to us) the author offered the startling and brilliant idea that Christ tasted death for all 'without God'. The first hand of the minuscule manuscript 1739 is one of only two Greek manuscripts to read this. In addition, it is supported by one Latin manuscript, and by several important early Christian writers including Origen, Ambrose and Jerome. Where the citations of an early writer are clear enough for us to reconstruct the text of the book from which he was quoting, the testimony is important. We then know that such and such a text was in circulation at such a time and such a place. This information can be of vital importance in reconstructing the history of the text, the stages of copying through which a writing passed.[8] The reading 'without God' is probably original. But the idea is likely to have fallen foul of later orthodoxy.[9]

THE GOSPELS

The four canonical Gospels appear to have come into existence in the last forty years of the first century. They constitute a vital stage in early Christianity's memories of the sayings and acts of Jesus, for they represent the transition from oral to written text. However, we must offer several cautions. First, we do not know that they were the first or the only representatives of that transition. Second, the oral tradition did not come to an end when written records were produced. Third, the original form of the Gospels is lost to us. The oldest extensive surviving copy of any Gospel dates from more than a century after the first writing down of that Gospel. We must allow for the possibility that the texts which survive do not represent what the evangelists wrote, but have been to some unknown extent moulded by subsequent readers and copyists. Indeed, when one begins to study them in detail, one is staggered by the amount of variation between the manuscripts. It is an established fact that written texts of all kinds are most likely to suffer extensive alteration in the earliest stages of their lives. Thus, a high proportion of these variations in the Gospel text occurred before the year 200. Certainly, the creation of variation did not cease thereafter. But there is strong evidence that many of the most significant differences had indeed come into existence by then. In order to understand the problem, we must first describe the witnesses to the text. Remember, we do not have autographs, or authoritative copies. There are simply a large number of separate copies, each unique. The number of copies of the *Gospels* is far greater than that of any other part of the New Testament. It consists of papyri, majuscules, minuscules and lectionaries. The oldest of these (P^{52}) is a tiny scrap of John's Gospel, written in the second quarter of the second century. It is very small, and the passage it covers contains, sadly, no significant reading. But three other papyri of particular value must be mentioned. One, copied in about 200, contains nearly all of John's Gospel (P^{66}). Another of a similar date is also extensive, preserving most of Luke, and most of John down to chapter 15 (P^{75}). This particularly significant manuscript shows all the signs, both in script and text, of being the result of careful and thoughtful production. The third (P^{45}) contains fragments of the four Gospels and Acts. It is somewhat later than the other two. It was found in the same place as the Chester Beatty manuscript of Paul's letters, and is in the same collection today. Unfortunately, there are no papyri of Matthew or Mark as extensive as P^{66} or P^{75}. For the value of these papyrus witnesses is that they are older than anything that had been known before they were discovered in the course of excavations in Egypt. Until then, the oldest copies were those important fourth-century majuscules mentioned in the description of witnesses to the text of Paul. The papyri break the 'Constantinian barrier', and have made it possible for scholars to scrutinize the theories they had founded on the majuscules. The theory had been of a number of 'recensions', distinctive 'editions' of the text, established in the fourth and fifth centuries. The most valuable was the Alexandrian text, represented above all by Codex Vaticanus. Another was the Antiochian text from which the main 'Byzantine' text of the majority of later manuscripts was descended. A third came to be known as the 'Western' text. It puzzled everyone, for it seemed to depart most bafflingly and aberrantly from the other two, and yet sometimes it seemed to have a preferable text. Hitherto, there had been three ways of working out the text of the third century and before. The first was from the citations of early Christian writers. Here Origen, the great theologian and exegete of Alexandria and Caesarea, rules supreme. His extensive commentaries on Matthew and John often contain the material from which the Gospel text known to him may be reconstructed. The second was to examine and compare the earliest translations of the Gospels. These were the Syriac and Latin versions, both with their origins in the second century. Where these two agreed, one had cross-bearings on a now lost Greek text of the second century from which they were both derived. It was noticeable that they did often agree, and that in these agreements they were often joined by the Western text. This increased the puzzle over the Western text for those who favoured one of the other text types as more original. It encouraged some people to prefer it to the others. The third way was to compare the various forms of text in variant readings, and by observation, historical knowledge and common sense to work out which form must be the cause of the others.[10]

The discovery of P^{45} in the 1930s, and of P^{66} and P^{75} in the late 50s, made it possible to put these theories to the test. P^{75} turned out, dramatically, to be either a precursor or an early member of the Alexandrian group. While not identical to Codex Vaticanus, it is so similar, and shows such similar thoroughness in its production, that the relationship is evidently close. But apart from this, there were no earlier representatives of the post-Constantinian text-types. There were manuscripts that offered promise of being Western, and then gave up being so. There were manuscripts that contained Byzantine readings, but then had a lot of non-Byzantine readings. With the exception of P^{75}, these papyri seemed to contain the pool of readings found in later manuscripts, but not to contain them in the distinctive blend that gave the later recensions their particular characteristics. There were a number of reasons for this change from second-century fluidity to fourth-century recensions. First, the success of the recensions was their promulgation by leading sees and figures, who saw the importance of agreed texts in cementing the unity of the Church; one might put this rather differently, and observe that control of the text was one way, along with the definition of orthodoxy and the prescription of the Canon, in which powerful figures strengthened their power. Until the fourth century there were no individuals or offices with the power successfully to do this. Second, such magnificent volumes as Codex Vaticanus or Codex Sinaiticus are the product of wealth and leisure. It is improbable that the Church of the Martyrs had sufficient of either. Indeed, it is perhaps unlikely that Christians of an earlier generation would have approved. Jerome, writing early in the fifth century, wrote caustically of those who produced luxurious codices while Christ was starving at their door. Even more significant than these two reasons is a third: that early Christians were not so interested in preserving the texts verbatim as in preserving what they considered to be the proper significance and meaning of the Gospels. This concept of faithful copying is most noticeable in the transmission of the words of Jesus. It may be illustrated with a few examples:

In the earliest Gospel to have been written, that according to Mark, Jesus offers the following pronouncement about the end time: 'But of that day or hour no one knows, not even the angels in heaven, nor the Son, except the Father' (13.32). Matthew (24.36) preserves this in his Gospel, with various small changes. But that Luke, the third of our evangelists to write, omitted the saying totally, may indicate that this denial of knowledge to Jesus soon became troublesome to Christians. Certainly, there is manuscript evidence from later times. A number of copies of Matthew, the oldest going back to the third century, omit the words 'nor the Son', as do several manuscripts of Mark.

At Luke 9.55 it is stated that Jesus rebuked the disciples' desire to bring down fire on the unwelcoming Samaritan village. This lack of information was considered unsatisfactory, and many manuscripts supply the words 'and he said, "You do not know of what manner of Spirit you are; for the Son of man came not to destroy men's lives but to save them."' These words appear to be a pastiche of Luke 19.10 and John 3.17, adapted to indicate what Jesus would have said on such an occasion. The first part of the saying was certainly in circulation in the second century, and the rest of it can be little more recent.

Finally, the reader is referred to the particularly striking example of Jesus' sayings on divorce and remarriage (Matt. 5.32; 19.9; Mark 10.11–12; Luke 16.18). There, in addition to marked differences between the English texts of each Gospel, there are further variants within each Gospel, so that more than a dozen different sayings are all put on to Jesus' lips.[11]

THE ACTS OF THE APOSTLES

The textual history and problems of Luke's second volume are different again from anything hitherto described. It is generally formulated as the book's existing in two separate forms, one long and the other short. These two forms are also generally associated with two manuscripts. The long form is represented by Codex Bezae, which in the Gospels is the chief representative of the Western text, and the short form by Codex Vaticanus, in the Gospels the best representative of the Alexandrian text. The situation is in fact rather more complicated than this: it has been argued that Codex Bezae presents a rather degenerate version of the longer text, which is found more purely in other representatives; in addition, various witnesses contain some but not all of the features of the longer text. But, before exploring the questions more fully, an example of the differences must be provided.

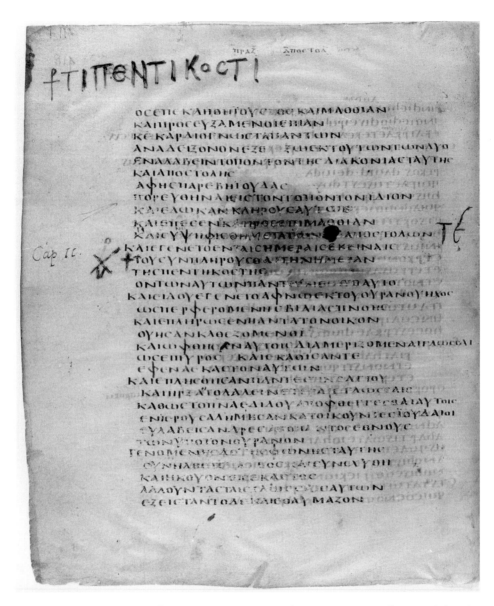

Figure 13.2 The opening of Codex Bezae (written in about 400). The Greek on the left and a Latin version on the right contains the variants at Acts 2.1 discussed in the text (in lines 12–19). The early Byzantine scrawl at the top records that it is the reading for Pentecost. 'Cap. II' in the margin is sixteenth or seventeenth century. By permission of the Syndics of Cambridge University Library.

Figure 13.3 Codex Vaticanus, the manuscript most influential in the formation of the text used by English copies of the New Testament, showing Acts 2.1–2. The letters were reinked in the medieval period. Vatican, Gr. 1209 (Codex Vaticanus) Acts 2.1–2 (p.1383). Copyright Biblioteca Apostolica Vaticana.

First, the shorter text (that on which the principal English versions are based), here translated out of Codex Vaticanus, of the passage Acts 2.1–2:

> When the day of Pentecost had come, they were all together in one place. And suddenly a sound came from heaven like the rush of a mighty wind, and it filled the whole house where they were sitting

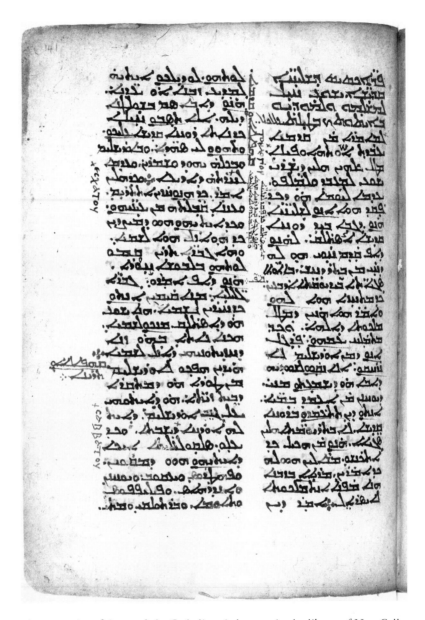

Figure 13.4 A manuscript of Acts and the Catholic epistles now in the library of New College, Oxford. It represents the Harklean Version, produced in 616 by Thomas of Harkel, a careful scholarly product. MS New Coll. C. 333 Fol. 141r. Copyright Bodleian Library, Oxford. By permission of the Warden and Fellows of New College, Oxford.

This is the same passage, as it is found in Codex Bezae:[12]

> And it came to pass in those days when the day of Pentecost had come,
> when they were all of them in one place, and behold suddenly a sound came
> from heaven like the rush of a wind of might, and it filled all of the house
> where they were sitting.

As in the Gospels, we find that other important witnesses to the text of Codex
Bezae are found in various languages. In Syriac there is the Harklean Version, a very
careful and unidiomatic translation of the Greek, produced in 616, and with useful
marginal notes on certain important readings. In Latin we have several important
manuscripts. In Coptic there is a manuscript written in a little-attested Middle
Egyptian dialect in the fourth century, which is complete as far as the beginning of
chapter 15. There are also some other interesting Greek witnesses, including a copy
containing also a Latin translation, written probably in Sardinia in the sixth century.
Called Codex Laudianus as a result of its ownership by Archbishop Laud, and now
in the Bodleian Library in Oxford, it is probably the actual manuscript the Venerable
Bede used when he was writing his commentary on Acts.

There have been three main explanations for the existence of the two versions of
the text: that the longer one is authentic, that the shorter is authentic, and that both
are the work of Luke's hand. There has always been least support for the first point
of view. It seems strange that copyists or readers should excise interesting and improv-
ing stories about the apostles, while it is readily understandable why they should
expand such material. Almost the only strong point in favour of the theory is the fact
that there seem to be places where the shorter text is rather clumsy where there is an
expansion in the longer text, as though it had been crudely reduced.

The case for two Lukan versions has been advanced several times, most recently
in an account that takes seriously the nature of an edition in the ancient world.[13]
As we have seen, this consisted of a limited private circulation, followed by wider
dissemination. It has been suggested that Luke wrote a version known to us as the
shorter text, which was read in his circle. As a consequence of readers' reactions,
Luke made marginal and interlinear additions and corrections. After a period of
neglect in the second century, an unknown editor produced the longer version from
Luke's corrected copy, sometimes confusing corrections for additions. The study of
the two versions is, therefore, a study not in the textual history of the book, but in
Luke's creative activity. This theory is interesting and not implausible. The traditional argument against it is that the two versions are sometimes contradictory, and
therefore cannot both be Lukan. This seems weak – if one believes the accounts to
be based on sources, then the author might have found what he considered to be
superior evidence; if, on the other hand, one considers Luke's literary creativity to
have played a large role in his composition, then one might suppose that he had
thought of a better way of telling the story. A more telling problem, and one to
which the present writer has devoted some study, is that the longer text itself appears
to have undergone a process of growth. Broadly speaking, the earlier forms of the
longer text of which we know appear to have been shorter than the later forms. For
example, the story of the baptism of the Ethiopian eunuch has passed through several

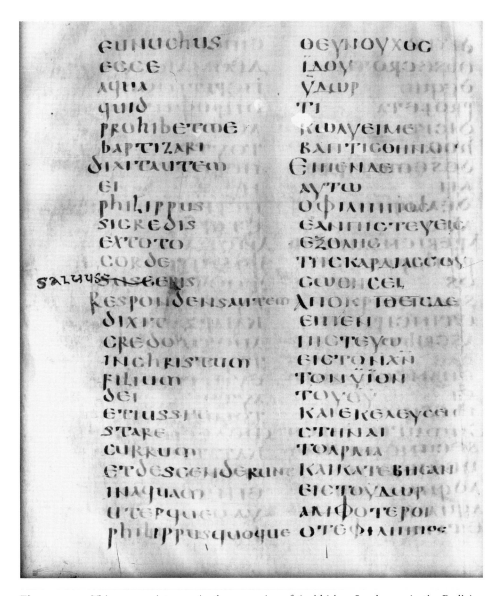

Figure 13.5 This manuscript once in the possession of Archbishop Laud, now in the Bodleian Library Oxford, has a Greek version, with a Latin translation on its right hand on each page. It shows Acts 8.37, when the manuscript supports the longer reading. MS Laud Gr. 35 fol. 70. Copyright Bodleian Library Oxford.

stages of development. Verse 37 is missing in the short version. As it is found in the main Greek witness to the longer version, it reads:

> Philip said to him, 'If you believe with all your heart he [sic] will be saved.'
> Answering he said, 'I believe in the Christ the Son of God.'

Other witnesses to the longer version present the eunuch's reply as 'I believe Jesus Christ to be the Son of God'.

The short version of verse 39 reads:

> When they came up out of the water, the Spirit of the Lord snatched Philip away . . .

The text of Codex Alexandrinus (not generally a witness to the longer text) and of some witnesses to the longer text runs:

> When they came up out of the water, the Holy Spirit fell upon the eunuch, and the angel of the Lord snatched Philip away . . .

This addition, along with the variation in verse 37, illustrates how readily such accounts were developed by early Christian readers and copyists, and indeed this example clearly illustrates the reasons for such development.

Another recent approach to the two texts has been less concerned with the question of originality, and instead has focused on the internal logic and ideas of the longer text. The contribution of 'Discourse Analysis' has played a key role here. Changes in word order or tense, the selection of one conjunction rather than another, may have played an important role in the way in which ancient readers understood the text. These apparently small changes in the longer text may be cumulatively significant in casting light on its development.[14] Additionally, it may be that certain theological and cultural presuppositions shed light on the growth of the longer text. In particular, it has been argued that some changes show the increasing anti-Jewish feeling of the third, fourth and fifth centuries, projected back into Luke's picture of the emergent church.[15]

A final example to illustrate the two texts of Acts may be taken from chapter 15 and the Apostolic Decree (verse 29). It is found in the shorter text of Codex Vaticanus as follows: 'that you abstain from what has been sacrificed to idols and from blood and from what is strangled and from unchastity'. The longer text of Codex Bezae runs, 'that you abstain from what has been sacrificed to idols and from blood and from unchastity; and whatever you do not wish to happen to yourselves, do not do to another'. The reading differs in the excision of the reference to 'what is strangled', a compromise in the keeping of Torah that was no longer relevant at a later date, and in the universalization of the specific commands in the negative formulation of the Golden Rule.

The picture, therefore, that emerges is of a text of Luke preserved most accurately, though by no means without blemish, by the witnesses of the short text form, particularly Codex Vaticanus. Alongside this there developed a text form that handled

Luke's text quite freely, considering it acceptable to expand or to rewrite sections in order to highlight certain points of doctrine or practice that could then be more clearly seen to have been done in such and such a way by the earliest church. Although the long text has little claim to be original, it deserves careful study, for it is a prime witness to the way in which early Christianity used and interpreted Acts.

THE CATHOLIC EPISTLES

The Catholic Epistles were generally, and from early times, contained in a single codex with Acts. But they have none of its textual complexities. There are, of course, many variations, some of great significance, and a number of them extremely difficult to elucidate. The text is currently being comprehensively edited in the first volume of the major critical edition being prepared by the Institute for New Testament Textual Research in Münster, Westphalia.[16] Although they were transmitted together their origins are quite separate, and it is some ways misleading to discuss them together. Jude and 2 Peter seem, however, to have a close relationship, and it has generally been agreed that part of the latter is derivative of the former. It appears that a small amount of harmonization between the two at a later stage of copying has made confusion worst confounded in sorting out this problem.

Several early papyri of this collection have been recovered, including P[72], a manuscript found with P[75] of Luke and John, and like it of a high quality.

THE BOOK OF REVELATION

This, the book least copied throughout the manuscript period of Christianity, has again a quite different textual history. Before it is explained, a little pure textual theory will help. The editor of classical texts in Greek or Latin will be used to dealing with a handful of manuscripts, perhaps all of them derived from one early medieval copy. Such an editor will study the variations between these witnesses, for the purpose of constructing a family tree or stemma, showing how they relate to one another. When that has been done, a large number of the variations within each witness may be shown to be secondary, the result of error or confusion within the copying. The process of restoring the original text is made easier by eliminating so many differences between the manuscripts.[17] This process has never been possible for the New Testament. Not only are there are too many copies; the task is made impossible by the ever-shifting alliances between manuscripts. Technically, the manuscripts are contaminated: they are not, to continue the genealogical analogy, pure descendants of those lost copies that we seek to reconstruct, but represent frequent intermarryings between different groups. The cause of the problem is simply that the New Testament books were copied too often.

All, that is, except for Revelation. There are under three hundred manuscript copies. Here, while it is not possible to create a stemma, one can divide all the manuscripts into families. There were two families, each of them containing two groups. The number of papyri of this book is small, and indeed the oldest copy to contain more than a fraction of the text is Codex Sinaiticus, which has it complete. Although some complicated theories of the stages by which this book came into being have been proposed, the manuscripts show no such extensive differences between one another. But a number of interesting problems arise. These include the number of the Beast at 13.18, given in some manuscripts as 666, and in others as 616. Greek numerals are given by the allocation of letters of the alphabet to the successive units, tens and hundreds, so that the difference is of a single letter. Various explanations for each number have been given, all depending upon the numerical value of various names of Roman emperors and wordings referring to the Roman state, and it seems likely (space prevents a proper discussion) that the number was deliberately changed in order to make the text relevant to a new crisis in the life of the Church. A variant that illustrates the problems of the lack of punctuation and of word division is found in the well-known verse 14.13. A translation without punctuation might run, 'Blessed are the dead who die in the Lord henceforth blessed indeed says the Spirit that they may rest from their labours for their deeds follow them.' 'Henceforth' may go with either the first or the second half of the sentence. A similar problem arises at the end of chapter 12. Should we read 'I stood', connecting the sentence with chapter 13, or 'It stood', finishing off chapter 12? The difference is one letter in the Greek.

It will be observed that the variation in this book is slight, and this should not be ascribed only to the relative infrequency of its copying, and to its less regular use (to this day it has never been part of the Orthodox lectionary cycle); but also to the nature of the text. The greatest variation in the New Testament texts exists in the Gospels, and particularly in those parts where one might expect there to be least: that is, the sayings of Jesus. An interesting situation emerges: from the number of copies, and its enthusiasm for producing them, early Christianity might appear to be very much a people of a book. But the degree to which they changed the text of those copies shows them to have felt not at all constrained to treat them with any particular reverence or caution. The curse pronounced at the end of Revelation upon those who added to or took away from 'the words of this book' may or may not have deterred readers and copyists. It was certainly not a general early Christian attitude to their texts. Along with the written text went a powerful belief in the continuing inspiration of the Church by God's Spirit, and a conviction that the meaning was being made plain in their midst. This showed itself in theological controversy of high import, particularly with regard to Christological and Trinitarian matters, by a willingness to tweak the text in the direction of what a particular reader or copyist considered to be the truth. It is likely that the original words of the heavenly voice at Jesus' baptism according to Luke (3.22) were 'You are my Son, today I have begotten you.' This may have seemed rather adoptionist at a later point, and were replaced by words taken from Matthew and Mark: 'You are my beloved Son, in you I am well-pleased.'[18] It was, as shown already, only from the fourth century, and initially even then only gradually, that the text began to be treated as fixed. Even so, there was never an overwhelming determination to remove all aberrant forms of text. This may be illustrated by examples of quite late manuscripts, tenth-century or later, that reproduce very early (even second- or third-century) types of text or groups of readings.

The study of the many manuscripts of the New Testament, in the early versions as well as in Greek, besides being in itself a fascinating pursuit, is of value not only in the quest for the earliest and original texts. It also casts light on the theological and social development both of Christianity and of the many cultures in which it grew.

NOTES

1 M. R. James, *The Apocryphal New Testament*, Oxford, 1924; revised edn ed. J. K. Elliott, Oxford, 1993.

2 For ancient books see B. M. Metzger, *Manuscripts of the Greek Bible: An Introduction to Greek Palaeography*, New York: Oxford University Press, 1981.

3 Although their solution did not win universal agreement, so that it has been modifed, see C. H. Roberts and T. C. Skeat, *The Birth of the Codex*, London: The British Academy, 1983.

4 The complete catalogue of all Greek New Testament manuscripts is K. Aland, *Kurzgefasste Liste der Griechischen Handschriften des Neuen Testaments* (ANTF 1), 2nd edn, Berlin: de Gruyter, 1994. For descriptions of the principal manuscripts, see K. and B. Aland, *The Text of the New Testament: An Introduction to the Critical Editions and to the Theory and Practice of Modern Textual Criticism* 2nd edn, Grand Rapids: Eerdmans; Leiden: E. J. Brill, 1989) and B. M. Metzger. *The Text of the New Testament: Its Transmission, Corruption, and Restoration*, 3rd edn, New York: Oxford University Press, 1992. For an account of each of the four groupings of manuscripts, see Part I of B. D. Ehrman and M. W. Holmes, *The Text of the New Testament in Contemporary Research: Essays on the Status Quaestionis. A Volume in Honor of Bruce M. Metzger* (SD 46), Grand Rapids, 1995.

5 For the role and use of books see Harry Y. Gamble, *Books and Readers in the Early Church: A History of Early Christian Texts*, New Haven: Yale University Press, 1995.

6 Harry Y. Gamble, *The Textual History of the Letter to the Romans* (SD 42), Grand Rapids: Eerdmans, 1977.

7 For important discussions of many other important readings in Paul, see G. Zuntz, *The Text of the Epistles: A Disquisition upon the Corpus Paulinum*, The Schweich Lectures of the British Academy 1946, London: The British Academy, 1953.

8 See Part Three of Ehrman and Holmes, *The Text of the New Testament in Contemporary Research*.

9 For this and other theologically motivated alterations to the text, see B. D. Ehrman, *The Orthodox Corruption of Scripture*, New York: Oxford University Press, 1993.

10 D. C. Parker, 'The Development of Textual Criticism since B. H. Streeter', *NTS* 24 (1977), 149–62.

11 See, for this last example, and for the issues discussed in general, D. C. Parker, *The Living Text of the Gospels*, Cambridge: Cambridge University Press, 1997.

12 The two Greek texts are given on facing pages in J. H. Ropes, *The Text of Acts*, Vol. 3: *The Beginnings of Christianity*. Part 1: *The Acts of the Apostles*, ed. F. J. Foakes-Jackson and K. Lake, London, 1926. They give a history of the text, ccxc–ccxcvii. An English translation of Codex Bezae was made by J. H. Wilson, *The Acts of the Apostles*, London: SPCK, 1924.

13 W. Strange, *The Problem of the Text of Acts* (SNTSMS 71), Cambridge, 1992.

14 See e.g. J. Heimerdinger, 'The Seven Steps of Codex Bezae: A Prophetic Interpretation of Acts 12', in D. C. Parker and C.-B. Amphoux (eds), *Codex Bezae: Studies from the Lunel Colloquium June 1994* (New Testament Tools and Studies 22), Leiden: E. J. Brill, 1996.

15 The most important such study is E. J. Epp, *The Theological Tendencies of Codex Bezae Cantabrigiensis in Acts* (SNTSMS 3), Cambridge, 1966, 1–40, 165–71.

16 *Novum Testamentum Graecum Editio Critica Maior* IV Catholic Letters, Instalment 1 James, Part 1 Text and Part 2 Supplementary Material, ed. B. Aland, K. Aland, Gerd Mink and Klaus Wachtel, Stuttgart: Deutsche Bibelgesellschaft, 1997; Instalment 2 The letters of Peter, 2000.

17 The process is succinctly described by P. Maas, *Textual Criticism*, tr. B. Flowers, Oxford: Clarendon Press, 1958. The wittiest as well as one of the profoundest discussions is A. E. Housman's 'The Application of Thought to Textual Criticism', *Proceedings of the Classical Association* 18 (1922), 67–84; reprinted in *The Classical Papers of A.E. Housman*, ed. J. Diggle and F. R. D. Goodyear, Vol. 3, Cambridge: Cambridge University Press, 1972, 1058–69.

18 See Ehrman's *The Orthodox Corruption of Scripture*.

BIBLIOGRAPHY

Aland, K., *Kurzgefasste Liste der griechischen Handschriften des Neuen Testaments* (ANTF 1), 2nd edn, Berlin: de Gruyter, 1994.

Aland, K. and B., *The Text of the New Testament: An Introduction to the Critical Editions and to the Theory and Practice of Modern Textual Criticism*, 2nd edn, Grand Rapids: Eerdmans; Leiden: E. J. Brill, 1989.

Ehrman, B. D., *The Orthodox Corruption of Scripture*, New York: Oxford University Press, 1993.

Ehrman, B. D., and Holmes, M. W., *The Text of the New Testament in Contemporary Research: Essays on the Status Quaestionis. A Volume in Honor of Bruce M. Metzger* (SD 46), Grand Rapids: Eerdmans, 1995.

Epp, E. J., *The Theological Tendencies of Codex Bezae Cantabrigiensis in Acts* (SNTSMS 3), Cambridge: Cambridge University Press, 1966, 1–40, 165–71.

Gamble, Harry Y., *The Textual History of the Letter to the Romans* (SD 42), Grand Rapids: Eerdmans, 1977.

—— *Books and Readers in the Early Church: A History of Early Christian Texts*, New Haven: Yale University Press, 1995.

Heimerdinger, J., 'The Seven Steps of Codex Bezae: A Prophetic Interpretation of Acts 12', in *Codex Bezae: Studies from the Lunel Colloquium June 1994*, ed. D. C. Parker and C.-B. Amphoux (New Testament Tools and Studies 22), Leiden: E. J. Brill, 1996.

Housman, A. E., 'The Application of Thought to Textual Criticism', *Proceedings of the Classical Association* 18 (1922), 67–84; reprinted in *The Classical Papers of A. E. Housman*, ed. J. Diggle and F. R. D. Goodyear, Vol. 3, Cambridge: Cambridge University Press, 1972, 1058–69.

James, M. R., *The Apocryphal New Testament*, Oxford, 1924; rev. edn ed. J. K. Elliott, Oxford: Oxford University Press, 1993.

Maas, P., *Textual Criticism*, trans. B. Flowers, Oxford: Clarendon Press, 1958.

Metzger, B. M., *Manuscripts of the Greek Bible: An Introduction to Greek Palaeography*, New York: Oxford University Press, 1981.

—— *The Text of the New Testament: Its Transmission, Corruption, and Restoration*, 3rd edn, New York: Oxford University Press, 1992.

Parker, D. C., 'The Development of Textual Criticism since B. H. Streeter', *NTS* 24 (1977), 149–62.

—— *The Living Text of the Gospels*, Cambridge: Cambridge University Press, 1997.

Roberts, C. H., and Skeat, T. C., *The Birth of the Codex*, London: The British Academy, 1983.

Ropes, J. H., *The Text of Acts*, Vol. 3: *The Beginnings of Christianity*. Part 1: *The Acts of the Apostles*, ed. F. J. Foakes-Jackson and K. Lake: London Macmillan, 1926, ccxc–ccxcvii.

Strange, W., *The Problem of the Text of Acts* (SNTSMS 71), Cambridge: Cambridge University Press, 1992.

Wilson, J. H., *The Acts of the Apostles*, London: SPCK, 1924.

Zuntz, G., *The Text of the Epistles: A Disquisition upon the Corpus Paulinum*, The Schweich Lectures of the British Academy 1946; London: The British Academy, 1953.

ADDENDUM

The reader's attention is drawn to an important recent study, which argues that the Greek New Testament was first produced as an edition, as part of a Christian edition of the entire Greek Bible made in the middle of the second century. This theory, which deserves to be taken very seriously, is at variance with some of what is argued above. In another work, the same author has argued that Paul himself produced a collected edition of four of his letters (Romans, 1 and 2 Corinthians, and Galatians), with Romans 16 as a cover note.

Trobisch, D., *The First Edition of the New Testament*, New York: Oxford University Press, 2000.
—— *Paul's Letter Collection: Tracing the Origins*, Bolivar, Missouri: Quiet Waters Publications, 2001.

The reader's attention is also drawn to a study of early Christian scribes and their role:

Haines-Eitzen, Kim, *Guardians of Letters: Literacy, Power, and the Transmission of Early Christian Literature*, New York: Oxford University Press, 2000.

CHAPTER FOURTEEN

THE DEAD SEA SCROLLS

—— ·◆· ——

George J. Brooke

BASIC DESCRIPTION

The term Dead Sea Scrolls refers to manuscript finds from several sites in the wilderness of Judaea mostly from the middle of the twentieth century. Although the discoveries at Masada and other locations have been very significant, the term Dead Sea Scrolls is most commonly associated with the manuscript finds from the eleven caves at or near Khirbet Qumran on the north-west shore of the Dead Sea. Between 1947 and 1956 eleven caves were discovered there either by local Bedouin or by archaeologists. Fragments of over 850 manuscripts have come to light.

Samples from the collection have been subject to accelerator mass spectrometer dating and for the most part it is clear that the manuscripts were produced during the last three centuries before the fall of the Second Temple in 70 CE. The pottery found in the caves with the fragmentary manuscripts contained some distinctive types that were also found on the site at Qumran where coin evidence in particular suggested more or less continuous occupation from about 100–75 BCE to 68 CE.

THE QUMRAN SITE

The site Qumran takes its name from the Arabic term given to the place that since the middle of the nineteenth century has been anglicized as Qumran. Some scholars have wondered whether behind the Arabic name there lies a biblical place name such as Gomorrah. Some confidence has been expressed in the view that the site is to be associated with biblical Secacah (Joshua 15.61), which name also occurs in the *Copper Scroll* four times.

There were five seasons of excavations at Qumran (1951, 1953–6) led by Père Roland de Vaux of the Ecole Biblique et Archéologique Française in Jerusalem. It soon became apparent that the caves and the site were linked in some way, since distinctive pottery types found in the caves were also to be found at the site. Though this link has sometimes been challenged, such challenges have not been successful, not least because several of the caves where manuscripts were found are very near to the site. The vast majority of scholars are thus happy to associate the scroll deposits in the caves with the principal period of occupation of the site itself.

Although the complete reports from the Qumran excavations have yet to be published, de Vaux presented his interpretation of the history of the site on several occasions. As a result the site is usually described in terms of the periods of its occupation, rather than stratigraphically. For the two centuries before the fall of the Jerusalem Temple in 70 CE, de Vaux divided the occupation of the site into two periods. Although he subsequently pushed the initial date of occupation back to the middle of the second century BCE, his first impression which is now strongly advocated by scrolls scholars and archaeologists alike was that the initial period of occupation began (Period Ia) at some point near the end of the second or the beginning of the first century BCE. A small rectangular courtyard, first constructed in the seventh or sixth century BCE was reoccupied and a round cistern reused. This small building was almost immediately expanded (Period Ib) into a complex of both large and small rooms with small industrial installations, such as those for making pottery. The water system was expanded and the cisterns from this period (and Period II) are of two types, those with limited steps or none at all, which were probably used for water storage, and those with divided steps across the whole of one end, which may well have served for bathing or ritual washing. For de Vaux the site was abandoned in 31 BCE when it was hit by a large earthquake and, on the basis of his interpretation of the coin evidence, not reoccupied until sometime shortly after the death of Herod the Great in 4 BCE. Recent reconsideration of the coin evidence from the Herodian period has resulted in the proposal that the period of abandonment was much shorter than de Vaux proposed and might not have been caused by the earthquake of 31 BCE. Nearly all are agreed, however, that the site was attacked by the Romans in 68 CE as they made their way up to besiege Jerusalem which fell in 70 CE. Thereafter there were intermittent periods of occupation, first probably by a small Roman garrison and then, later, probably by some Jewish rebels, at the period of the Bar Kokba revolt (132–35 CE).

The function of the Qumran site has been much debated. Arguments depend principally on three factors. Firstly, consideration must be given to various features of the site itself. Its proximity to several of the caves where manuscripts were found is a strong argument in favour of linking the caves and their contents with the site, and the presence of inkwells on the site suggests that at least some writing was done at Qumran. Furthermore, several characteristics of the site suggest that it was occupied by a group who worked, ate and deliberated together. Over 1,000 bowls and plates were found stored adjacent to a large communal room whose sloping floor onto which water could be diverted from a conduit strongly suggests that it was a common dining area that could be easily and thoroughly cleaned. In several locations throughout the site, but not in any rooms, deposits of animal bones were found buried in jars. No adequate explanation for these deposits has been made; it is unlikely that the bones were the remains of sacrifices, but they could have come from some special community celebrations. The cisterns which are more obviously for bathing purposes (*mikvaot*) suggest that the Jewish community who lived there was concerned with ritual purity.

Now that de Vaux's identification of one locus as a toilet has been rediscovered, some might argue that its presence goes against identifying the occupants of the site as the Essenes, since the evidence of Josephus (*War* 2.148–49) would suggest that they only went to the toilet at a distance from the site. Several other features have commonly been used to argue against the identification of the occupants as sectarian in general or as Essene in particular, but none of these features can be viewed as incontrovertibly challenging such an identification. The supposed poverty of the Essenes is thought to be compromised by the large number of coins found at the site, especially the three hoards of silver Tyrian shekels. The substantial pillar bases and significant quantities of expensive stoneware and glass are also just as capable of being understood as the result of communal wealth based on individual vows of poverty as they may be suggestive of the individual wealth of the occupants of the site. In fact, the simplicity of the pottery types, the absence of imported fine wares, the lack of any elaborate architectural decoration on the site such is found at Masada or Herodian Jericho, all strongly suggest that the site was the scene of a Jewish community whose priorities lay elsewhere than in generating wealth.

Secondly, the site needs to be placed into its wider context for comparative purposes; in several respects it is unlike nearby contemporary sites, but in some respects it shares certain features with them. Those who liken Qumran to a fortress underestimate the weakness of its defences in comparison with other Hasmonean and Herodian fortress sites. Those who argue that it should be likened to a fortified farmhouse or villa fail to appreciate the elaborate complexity of the Qumran site, even though its basic rectangular design corresponds with what is known of such contemporary fortified farmsteads. Nevertheless, consideration of the archaeological context makes it clear that the cylindrical jars and peculiar oil lamps found at Qumran are not unique to the site, though as elsewhere, notably at Jericho, these seem to be datable to the Herodian period or later. Claims have been made too about the distinctiveness of the Qumran cemetery and the religious significance of the burials there, but similar shaft burials have been discovered at Ein el-Ghuweir, in Jerusalem and on the eastern shores of the Dead Sea.

Thirdly, there is written evidence of two kinds. The description of the site by Pliny the Elder (*Natural History* 5.73) has been much disputed. Although he never actually visited the Judaean wilderness, Pliny describes the Essenes as residing to the west of the Dead Sea and mentions that 'below them (*infra hos*)' is found Engedi. Even if this is taken literally to mean that the small set of first century CE dwellings on the plateau above Engedi is to be identified as an Essene settlement, the identification of Qumran as also such a settlement is not thereby automatically excluded. Most scholars, however, prefer to understand Pliny's phrase to mean that Engedi was 'to the south of' or 'down river from' the settlement he describes, which could thus readily be identified with Qumran.

The second kind of literary evidence comes from the Qumran site itself. In 1996 two Hebrew ostraca were found in the wall that runs along the terrace to the south of the main group of buildings. Though it is unlikely that the technical term for the community (*yaḥad*) is to be read on the better preserved of these ostraca, as has been claimed, the text is clearly a deed of gift concerning a slave and agricultural property. If the named beneficiary was the community bursar, then the ostracon strikingly illustrates the practice of the community in having property assigned to the group and formally registered, and so may justifiably be used to confirm the communal activities referred to elsewhere in the sectarian scrolls found at Qumran (1QS 6.18–20).

THE CAVES

General descriptions of the Dead Sea Scrolls (such as this) often tend to treat the manuscript collection of the eleven caves as a unity and to assume that all the caves served the same function for hiding the manuscripts at some particular catastrophic moment, such as the arrival of the Romans in the region in 68 CE. However, a more careful consideration of each cave suggests that some of them served distinct functions.

Caves 1, 3 and 11 are found in the cliff face above Qumran; they are all naturally formed. In cave 1 all the scrolls had been carefully stored in sealed jars as if in a genizah. Indeed it is quite likely that the manuscripts from cave 1 were already slightly damaged when placed there, and so were no longer in use. On the other hand, the caves in the marl terrace on which the Qumran site is located and on the one adjacent to it were formed by hand; because of their proximity to the site of Qumran these caves seem to have served a variety of functions. Not many manuscript fragments were found in cave 8, but there was a considerable number of leather tabs and ties; perhaps that cave was used as a small workshop for finishing off manuscripts. Cave 4 produced by far the largest number of fragments, belonging to over 550 manuscripts, including several copies of some compositions; it seems as if that cave was some kind of working repository for the site, not unlike a limited-access library stack. Perhaps some of its contents were regularly consulted as exemplars from which other manuscript copies could be made, but other items, such as the tefillin and mezuzot, seem to have been deposited merely for safe-keeping. The cave was certainly prepared well before any Roman advance and, as the holes in the wall suggest, it had an elaborate shelving system, none of which has survived. Cave 7, which can only be reached by walking through the Qumran site itself, was found to have manuscript fragments written only in Greek; though some Greek fragments were also found in cave 4, it seems as if cave 7 may have been a depository with special significance.

THE MANUSCRIPT FINDS

Background information

The manuscripts from Qumran are referred to in two ways: either by cave number, the letter Q (for Qumran), and the manuscript number or by cave number, the letter Q and an abbreviated title. Thus the principal *Commentary on Genesis* from the fourth cave is designated either as 4Q252 or as 4QCommGen A. In this case the capital A signifies that other works labelled as *Commentaries on Genesis* are probably not copies of the same composition; different manuscripts containing the same composition are designated with a small raised letter, indicating the copy number (e.g. 4QIsa[a] is the first copy of Isaiah from Qumran's cave 4). Lists of all the manuscripts from Qumran can be found in several different reference works. References to any particular item in many of the more fragmentary manuscripts are given by fragment number, column number (usually in small Roman numerals), and line number; in the better preserved manuscripts often column (commonly in standard numerals) and line number suffice.

The Qumran manuscript collection has both unity and diversity. It is best to be clear about its material diversity to begin with. Writing has been found predominantly on leather (parchment) fragments and scrolls, but there are several papyrus manuscripts too and also inscriptions on pieces of pottery (ostraca) and jars. There is also the famous *Copper Scroll*, which was made of three pieces of thinly beaten copper on which letters were impressed with some kind of engraving tool.

The majority of the scrolls are written in Hebrew, mostly in various forms of square script, but some of the Pentateuchal books and Job are represented in paleo-Hebrew, and the paleo-Hebrew alphabet is also used for the four letters of the divine name (the tetragrammaton) and for other divine epithets in some biblical and non-biblical scrolls. In addition to the biblical scrolls and some other compositions, it can safely be said that all the obviously sectarian compositions are extant only in Hebrew, as if the sect responsible for them was trying to make a point that identified them as continuous with the Israel of an earlier age. 4Q464 3 i 8, probably a sectarian composition, seems to describe Hebrew as 'the holy tongue'.

The Hebrew found in all these compositions is very diverse. Not only may changes and developments in the language over 300 years or more be represented in the scrolls, but also there are different ideolects: some compositions are in a deliberately archaizing style of Hebrew that tries to imitate the biblical books in various ways, whereas others use forms and vocabulary that may have been closer to the spoken forms of Hebrew, both cultic and non-cultic, of late Second-Temple period Palestine. An example of this is *Miqṣat Maʿaśe Ha-Torah* (*MMT*), 'some of the preceipts of the Torah', which is a second century BCE open letter recommending adherence to particular legal interpretations.

The Aramaic of Qumran is also diverse and there has been a considerable debate about how much of what is found in the Aramaic scrolls reflects the spoken language of much of the population of Palestine at the time. The extent to which one can use the scrolls for the reconstruction of the everyday language of Hillel, Jesus and others is thus controversial. A few scrolls are in Greek. At Qumran all these are literary texts, not business documents, apart from 4Q350. Though several ingenious suggestions have been made, as yet unexplained are several combinations of Greek letters that occur at the end of some of the units of text in the *Copper Scroll*.

The scrolls provide us with an unparalleled amount of information concerning the preparation and production of manuscripts in the late Second-Temple period. The scrolls that are assembled from pieces of animal skin are of various sizes and are prepared in a variety of ways. Many are ruled by gentle incision both horizontally for writing under, and vertically to demarcate margins. Such ruling is based on the use of guide dots in the margins. On some sheets of parchment the column width is regular, but on others there are commonly wider margins for the right-hand columns on the sheet than for those on the left. Some scrolls are prepared so as to contain large amounts of text, such as 1QIsaᵃ, which contains the whole of the book of Isaiah in 54 columns (7.34 m), and the principal copy of the *Temple Scroll* (11Q19; reconstructed length is c. 8.75 m), of which parts of sixty-six columns are extant. At least one 'scroll' is simply a single piece of leather with just one column of writing (4Q175).

The scrolls attest to a wide range of scribal practices. With regard to the layout of the text, it is evident that compositions were presented in paragraphs marked by spacing on the line, by the scribe starting a new line, or by the use of a new line and indentation. Occasionally a whole line is left blank. Major units of text are often indicated by the use of marginal markings of various shapes. As the composition was written out, mistakes were corrected in a number of ways: by erasure, by crossing out, or by cancellation dots above and beneath the incorrect letters. Omissions are sometimes made good, either by the same scribe or by a subsequent corrector; omitted text is supplied between lines or even in the margins. The texts themselves are presented in a variety of different scribal spelling practices. These practices are commonly ascribed to one of two groups, though in practice few manuscripts belong consistently within one particular scribal system. One group reflects a generally brief system of spelling which uses few consonants to represent vowel sounds, as is found in much of the Masoretic textual tradition of the Hebrew Bible. The other group reflects a fuller spelling system, even for some biblical books. Since a majority of the sectarian compositions survive in the fuller spelling, it may justifiably be supposed that the non-sectarian biblical and non-biblical works that are written in a similar spelling practice were copied by members of the community, whereas others may have been brought into the community from outside.

The library

It is probably correct to talk of the collection of manuscripts from all eleven caves as forming a library. Although the scrolls are written in two basic scribal systems and several variations of them, and although the collection contains both sectarian and non-sectarian materials, several factors point to the overall cohesion of the manuscripts. Even though some of the caves may have had manuscripts put in them at different times, it is remarkable that the largest surviving manuscript deposits, from cave 1 in the foothills above Qumran, from cave 4 within a stone's throw of the Qumran buildings, and from cave 11, which is furthest from Qumran, share certain features. In addition to various biblical books, the *Rule of the Community* is best known from its cave 1 copy, but up to ten versions of it have also been found in cave 4 (4Q255–64) and it is also suggested that it may have been part of the cave 11 deposit (11Q29); a copy was probably also deposited in cave 5 (5Q11). Other compositions that occur in more than one cave include the book of *Jubilees* found in cave 1 (1Q17–18), in cave 4 (4Q176a, 4Q216–24, 4Q482–3), and in cave 11 (11Q12) as well as in caves 2 (2Q19–20) and 3 (3Q5). The *Temple Scroll* may have been found in cave 4 (4Q365a?; 4Q524), though the principal copies come from cave 11 (11Q19–21). The Aramaic *New Jerusalem* text was found in cave 1 (1Q32), in cave 4 (4Q232 [in Hebrew], 4Q554–5) and in cave 11 (11Q18), as well as in caves 2 (2Q24) and 5 (5Q15).

The manuscript deposits also share certain other features. All of them are principally concerned with literary compositions; there are virtually no business documents to be found in the whole collection. Among the calendar, prayer and festival texts none completely contravenes the 364-day solar calendar explicitly attested in several places and that lies behind such compositions as the *Temple Scroll*. Furthermore, certain contemporary Jewish compositions are lacking, such as 1 and 2 Maccabees, the book of Judith, and the book of Esther, all of which must have been in circulation at the time the site was occupied and the caves used. The religious or political sentiments expressed in those works seem not to have been welcome at Qumran. In addition, no non-Jewish literature has been discovered in the caves; one might have expected there to be some, if the deposits in the caves were from the great libraries of Jerusalem.

There is a rich range of literary materials in this Qumran library and several different ways of classifying them, but here I suggest that the compositions can be grouped under five headings. The first four are arranged here so as to make the important point that the movement and community responsible for collecting and transmitting these texts is seen clearly to be aligning itself with biblical Israel. Although some of the sectarian compositions allude to scripture only implicitly, the vast majority of literary works found in the caves can be seen either as biblical or as heavily dependent on biblical traditions. The community thought of itself as the only true remnant of Israel in the eschatological period; in its own self-understanding it was not post-biblical but on the verge of inheriting all that was promised to them as penitent exiles.

1. In the first place many of the compositions are copies of biblical books. Care must be exercised in assessing the manuscripts that can be assigned to this category. In strict terms the label 'biblical' is an anachronism for the last three centuries before the fall of the Temple in 70 CE; it also suggests misleadingly that the manuscript remains are in the form of books. Nevertheless approximately 200 of the 850 manuscripts from the Qumran caves can be broadly defined as biblical. It is often stated that there are copies of all the compositions later found in the three parts of the Hebrew scriptures (Law, Prophets and Writings) except Esther, but it should also be noted that there is only the smallest fragmentary evidence for the books of Ezra–Nehemiah (4Q117) and Chronicles (4Q118).

From the several references to what God commanded 'by the hand of Moses and by the hand of all his servants the Prophets' (e.g. 1QS 1.3), it is clear that the Law and the Prophets were understood as authoritative, though whether the Prophets included also the historical books remains uncertain. In 4Q397 14–21 10–11, a first century BCE manuscript, we read of 'the Book of Moses [and] the books of [the Pr]ophets and in Davi[d]', and the text seems to continue with reference to the deeds of former generations; perhaps this is a reference to a four-part authoritative collection of scriptures: 'Moses' designating the five books of the Law, 'the Prophets' describing the writings of the three major and twelve minor literary prophets (and possibly Daniel; cf. 4Q174 1 ii 3), 'David' referring to the Psalms or perhaps even to the collection of writings of which the Psalms are usually put in first place, and 'former generations' possibly referring to the history books. With such a notice can be compared the definitions in the Greek Prologue to Ben Sira (c. 132 BCE), in Luke 24.44 and elsewhere. If citation is also used as a criterion for helping us determine what was authoritative at Qumran, then the book of *Jubilees* should also be included (CD 16.3–4; 4Q228) as also some Levi composition (CD 4.15). Since the New Testament's letter of Jude 14–15 refers to the writings of *Enoch* in an authoritative way, perhaps the considerable number of *Enoch* manuscripts found in the Qumran caves indicates that they were held in esteem there too.

Within the authoritative collection it seems as if the biblical books given a particular place of honour included Genesis, Deuteronomy, Isaiah, most of the Twelve

Minor Prophets, and the Psalms, which circulated in at least two different group-ings. Both the number of manuscript copies to survive and also the frequent citation of and allusion to these works suggest that these books formed a sort of 'canon within the canon' for their collectors. Perhaps it is particularly in these books that there is an indication of the theological concerns of the community. Interest in Genesis would have provided ancient patriarchal authority for the community's prac-tices, Deuteronomy's law for the land (Deuteronomy 12–26) could have been used to justify in many ways the strict and exclusivist interpretation of the Law found in the rest of the sectarian compositions, Isaiah and the Twelve were the sources of many of the eschatological views of the community and the movement of which it was a part, and the Psalms, variously collected, were viewed both as prophecy (cf. 11QPs^a 27.11) and as a live part of worship.

If the Qumran biblical scrolls give a strong indication of which scriptural books were considered authoritative by the sect and probably also the wider Jewish commu-nity, they also show that the two centuries before the fall of the Temple in 70 saw a gradual move towards a standard form of the text of each book. Four principal theories have been put forward to categorize and explain the textual pluralism of the Qumran biblical manuscripts. F. M. Cross is most commonly associated with the theory of local texts, in which the evidence is variously associated schematically with Jewish scribal schools in Babylon, Egypt and Palestine. S. Talmon has offered an alternative view, arguing that the pluralism now evident is simply the result of which Jewish communities survived; the variety was probably even greater than is now discernible. E. Tov has argued that although a few biblical manuscripts at Qumran can be linked with the increasingly authoritative proto-Masoretic text, with the Hebrew Vorlage of the LXX, and with the Samaritan tradition, nevertheless each manuscript should be viewed as having certain independent features that are not easily classifiable; furthermore, Tov has noted that several biblical manuscripts are written in the scribal system found in the majority of the non-biblical manuscripts containing sectarian compositions and these should be viewed as a category on their own. E. Ulrich has moved the discussion in another direction by proposing that each biblical book should be viewed in turn and by observing that for some of the biblical books there existed side by side two or more literary editions: as can be seen in the case of Jeremiah, it was not always the oldest edition that became authoritative in the later rabbinic tradition. Whatever the case, the biblical scrolls from Qumran now form a very significant part of the modern scholarly understanding of how the various books of the Bible were being transmitted in the late Second Temple period.

2. The second overarching literary category contains texts that are in some way related to the Law (Torah) and its practice. Compositions that can be grouped under this heading include both sectarian and non-sectarian materials. In addition to various manuscript copies of the five books of the Law, several compositions are non-sectarian re-presentations of the Law. There are five versions of the *Reworked Pentateuch* (4Q158, 4Q364–7), which is not dissimilar to the Samaritan Pentateuch in purpose and even in the form of its text. This composition adjusts the text of the books of the Law in various minor ways so that its consistency is enhanced and its style and grammar improved. From time to time, more substantial alterations are included, such as the so-called Song of Miriam in 4Q365 6a ii 1–7, a poetic composition that

immediately precedes Exodus 15.22 and which seems to suggest that Miriam and her female companions sang a different song from that which Moses and the men had sung as recorded in Exodus 15.1–18. This previously unknown Song of Miriam shares certain features of the victory songs associated with Jewish women in the late Second Temple period, such as Judith (Judith 16.1–17) and Mary (Luke 1.46–55).

The many copies of the book of *Jubilees* and of compositions somewhat similar to it (e.g. 4Q225–7) reflect a similar interest in rewriting the biblical accounts of Genesis and Exodus so as to have particular halakhic views incorporated within an authoritative text. The book of *Jubilees* is cited with authority in other compositions found in the Qumran caves, such as the *Damascus Document* (CD 16.3–4) and the aptly named 4QText with a Citation of *Jubilees* (4Q228). It is well known, for example, that the author of *Jubilees* almost certainly wrote against the custom of some contemporary Jews when he spoke against nakedness. The *Temple Scroll* shares many features with *Jubilees* and seems to have been compiled as a collection of rewritten laws derived from Exodus 34 to Deuteronomy 22. Though it may have been re-edited subsequently at Qumran, it probably comes from the time of John Hyrcanus, before the Qumran community had come into existence.

Legal materials are found at Qumran in a variety of genres in addition to those of the Rewritten Bible. In these predominantly sectarian works direct dependence on particular scriptural passages is usually implicit and some of these compositions share features with later rabbinic collections of legal interpretations (*halakhot*) such as are found, for example, in the Mishnah. The sets of purity regulations (4Q274–84a) are a typical example of how various legal matters were sometimes grouped together according to their subject matter.

In six copies of what is compiled like an open letter (4QMMT = 4Q394–9), an author is concerned to identify his own group as having practices that his addressees would find appropriate, while others known both to him and his audience would find themselves in disagreement and so excluded. The body of this letter is a list of legal interpretations that are in effect rulings to which the addressees are invited to subscribe in the interests of their own justification and for the sake of Israel. Among the matters for which rulings are given can be found views on the right sacrificial practice for the Temple, a set of rulings concerning tithing, rulings to enforce the strict sanctity of Jerusalem, and rulings concerning meal practices. Some of these can be linked with biblical passages which they expound, but most are only indirectly related to the Law.

In the sectarian rule books, there are similar lists of rules to which readers are expected to adhere: these rule books rarely cite the Torah, but supplement it with particular regard to the life of the community, both narrowly and more widely defined. It is difficult to know how all the rule books should be related to one another. The *Rule of the Community* exists in several versions. In its cave 1 form it opens with a recollection of the liturgical basis of the admission of new members, contains a section of instruction about the two spirits, rehearses sets of rules for the hierarchical organization of the community with reference to the circumstances that have given rise to the need for such sectarian withdrawal, and concludes with a reflective poem in the first-person singular, which stresses the inadequacy of all human attempts to live up to divine demands. The authority structure this version reflects involves members obeying rulings constructed by the Sons of Zadok, a leading priestly group. In some of the versions of the same composition from cave 4, there are similar sets of rules, but the overall text is much shorter than the cave 1 counterpart and the structures of the community seem to have changed somewhat. In place of the priestly Sons of Zadok can be read the more broadly democratic 'many'; authority seems to be based in the whole eligible community. It is not yet known precisely what relationship these two versions of the *Rule of the Community* have to one another and to any social reality at Qumran or elsewhere. There could have been a priestly reorganization of an earlier less hierarchical community, or the course of events may have been the other way round with the priestly leadership subsequently replaced by something more democratic. The regular understanding of how sectarian groups organize themselves and change over the years would suggest the former, but the relative dating of the manuscripts containing these variant versions would suggest the latter. Perhaps it was both, with the rediscovery of an originally more egalitarian practice after the community had had a period organized in a strict hierarchy.

The problem of relating the texts to the communities they represent does not stop with the *Rule of the Community*. Two compositions are appended to the cave 1 version of the *Rule*: another Rule and a set of blessings. This second Rule book is generally known as either the *Rule of the Congregation* or as the *Messianic Rule*. Like the *Rule of the Community* it depicts a community under the authority of the Sons of Zadok, the priests, but it also defines itself as 'a rule for the congregation of Israel in the last days' (1QSa 1.1). Although this definition might imply that the *Rule* is only for the future eschatological period, it could also be that several elements in the *Rule* reflect the ongoing practices of a community. For example, after describing the meal at which the eschatological priest presides in the presence of the Messiah of Israel, the text concludes, 'and according to this statute one shall act at every meal when at least ten men are gathered' (1QSa 2.21–2). Significantly in this *Rule*, there is explicit mention of the need for women and children to be instructed in the precepts of the covenant.

There is yet another rule book, the so-called *Damascus Document* (also known as the *Zadokite Fragments*), which falls principally into two parts. In the first (equivalent to CD A 1–8) there is a threefold summons to repentance followed by various exegetical passages that contain veiled descriptions of the history of the community, including its stay in the Land of Damascus (which a majority take as a code-word for Qumran). The second part is a set of rules for local communities. Among the rules are those which clearly imply that members of this group are married and interact in business dealings during the week with non-members, even Gentiles. Josephus describes the Essenes as being of two kinds, the celibate and the marrying. Perhaps the *Damascus Document* reflects the practices of those communities widely spread throughout Palestine in which marriage was permitted.

The overall characteristics of these various sectarian legal texts are patriarchal and priestly; they also pay special attention to purity. The patriarchs are presented in a positive light and as observant practitioners of the Law, even before it was given by Moses. Not surprisingly their practices correspond more or less with those of the communities reflected in the sectarian rules. Perhaps the patriarchs are being used to make the claim that the contemporary practices of the community are of greater antiquity and therefore of greater authority than those of other Jews at the time. The practices of the patriarchs and the community they reflect are generally to be understood as stricter than those that can be surmised as characterizing the groups against which works such as the *Temple Scroll* or *MMT* may have been written. In particular, purity regulations are interpreted strictly and extended to ensure that no possible infringement might occur. Matters of cultic legislation are dealt with extensively. Even though the members of the Qumran group probably did not participate in the rites and ceremonies of the Jerusalem Temple, they looked forward to a time when God would establish the eschatological Temple in which their priests alone would be competent to officiate. This was so because the community alone knew how to behave appropriately in the last days.

3. A third overarching literary category relates broadly to the biblical prophetic traditions. As with the Law, so within this category there also survive non-sectarian Rewritten Bible compositions such as the *Paraphrase of Kings* (4Q382), the extant fragments of which are chiefly concerned with Elijah and Elisha, and the *Visions of Samuel* (4Q160). There are also compositions containing traditions about other prophets such as Jeremiah (4Q383–4, 385a, 387, 387a, 389, 390) and Ezekiel (4Q385, 385b, 385c, 386, 388, 391).

Among the compositions clearly sectarian in origin are those with a thoroughgoing eschatology. The *Pesharim*, so-called from their formulaic use of the Hebrew word *pesher* (interpretation), are commentaries on Isaiah and most of the books of the Twelve Minor Prophets. The sectarian commentator cites a section of the prophetic text and then provides commentary in which the scriptural text is related directly to circumstances contemporary with the community whose experiences are described as taking place within the 'end of days'. Several other thematic commentaries have a similar agenda, linking biblical passages to the experiences and aspirations of the community. Among those aspirations are hopes that three eschatological figures would appear soon, a prophet, a priest messiah and a prince messiah. In compositions from the latter half of the first century BCE, the prince messiah is increasingly identified as the Branch of David (4Q161, 4Q174, 4Q252, 4Q285).

In addition several compositions depend upon prophetic traditions for their description of future events. The copies of the *War Rule* (1QM, 4Q285, 4Q491–7) in which the rules of engagement are provided for the series of eschatological battles is a composite work, much of which depends heavily on traditions found in the book of Daniel. Several other Danielic compositions rehearse the epochs of history with an eschatological conclusion (4Q243–5) or rework various visionary traditions such as are found in Daniel itself (4Q246). Whereas the *War Rule* is clearly a sectarian composition, the other Danielic works are probably not. There is also an intriguing list of false prophets (4Q339), the existence of which strongly suggests an ongoing interest in and practice of prophecy in the movement.

4. The fourth set of literary materials from the Qumran caves can be associated in one way or another with the works found in the Writings. Several compositions contain rewritten forms of the biblical psalms (4Q380–1). There are also numerous manuscripts that contain prayers and other liturgical texts for private or communal use: *Prayers for Festivals* (4Q507–9), *Daily Prayers* (4Q503), a confession ritual

(4Q393), and individual blessings (4Q434–7). There are also blessings and liturgical descriptions of various kinds: the *Blessings* texts (4Q286–7), the corresponding *Curses* (4Q280), and the *Songs of the Sabbath Sacrifice* (4Q400–7, 11Q17), which are arranged in a sequence of thirteen for a quarter of a fifty-two-week year, with the twelfth being a description of the divine throne-chariot. Because of the generally traditional character of liturgical language, it is often particularly difficult to discern whether or not these prayer texts are sectarian. The *Prayer for King Jonathan* (4Q448), probably a prayer on behalf of Alexander Jannaeus, would seem definitely to be non-sectarian, whereas the eschatological blessings (1QSb), which form an appendix to the *Rule of the Community* in its cave 1 form, are almost certainly sectarian.

The poetic compositions also include several versions of the *Hodayot* or *Thanksgiving Hymns* (1QH, 1Q36, 4Q427–32). These poems, which are also replete with biblical imagery, are clearly sectarian in mood. In several of the individual thanksgivings the poet speaks of his gratitude in being chosen by God to be a true member of the covenant people. He has suffered persecution at the hands of his enemies in a way similar to that assigned to the servant in Isaiah 52.13–53.12. A majority of interpreters reckons that at least some of these poems were composed by the Teacher of Righteousness, the leader of the group at some point, probably in the mid-second century BCE, before the occupation of Qumran, or possibly as the community embraced its wilderness location.

Providing the appropriate calendrical setting for the use of many of these liturgical pieces, there are among the Qumran finds a significant number of compositions concerned with calendrical matters, nearly all of which seem to be sectarian in origin. These include the introduction to one of the copies of *MMT* (4Q394), the list of calendrical signs (4QOtot = 4Q319), the delineation of the priestly courses (4Q320–30, 337), the description of the phases of the moon (4Q317) and the zodiacal calendar with brontological features (4Q318), which allows the knowledgeable interpreter to declare what will happen when it thunders at particular times in the moon's cycle. All these texts are related to the kind of cosmological knowledge which is sometimes contained in wisdom compositions.

Indeed several works found at Qumran reflect the ongoing production of wisdom collections in the Second Temple period such as are found in the biblical books of Proverbs and Ecclesiastes. A set of ethical admonitions and cosmological teaching is to be found in the non-sectarian composition known as *Instruction* (1Q26, 4Q416–18, 4Q423). Some other wisdom texts are also thought to be non-sectarian, particularly because they contain reflections on creation of a universalist character (4Q307–8, 4Q408–13). Among the sectarian wisdom traditions are the *Mysteries* composition, which attempts to describe various cosmological secrets (1Q27; 4Q299–301), the wisdom text with a set of beatitudes (4Q525), and the physiognomical texts (4Q186, 4Q534, 4Q561).

5. The fifth category consists of all those literary compositions that cannot readily be seen as directly or indirectly dependent on biblical exemplars. The best known of these is the *Copper Scroll*, which provides details of sixty-four locations where gold, silver and various priestly accoutrements are hidden away. A minority of scholars considers that the discovery of this scroll in cave 3 proves that the whole collection of manuscripts was brought to the desert region from Jerusalem shortly before the

capture of Jerusalem by the Romans and that therefore the scrolls and the Qumran site have nothing to do with one another. Others are more inclined to suggest that the scroll exemplifies a link that was re-established between the occupants of Qumran and the Temple at the time of crisis before the Jewish Revolt (66–74 CE). Support for such a view is sometimes sought in the discovery of the *Songs of the Sabbath Sacrifice* at Masada, a composition otherwise known only from the Qumran caves, and which could have been brought to Masada by a community member who was sympathetic with those trying to make their last stand against Rome. Other scholars still suggest that the treasure listed in the scroll was the accumulated wealth of the Essene movement; over 200 years, it is argued, very large sums of money would have been transferred into the care of the community's bursar. Yet others see the *Copper Scroll* as having been placed in cave 3 at a somewhat later date, and that its treasure represents the amassing of the Temple tax after the destruction of the Temple when there was nothing for it to be spent on. Whatever theory is followed, it remains the case that nobody has satisfactorily explained precisely how the quantities of treasure listed in the scroll should be translated into modern equivalents, nor has anybody yet found any of the treasure, either because it is impossible to identify its locations with sufficient precision or because others have long ago discovered it and taken it away.

Among other miscellaneous compositions included are a few letters (4Q342–3), some deeds recording various legal transactions (4Q344–9), and some accounts (4Q350–8); it is not completely clear whether these all come from Qumran or were allocated to the collection on the hearsay of those from whom they were bought. From cave 10 there is only a single ostracon.

THE CLASSICAL SOURCES

Alongside all the manuscripts from the eleven Qumran caves three classical authors have played a major role in discussions about the identity of the occupants of Qumran and the wider movement of which they may have been a part. The oldest source is Philo (c. 30 BCE – 45 CE). In two places (*Quod omnis probus liber sit* 75–91; *Apologia pro Iudaeis* 1–18) he writes about the Essaioi, a label he relates to the Greek word for holiness (*hosios*). Philo describes them in somewhat idealized terms as a group of over 4,000 celibate men who have enthusiastically embraced poverty, sharing what possessions they have, in order to dedicate themselves utterly to the service of God. He notes their stress on purity and that they live as voluntary associations in towns, villages and large groups throughout Palestine.

In another work (*De contemplativa* 1–2, 11–40, 63–90) Philo describes the Therapeutae, a group living primarily in Egypt, who share many features with the Essenes he has described elsewhere and whom Josephus also described, especially with regard to their daily living practice and reverence for the Torah and its study. Though it is impossible to equate the two groups as branches of the same movement, the Therapeutae also share several features with the Qumran community, even certain details such as being required to gesticulate with the right hand alone (77; cf. 1QS 7:15), and the observance of a festival calendar made up of seven-week units (65; cf. 11QTemple[a]).

The description in Pliny the Elder's *Natural History* (5.17.4), composed shortly after 70 CE, is the most significant classical source in debates about who lived at Qumran. Pliny describes the Esseni as a contemporary celibate group living a life of communal poverty on the western shore of the Dead Sea with only the palm trees for company. His remarks on the precise location of the group are somewhat ambiguous as has already been mentioned. Most scholars are happy to locate Pliny's group at Qumran, understanding that 'below' means either 'down river' or 'south' and suggesting that his reference to them in the present tense is explicable either through his lack of precise first-hand information or through the use of a source written before the likely destruction of Qumran in 68 CE. In addition, some Essenes may have moved into cells above Engedi in the first century CE; there is no need, however, to insist that that was the only place in the area where they had ever been resident.

The third major classical author who has influenced the debate is Josephus, the Jewish historian whose writings date from the last quarter of the first century CE. In both the *Jewish War* and in his *Jewish Antiquities* he writes about the Essenes as a group. He also mentions certain individual Essenes by name: Judas (*War* 1.78–80; *Antiquities* 13.311), a contemporary of Aristobulus Antigonus (ruled 105–104 BCE); Menahem (*Antiquities* 15.371–79), who apparently encountered Herod when a child as well as later when he was king and who supposedly was responsible for Herod's favourable disposition towards the Essenes; Simon (*War* 2.113; *Antiquities* 17.345–48), a contemporary of Archelaus (4 BCE – 6 CE); and John (*War* 2.567; 3.11), who was active in the Jewish Revolt in 66 CE.

The lengthiest description of the Essenes is in Josephus' *War* (2.119–61) in the context of describing the principal schools of thought in Palestinian Judaism at the time of the political unrest in 6 CE. Josephus describes how they are spread in small groups throughout Palestine and are particularly noted for the way they share their possessions. He comments on their regular prayers, especially noting those before sunrise, on their disciplined work schedules, and on their ritual washings and common meals. He notes how they refrain from taking oaths and assiduously study sacred texts. The process of admission to the group Josephus outlines corresponds closely with what is known from the *Rule of the Community*, though it is not exactly the same. The description of the organization of the community is entirely compatible with what can be reconstructed from the various rule books. One detail is commonly and rightly highlighted: Josephus notes that spitting in the middle of the company is expressly forbidden (cf. 1QS 7.13). He comments on their bravery in the face of the Romans and notes their beliefs in the afterlife, but only by speaking of their view concerning the immortality of the soul, which is not confirmed in the sectarian scrolls. He remarks that not all Essenes follow the same path of sexual abstinence – there are some who marry. One way of reading the sectarian documents from Qumran is to suppose that the majority of Essenes who did not live at Qumran were of the marrying kind, while those at Qumran and perhaps at some other important centres were abstinent as if they were in the Temple or the line of battle, for both of which biblical injunctions concerning sexual abstinence applied.

The later description of the Essenes in Josephus' *Antiquities* is shorter than that in the *War* but contains several details also found in the account of Philo, such as the numbering of the Essenes at 4,000, noting their interest in agriculture and the absence of slavery in the movement. As has sometimes been noted, the principal differences between what Josephus says and what can be reconstructed from the scrolls about the community's organization and beliefs are to be found in the *Damascus Document*. It is thus quite possible that Josephus had some kind of direct knowledge of the movement, since he claims to have tried to be an Essene (*Life* 10–11), but that his familiarity was limited in several respects.

Overall the numerous similarities between these three classical sources on the Essenes and what can be known on the basis of the scrolls and the archaeological evidence about the group at Qumran and the wider movement of which it was a part is best explained by suggesting that the inhabitants of Qumran from the beginning of the first century BCE until the destruction of the site in 68 CE are to be identified with an evolving section of the Essenes in some form. Over a period of nearly 200 years such a movement is bound to change and it is clear from both the classical sources and from the Qumran sectarian scrolls that the agreements in detail between the two groups of sources far outweigh the few general differences, most of which can be discerned in the differences between the *Damascus Document* on the one hand and Philo and Josephus on the other. This does not exclude the possibility that in some respects their views at some points in their history could have been close to those of other groups: several scholars have justifiably noted how a few of the prescriptions in the *Temple Scroll* and *MMT* echo what later rabbinic sources ascribe to the Sadducees, while others have noted similarities to some of the views of the Pharisees.

A BASIC HISTORICAL OUTLINE

Several historical details emerge from the scroll remains, though quite how all these should be understood is still a matter of some considerable debate.

The period of the *Damascus Document*

The historical self-understanding of the movement of which the Qumran residents were a part is presented in its classic form in the so-called *Damascus Document*. The opening column of the version of the A text, which has survived from the Geniza of the Ben-Ezra Synagogue in Cairo, describes how God visited a remnant of Israelites 390 years after the destruction of Jerusalem by the Babylonians. If they were able to calculate the date of that event accurately, then this divine visitation took place in 196 BCE. For twenty years, the text continues, the newly founded community was leaderless, but then a Teacher arose to lead it, the so-called Teacher of Righteousness. This may have happened during the period of political and religious turbulence leading up to the Maccabean Revolt that broke out in 167 BCE.

The Teacher of Righteousness or Righteous Teacher is an enigmatic figure. He features in only a very few scrolls: the *Damascus Document*, the *Psalms Pesher* and the *Habakkuk Pesher*. Nowhere is he named. From the *Psalms Pesher* we learn that he was a priest. Several scholars have suggested that he may even have been a high priest, the one who was displaced by Jonathan Maccabee, when he assumed the high priesthood in 152 BCE. Such an interpretation, taken together with the literal reading of the *Damascus Document* would suggest that this Teacher was active from about 176 BCE for a generation, a period that would encompass the high priesthood of the time (149–142 BCE) for which no ancient source records the name of the high priest.

Those who understand that the Teacher of Righteousness was this displaced high priest commonly suppose that his community was fully established as a separatist group only after his removal from office in Jerusalem. Such modern interpreters also often assume that this group formation was contemporary with the occupation of the Qumran site itself. However, as has already been noted, it is highly unlikely that the first phase of the occupation of Qumran should be dated earlier than about 100 BCE. If the teacher is indeed to be associated with the deposed high priest of 149–142 BCE, then he led the movement initially in Jerusalem or elsewhere, not at Qumran.

The *Damascus Document* envisages that after the death of the Teacher there will be a final forty-year period before the end of all things. If the dates in the text are made into a total symbolic period of ten jubilees (490 years), and if the author could calculate the time since the Babylonian destruction of the Temple in 586 BCE, then it can be supposed that the *Damascus Document* itself was written sometime shortly before 96 BCE.

John Hyrcanus and his two sons, Aristobulus and Alexander Jannaeus

John Hyrcanus, the Maccabean high priest–ruler (134–104 BCE) is not explicitly named in any of the Qumran scrolls, but two compositions seem to reflect something of his life and times. He was a cultic reformer who was also concerned to centralize his power base in Jerusalem. The *Temple Scroll*, which survives in several copies, seems to refer to some of John's Temple reforms, notably the changes he made to the system for slaughtering sacrificial offerings (cf. Mishnah *Ma'aser Sheni* 5.15). The *Temple Scroll* describes arrangements for slaughtering that can be understood as reflecting what John introduced, and it does so favourably. One may suppose that those responsible for writing the particular section of the *Temple Scroll* approved of John's actions. Providing one allows that the *Temple Scroll* was compiled by members of the Teacher's movement, all this could be significant in implying that the community still exercised influence in Jerusalem in the last quarter of the second century BCE. There is thus no need to place them at Qumran then.

However, both the Jewish historian Josephus and other classical Jewish sources comment that at some point during his rule John Hyrcanus became involved in a power struggle and his political support switched from one group to another. If those responsible for the *Temple Scroll* had been inclined to view his actions favourably, possibly even influencing some of the reforms he introduced into the Temple itself, then by the end of his reign it is quite possible that they were no longer his supporters and something of the political turmoil at the end of the reign of Hyrcanus might have contributed to the establishment of the community at Qumran.

It is likely that such unease with John Hyrcanus is reflected in another composition found at Qumran. In the single column *Testimonia* (4Q175), four texts are cited as authoritative: the first three scriptural texts are probably cited as proof-texts for the three expected eschatological figures who would act as divine agents in the end days, the prophet, the princely messiah, and the priestly messiah. The fourth extract is also found in a rewritten form of Joshua, now entitled the *Apocryphon of Joshua*. Building on the language and phraseology of Joshua 6:26, it refers to a man of Belial who is accursed and to two 'vessels of violence', a phrase borrowed from Genesis 49.5 where it refers to Simeon and Levi. Thus in *Testimonia* the text may refer to the accursed man's two sons. The action for which they are all chiefly cursed is the rebuilding of Jerusalem in an inappropriate way. *Testimonia* is commonly dated to the first quarter of the first century BCE and was almost certainly copied by the same scribe who copied the first cave version of the *Rule of the Community* (1QS). Perhaps the negative counterparts to the eschatological prophet, prince and priest were John Hyrcanus and his two sons Aristobulus and Alexander Jannaeus.

Yet another text is also commonly related to the historical circumstances of the reign of Alexander Jannaeus. The principal fragment of the *Nahum Pesher* (4QpNah) refers to a time period from Antiochus to Demetrius. Because of other matters described in various veiled ways in the *Commentary*, these two figures are widely considered to be the Seleucid kings Antiochus IV Epiphanes and Demetrius III Eukairos. Most famously the commentary refers to an incident when a furious young lion hanged people alive, a euphemism most probably for crucifixion. Classical sources inform us that Alexander Jannaeus crucified 800 Pharisees in 88 BCE because they had treasonably invited the Seleucid Demetrius III to assist them in their attempt to remove Jannaeus from the high priesthood. The *Nahum Pesher* speaks of three groups under the epithets of Judah (the community), Ephraim (the Pharisees; 4QpNahum 3–4 i 12), and Manasseh (the Sadducees; 4QpNahum 3–4 iii 9–10) whose principal characteristics and interactions seem to correspond well with what little is known of the Pharisees and Sadducees of the time of Alexander Jannaeus.

A further text may also refer to this period. As is confirmed by his bilingual coins, Alexander Jannaeus' Hebrew name was Jonathan. One scroll from cave 4 (4Q448) survives only in a small piece, which comes from the opening of the scroll, since the tab for tying the scroll together also survives. Three somewhat strangely placed columns are extant, two of which seem to belong together and in at least one place mention a King Jonathan. Most scholars identify this Jonathan with Alexander Jannaeus and suppose that the two-part poem is a hymn and prayer on behalf of the king. A minority view is inclined towards thinking of the Jonathan of this text as Jonathan Maccabee, even though that Jonathan is called king in no other ancient source. This text is probably not sectarian but could have been brought to Qumran by somebody joining the movement having become disenchanted with what those in power in Jerusalem were doing.

Alexandra Salome and the subsequent civil war

Few proper names survive in any of the Qumran scrolls. However, it is quite clear that in one annalistic historical composition (4Q331–2), a certain time of year is associated with events that took place during the reign of Salome Alexandra, Alexander Jannaeus' widow who became queen after his death and who ruled from 76–67 BCE.

In addition the same or a very similar historical composition (4Q333) refers to a certain Aemelius who is associated with killing. Almost certainly this Aemelius is to be identified with Aemelius Scaurus who was Roman Governor of Syria (65–62 BCE) at the time of Pompey's intervention in the civil strife that had broken out between the followers of Hyrcanus and Aristobulus, Alexander's two sons. Salome Alexandra had favoured passing the succession to her moderate and somewhat weak son Hyrcanus, but the more nationalistically minded Aristobulus had seized control and in so doing provoked civil unrest. When Pompey intervened in Jerusalem in 63 BCE, his forces attacked those of Aristobulus, displacing him in favour of Hyrcanus who was then set up as a Roman puppet ruler. It is difficult to determine the significance of these slender references to events in the 60s of the first century BCE, but it seems that the writer of the *Historical Text* disapproved of Aemelius's action and so may have been a sympathizer of the more hardline Aristobulus.

The Herodian period

Josephus describes how the Essenes had certain privileges from Herod and how Menahem the Essene had interacted with him, gaining his approval. If the Qumran community and the wider movement of which it was a part were Essenes, then it is likely that the whole group experienced Herodian favour. The community site at Qumran was just a few miles south of Herod's winter palace at Jericho. It is unlikely that he would have tolerated the community, if they had been outspoken in their opposition to him.

One real possibility is that when Herod announced his intention to rebuild the Temple, the hopes of some of the Qumran Essenes were raised and they made a copy of their *Temple Scroll* (11Q19 was copied sometime in the latter half of the first century BCE) as a blueprint for his grand scheme. Some of the dimensions of the Herodian Temple do indeed seem to mirror what can be reconstructed on the basis of the *Scroll*, but the overall Herodian project was nowhere near as large as the *Temple Scroll* demands.

From Herod to the fall of the Masada

In the surviving fragments from the Qumran caves the majority of proper names that can be identified with known figures belong to the first half of the first century BCE. We can conclude that this was a period when the community had ongoing political concerns. Although there may have been some interaction with religious institutions and political leaders after the Roman invasion of 63 BCE, no Qumran texts refer to it explicitly. Many manuscripts are dated typologically to the Herodian period, so the community itself was not entirely inactive after 63 BCE, but it may have become somewhat more withdrawn as the expected end seemed to recede further and further into the distance. The outbreak of war in 66 CE may have encouraged some Essenes to become activist once again. The discovery of a copy of the *Songs of the Sabbath Sacrifice* at Masada may indicate that at the end of the war some members of the movement joined with those who made their final stand against the Romans there.

CONCLUSIONS

The discoveries of the Dead Sea Scrolls are sometimes described as the greatest archaeological finds of the twentieth century. However one might measure such matters, it is clear that the scrolls are very significant. They have opened up a new chapter in how the transmission of the texts of the various biblical books is best understood. The plurality of the textual evidence for many of the biblical books is striking and cannot be lightly dismissed. The pluralism within Palestinian Judaism in the three centuries before the fall of the Temple in 70 CE has long been known, but the scrolls provide primary data which now enable scholars to see that much of the pluralism rested in arguments about the right interpretation of the Law, as well as in various cultic disputes concerning the calendar and the priesthood. Reaction to changing political circumstances also provoked different responses in the various segments of Jewish society. While the Qumran community may not continually have been as withdrawn as many have supposed, nevertheless it seems to have put its hopes principally in eschatological divine intervention rather than in physical resistance. The aspirations of the members of the movement were never vindicated as they hoped, but their legacy has resulted in a revitalizing of the study of the late Second Temple period from a distance of two millennia. The scrolls have changed the way in which the transmission of the Hebrew scriptures is viewed and they have altered how the origins of both early Judaism and early Christianity are suitably described.

BIBLIOGRAPHY

Texts and translations

Most of the manuscripts have now been published in their official editions in the series Discoveries in the Judaean Desert (Oxford: Clarendon Press, 1955–) under a series of general editors (currently E. Tov). These are also available on CD ROM (Leiden: Brill, 1999). Some manuscripts such as the *Temple Scroll* have been published in principal editions apart from the official series. A handy compendium of all the principal fragments is available in transcription with English translation in F. García Martínez and E. Tigchelaar, *The Dead Sea Scrolls Study Edition* (Leiden: Brill, 1997–8; pbk 2000). The English translations are available separately in F. García Martínez, *The Dead Sea Scrolls Translated* (2nd edn; Leiden: Brill, 1996). English translations are also available in G. Vermes, *The Complete Dead Sea Scrolls* (London: Penguin Books, 1998), and in M. Wise, M. Abegg, E. Cook, *The Dead Sea Scrolls: A New Translation* (San Francisco: HarperCollins, 1996). An English version of the biblical manuscripts can be found in M. Abegg, P. Flint, E. Ulrich, *The Dead Sea Scrolls Bible* (San Francisco: HarperCollins, 1999).

Basic reference works

Two significant reference works are P. Flint and J. C. VanderKam (eds), *The Dead Sea Scrolls after Fifty Years* (Leiden: Brill, 1998–9) and L. H. Schiffman and J. C.

VanderKam (eds), *The Oxford Encyclopedia of the Dead Sea Scrolls* (New York: Oxford University Press, 2000). Recent bibliography is listed in F. García Martínez and D.W. Parry, *A Bibliography of the Finds in the Desert of Judah 1970–95* (Leiden: Brill, 1996). Ongoing scholarly discussion can be found in many journals, especially *Dead Sea Discoveries* (G. J. Brooke, L. H. Schiffman, J.C. VanderKam [eds], Leiden: Brill), and *Revue de Qumrân* (F. García Martínez, E. Puech [eds], Paris: Gabalda).

Introductions and other studies

The most reliable introductions to the Dead Sea Scrolls are by F. García Martínez and J. Trebolle Barrera, *The People of the Dead Sea Scrolls* (Leiden: Brill, 1995), L. H. Schiffman, *The Dead Sea Scrolls Reclaimed* (Philadelphia: Jewish Publication Society, 1994), H. Stegemann, *The Library of Qumran* (Leiden: Brill, 1998), and J. C. VanderKam, *The Dead Sea Scrolls Today* (London: SPCK, 1994). Good introductory surveys are provided by O. Betz, 'The Essenes', and J. Campbell, 'The Qumran Sectarian Writings', in *The Cambridge History of Judaism*, Vol. 3 (ed. W. Horbury, W. D. Davies, J. Sturdy, Cambridge: Cambridge University Press, 1999), 444–70 and 798–821. G. Vermes, *An Introduction to the Complete Dead Sea Scrolls* (London: SCM Press, 1999) provides a survey of some of the principal texts and his long-established version of the consensus view.

More detailed but very accessible studies are J. J. Collins, *Apocalypticism in the Dead Sea Scrolls* (London: Routledge, 1997), J. J. Collins, *The Sceptre and the Star* (New York: Doubleday, 1995), P. R. Davies, *Qumran* (Guildford: Lutterworth Press, 1982), D. Harrington, *Wisdom Texts from Qumran* (London: Routledge, 1996).

HEBREW INSCRIPTIONS

——·◆·——

Graham Davies

INTRODUCTION: THE VALUE OF EPIGRAPHY

The study of inscriptions (or epigraphy) is a branch of archaeology that can make a contribution of special importance to the understanding of a literary text like the Bible, for several reasons. The content of these texts can, in a very general way, shed light on many aspects of life in the biblical period, religious, social, economic and political, just like other archaeological discoveries, but with the added clarity that words can give. Sometimes, though not very often, inscriptions even have a direct relationship to particular biblical passages, either because they refer to the same events or objects or because their style or phraseology is mirrored in the more complex literary works of the Bible. Again, inscriptions show how Hebrew and related languages were written in the biblical period itself and they may also provide some valuable clues to the extent and uses of literacy in ancient Israel. For reasons such as these archaeologists excavating at the site of a major ancient city often dream of finding a great quantity of inscriptions, or even an archive, and the discovery of even one such text is always a cause of excitement and anticipation of what it will say when it has been deciphered.

The number of ancient Hebrew inscriptions now known is probably larger than most readers of the Bible would imagine. If we limit ourselves to the period before 200 BC, the figure for published items was around 1,550 at the time of writing (September 1997) and is growing every year. While this figure remains small when compared with the many thousands of texts known from some of the great cities elsewhere in the ancient Near East, and nearly 1,000 of the Hebrew inscriptions are inscribed seals and seal-impressions containing only two or three words each, this is still a sizeable supplement to the corpus of written Hebrew from the biblical period. The texts are of the most varied kinds, from lists of names to carefully composed letters and from single letters of the alphabet and abbreviations to fragments of what must originally have been large stone tablets mounted on a wall for everyone to see.[1] There are also considerable numbers of texts (approaching 900 in all) written in the Canaanite, Aramaic, Ammonite, Moabite, Edomite, Philistine and Phoenician languages by various of Israel's neighbours in Palestine and Transjordan. Some of these that are of great relevance to biblical studies will be mentioned below.

THE WRITING OF HEBREW INSCRIPTIONS

I shall begin with some general remarks about the writing of Hebrew as it is reflected in the inscriptions. First, *materials and methods*.[2] A broad distinction can be made between incised writing using a metal stylus (Hebrew *ḥeret*, sometimes *'eṭ*, Jer. 17.1) or another hard object, on stone, metal, wood or the hardened clay of a pottery vessel; and the use of a pen (also *'eṭ*, Ps. 45.2; Jer. 8.8) and ink, mainly on broken pieces of pottery (ostraca) as far as the extant evidence goes. But one papyrus from Wadi Murabaat, near the Dead Sea, has survived from the seventh century BC – in fact it was used twice, once for a letter and then later for a list of names and quantities (of grain?) – and it is clear from the impressions of papyrus on the back of some *bullae* (see below) that this material was in fact quite widely used. The moist conditions in most of Palestine were not as favourable to its preservation as those in Egypt, for example. Seals were occasionally made of metal but generally of stone, often precious coloured stone, and they were pressed into clay while it was still soft, the writing being inverted on the seal but true on the impression, which might be on the handle of a jar or a lump of clay (*bulla*) placed over the string that tied up a papyrus scroll. The Hebrew word *seper*, often translated 'book', probably never refers in the biblical period to anything like a modern book, which did not yet exist, but is a general word for any kind of written document from a letter (as frequently in the Lachish ostraca) to a lengthy literary work such as the text about Balaam to be described below or the 'book' of the law (Deut. 28.61 etc.).

Secondly, the *script*. Hebrew and its sister languages were written from right to left in an alphabetic script that had its origins in the middle of the second millennium BC.[3] The classical scripts of ancient Egypt and Mesopotamia used characters that represented syllables or even whole words, and consequently the number of symbols was very large. Two simpler systems of writing, simpler at least to write but not to decipher, were devised in the Levant, both based on the alphabetic principle of a single (consonantal) sound being represented by each sign. One system, known mainly from the vast archives of texts found at Ugarit (Ras Shamra) in Syria, was a simplified version of the Mesopotamian cuneiform script with just thirty characters. A few texts in a script like this are known from Palestine, but its use was short-lived: all the examples known are from between about 1400 and 1200 BC. The other system drew its inspiration from Egyptian hieroglyphs and began with the same 'pictorial' basis, but employed the 'acrophonic' principle, that is, the sign represented only the first sound ('letter') of the word for the object portrayed. The earliest such inscriptions go back to at least 1500 BC. Comparatively few examples of this 'proto-Canaanite' script are known, but an important subgroup are the 'proto-Sinaitic' inscriptions from Serabit el-Khadim in the Sinai peninsula, which one recent study holds to be the oldest of all.[4] It was from this latter system that the scripts of the early first millennium in Palestine, and in due course the Greek alphabet and our own, were developed.

The letter-forms in use during pre-exilic times (down to the early sixth century BC) were very different from those seen in modern printed Hebrew Bibles or even medieval manuscripts. To distinguish this script from the later 'square script' it is generally referred to as 'palaeo-Hebrew'. Although it was largely superseded by the square script among Jews, it has been retained (in a modified form) by the Samaritans to the present day and it is also found on some Jewish coins of the Hellenistic and Roman periods, as well as in a number of biblical manuscripts from Qumran. In the inscriptions there is no full system for marking the vowels (such a system was introduced only in the sixth or seventh century AD) and no punctuation except for the frequent but not universal use of a dot as a word-divider between words. There are several early inscriptions in which part or all of the alphabet is written out, either in exactly the order still used (Lachish, Kuntillet Ajrud once) or with the single difference that *pe* is placed before ʿ*ayin* rather than after it (Kuntillet Ajrud twice: the same order appears in Lam. 2.16–17; 3.46–51; 4.16–17 in alphabetic acrostic poems in the Bible, whereas Lam. 1.16–17 has the normal order). One of the earliest inscriptions that may be Hebrew, from Izbet Ṣartah, also has this variation, together with two others that may be simple errors. Similar abecedaries are known from neighbouring peoples and it is plausible to associate them with the process of learning to write, perhaps in some kind of school. Whether there were schools in ancient Israel is a much debated matter, but such sequences of letters, especially when they are combined with other likely school exercises such as standard letter introductions (as at Kuntillet Ajrud) or lists of numerals (as at Tell el-Qudeirat) give strong support to the more indirect evidence that has been brought forward in support of their existence. Certainly there must have been some means by which scribes were trained to write in the fluent regular script of many inscriptions and to use the system of numbers and other signs largely borrowed from Egypt.[5]

This leads directly to questions about literacy and the uses of writing in ancient Israel, for which the inscriptions provide important but not entirely undisputed evidence. Many of the documents come from either administrative archives in major cities (e.g. Samaria, Lachish, Jerusalem) or royal outposts (Arad) or from the specialized craft of the seal-cutter, and so suggest that writing was largely the province of professional scribes. But there are also a number of more crudely written inscriptions, for example marks of ownership on jugs or graffiti in caves, which show that the ability to write was not limited to such circles, at least where short, simple texts were concerned. What can be said about the beginning and the spread of writing in ancient Israel? There is no doubt that the great majority of the inscriptions so far known come from the eighth century or later: a recent very careful study dated only twenty-two items to the tenth and ninth centuries.[6] In particular the large administrative archives only begin to appear in the first half of the eighth century (Samaria) and the biggest concentrations are from the late seventh and early sixth centuries (Arad, Lachish, etc.). On this basis some would conclude that writing only became widespread in Israel in the eighth century. Against this it is pointed out (especially by A. R. Millard) that this ignores the possibility that in earlier centuries perishable materials such as papyrus were used more exclusively and these simply have not survived in Palestine as they do in Egypt.[7] Evidence for the use of papyrus, though at a later period, has already been noted. Surviving texts, in some cases of considerable extent, from neighbouring peoples also strongly suggest that the use of writing was well known in the early Israelite monarchy. The earliest inscriptions of any length from the Phoenician cities to the north are from the eleventh and tenth centuries (Byblos) and there are several substantial inscriptions of the ninth century deriving from Israel's neighbours in the east and north-east: the inscription of Mesha (the Moabite Stone), the Amman Citadel inscription, the Deir ʿAlla plaster texts and, the most recently discovered, the Aramaic inscription from Tel Dan. It is hardly reasonable to deny to Israel a degree of competence so clearly attested among their neighbours, even if the accidents of discovery have not so far produced a comparable text in Hebrew.

THE EARLIEST TEXTS FROM IRON AGE PALESTINE

In its earliest form the Hebrew script was close to its Phoenician parent and as a result there is debate about whether some of the earliest alphabetic inscriptions from Palestine are Hebrew or Canaanite. Recent historical studies of the origins of the Israelites, which have tended to emphasize the Canaanite element in early Israel, only make the arguments more complex. However, on the basis of the places where they were found being within the Israelites' boundaries, a case can be made for regarding the texts from the early Iron Age described in the rest of this paragraph as being at least possibly Hebrew. Five inscribed bronze arrowheads with the words *ḥṣ ʿbdlb(ʾ)t*, 'arrow of ʿAbdlabi(ʾa)t', are dated to the late twelfth century and are said to come from el-Khadr, 3 km (2 miles) west of Bethlehem, close to the Iron I site of Giloh.[8] They belong to a group of similar arrowheads, not all inscribed, which have mainly been found in southern Lebanon. El-Khadr lies within the area occupied by the tribe of Judah, but the owner of these arrowheads bore a name taken to mean 'servant of the Lioness', which might be a title of the Canaanite goddess Anat. On one of the arrowheads ʿAbdlabiʾat is actually called 'son of Anat'. As will appear later, such names can be a valuable clue to the religion of the communities in which they were used, and this name has a good Canaanite pedigree. If these arrowheads belonged to an early Israelite, he was not a very orthodox one! In the excavation of the Iron I site at Izbet Ṣarṭah, 19 km (12 miles) east-north-east of Tel Aviv on the edge of the hills claimed by the tribe of Ephraim, an ostracon was found containing about eighty crude incised letters in five lines.[9] The first four lines appear to be meaningless sequences of letters, but the bottom line is the alphabet already mentioned, which exceptionally is written from left to right. Probably the whole piece is an exercise of someone at a very basic stage of learning to write. The 'Gezer Calendar' of the tenth century, incised on a small limestone tablet now in Istanbul, may also be a writing exercise.[10] Gezer was an important centre, which, according to 1 Kings 9.15–16, was captured by the Egyptian Pharaoh from its 'Canaanite' (more likely Philistine) rulers and given as a dowry to his daughter when she married Solomon, who made it one of his fortified cities. If the text belongs quite late in the tenth century, as seems likely, this would place it in the period when Gezer was an Israelite city and make its classification as Hebrew probable. The contents of the text are most interesting:

> Two months thereof [are for] ingathering. Two months thereof
> [are for] sowing. Two months thereof [are for] late sowing.
> A month of cutting flax.

A month of barley harvest.
A month of harvest and measuring.
Two months thereof [are for] pruning.
A month of summer fruit.
Abi[jah?].

This is clearly a description of the agricultural year beginning, somewhat curiously, at the end of the yearly cycle in the late summer with the 'ingathering' of olives and grapes. The words for 'ingathering' and 'harvest' are identical to those used in Exodus 23.16 for two of the major religious festivals and this shows how closely Old Testament worship was originally tied to agricultural life. The name at the end may be that of the trainee scribe.

FOUR TEXTS FROM ISRAEL'S NEIGHBOURS TO THE EAST

The few inscriptions of the tenth and ninth centuries that are more definitely Hebrew are short and uninteresting, and it is more worthwhile to digress briefly and discuss the four ninth-century inscriptions from Israel's neighbours that were mentioned above. The best known is the inscription of Mesha king of Moab, often called the Moabite Stone.[11] It was found at Dhiban, ancient Dibon, east of the Dead Sea in 1868 and is now in the Louvre. The Moabite language is practically indistinguishable from Hebrew, at least in its written form. The text begins:

I am Mesha, son of Chemosh[-yat], king of Moab, the
Dibonite. My father reigned over Moab for thirty years, and I
reigned after my father. I built this *bamah* for Chemosh in QRḤH,
   a *bamah*(?)
[of deli]verance, for he delivered me from all attacks (on me) . . .
   (lines 1–4)

From the end of line 4 a long section deals with Moab's wars with the kings of Israel, beginning with Omri, who is named twice; there follow further references to Mesha's building works and, finally, a damaged section that describes fighting in Horonaim. The Bible contains no specific account of Omri's war with Moab (but see 1 Kgs 16.27 for his 'power'). However, Moab's subjection to Israel is presupposed by the account in 2 Kings 3 of a 'rebellion' by King Mesha and an attack on Moab from the south by an alliance of Israel, Judah and Edom. The overall outline of this account is very similar to what Mesha himself records, at least if Horonaim was in the south of Moab, and there is some evidence for this (Isa. 15.5). The inscription is thus a valuable historical source for events in the middle of the ninth century BC. It also sheds some light on Moabite religion: the national god is Chemosh, who is mentioned eleven times (cf., e.g., 1 Kgs 11.7) and what is said about him corresponds closely to claims made in the Old Testament about Yahweh (note in the extract above: 'he *delivered me* from all attacks [on me]'). Other aspects of the religion are also similar to Yahwism, for example the use of *bamah* (often translated 'high place' in the Bible) as a regular word for a shrine (as in 1 Sam. 9.12–14) and the practice of 'utter destruction' or more precisely 'sacrifice by destruction' (*ḥerem*), when an enemy city was captured.

A stone inscription discovered in excavations on the Citadel at Amman (ancient Rabbath-Ammon, the capital city of the Ammonites) has been dated to the middle of the ninth century.[12] It contains only eight lines, which are damaged at both the beginning and the end. It apparently records a prophetic oracle in the name of the Ammonite god Milcom, which includes both instructions about building and assurances to the king of victory and prosperity. The precise meaning is not at all clear, but one line appears to say that 'in all the rows (of pillars?) the righteous shall spend the night'. This and other aspects of the text have suggested to some scholars that the prophecy may have provided the god's authorization for the building of a temple.

The Balaam inscription, written in ink on plaster, from Tell Deir ʿAlla in the central Jordan Valley, is certainly an account of prophetic phenomena.[13] It was found during excavations in 1967, broken into countless pieces after falling with the wall on which it was mounted as a result of an earthquake. The date of this destruction forms a *terminus ante quem* for the writing of the inscription and the excavators now propose a date for this c. 800 BC on the basis of carbon-14 dating of organic remains in the same level. This would put the inscription itself in the late ninth century. Some scholars prefer a slightly later date. There has been much argument about the language of the inscription. It bears some characteristics of Aramaic, but not enough to convince all. It may be a hitherto unknown local language or dialect. The script is certainly related to the Aramaic scripts and this would fit well in the later ninth century when Transjordan was under Aramaean domination (2 Kgs 10.32–3: see also below), whereas in the eighth century this area was recovered by Israel (2 Kgs 14.25; Amos 6.13).

The inscription, as its name implies, describes an episode (possibly more than one) in the life of Balaam son of Beor, known from Numbers 22–4 as a prophet who was active in Transjordan. The new text bears no direct relation to the biblical story and it presents Balaam as an entirely pagan prophet. It begins as follows:

> [This is the doc]ument [about Bala]am, [the son of Be]or, the man (who is) a seer of the gods. He it was to whom the gods came by night [and they spoke to hi]m according to El's command and they said to [Bala]am, the son of Beor, thus: . . . shall make . . . And Balaam rose up the next morning . . . And he co[uld] not [eat, and he fa]st[ed], and his people came to him. And th[ey said] to Balaam, the son of Beor: Why are you fasting? [And w]hy are you weeping? And he said to them: Sit down! I will tell you what Shagg[ar will do]. And come, see the work of the go[d]s! [The god]s gathered together and the Shaddai-gods took up their position in the assembly, and they said to Sh[aggar]: You may break the bolts of heaven . . . (after Smelik 1991: 83–4)

Balaam had evidently brought a message of doom and the less well preserved lines that follow may be his explanation of the reason for the gods' judgement. The name of the god in whose name Balaam speaks here seems to be Shaggar, a lunar deity

known from Ugaritic and Mesopotamian texts. Nevertheless there are some interesting similarities of detail to the biblical narratives about Balaam: there too Balaam
'sees the vision of the Almighty (*Shaddai*)', he has a vision in the night, his father's
name is Beor, he comes from Mesopotamia and he is expected to deliver a message
of doom (Num. 22.5, 8–13; 24.4, 16).

The Deir 'Alla text gives no indication of whether Balaam was a figure of the
recent past when it was written or an ancient seer whose teachings had been preserved
in a similar way to those of the biblical prophets. The biblical references place
Balaam in the context of Moabite hostility to the Israelites' original settlement in
Canaan, which would favour the latter alternative, but the possibility cannot be
discounted that this association is anachronistic and that the biblical stories originally belonged to the time of some later war with Moab, closer to the date of the
Deir 'Alla text.

Most recently, in 1993 and 1994, in excavations at Tel Dan in northern Israel
three pieces of a basalt stele have been found, probably originally written in the late
ninth century.[14] The script fits such a date and the broken pieces were found in
secondary use in a pavement of the early eighth century. The language of the text
is Aramaic and the contents, which refer to Hadad as the writer's god and to his
victories over at least one Israelite ruler, imply that the stele was originally set up
by a Syrian ruler, presumably after his conquest of Dan. The breaking up of the
stele and its reuse as paving stones presuppose that the city had by then been liberated from Syrian control. This sequence of events corresponds in general terms to
what can be learned from the biblical narratives about relations between Syria/Aram
and Israel when Hazael conquered large areas of Israelite territory (see the passages
cited above, p. 275). The stele seems to have included the names of two Israelite
kings, '[ ]ram son of . . . king of Israel' and '[ ]iah son of . . . [kin]g of the House
of David (i.e. Judah, Aram. *bytdwd*)'. This interpretation of the final phrase has been
disputed, but it is most probably correct. If these two kings were contemporaries,
they can only be Jehoram of Israel and Ahaziah of Judah, who ruled according to
the biblical chronology in the 840s. There is, however, then a serious historical
problem because, while 2 Kings 8.28 does refer to these two kings fighting against
Hazael (and to the wounding of Jehoram), in a later passage they are said to have
been killed by Jehu, who seized the throne of Israel from Jehoram c. 842 (2 Kgs
9.14–28), whereas the stele seems to say that Hazael killed them both.

INSCRIPTIONS FROM THE NORTHERN
KINGDOM OF ISRAEL

In the early eighth century there begin to be some inscriptions of some length
written by inhabitants of the northern kingdom of Israel itself. What are probably
the earliest of these come, rather surprisingly, from an outpost in the desert in the
far south, known today as Kuntillet Ajrud.[15] Three features of these texts, which
include inscriptions incised on stone and clay vessels, but also some written in ink
either on wall-plaster or on the outside of storage jars (pithoi), link them to the
northern kingdom. One text refers, it seems, to 'Yahweh of Samaria', a specific
manifestation of the national god in the capital city; at the end of theophoric names

the divine name appears as -*yw* (-*yaw*) rather than -*yhw* (-*yahu*), following the northern pronunciation (cf. the Samaria Ostraca below); and some inscriptions are in the Phoenician script, which is attested otherwise only in the north. What brought northerners to this desert area is uncertain, but the semi-fortified character of the building in which the inscriptions were discovered and the objects found in it make trade rather than religion the most likely explanation. The texts are, however, chiefly interesting for the light they shed on the religion of those who wrote them. The Phoenician texts mention Baal and El as well as Yahweh and there are several references to Yahweh's *asherah*, which has been understood both as a cultic object, perhaps a stylized tree representing a goddess of fertility, and as the name of the goddess herself. Further references to this goddess or her cult symbol (which are also mentioned in the Old Testament) appear in somewhat later inscriptions from the Philistine city of Ekron and a burial inscription from Khirbet el-Qom in Judah. These are important indications of the worship of a Canaanite goddess among the Israelites (and the Philistines), but to judge from the relatively few epigraphic references to her she was in no sense a rival to Yahweh in the way that Baal was.

A slightly later group of texts, from Samaria itself, provides further evidence for the popularity of Baal worship in Israel referred to in the Old Testament (see 1 Kgs 16.31–3; 2 Kgs 10.18–28; Hosea *passim*). These are the Samaria Ostraca, found during excavations of the acropolis of the Israelite capital in 1910.[16] They appear to be receipts of some kind, most likely records of annual contributions to the palace provisions by the farmers of (royal?) estates in the kingdom. Many of the texts follow one of the following patterns:

> In the ninth year. From Quṣeh. For (*or* of) Gaddiyaw. A jar of old wine. (no. 6)

> In the tenth year. From Seper. For (*or* of) Gaddiyaw. A jar of clear (literally 'washed') oil. (no. 16)

> In the 15th year. From Heleq. For (*or* of) Aša (son of) Ahimelech. Heleṣ. From Haṣerot. (no. 22)

The first two types record a date, a place from which the produce came, the name of the person who received (or sent) it, and the nature of the produce. The third type contains additional names of persons and places (including the district as well as the town), but no indication of the nature of the produce. Many of the place-names can be identified with districts, clans or towns in the vicinity of Samaria that are known from references in the Bible or names of modern Arab villages. The personal names provide some evidence of religious affiliations. Many names in biblical times were theophoric, that is, they included the name of a god, and it is reasonable to suppose that the god in question was revered by the parents of the person so named. The personal names in the Samaria Ostraca are of various types (and some may be of Egyptian rather than Israelite origin), but those including a form of the name Yahweh are only slightly more numerous than those formed with 'Baal'. For example, alongside Abiyaw, 'Yahweh is my Father', there is Abibaal, 'Baal is my Father'. It is true that the word *baʿal*, which means 'lord' or 'husband', was sometimes used as a title for Yahweh (cf. Hos. 2.16), but it is unlikely that all the onomastic evidence can be explained in this way. It probably indicates that among the families who sent their produce to the royal palace there was quite a high proportion who worshipped Baal as well as or instead of Yahweh.

Finally, the dates. Only three dates appear on the surviving ostraca, referring to the ninth, tenth and fifteenth years of one or more kings. The style of the pottery used for the ostraca and the script point to the first half of the eighth century. Around this period the Bible knows of only three kings who reigned over Israel for fifteen years or more, Jehoahaz (c. 815–801), Joash (c. 801–786) and Jeroboam II (c. 786–746).[17] At the latest, therefore, the 'fifteenth' year group would belong to approximately 772 BC and the 'ninth year' and 'tenth year' groups would be somewhat earlier.

Two seals of royal officials from the northern kingdom are also of great interest. The seal of 'Shema servant of Jeroboam' was found in excavations at Megiddo in 1904 and will come from the long reign of Jeroboam II.[18] It is larger than most Israelite seals and bears a fine representation of a roaring lion. Unfortunately the original seal was lost and only a bronze cast of it survives. Very recently a seal with a similar inscription, whose precise provenance is as often unknown, was published: it bears the name of 'Abdi servant of Hoshea', Hoshea (c. 732–724) being the last king of the northern kingdom.[19] In this case a human figure is engraved in an 'Egyptianizing' style on the seal and there is a winged sun-disc beneath him that betrays a similar cultural background. (Similar seals of 'servants' of three eighth-century kings of Judah, Uzziah, Ahaz and Hezekiah, are also known.[20]) The 'servant of the king' (this form of the title appears on several other Hebrew seals) was a high office of state, known also from the Old Testament (cf. 2 Kgs 22.12), a predecessor of the modern 'minister of the crown'.

INSCRIPTIONS FROM THE SOUTHERN KINGDOM OF JUDAH

From the southern kingdom of Judah a few inscriptions are known that date to the first three-quarters of the eighth century, but they are mainly lists of names or 'delivery notes' of the same general kind as the Samaria Ostraca. It is only in the last quarter of the century, corresponding to the reign of Hezekiah and the time of the prophet Isaiah, that we begin to have evidence of fuller texts. But this evidence is suddenly quite extensive, so that either there was a great increase in literacy at this time or similar evidence for earlier periods has not survived. This might be because perishable materials were used or because, as A. R. Millard has suggested, finds made by archaeologists tend to be from the years immediately preceding a major destruction, and Judah escaped such a catastrophe until the Assyrian invasion under Sennacherib in 701.[21]

The largest group of these inscriptions are over twenty ostraca from the fortress of Arad, which lay east of Beersheba on the southern border of Judah, close to the desert. Once again, many of them are evidently administrative documents, usually quite brief. But one is a letter (no. 40) that refers to troubles with Judah's Edomite neighbours on the southern border and asks for information about the difficulties to be passed on to 'the king of Judah'. The writers seem, from the deferential language they use ('my lord . . . your servant'), to be officials or army officers who are subordinate to Malcijah, the recipient of the letter and probably the commanding officer at Arad then.[22]

There are also several inscriptions of this period from Jerusalem. Some, again, are short administrative records that in isolation do not tell us very much. But several carved in stone indicate the use of writing for more substantial texts. The best known is the Siloam Tunnel inscription, discovered at the lower end of an underground channel that brought the waters of the Gihon spring on the east slope of Jerusalem to a point in the south where they were more easily accessible to inhabitants of the new western quarter of the city.[23] The text is worth quoting in full:

> . . . the breakthrough. And this is the story of the breakthrough. While the stoneworkers were wielding their picks, from both sides, and when there were still three cubits to dig through, a man's voice was heard calling to his mate, because there was a crack in the rock from right to left. On the day when they broke through the stoneworkers struck the rock from both sides, pick against pick, and then the waters flowed through from the spring to the pool, a distance of 1200 cubits. The height of the rock over the heads of the stoneworkers was 100 cubits.

Although inscribed on a well-prepared surface and in a fine script, the text does not conform to the usual ancient Near Eastern pattern of building inscriptions, which attribute public works to the king and describe the whole construction and not just its final stage. The location of the inscription, where it would rarely be seen, is also unusual. Someone, perhaps the official in charge of the work, evidently thought that such a major feat of engineering should be commemorated on the spot.

On the opposite side of the Kidron valley, at the foot of the slope on which the Arab village of Silwan now stands, a large number of well-made chamber-tombs have been found, and in four cases inscriptions survived by their entrances. The most interesting of these, now in the British Museum, reads as follows:[24]

> This is [the grave of . . .]iah, who was 'over the house'. There is no silver or gold here, but only [his bones] and the bones of his maidservant with him. Cursed be the person who shall open this [grave].

The phrase 'over the house' was a title for another leading official at the royal court, 'house' referring here to the palace, and 'royal steward' is a good paraphrase. Several such officials are known, both from the Old Testament (e.g. 1 Kgs 4.6) and from a seal and seal-impressions that have come to light in modern times. One such official, Shebna, is rebuked by the prophet Isaiah for the extravagant tomb he had prepared for himself (Isa. 22.15) and, given the likely date of this inscription, it has been tempting to read the partially preserved name as a fuller form of his name, Shebaniah.

Further evidence of royal administration, though its precise significance is uncertain, comes from stamped seal-impressions on the clay handles of a type of storage jar found in excavations at many sites in Judah. These are of two types. One has the phrase *lmlk*, 'For (*or* of) the king', together with one of four place-names: Hebron, Socoh, Ziph and Mamshat (the vowels of the last name are uncertain).[25] The first three names were towns in the outlying parts of the kingdom, which may have been depots for supplies under royal control. Mamshat is a mystery, as no place of that name is known at the time. A popular and plausible suggestion is that it stands for the capital Jerusalem, but no convincing explanation of how this is so has been given. The other types of stamp that may be relevant here contain, like many others, the names of individual persons and their patronymics. But the large number of some such stamps that survive, and the fact that they appear regularly on the same type of jar as the *lmlk* stamps, has suggested that they may belong to officials at one or other of these depots, who marked consignments of produce as they arrived or were despatched to where they were needed.[26]

Far fewer inscriptions are known from the first half of the seventh century. This may, at least in part, be due to the depletion in the territory of Judah after Sennacherib's invasion in 701. The largest number come from Jerusalem, but except for one they are ostraca with little legible content. The exception is part of a formal inscription on stone on which a few tantalizing words can be read.[27] Both the script and the thickness of the stone suggest that it was originally part of a large stele (comparable perhaps to the Moabite Stone) on which building works, for example, may have been recorded. Two other fragments of stelae are known, one from Samaria and one from Jerusalem: the latter contains what may be a date, 'on the seventeenth [day of the] fourth [month]'. These fragments point to the existence of, probably royal, 'display inscriptions' in the capital cities of Israel and Judah.

By contrast, a much more mundane use of writing is represented by the sixty-two inscribed jar handles found in excavations at el-Jib (Gibeon), a few miles north of Jerusalem.[28] The archaeological evidence clearly associates these handles with the huge centre of wine production that existed here in the eighth and seventh centuries BC. Typically the inscriptions (which are poorly written) consist of the name 'Gibeon' followed by two personal names, presumably the names of the vineyard owner(s) and/or the wine merchant(s) who produced and stored the wine. One of the names, represented by the letters *gdr*, has been the subject of great discussion, but there are strong reasons for reading it as the personal name Gedor (cf. 1 Chr. 8.31; 9.37). The inscriptions thus correspond to modern wine labels. Isolated inscriptions from other sites describe wine as 'smoky' or 'dark' (unless the words in question are again place-names).[29]

Other inscriptions from this period are the papyrus from Wadi Murabaat (p. 271) and two groups of very interesting texts from unpromising provenances, a burial cave at Khirbet Beit Lei in western Judah and a fortress in the desert south-east of ancient Arad, now known as Ḥorvat ʿUza. The burial cave inscriptions are of two kinds.[30] One consists of curses, in the fullest case (probably) against 'whoever erases (this)', a formula known from other inscriptions in both Hebrew and Phoenician. The others, which may or may not be connected, are a collection of prayers and hymns addressed to Yahweh. One simply asks, 'Yahweh, deliver (us/me)!' A second, as generally understood, praises Yahweh as 'the God of all the earth' (cf. Ps. 97.5; Isa. 54.5) and 'the God of Jerusalem'.[31] A third has been understood both as a prayer and as a thanksgiving: according to some scholars it refers to Jerusalem by the name 'Moriah' and the phrase 'the abode (*nwh*) of Yah, Yahweh'. These graffiti are informative about the piety of at least some rural folk in the time around or shortly after the Assyrian invasion of Judah in 701 and Isaiah's prophetic ministry: they show that devotion to the religious significance of Jerusalem was not limited to the capital itself.

Thirty ostraca were discovered at Ḥorvat ʿUza in the 1980s, but only five of them have been fully published so far.[32] One is a (probably later) Edomite letter, with a greeting in the name of the Edomite god Qôs. Three are lists of names, probably of Judaean military officers and their subordinates, and in one case place-names indicate where the men came from. Alongside these administrative documents is one that has been described as a 'literary' text, but its interpretation is still disputed. It appears to open by placing two alternative options before an individual and then to threaten that individual ('you') that a third party ('he') will violently punish him: the final words are 'your grave will be desolate'. The style is elevated and very similar to some prophetic passages, but there is no explicit indication in the surviving text that the 'he' is a god, as one would expect if it were a prophetic threat. But such an interpretation remains possible.

ARCHIVES AND OTHER TEXTS FROM THE LATE MONARCHY PERIOD

From the later seventh century and the early sixth century, which may conveniently be taken together, there is once again an abundance, relatively speaking, of epigraphic material, including especially the large archives of ostraca from Arad and Lachish. This is probably connected with the revival and expansion of Judah in the time of Josiah. Of the 107 Hebrew ostraca found at Arad nearly half are now dated to the end of the monarchy. They include the so-called 'Eliashib archive', a group of eighteen letters addressed to Eliashib, who was apparently the commander of the fortress at Arad at the time.[33] All but one of these, together with two other ostraca, were found together in what seems to have been a record office, perhaps (to judge from the content of the letters) for the distribution of provisions. One example must suffice:

> To Eliashib. And now, give to the Kittim 2 *bat* of wine for the four days and 300 [loaves of] bread and a *homer* full of wine. You shall take it round tomorrow, do not delay. And if there is any vinegar left, you shall give it to them. (no. 2)

Clearly Arad was a sort of depot from which supplies of bread and wine (and in other cases grain or oil) were delivered to military units nearby. In some ostraca specific dates are mentioned, and 'sealing' of the jars. The 'Kittim' named here appear several times in the ostraca: the term refers to Cyprus or the Greek islands generally in the Old Testament (e.g. Jer. 2.10). Probably Greek mercenaries in the Judaean army are meant. In general the Arad Ostraca seem to reflect a calm situation for the garrisons on the southern border of Judah. Only in two cases are there clear references to the wider political background. Ostracon 88 reads like the first orders of a new Judaean king:

I have become king in [all?] . . . strengthen [your?] arms . . . the king of Egypt . . .

Its fragmentary preservation is tantalizing, the more so as Egypt played an important role in the politics of the time. Ostracon 24 calls on Eliashib, by royal authority, to send assistance to Ramat-Negeb to prevent an Edomite incursion there. It is likely that this ostracon, and perhaps others too, relates to the time in 598/7 when Judah was invaded by the Babylonians and its Edomite neighbours to the south and east took the opportunity to move into southern Judah (cf. Jer. 13.19). Reference has already been made in passing to the Edomite ostracon from Ḥorvat ʿUzza and in later centuries this whole area came under Edomite control, as reflected in the later Greek name for it, Idumaea.

The Lachish Ostraca, several of which are in the British Museum, bear more marks of a time of crisis.[34] Twenty-one inscriptions were discovered in the debris of the final destruction of Iron Age Lachish, a major city, about 40 km (25 miles) south-west of Jerusalem, in a room of the outer city gate. The date of this destruction was shortly before the final capture of Jerusalem by the Babylonians in 586 and the deportation of many of its inhabitants into exile. Jeremiah 34.7 is evidence that Lachish was one of the last cities outside Jerusalem to fall to the Babylonians. The majority of these ostraca are letters and the whole group is sometimes loosely referred to as 'The Lachish Letters'. Three of them name the recipient, perhaps the governor of Lachish, as Yaush, and the deferential language ('my lord', 'your servant') shows that the writers are subordinate officials, presumably in neighbouring towns. The number of references to letters (strictly 'documents', *separîm*, but for this meaning see 1 Kgs 21.8, etc.) in these texts gives the impression of a rapid interchange of messages between the officials in the area and also between them and the capital. At one point there is a reference to 'watching for the signals of Lachish'. One letter appears to criticize instructions from Jerusalem as being likely to weaken morale. Another speaks of a report that the army commander, Coniah by name, was on his way to Egypt, probably to negotiate for Egyptian help in the crisis of the Babylonian attack (cf. Jer. 37.5). It is fascinating to read these documents against the background of the later chapters of Jeremiah, in which different policies for dealing with the Babylonian threat are considered and accusations of collaborating with the enemy are targeted on Jeremiah himself. The Lachish letters also contain two clear references to a 'prophet' (*hnb'*). One contains only the fragmentary phrase '[ ]iah the prophet', but the other is slightly more informative:

> The letter of Tobiah the servant of the king which came to Shallum son of Yaddua from the prophet, saying 'Beware!' – your servant sent it to my lord. (no. 3)

It was suggested early on that this prophet might be Jeremiah. But there is no real basis for this, and the book of Jeremiah itself attests that he was by no means the only prophet in Jerusalem at the time.

Two smaller groups of ostraca from a little before the final death-throes of the monarchy add in different ways to our knowledge of contemporary life. During excavations of a fort near Yavneh-Yam on the coast south of Jaffa, six ostraca were identified.[35] On five of them only a few letters could be read, but they seem to be delivery notes of some kind. The sixth inscription was well preserved and quite different in type, and it deserves to be quoted in full:

> Let my lord, the commander, hear the word of his servant. Your servant is a reaper. Your servant was in Hasar Asam, and your servant reaped and measured out and stored [the grain], as on [other days], before stopping. When your servant had measured the crop and stored it as on [other] days, Hoshaiah son of Shobay came and took the garment of your servant, and all my companions will bear witness for me – those who reaped with me in the heat of the [sun] – my companions will bear witness for me. Truly I am innocent of [guilt, so let me have] my garment back and let me get full recompense [*or* 'And if not (i.e. even if I am not innocent of the charge against me)']. It is the duty of the com[mander to recover the garment] of his serv[ant, so may you show] him pi[ty and hear] the [appeal of your se]rvant and not be silent [i.e. inactive] . . .

The translation of the last few lines is not entirely certain, but the text is clearly an appeal from a farm labourer to the fort commander, who presumably had judicial authority, for the return of a garment that had been taken from him. His protest of innocence shows that there was another side to this dispute, but the strength of his demand suggests that he had right on his side, in the form of the laws forbidding the retention overnight of a garment taken in pledge, that is, as guarantee for a loan (Exod. 22.26–7; Deut. 24.12–13).

The other group of ostraca comes from Tell el-Qudeirat, a fortress in the desert to the south of Judah, which is generally thought to mark the site of Kadesh-barnea named in the stories of the wilderness journeys after the Exodus (see, e.g., Deut. 1.2, 19, 46).[36] Seven ostraca were found here in the final stratum of the fortress, from the late seventh century. They are all apparently scribal exercises, or aids to the education of scribes. One contains what may be part of an alphabet, another repeated words: but the rest are full of signs for numbers and measures such as the shekel or the gerah. In some cases the numbers or quantities were written out in sequence: 1, 2, 3, 4, 5, 6, 7, 8, 9, 10, 20, 30, 40, 50, 60, 70, 80, 90, 100, 200, 300, 400, 500, 600, 700, 800, 900, 1000, 2000 . . . up to 10,000. Not all the sequences are complete, and sometimes the order is mixed up. One gains the impression that a teacher would write out, or perhaps dictate, the numbers for a trainee scribe to copy. In one case the same number, 2,382, is written several times on the same ostracon – was this a punishment, perhaps, for a lazy pupil? Two features of these inscriptions deserve comment. The numerical symbols (and some of the others) are close to the system used in the Egyptian hieratic script. In fact many of these same symbols appear elsewhere: for example at Arad and on inscribed stone weights from a number of sites. Evidently in this respect Hebrew scribes borrowed from the highly literate civilization of Egypt to the south. It was not the only such borrowing of which we know: for example the names of some of the state officials at the Judaean court seem to be modelled on those of Egypt, and a section of the book of Proverbs

(22:17–24:22) has so many similarities to the Egyptian Instruction of Amenemope that literary dependence on the part of Proverbs has seemed likely to most scholars. The other peculiarity is that such inscriptions are there at all. Why should quite complex scribal exercises be found in a far-off fortress, rather than in one of the major cities of the country? A similar question can be raised about some of the inscriptions from Kuntillet Ajrud. It is perhaps a possibility that scribes were sent to an outlying part of the kingdom to learn their craft away from the distractions of the city, rather like a public school in the heart of the English countryside. But it is more likely that these examples are the exceptions rather than the rule and relate to the training of scribes to serve specifically in the army. It is clear from the Arad and Lachish Ostraca that by the end of the monarchy period a good deal of military communication, whether about provisions or about the movement of troops, was being done in writing. It must then be regarded as largely a matter of chance that so far much of the evidence for scribal education comes from military outposts far from Jerusalem. But perhaps not entirely chance. In the cities it is likely that papyrus would have been more easily available and, if it was used there for such exercises, the perishable material would not survive and this would explain the absence of evidence where it might be most expected to be found.

Archaeology is full of surprises, but it could not have been expected, when excavations began at some tombs near St Andrew's Church in Jerusalem, that the finds would include two inscriptions that bear a remarkable resemblance to a passage in the Old Testament.[37] Beneath one of the tombs was a repository in which grave-goods and bones from earlier burials had been thrown to make room for new interments. Among the grave-goods were two small silver scrolls, and when they were unrolled it gradually became clear that the texts on them included, along with personal names and some other words, phrases from the priestly blessing in Numbers 6.24–6:

> May Yahweh bless [you and] keep you; may Yahweh make [his fa]ce shine [upon you] . . . (Scroll 1)

> May Yahweh bless (you) and keep you; may //Yahweh// make his face shine [upon] you, and give you peace. (Scroll 2)

The first text is broken at the end and may have included the same final phrase as the second, but neither text includes the words 'and be gracious to you; may Yahweh lift his countenance upon you', which are found in the biblical passage. The texts are not simply extracts from a biblical manuscript. But the occurrence of even a part of the well-known blessing on what seems likely to have been a kind of amulet, probably worn around the neck, is of great interest. The majority of the grave-goods in the repository are from the seventh and sixth centuries and the small, crude writing on the scrolls, while difficult to date, is compatible with an origin around the time when Jerusalem was conquered by the Babylonians.

CONCLUSION

Many more examples could have been included in this survey, some with possible correlations with persons mentioned in the Bible or with the practice of religion.[38]

Enough has been said, however, to show the widespread use of writing in the later monarchy period and to suggest that, on a more limited scale, it was known earlier as well. The inscriptions also shed light on many aspects of everyday life in ancient Israel and Judah, as indicated at the beginning. They give a glimpse of agricultural life, royal bureaucracy, the training of scribes, military affairs and a variety of religious practices. Occasionally there are more direct references to events or personalities (especially kings) mentioned in the Bible.

NOTES

1 For an analysis of the genres represented see J. Renz and W. Rollig, *Handbuch der althebräischen Epigraphik*, Vol. 2/1: *Die althebräischen Inschriften*. Part 2: *Zusammenfassende Erörterungen, Paläographie und Glossar*, Darmstadt: Wissenschaftliche Buchgesellschaft, 1995, 1–33.

2 See in general G. R. Driver, *Semitic Writing: From Pictograph to Alphabet* (Schweich Lectures 1944), 3rd edn, London: Oxford University Press for the British Academy, 1976, 78–87.

3 Driver 1976: 128–97; J. Naveh, *The Early History of the Alphabet*, Jerusalem: The Magnes Press, 1982.

4 B. Sass, *Studia Alphabetica: On the Origin and Early History of the Northwest Semitic, South Semitic and Greek Alphabets* (Orbis Biblicus et Orientalis 102), Freiburg: Universitätsverlag; Göttingen: Vandenhoeck & Ruprecht, 1991, ch. 2.

5 A. Lemaire, *Les écoles et la formation de la Bible dans l'ancien Israël* (Orbis Biblicus et Orientalis 39), Freiburg: Universitätsverlag; Göttingen, Vandenhoeck & Ruprecht, 1981; G. I. Davies, 'Were There Schools in Ancient Israel?' in J. Day, R. P. Gordon and H. G. M. Williamson (eds), *Wisdom in Ancient Israel*, Cambridge: Cambridge University Press, 1995, 199–211.

6 See the tables in Renz and Rollig, *Handbuch der althebräischen Epigraphik*, Vol. 1: *Die althebräischen Inschriften*. Part 1: *Text und Kommentar*, Darmstadt: Wissenschaftliche Buchgesellschaft, 1995, 11.

7 A. R. Millard, 'The Knowledge of Writing in Iron Age Palestine', *Tyndale Bulletin*, 1995, vol. 46, 207–17.

8 J. C. L. Gibson, *Textbook of Syrian Semitic Inscriptions*, vol. 3, Oxford: Clarendon Press, 1982, 1–8; R. Deutsch and M. Heltzer, *New Epigraphic Evidence from the Biblical Period*, Tel Aviv-Jaffa: Archaeological Center Publication, 1995, 11–38.

9 G. I. Davies, *Ancient Hebrew Inscriptions: Corpus and Concordance*, Cambridge: Cambridge University Press, 1991, no. 35.001; K.A.D. Smelik, *Writings from Ancient Israel*, Edinburgh, T. & T. Clark, 1991, 20–1.

10 Davies 1991: no. 10.001; Smelik 1991: 21–7; J. C. L. Gibson *Textbook of Syrian Semitic Inscriptions*, Vol. 1: *Hebrew and Moabite Inscriptions*, Oxford: Clarendon Press, 1971, 1–4.

11 Smelik 1991: 31–50; Gibson 1971, 1: 71–83.

12 W. E. Aufrecht, *A Corpus of Ammonite Inscriptions* (Ancient Near Eastern Texts and Studies 4), Lewiston: The Edwin Mellen Press, 1989, 154–63; Smelik 1991: 89–90.

13 J. Hoftijzer and G. van der Kooij, *Aramaic Texts from Deir ʿAlla* (Documenta et Monumenta Orientis Antiqui 19), Leiden: E. J. Brill, 1976; M. M. Ibrahim and G. van der Kooij, 'The Archaeology of Deir ʿAlla Phase IX', in Hoftijzer and van der Kooij (eds), *The Balaam Text from Deir ʿAlla Re-evaluated*, Leiden: E. J. Brill, 1991, 16–29; Smelik 1991: 79–88.

14 A. Biran and J. Naveh, 'An Aramaic Stele Fragment from Tel Dan', *Israel Exploration Journal*, 1993, vol. 43, 81–98; idem, 'The Tel Dan Inscription: A New Fragment', *Israel Exploration Journal*, 1995, vol. 45, 1–18.

15 Davies 1991: nos. 8.001–23; Smelik 1991: 155–60.

16 Davies 1991: nos 3.001–7; Smelik 1991: 55–62; Gibson 1971, 1: 5–13.

17 The dates cited in this chapter are taken from J.A. Soggin, *An Introduction to the History of Israel and Judah*, London: SCM Press 1993.

18 Davies, op. cit., no. 100.068; Smelik, op. cit., 144; Gibson 1971, 1: 62–3.

19 A. Lemaire, 'Name of Israel's Last King Surfaces in a Private Collection', *Biblical Archaeology Review*, 1995, vol. 21/6, 48–52.
20 Davies, op. cit., nos 100.065, 067, 141, 321; Smelik, op. cit., 144–5; Gibson, 1: 62.
21 A. R. Millard, 'The Last Tablets of Ugarit', in *Actes du colloque 'Le pays d'Ougarit autour de 1200 av. J.-C.'* (Ras Shamra-Ougarit 11), Paris: ERC, 1995, 121–2.
22 Davies, op. cit., no. 2.040; Smelik, op. cit., 103–4.
23 Davies, op. cit., no. 4.116; Smelik, op. cit., 68–71; Gibson, op. cit., 1: 21–3.
24 Davies, op. cit., no. 4.401; Smelik, op. cit., 72–5; Gibson, op. cit., 1: 23–4.
25 Davies, op. cit., nos 105.001–20; Smelik, op. cit., 133–5; Gibson, op. cit., 1: 64–6.
26 Y. Garfinkel, 'The Distribution of Identical Seal-Impressions', *Cathedra*, 1984, vol. 32, 35–52 (Heb.).
27 Davies, op. cit., no. 4.125 (cf. 3.312 and 4.120); Smelik, op. cit., 55, 76.
28 Davies, op. cit., nos 22.001–62; Smelik, op. cit., 132–3; Gibson, op. cit., 1: 54–6.
29 Davies, op. cit., nos 1.025, 030, 26.001.
30 Davies, op. cit., nos 15.001–8; Smelik, op. cit., 165–7; Gibson, op. cit., 1: 57–8.
31 For a different interpretation see P. D. Miller, 'Psalms and Inscriptions', *Vienna Congress Volume* (Vetus Testamentum Supplements 32), 1981, 320–3.
32 Davies, op. cit., no. 37.001; I. Beit-Arieh and B. Cresson, 'An Edomite Ostracon from Ḥorvat ʿUza', *Tel Aviv*, 1985, vol. 12, 96–101; I. Beit-Arieh, 'An Inscribed Jar from Ḥorvat ʿUza', *Eretz Israel*, 1993, vol. 24, 34–40 (Heb.); I. Beit-Arieh, 'A Literary Inscription from Ḥorvat ʿUza', *Tel Aviv*, 1993, vol. 20, 55–63.
33 Davies, op. cit., nos 2.001–18; Smelik, op. cit., 105–13; Gibson, op. cit., 1: 49–54.
34 Davies, op. cit., nos 1.001–21; Smelik, op. cit., 116-31; Gibson, op. cit., 1: 32–49.
35 Davies, op. cit., nos 7.001, 003–7; Smelik, op. cit., 93–101; Gibson, op. cit., 1: 26–30.
36 Davies, op. cit., nos 9.001–6, 009.
37 Davies, op. cit., nos 4.301–2; Smelik, op. cit., 160–2.
38 E.g. the *bulla* of Berechiah (Baruch?) son of Neriah the scribe (Davies, op. cit., no. 100.509; Smelik, op. cit., 146–7) and several objects inscribed with the word 'holy' (Davies, op. cit., nos 2.104, 5.005, 24.014, 99.001; Smelik, op. cit., 162–3).

BIBLIOGRAPHY

Avigad, N. and Sass, B., *Corpus of West Semitic Stamp Seals*, Jerusalem: Israel Academy of Sciences and Humanities, 1997.

Davies, G. I., *Ancient Hebrew Inscriptions: Corpus and Concordance*, Cambridge: Cambridge University Press, 1991.

Driver, G. R., *Semitic Writing: From Pictograph to Alphabet* (Schweich Lectures 1944), 3rd edn, London: Oxford University Press, 1976.

Gibson, J. C. L., *Textbook of Syrian Semitic Inscriptions*, Vol.1: *Hebrew and Moabite Inscriptions*, Oxford: Clarendon Press, 1971.

Hestrin, R., et al., *Inscriptions Reveal: Documents from the time of the Bible, the Mishna and the Talmud*, 2nd rev. edn, Jerusalem: Israel Museum, 1973.

Hestrin, R. and Dayagi-Mendels, M., *Inscribed Seals: First Temple Period, Hebrew, Ammonite, Moabite, Phoenician and Aramaic*, Jerusalem: Israel Museum, 1979.

Renz, J. and Röllig, W., *Handbuch der althebräischen Epigraphik*, Vol. 1, *Die althebräischen Inschriften. Teil 1: Text und Kommentar*; Vol. 2/1: *Die althebräischen Inschriften. Teil 2: Zusammenfassende Erörterungen, Paläographie und Glossar*; Vol. 3: *Texte und Tafeln*, Darmstadt: Wissenschaftliche Buchgesellschaft, 1995.

Smelik, K. A. D., *Writings from Ancient Israel*, Edinburgh: T. & T. Clark, 1991.

CHAPTER SIXTEEN

THE CAIRO GENIZAH

———·•·———

Stefan C. Reif

Great religions, like ordinary individuals, constantly reinterpret the ideas and events of their past in the light of current developments and future expectations. Those curious to know the nature of beliefs and practices many centuries ago are therefore always anxious to remove the intellectual deposits of later periods and uncover materials that represent earlier layers of information. Manuscripts represent a major component of such materials and if they greatly pre-date what has previously been available, and have lain undisturbed for centuries, they assume even greater importance. Modern students of the Hebrew Bible, who are naturally keen to understand how that remarkable source of religious inspiration was used and interpreted by the Jews at critical periods in their history, have been greatly assisted by the discovery of two outstanding caches of such documents, the first made in 1947, and the second in 1897. The scrolls from the Judean desert illuminate many of the religious ideas and customs of Jewish groups in the last years of the Second Temple period and during the time when Christianity and Rabbinic Judaism were taking form, and their relevance to the history of biblical texts and interpretation has been discussed in an earlier chapter. The thousands of manuscript fragments from the Cairo Genizah, though dating from almost a thousand years later, are equally important for our understanding of equivalent developments in the early medieval period. Neither the transmission of the text nor the history of its interpretation has consistently stood at the centre of the kind of 'Old Testament' scholarship that has predominated since the middle of the nineteenth century. There has, however, been a growing tendency in recent years to rectify such neglect and in this connection to pay more attention to the evidence from manuscript treasures. To that end, what needs to be offered in this chapter is a brief explanation of the origins of the Cairo Genizah, followed by a summary of the significance of its stained, worn and crumpled folios for various aspects of biblical study.

The earliest occurrences in Hebrew literature of the root *gnz* are in the books of Ezekiel, 1 Chronicles and Esther where it refers to the storage of valuable items, with a similar usage in the Aramaic sections of Ezra. Given that the first of these examples carries the Persian suffix *-ak* and that aspects of these texts may reflect a Persian imperial environment, it is probable that the entry into Hebrew was through Persian. Nevertheless, the root is attested not only in Hebrew and Aramaic but also

Figure 16.1 Synagogue official searching a hole in the ground for Genizah treasures in Basatin Cemetery, Cairo, c.1979 (Cambridge University Library).

in Arabic, Ethiopic and Late Babylonian with the meanings of 'hide', 'cover' and 'bury' and it therefore had early use if not authentic origins in the Semitic world. In the talmudic and midrashic literature of the first few Christian centuries, it carries similar senses and is used to describe special treasures stored away by God, such as the Torah and the souls of the righteous. In those sections of such literature that relate to Jewish religious law (*halakhah*), however, the root takes on a technical sense describing the removal from circulation of some item that is or has at some stage been regarded as sacred, whether legitimately or illicitly, and is now ruled in-appropriate for ritual use. Such items may include religious texts controversially purporting to be canonical or authoritative, materials once used in worship, capri-cious transcriptions of the tetragrammaton, or effects about whose status there is unresolvable doubt. As Jewish law developed and synagogal ritual became more formalized, it became customary for communities to set aside a *bet genizah*, or simply *genizah*, into which could be consigned texts of the Hebrew Bible that were damaged or worn, as well as other Hebrew texts, including tracts regarded as heretical, that contained biblical verses or references to God. The rationale for such behaviour lay in an interpretation of the third commandment that proscribed the obliteration of the name of God but the principle appears to have been extended by many Jewish communities to the protection of a variety of Hebrew and Jewish literature, all of which might lay some claim to a degree of sacredness. If it is true that the adoption of the codex by the Jews in about the eighth century led to an explosion of Jewish literary activity, the problem of the disposal of obsolete items must soon have become a pressing one and the use of a *genizah* a more frequent and standard occurrence.

If such an extensive application of the law was indeed a feature of oriental Jewish communities of the post-talmudic and early medieval periods, it is only to be expected that *genizot*, or what would be defined by modern scholars as precious archival collections, were amassed in many areas of Jewish settlement. There is indeed evidence that where some communities made 'assurance double sure' by burying the unwanted texts in the ground to await the natural process of disintegration, there were others that removed them to caves or tombs, sometimes storing them first in suitable vessels. It is perfectly plausible that the Qumran scrolls represent just such a *genizah*, although there is clearly room for dispute about the immediate reason for the removal. Sadly, however, the survival rate of such *genizot* has not proved impressive, the ravages of time and climate on the one hand and the vicissitudes of Jewish history on the other either ensuring a return to dust or denying later generations adequate knowledge of where a search might even be commenced. Fortunately, however, in at least one case, the first stage of consignment into the synagogue *genizah* appears not to have been followed by removal to a cave or burial place and scientific study of Jewish literature has consequently been greatly enriched.

The Jewish community of Fustat or Old Cairo appears to have been established soon after the Muslim conquest of Egypt in the seventh century and to have settled in the area of the old Byzantine fortress known as 'Babylon'. There is certainly testimony to a synagogue in the ninth century and it is possibly on the site of that house of worship, perhaps formerly occupied by a church, that the Ben-Ezra Synagogue was built or rebuilt in the eleventh century. The survival of that community *in situ* for 900 years; the dry climate of Egypt; the central importance of the city to Muslim and Jewish history for a number of centuries; and the reluctance of the Jewish communal leaders to take any action in the matter of its *genizah* other than to expand its contents with all forms of the written word – all these factors contributed to the survival there of a collection of fragmentary Jewish texts that is historically at least as significant as the Qumran scrolls.

The 'Cairo Genizah', as it has come to be called, has bequeathed to the modern historian of Hebrew literature well in excess of 200,000 items, or about 800,000 folios, of text mainly dating from about a thousand years ago, written in various languages, but particularly in Hebrew, Aramaic and Arabic, on papyrus, vellum, cloth and paper, and containing a wide variety of subject matter. In addition to the field of Bible studies, such disparate topics as rabbinics, philology, poetry, medicine and magic have been virtually revolutionized by the Genizah discoveries and the more mundane documents found among the fragments have made possible a reconstruction of daily Jewish life in the Mediterranean area during the Fatimid period. Although scholarly visitors and dealers during the second half of the nineteenth century ensured that famous libraries in St Petersburg (Leningrad), Paris, London, Oxford, Cambridge and New York ultimately each acquired thousands of fragments,

Figure 16.2   Ben-Ezra Synagogue, view from outside, 1979 (Cambridge University Library).

and that other institutions also took smaller shares of the spoils, it was the Reader in Talmudic and Rabbinic Literature at the University of Cambridge, Dr Solomon Schechter, who made a famous journey to Cairo in the winter of 1896–7 to investigate the precise source of the fragments that had been arriving from Egypt. Having located it in the Ben-Ezra Synagogue, he persuaded the Chief Rabbi of Cairo, Rabbi Aaron Raphael Bensimon, to allow him to remove 140,000 items to Cambridge and thereby to create there a mecca for Genizah scholarship.

The study of the Hebrew Bible has been one of the fields most closely affected by the results of such scholarship. What emerges from the latest international research relates not only to the content of the fragments but also to the nature of the medium by which the text was transmitted. While this latter field of study is still at an early stage, it is becoming clear that Jewish scribal techniques made major advances from the ninth century onwards and that this had a significant impact on the quality and consistency of the scrolls used for synagogal rites and on the early development of the biblical Hebrew codex. Differences in format between early and

Figure 16.3   Genizah entrance in a wall of the Ben-Ezra Synagogue in Cairo
(Cambridge University Library).

late Genizah material stand testimony to the degree to which the technical details
of Hebrew Bible production were of increasing importance to Jewish custom. As far
as the synagogal scroll is concerned, it has recently been pointed out that the initial
opposition to the Arabic *raq* among the oriental rabbinic authorities gradually
gave way to its adoption. The methods used, which included soaking in water and
lime rather than tanning, and were probably influenced by European techniques,
produced a better quality of split skin. Initial examination of the Genizah evidence
appears to confirm an increasing preference for the improved product. With regard
to the codex, used for purposes other than that of the synagogue ritual, the simple,
even primitive, folios and codices gradually gave way to altogether more elaborate
and systematically produced volumes. A whole range of scribal techniques evolved,
qualities of vellum began to be differentiated, and paper began to challenge the
place of vellum as the primary material for the transcription of texts. Quires were
composed with greater care and consistency, catchwords were included, sections
numerated, lines justified in a variety of ways, folios pricked and ruled, and the
ruling-board was employed to facilitate the planning of the lines. Standards of illus-
tration and illumination gradually improved, making use not only of the more
oriental style of micrography but also of art forms that were more typical of the
West. The private and public libraries that began to spring up in North Africa,
including Egypt, as early as the ninth and tenth centuries, included numerous examples of biblical texts.

Figure 16.4   Schechter at work at Cambridge University Library 1898
(Cambridge University Library).

As far as the consonantal text and its layout are concerned, it is perhaps not surprising to find that most of the Genizah texts may be linked to one or other of the major medieval codices that served as models for copyists, such as those of Aleppo, St Petersburg and Cairo, and that the variants, though certainly worthy of attention, are not therefore substantial in number or significance. Some are valuable and reflect genuine readings, others are simply the result of careless or unprofessional copying. For use in textual criticism, they must all be individually assessed. Where major discoveries and novel historical assessments have been made has been in the area of vocalization systems for the Hebrew Bible. It is now clear that the standard Tiberian system of Ben-Asher, so sanctified since the period of late manuscripts and early prints by both tradition and scholarship, was only one of a number of such systems that were in vogue throughout the Jewish world from the period of the earliest systematic Masoretic activity, say in the eighth and ninth centuries, until their almost total replacement by the standard system some five or six hundred years later. Three major systems, one supralinear Palestinian, one sublinear Tiberian, and one supralinear Babylonian are clearly attested, and combinations of the various systems were also devised in an effort to create a more sophisticated reflection and record of Hebrew pronunciation. Although such variant systems gave way to the Ben-Asher method before the invention of printing and that method was 'codified'

Figure 16.5   T-S K11.54. Ruling board for use by scribe (*mastara*)
(Cambridge University Library).

in the Bible produced by Jacob ben Asher and published by Daniel Bomberg in
Venice in 1524–5, remnants of non-standard vocalization systems may still be found
in non-biblical Hebrew texts throughout the sixteenth century.

It is of course self-evident that the earliest history of traditions concerning the
pronunciation and transmission of the Hebrew Bible must go back to the biblical
period itself. The talmudic rabbis too spoke of authoritative versions of both the
text and the manner of reading it and followed a number of principles concerning
the explanation and exegetical exploitation of textual curiosities. The definition and
recording of vowel-points would appear, however, to be a development of about the
seventh century. Whether inspired by the Syriac Christian example, by Muslim
concern for the accuracy of the Qur'an, or by an internal feud with the Karaite Jews
who preferred the biblical to the rabbinic traditions, a novel attention to the accurate recording of the vocalized text of the Hebrew Bible created a whole new field
of Jewish scholarship, among both Karaites and Rabbanites. The Genizah evidence
is not early enough to shed light on the initial stages of such scholarship but it does
contribute generously to our knowledge of its subsequent expansion. Schools of
Masoretes (from the Hebrew root *msr* meaning 'to count' and then 'to transmit')
flourished in the two main centres of Jewish population, Palestine and Babylon, and

made it their task to surround the text of the Hebrew Bible with vowel-points that reflected their pronunciation tradition, cantillation signs that recorded the melodies used for its synagogal chant, and explanatory notes that inevitably testified to their understanding of the text, whether inherited or newly fashioned. Such a tendency towards the canonization of an aspect of liturgical expression may well have owed a good deal to the formalization of synagogal procedures that was characteristic of developments in the geonic period.

Both Karaites and Rabbanites were active in the Masoretic process and it seems that much of the impetus came from the biblical scholars among the former. It is indeed not always an easy matter to distinguish which of the famous personalities associated with the early history of the Masorah belonged to one group and which to the other. What is clear is that scholars are now in a better position to understand the identifying features of each method and the basic differences between the various schools. Treatises and scholars, hitherto unknown or accorded scant recognition in later manuscripts, have been more clearly identified and new sets of vocabulary and terminology have been uncovered. Such an interest in the text read and translated before the congregation in the synagogue naturally had an effect not only on exegesis (as will shortly be noted), but also on the development of Hebrew philological studies. Once texts and their interpretation became more consistent and authoritative, the way was open for comparisons to be made by keen linguists of the features of the various Semitic languages known to them. Grammatical rules were consequently drawn up, textbooks and dictionaries compiled, and the literal interpretation of the biblical verse given a boost by such systematic approaches. It should not be forgotten that such grammatical and philological studies provided the foundations on which was built much of the interpretation of the Hebrew Bible, by both Christians and Jews, in the later medieval and modern times.

In the earliest years of Genizah research, now over a century ago, the discovery of the Palestinian triennial cycle for both the Pentateuchal and prophetic weekly readings generated great excitement and led scholars to believe that they were now in a position to reconstruct what precisely had been read in the synagogue on particular sabbaths of the year from as early as the time of Jesus. Attempts were therefore made to relate the homilies of both the New Testament and the rabbinic midrashim to the Palestinian cycle and to establish the precise time of the year in which it commenced. More recent work has moved away from such theories and demonstrated that the primary sources bear witness not to one Palestinian cycle and one Babylonian but to a number of possible variations in the Holy Land and to the possibility that each influenced the other from the talmudic to the medieval period. Although the Babylonian cycle as it emerged from the Iraqi talmudic centres in and around the tenth century came to dominate Jewish synagogal practice worldwide, the reports of the traveller Benjamin of Tudela in the twelfth century and Genizah material from the thirteenth testify to the continuing struggle waged by the community of Palestinian emigrés in Cairo to maintain their own traditions and to withstand the pressure to conform to the customs of the Babylonian academies. It is not, however, only the liturgical traditions of the synagogue that are represented in the Genizah collections since Syriac and Greek versions are to be found there, albeit lurking under later Hebrew texts in a number of palimpsests dating back as early as the fifth or

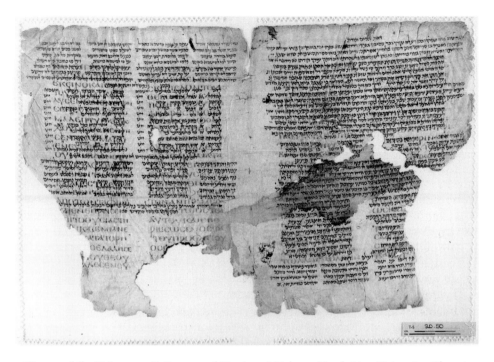

Figure 16.6   T-S 20.50. Palimpsest of Greek and Hebrew (Cambridge University Library).

sixth century. Those redoubtable women who inspired Schechter's trip to Cairo and then worked enthusiastically with him on sorting his finds at Cambridge University Library, Mrs Agnes Lewis and Mrs Margaret Gibson, were given responsibility for the Syriac texts and edited thirty-four of these. They count among the earliest set of Palestinian (and one Edessene) texts of the Syriac Bible, covering four books each in the Old and New Testaments.

Other palimpsests dating from between the fifth and ninth centuries contain Greek texts of the Gospels, Acts and 1 Peter, of Origen's *Hexapla* on Psalm 22 and of Aquila's renderings of parts of Psalms 90–103 and Kings. Aquila's version, written in the second century probably under the influence of Rabbi Akiva, was profoundly literal, no doubt for good theological reasons, and was widely used by Jewish communities in the Greek-speaking diaspora; hence its inclusion in the columns of the *Hexapla*. Since the Genizah fragments are derived from an independent text of Aquila and not from the *Hexapla* and have been dated to the fifth or sixth century, it is possible to regard them as evidence that these Jewish communities continued to use his version until the conquest of the Near East by the Arabs in the seventh century and the subsequent linguistic takeover of the area by Arabic. On the other hand, unless such Jewish communities were more theologically liberal than has hitherto been supposed, the presence of palimpsests of New Testament texts is perhaps more convincingly explained as the result of the acquisition by Jews (through Muslims?) of second-hand writing material from Christian sources. The nearest Jewish Aramaic equivalent to Aquila is the authoritative and synagogal translation ascribed to a contemporary of his, the proselyte Onqelos. Whether or not Aquila is, as has some-times been suggested, identical with Onqelos is not clarified by the Genizah texts, but they do have much to add to our knowledge of the development of that popular genre of Aramaic translation known simply as *targum*.

Examples of Onqelos, Jonathan, Palestinian and fragmentary targums are to be found and are naturally important for the textual (and perhaps pre-textual) history of these versions. It is, however, in the area of more diverse targumic material that surprise discoveries are still being made. Some items are directly related to festivals or other special occasions and to their synagogal lectionaries, while another variety constitutes aggadic expansions often inserted into Onqelos texts. One genre provides poems on themes such as the death of Moses, or the praiseworthiness of the month of Nisan, or of Jonathan ben Uzziel, and there are others that abbreviate Onqelos, provide Masorah for the same version, offer a Judaeo-Arabic translation of Palestinian targum, or incorporate halakhic interpretations of verses that run counter to what is found in the Talmud. It should also be noted that the collections of targums may reflect a particular lectionary cycle, Pentateuchal or prophetic, which may turn out to be novel for records of either Babylonian or Palestinian traditions. A recently published description of the targumic manuscripts in the Cambridge Genizah collec-tions lists over 1,600 items, dating from the ninth to the fourteenth centuries, and this would indicate that there are from Cairo well over 2,000 pieces of targum that are generally older than any other manuscript attestations to medieval targumic traditions, a fact of profound significance to the latter's textual as well as exegetical study.

Because the custom of translating the Hebrew Bible into Aramaic was an ancient one, prescribed by Jewish religious law (*halakhah*), it was not abandoned when Arabic replaced Aramaic and Greek as the predominant Jewish vernacular but was incor-porated with an Arabic rendering into a trilingual version. Such Judaeo-Arabic renderings of the biblical readings, written in Hebrew characters and reflecting the popular Arabic dialect of the Jewish communities, appear to have come into exis-tence at least as early as the ninth century. They provided the inspiration for the tenth-century leader of the Babylonian Jewish community, the Egyptian scholar Saʿadya ben Joseph of Fayyum (882–942), to compose his own Judaeo-Arabic version, the text and spelling of which were destined to become the standard translation for the oriental Jewish communities for the remainder of the medieval period. But Saʿadya was not only a translator of the Hebrew Bible; he also composed a commen-tary, more and more of which has recently come to light and has demonstrated how, as a philosopher, he struggled to rationalize much of Scripture but without over-doing the degree of literalness. The exegetical work of his successor as head of the Sura *yeshivah*, Samuel ben Ḥofni, has also been rescued from the Genizah and is char-acterized by his desire to impose systems of classification on his treatment of the biblical texts.

Of other exegetical material in Hebrew and Arabic from that same Egyptian source, some is extended, some brief; there are those who make use of the latest syntactical and philological theories while others prefer traditional midrashic methods; philoso-phy inspires one commentator, kabbalah another. New discoveries reveal for the first

time how scholars such as Judah ibn Balaam and Moses ibn Gikatilla handled difficult verses from the Hebrew Bible in the intellectual atmosphere of eleventh-century
Spain. By then, the tensions between the literal and applied senses of Scripture had
grown and the cause of the former was then carried forward in Spain and France while
the latter tended to recover an honoured place as the situation of Jews in the Orient
deteriorated after the period of the Fatimid dynasty. The move towards the literal
interpretation had been championed by the Karaites, whose linguistic interest and
textual orientation in the golden age of their biblical studies in tenth- and eleventh-
century Jerusalem led to a high level of lexical and syntactical exegesis. Suspicious as
they were of the rabbinic traditions, they produced their own word-for-word translations, alternative renderings, and interpretations, amounting to what a recent
researcher has defined as 'scientific literalism'. There is no doubt that the Karaites and
Rabbanites exercised both positive and negative influences on each other and that
the Rabbanites were torn between a desire to steal the copyright of the devil's best
tunes and the need to avoid betraying what they saw as the authentic nature of the
talmudic-midrashic interpretation of Scripture. The Karaites too were not without
their polemical intent, as is indicated by the strange phenomenon of surviving folios
of their Bibles from Palestine and Egypt in the eleventh and twelfth centuries that
record the text of the Hebrew Bible in Arabic characters with Hebrew vowel-points.

Figure 16.7   T-S Ar.41.18. Hebrew Bible in Arabic characters
(Cambridge University Library).

If Geoffrey Khan's theory is correct, such an idiosyncratic system was employed as a means of retaining an independent religious identity in the face of Rabbanite influence and incursion. Other strange combinations of languages that occur in the Genizah include Judaeo-Greek, Judaeo-Persian, Judaeo-Spanish and Judaeo-German, and a number of texts in these Jewish dialects written in Hebrew characters testify to the manner in which their speakers understood and approached the Hebrew Bible.

Whatever the variety of their exegetical intent, their literary structure, and their geographical and chronological provenance, what all midrashim have in common is that they represent in one way or another a major history of Jewish commentary on the Hebrew Bible. It is therefore not surprising that contemporary understanding of the development of such an important rabbinic genre in the post-talmudic period also owes much to Genizah research. Hitherto, the earliest manuscripts were medieval, from the early periods of major Jewish settlement in European countries, while now there are thousands of fragments written at a much earlier date and representing older textual traditions. Such traditions are more likely to preserve the authentic form of the midrash since later editions and copyists tended to treat anything unusual as erroneous and to harmonize it with what had already become standard or authoritative for them. While such a statement may be made about all the well-known midrashim of the 'classical' talmudic period, for which the Genizah provides useful textual variants, it is especially true of the halakhic midrashim dating from then, such as the *Mekhilta of Rabbi Ishmael* on Exodus, *Sifra* on Leviticus and *Sifrey* on Numbers and Deuteronomy, the original halakhic statements of which were not always permitted to survive. Halakhic midrashim for which no complete codices survive have also surfaced in the Genizah collections and considerably expanded the horizons of the Hebrew literary historian. Fragments have been identified of the *Mekhilta of Rabbi Shim'on bar Yoḥai* on Exodus, of the *Sifrey Zuṭah* on Numbers and of the *Mekhilta* on Deuteronomy, and these have been or are being exploited for the creation of new scientific editions.

In the standard aggadic field too, discoveries of new midrashim, particularly of the *Tanḥuma Yelammedenu* homiletical variety on the Pentateuch and of the exegetical treatments of the hagiographical books such as Proverbs and Ecclesiastes, have added greatly to our knowledge of developments during the post-talmudic and early medieval ages, and the identification of new anthologies from the last period of midrashic activity have demonstrated how use was made of earlier material to build up a Jewish exegetical overview of biblical texts. Perhaps more important than anything else, there is a whole fresh set of new or little-known midrashim that testify to the fact that medieval Jewish interpretation of the Hebrew Bible could be distinctly colourful and heterogeneous. Fanciful expansions of biblical accounts, apocalyptic visions and mystical works were among the earliest midrashim acquired from the Genizah and quickly published by various scholars. As such a variegated approach to the Bible gave way to the more linguistic and philological commentaries of the tenth, eleventh and twelfth centuries, so the written evidence from the Genizah also records the influence of the centralized Babylonian authorities in inspiring the change and thereby thwarting some of the Karaite efforts to discredit rabbinic interpretation as lacking the serious, literal dimension.

Figure 16.8   T-S K5.13. Child's Hebrew alphabet primer (Cambridge University Library).

Since the Genizah contains not only literary items but also mundane documentary material, it is not surprising to find fragments relating to the place of the Hebrew Bible in everyday Jewish life. Since an ability to read simple biblical and rabbinic Hebrew was a prerequisite for active participation in synagogal worship, most of the male community was introduced to the Bible at an early age. Simple texts, sometimes in alphabet primers, were used by children, and girls were sometimes educated in the Bible, particularly bright ones becoming teachers of the subject. In one sad little Genizah fragment, a father bewails the loss of such a daughter, recalling her intellect, her knowledge of Torah and her piety, as well as the lessons he used to give her. Items from the Genizah are also significant in writing the history of both the illumination of the Hebrew Bible and the melodies used for chanting it. Incipits and colophons are on occasion colourfully treated in an oriental style, while the famous eleventh- and twelfth-century Jewish proselyte from Christianity, the Catholic priest John Oppidans, converted as Obadiah Ha-Ger, took the trouble to record for posterity the music to be used for particular parts of the contemporary Jewish liturgy, including biblical verses. Fragments of incunables and early editions of the printed Hebrew Bible, some of them on vellum and others not yet with vowel-points, are another feature, albeit a limited one, of Genizah collections.

It remains only to make brief reference to items that are either already widely familiar or are only indirectly related to biblical studies. The recovery of the Hebrew

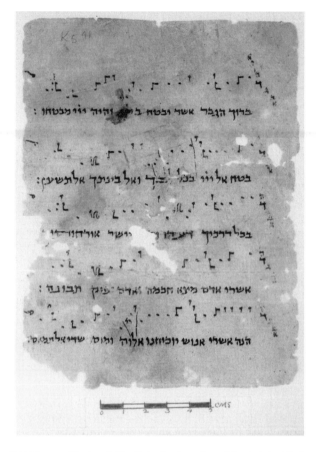

Figure 16.9   T-S K5.41. Music of Obadiah the Proselyte (Cambridge University Library).

text of Ben Sira or Ecclesiasticus from the Genizah is a well-rehearsed story. The first such fragment to come to light, brought to Cambridge from Egypt by Mrs Agnes Lewis and Mrs Margaret Gibson, was enthusiastically identified by Solomon Schechter and acted as a catalyst for his expedition to Cairo and for other identifications elsewhere, particularly in Oxford, London and Paris. Indeed, it is now clear that some such fragments had been retrieved from the Genizah in earlier years and there was considerable competition between various academic institutions, particularly Oxford and Cambridge, in the matter of prior claims and publication. A whole set of fragments, some of them from as early as the tenth century, surfaced in Cambridge during Schechter's initial sorting of his Cairo material and were published by him and Charles Taylor as a new Hebrew edition, followed by a handsome portfolio of facsimiles two years later. If that was insufficient to prove that there had been an original Hebrew in the second century BC, the further work of Segal and Schirmann and Yadin's discovery at Masada of texts that tallied with the oldest Genizah version completed the process of the book's rehabilitation to Hebrew literature of the Second Temple period.

Figure 16.10   Mrs Gibson and Mrs Lewis in academic gowns
(Westminster College, Cambridge).

A less immediate fame was achieved by the *Zadokite Fragment* or *Damascus Document*
(= CD). Although Schechter and Louis Ginzberg both recognized the importance of
the two Genizah manuscripts of this work and offered some explanations that have
generally stood the test of time, no scholar was able to place it in its precise historical and theological context until the discovery of the Dead Sea Scrolls exactly fifty
years after the arrival of the Genizah pieces in Cambridge. Once fragments of the
same work had been identified among the Qumran treasures, it became possible to
trace the origin of CD. And now more material has come to the fore from among
the Qumran manuscripts that show the Genizah version to be a reliable copy of the
earliest texts; a little less than half of an original tract that constituted an admonition and corpus of Torah interpretation and sectarian rulings; and a composite work
belonging to a Qumran legal corpus, at times related to Sadducean and proto-rabbinic
traditions. In addition, the Genizah provides us with texts of Tobit in Hebrew and
the *Testament of Levi* in Aramaic.

How is one to account for the survival of such material, in some sort of context,
from Second Temple Judea to tenth-century Cairo? It is possible that the rabbinic
tradition was central through these centuries and was lukewarm about such items,
which found greater acceptance among Karaites, fringe groups and non-Jewish
communities and made only occasional, haphazard appearances in the more normative synagogues. Alternatively, the rabbinic tradition was less central than it later
imagined itself to have been, and historians should be seeking to uncover major
Jewish religious trends during the first Christian millennium that manifest

themselves in a variety of ideologies that were, for their part, unenthusiastic about rabbinic developments. Whatever the nature of such alternative 'Judaisms', it would have been natural for talmudic Judaism to have played down their importance and condemned their literature, perhaps not always with success. At periods of literary expansion, such as the one represented by the classic Genizah texts, the drive towards the adoption of written, and therefore authoritative versions (and broader, syncretistic vistas?) may have been one of the factors leading to the temporary acceptance within the talmudic communities of a greater variety of compositions than that sanctioned in some earlier or later contexts. For some historians, the answer is even simpler and is to be found in the fact that texts were hidden away in caves and surfaced from time to time. But would Jewish communities indiscriminately embrace such texts as part of their sacred literature?

Finally, it should be noted that neither Jesus nor Christian liturgy escape mention among the Genizah fragments. The rather uncomplimentary and folkloristic account of the life of Jesus known as *Toledot Yeshu* is well represented and no doubt made the persecuted Jews of the Middle Ages feel a little better, while no wholly satisfactory reason can be offered for the existence in the Cairo Jewish community of parts of a Nestorian Syriac hymn-book. Perhaps these thirteenth- or fourteenth-century texts belonging to a feast of the Virgin Mary were sold as scrap when the Nestorian community faded out of existence in Cairo at that time or shortly afterwards. Such a surprising find should alert us to the fact, if it is not already patently obvious, that there is hardly any area of medieval Near Eastern studies that is not illuminated by the fragments from the Ben-Ezra Synagogue of medieval Fustat.

GLOSSARY

Aggadah (telling): rabbinic religious lore and theology in the talmudic and midrashic corpora, to be contrasted with *halakhah*, which is its legal equivalent.

Genizah (storage): the rabbinic tradition of consigning sacred texts, no longer to be used, to a storage room, cave or underground burial, and a place where that process has taken place.

Geonim (excellencies): the heads of the rabbinic academies in Iraq from the seventh to the twelfth centuries.

Halakhah (procedure): rabbinic religious law, to be contrasted with aggadah, which is its non-legal equivalent.

Kabbalah (tradition) the traditional study and practice of Jewish mysticism.

Karaites and Rabbanites: the two dominant groups of Jews in the early Middle Ages, the former devoted to a more literal interpretation of the Hebrew Bible and rejection of the authority of the Talmud, while the latter adhered to the rabbinic exposition of Jewish religious law and of the Hebrew Bible.

Masorah (transmission): the careful study and transmission of the reading, pointing and chanting of the traditional Hebrew text of the Hebrew Bible.

Midrash (interpretation): the rabbinic system of interpreting the Hebrew Bible and any one of a number of collections of material that follow such a system, most of them compiled in the first Christian millennium.

Palimpsest: a manuscript that has been overwritten, with the previous text imperfectly erased.

Raq: skin used by the Muslims for recording texts, especially the Qur'an.

Sadducees: a Jewish sect of the pre-Christian period at odds with the Pharisaic or proto-rabbinic groups and more devoted to the temple, priesthood, ritual purity and more literal interpretation of the Hebrew Bible.

Talmud (study): an authoritative corpus of rabbinic instructions and traditions dating from the first few Christian centuries and given a fixed literary form by the eighth century.

Targum (translation): traditional rabbinic translation and interpretation of various parts of the Hebrew Bible in Aramaic.

Torah (learning): the Pentateuch or the whole Hebrew Bible, or the sum total of Jewish religious teaching.

Yeshivah (sitting): a learning session and, by extension, the place where talmudic and halakhic study has taken place for about 2,000 years.

FURTHER READING

Documentation and further details of various aspects of the subject in English may be found in the following books and articles:

Beit-Arié, Malachi, *Hebrew Codicology: Tentative Typology of Technical Practices Employed in Hebrew Dated Medieval Manuscripts*. Rev. edn. Jerusalem, 1981. One of a number of important books by Beit-Arié on various aspects of the study of Hebrew manuscripts.

Blau, Joshua and Reif, Stefan C. (eds), *Genizah Research after Ninety Years: The Case of Judaeo-Arabic*. Cambridge, 1992. A collection of essays that exemplifies the range of subjects written in one of the major Jewish languages represented in the Genizah.

Broshi, M., *The Damascus Document Reconsidered*. Jerusalem, 1992. Useful essays on the current state of various aspects of research into CD by Broshi himself and by E. Qimron and J. Baumgarten, as well as an excellent bibliography by F. García Martínez.

Chiesa, B., *The Emergence of Hebrew Biblical Pointing*. Frankfurt, 1979. A brief monograph tracing the background to the development of the various systems.

Dotan, Aron, 'Masorah' in *Encyclopaedia Judaica* 16, cols 1401–82. An excellent summary of the history and importance of Masoretic studies.

Goitein, S. D., *A Mediterranean Society: The Jewish Communities of the Arab World as Portrayed in the Documents of the Cairo Geniza*. 6 vols, including the index volume by Paula Sanders. Berkeley, 1967–93. An outstanding study of Oriental Jewish life in the Middle Ages based on Genizah sources.

Haran, M., 'Bible Scrolls in Eastern and Western Jewish Communities from Qumran to the High Middle Ages', *Hebrew Union College Annual* 56 (1985), 21–62. A detailed and reliable account of how the Hebrew Bible was copied by generations of scribes.

Kahle, Paul, *The Cairo Geniza*. 2nd edn. Oxford, 1959. Outdated in some respects and out of print, but not difficult to obtain, and certainly important for the history of Genizah research.

Khan, Geoffrey, *Karaite Bible Manuscripts from the Cairo Genizah*. Cambridge, 1990. A thorough and carefully argued examination of some unusual Bible texts.

Klein, M. L., *Targum Manuscripts in the Cambridge Genizah Collections*. Cambridge, 1992. A sound, scholarly description of many hundreds of targumic items from the Genizah.

Lambert, Phyllis (ed.), *Fortifications and the Synagogue: The Fortress of Babylon and the Ben Ezra Synagogue, Cairo*. London, 1994. An attractive collection of essays and plates on all aspects of the history of Ben Ezra as a building and a community in medieval and modern times.

Petuchowski, J. J., *Contributions to the Scientific Study of the Jewish Liturgy*. New York, 1970, introduction, xvii–xxi. The literature on the lectionaries used in the synagogue is summarized and briefly analysed.

Polliack, M., *The Karaite Tradition of Arabic Bible Translation: A Linguistic and Exegetical Study of Karaite Translations of the Pentateuch from the Tenth and Eleventh Centuries C.E.* Leiden, 1997. A close study of important developments, hitherto documented and examined only to a limited degree.

Price, A. Whigham, *The Ladies of Castlebrae*. Gloucester, 1985. A joint biography of Mrs Agnes Lewis and Mrs Margaret Gibson that is entertaining and informative.

Reif, Stefan C., *A Guide to the Taylor–Schechter Genizah Collection*. 2nd edn. Cambridge, 1979. A useful booklet briefly introducing the history and contents of the Collection, with some plates. Out of print but available online.

—— 'A Midrashic Anthology from the Genizah', in *Interpreting the Hebrew Bible*, eds. J. A. Emerton and S. C. Reif. Cambridge, 1982, 79–125. An analysis, edition and translation of an unusual midrashic compilation.

—— *Published Material from the Cambridge Genizah Collections: A Bibliography 1896–1980*. Cambridge, 1988. Details of the books and articles published on the Cambridge Genizah, indexed according to classmark, author and title.

—— 'Aspects of Mediaeval Jewish Literacy', in *The Uses of Literacy in Early Mediaeval Europe*, ed. R. McKitterick. Cambridge, 1990, 134–55. A survey of the written material used by the Oriental Jewish communities in the early Middle Ages and how it came to be extensive.

—— 'The Cairo Genizah and its Treasures, with Special Reference to Biblical Studies', in *The Aramaic Bible*, eds D. R. G. Beattie and M. J. McNamara. Sheffield, 1994, 30–50. A summary of the Genizah's importance for many aspects of biblical study.

—— 'The Discovery of the Ben Sira Fragments' in *The Book of Ben Sira in Modern Research*, ed. P. C. Beentjes. Berlin, 1997, 1–22. An account of how the original Hebrew was recovered from the Genizah.

—— 'Aspects of the Jewish Contribution to Biblical Interpretation', in *Cambridge Companion to Biblical Interpretation*, ed. J. Barton. Cambridge, 1998. A summary of Jewish study of the Hebrew Bible, comparing and contrasting it with recent 'Old Testament studies'.

Richler, Benjamin, *Hebrew Manuscripts: A Treasured Legacy*. Cleveland and Jerusalem, 1990. A popular but informed introduction to the subject, with plates and samples of handwriting, and a chapter on the Cairo Genizah by Robert Brody.

Sokoloff, M. and Yahalom, J., 'Christian Palimpsests from the Cairo Geniza', *Revue d'histoire des Textes* 8 (1978), 109–32. A helpful listing of the relevant items and the studies made of them.

Stemberger, G., *Introduction to the Talmud and Midrash*. ET Edinburgh, 1996. Originally an updated version of Hermann Strack's classic, but now an important work in its own right, with the latest scholarly data.

Yeivin, I., *Introduction to the Tiberian Masorah*. ET Missoula, 1980. A reliable study of the subject and one of the few available in English.

THE GNOSTIC GOSPELS

———•◆•———

Alastair H. B. Logan

INTRODUCTION

Gnostic and canonical gospels

The problem of 'gnostic gospels' is twofold; it involves both the question what is a gospel and the definition of 'gnostic'. Indeed the first question, what is a gospel, comes into sharp focus precisely when dealing with 'gnostic gospels', particularly those works from the Nag Hammadi Coptic library so entitled (the *Gospel of Truth* (NHC I,*3* AND XII,*2*), the *Gospel of Thomas* (NHC II,*2*), the *Gospel of Philip* (NHC II,*3*), the *Gospel of the Egyptians* (NHC III,*2* and IV,*2*), and the *Gospel of Mary* from the Berlin Coptic Gnostic papyrus (BG 8502,*1*)). The latter also contains versions of Nag Hammadi texts significant for defining gnostic 'gospels' (the *Apocryphon of John*: NHC II,*1*, III,*1*, IV,*1* and BG 8502,*2*, and the *Sophia of Jesus Christ*: NHC III,*4* and BG 8502,*3*). As we shall see, in several cases the term 'gospel' appears to be a later addition to a more original title, which often relates to 'secret sayings' or a 'secret book' (*apokryphon*) or 'apocalypse'; other texts from Nag Hammadi similarly entitled but without the tag 'gospel', for example the *Apocryphon of James* (NHC I,*2*), the *Dialogue of the Saviour* (NHC III,*5*), the *Apocalypses of James* (NHC V,*3* and *4*) and the *Book of Thomas* (NCH II,*7*), must be kept in mind when discussing gnostic 'gospels'.

The use of the term 'gospel' in some of these texts certainly seems to imply both awareness of and deliberate relation to the canonical gospels. Irenaeus of Lyons, in *Against Heresies*, his attempted refutation particularly of Valentinian gnostics composed around 180, claims that they boast of having more gospels than the four canonical ones themselves. According to him they have a work entitled 'the Gospel of Truth', recently written by them, totally unlike the apostles' gospels, so that not even the name 'gospel' is free of their blasphemy. There can only be, Irenaeus concludes, the four gospels, no more, no less; since God has created everything suitably and in order, the gospel should be well composed and laid out (*Against Heresies* 3.11.9).

Whether this 'Gospel of Truth' is the same as that found in two Nag Hammadi codices or not (see below), Irenaeus's comments are significant, both in that they are among the first incontestable references to the term 'gospel' as designating written documents apparently very similar to our present versions (including John), and in

Figure 17.1 The Nag Hammadi codices, from a photo taken by Jean Doresse in Cairo in 1949. Photo by courtesy of the Institute for Antiquity and Christianity, Claremont, California.

that they show awareness of the term being used by Christian gnostic groups acquainted with the canonical gospels to refer to texts that were very different. Irenaeus's criteria for the nature and number of the gospels (as being transmitted by apostles or pupils of apostles and reflecting the four world zones, spirits and cherubim of Ezekiel and Revelation, and hence the fourfold character of Jesus Christ versus Marcion, Ebionites and Valentinians, etc., who appealed to less or more gospels), despite their tendentious character, are a kind of ancient counterpart of modern arguments that would classify the four canonical gospels as a unique genre.

The first thing to strike one about the gnostic gospels is their very varied character, with none at all comparable to the canonical gospels. The latter, with their distinctive combination of narrative, sayings material, miracle stories and passion narrative, form a complex literary genre that scholarly consensus would now classify as a subtype of narrative analogous to the lives of the Israelite prophets or the Graeco-Roman life/*bios* (Vorster 1992: 1077–9). Thus although some gnostic gospels have narrative elements, these are usually peripheral and subsumed into another literary genre, sayings collection in the case of the *Gospel of Thomas*, or, in the case of the *Gospel of Mary*, revelation dialogue or discourse of the risen Christ with his disciples, the genre most characteristic of gnostic groups and texts (e.g. *Apocryphon of James*, *Apocryphon of John*, *Dialogue of the Saviour* and the *Pistis Sophia* of the Askew Codex: Perkins 1980). Again while some of these have obvious relations to the canonical gospels (the *Gospel of Thomas* with considerable overlap with Q, the hypothesized common source of Matthew and Luke, the *Dialogue of the Saviour* including a collection of Jesus' sayings similar to that in *Thomas*, and developing discourses of the

Saviour similar to those of John's Gospel (Koester 1990: 173–87), the *Gospel of Mary* with some allusions), other texts actually entitled 'gospels' neither bear any significant relation to the canonical gospels, nor are they revelation discourses. Thus the *Gospel of Philip*, despite its echoes of Matthew and John and allusions to the Lord's sayings, is a 'didactic and hortatory treatise' (Wilson 1976: 664) or an example of the genre 'collection' (Turner 1996: 240ff.), the *Gospel of Truth* is a 'meditation or sermon' (Koester 1984: 1474) or a 'hortatory, laudatory address' (Helderman 1988: 4072), and the *Gospel of the Egyptians* an esoteric treatise describing the salvation history of Sethian gnostics.

Conversely, some scholars would see the *Gospel of Thomas*, extant both in Coptic in full and in Greek in fragmentary from in three Oxyrhynchus papyri (POxy 1, 654, 655) as incorporating pre-synoptic gospel tradition. They detect in it a wisdom sayings source overlapping significantly with Q, the hypothetical synoptic sayings source posited by many, particularly American, New Testament scholars (Kloppenborg 1987). Where the two overlap, such scholars have argued that many sayings in *Thomas* appear to be more original or to have developed more original forms than their synoptic versions. Accordingly they argue for the autonomy of this material, seeing it as evidence of one of the earliest stages of gospel formation as reconstructed by them, namely a sayings gospel like Q. Hence, for them, *Thomas* is a document of fundamental importance in reconstructing the history of the gospel tradition (Koester 1990: 75ff.). Conversely other scholars would argue for the essential dependence of *Thomas* on the synoptic tradition (Tuckett 1988), or reject the proposed genre of sayings gospel (Meier 1991: 144). Certainly, as it stands, the text has been subject to redaction, including a gnosticizing interpretation which promotes the salvation of the individual by a self-knowledge that implies hidden mysteries (Arnal 1995: 478ff., cf. sayings 21–2). And as regards the second question noted at the outset, the definition of 'gnostic', it is striking that the earliest most probable allusion to the *Gospel of Thomas*, a version of saying 4, occurs in the *Refutation of All Heresies* of Pseudo-Hippolytus of Rome, written before 222 CE, which speaks of its use by the Naassene sect, who called themselves 'gnostics'.[1]

Thus the *Gospel of Thomas* emerges as a pivotal text both as regards the question of the definition and development of the genre 'gospel' and of the canonical gospels in particular, and as regards the definition of 'gnostic'. And its existence within a collection of texts, some of which are dubbed 'gospels', and many of which seem to reflect the views of groups whom Irenaeus of Lyons, author of the earliest surviving heresiological work, entitled 'Detection and overthrow of the falsely so-called *gnosis* (knowledge)', identifies as 'gnostics' and Valentinians, is evidently no accident. Certainly one scholar has attempted to deny that the Nag Hammadi Coptic texts are the library or libraries of the extremely varied gnostic sects identified by the fathers, largely on the basis of a lack of correlation. Such sects, he argues, are largely inventions of the fathers, and the texts are united only by an ascetic tendency, being intended for individual meditation (Wisse 1971). Moreover, the whole concept of 'gnosticism' as a homogeneous phenomenon with certain characteristics (dualism, anti-cosmicism, etc.) has been attacked (Williams 1996). Indeed, a widespread view today, appealing to evidence from the covers, is that the Nag Hammadi texts were not the library of a gnostic sect or sects but were collected and copied by monks in

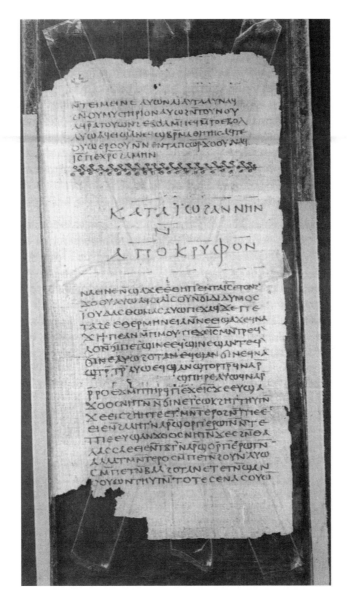

Figure 17.2 The end of the *Apocryphon of John*. Photo by courtesy of the Institute for Antiquity and Christianity, Claremont, California.

that area, precisely where Pachomius, the pioneer of cenobitic monasticism, founded his first monastery (Wisse 1978).

But were they originally composed by monks, let alone collected or copied by them? The Nag Hammadi codices, despite their varieties of genre and content, including Christian and pagan texts, do not seem to suggest a haphazard process of monastic collection and copying, and could make sense as the collection of a particular group or groups. I have recently argued that they are indeed the collection of a Christian cult group who called themselves 'gnostics', centring on their 'classic' myth and cult of initiation as reflected in their fundamental text, the *Apocryphon of John* (Logan 1996; 1997).

This group (including Irenaeus' 'Barbelognostics' and 'Ophites', the Naassenes of Pseudo-Hippolytus, the Christian 'heretics' attending Plotinus' lectures in Rome in the 260s, the gnostics, Sethians and Archontics of Epiphanius of Salamis, and the Sethians or 'immoveable race' of many Nag Hammadi tractates) was united in their understanding and experience of fall and restoration. This was seen in terms of the myth of a fallen heavenly Sophia figure, and their rebirth as Christs in baptism and chrism, after the pattern of the primal anointing of the Son, the third person of the gnostic triad of Father, Mother and Son. As is said of the Naassenes, Sethians and Archontics, such groups collected all manner of relevant material to illustrate and confirm their myth and doctrine.[2]

As regards the coherence of individual codexes, it has recently been argued that they themselves demonstrate a certain logic in their ordering (Williams 1996: 235ff.), something that might cast light on those texts entitled 'gospels'. Analysis of the manuscripts, scribal hands, and so on, has suggested a collection of subcollections from different locations. It is surely significant that the *Apocryphon of John* comes first in three codexes from distinct groupings in terms of scribal hand and codex construction, and in a recurrent pattern in which it is followed by the same few texts, of which three are entitled 'gospel' (*Gospel of the Egyptians, Gospel of Thomas, Gospel of Philip*).[3] Now the first two of several rationales for composition suggested by Williams are a 'history of revelation' arrangement and an imitation of the order of Christian scripture. The *Apocryphon*, setting out as it does the primordial revelation and history of salvation, reinterpreting the early chapters of Genesis, could be considered the gnostic equivalent of the Old Testament, the 'scripture' of the early Christians. This is then followed by further ancient testimony (e.g. *Gospel of the Egyptians, Eugnostos*: NHC III and IV) and Christ's revelation to his disciples (*Sophia of Jesus Christ, Dialogue of the Saviour*: BG and NHC III), or Gnostic equivalents of the New Testament (gospels, letters-cum-treatises, apocalypse, etc.), dealing with salvation (the Saviour's coming and his sayings, the battle with opposing powers over the soul, etc.) and eschatology (resurrection of the flesh, apocalypses, judgment; i.e. the remaining tractates of NHC II).

This evidence of order and pattern, suggesting an alternative set of 'scriptures' to the mainstream one, existing in at least four distinct collections, far from supporting the Pachomian monks' hypothesis, would seem to imply the activity of a Christian gnostic group or groups, composing, copying, assembling collections of relevant sacred writings. For the texts do seem to have been assembled with a certain logic,[4] with some coherence supplied by the order: the opening text as primal or decisive revelation ('scripture') supplies the criterion by which to interpret the rest. Thus the largely Valentinian treatises of codex I (including the *Gospel of Truth*), clearly deliberately ordered, are introduced by the apparently non-Valentinian *Apocryphon of James* as a kind of 'gospel', a revelation dialogue of the Saviour with James and Peter, who then experience an ecstatic ascent with apocalyptic features.[5] The Thomas literature (*Gospel* and *Book of Thomas*), which is generally thought not characteristically gnostic but to derive from the ascetic Syrian Thomas tradition, and which it has been argued was known to and influenced Valentinus and his school (Layton 1987: 359ff.), I would suggest fitted very well into the gnostics' ascetic tendency and overriding concern for the nature and destiny of the soul, as the use of *Thomas* by the Naassene branch demonstrates. The presence of other very varied material in the Nag Hammadi library can be seen in the same light.

GNOSTIC GOSPELS: AN OVERVIEW

Having considered the question of the definition of 'gospel' and looked at the 'gnostic' texts entitled 'gospel' in their relation to the canonical gospels and in their context, the libraries of gnostic cult groups, we now need to consider the gnostic gospels in more detail. As already indicated, the *Gospel of Thomas* would seem to be a pivotal work, both as regards the development of the synoptic gospel tradition, but also with regard to the development of gnostic movements, both the gnostics and the Valentinians. Therefore, I shall first deal with it and then more briefly with the other gnostic gospels.

Gospel of Thomas

As indicated, the *Gospel of Thomas* is a collection of sayings of Jesus of various sorts, including prophecies, proverbs and parables, usually in dialogue with his disciples individually or as a group, which betrays no overall pattern, but often links sayings by catchword. Significantly, whereas the Coptic has the past tense (or 'historic present'?), the Greek of the fragments has the present ('Jesus says'). The title 'gospel' seems a later addition, with the more appropriate designation contained in the opening words: 'These are the secret sayings which the living Jesus spoke and which Didymus Judas Thomas wrote down.'[6] However, both POxy 654 and the Naassenes confirm the overall theme of the work and the order of the opening sayings (especially 2–5), while the latter clearly attest the attribution of the title 'gospel' to the work by the third century.[7] Moreover, it evidently sums up the Naassene esoteric teaching, according to Pseudo-Hippolytus. And this issue of the opening words and designation raises the question of the genre of the *Gospel of Thomas*. I have already spoken of its general designation by a number of scholars as a sayings collection, or sayings gospel, like Q, but also of the criticism and rejection of such a genre. Can we be more precise?

In a landmark essay, James Robinson claimed to identify the genre of *Thomas* as that of *logoi sophon*, 'words of the wise' (Robinson 1971), pointing not only to Jewish examples, such as Proverbs, Ecclesiastes, Wisdom of Solomon, *Testaments of the Twelve Patriarchs*, and *Pirke Abot*; and gnostic examples, such as the *Apocalypse of Adam* but also to pagan versions and Christian instances such as Q. Robinson also went on to point out the essentially fluid, dynamic character exhibited by genres and attempted to trace the history of the sayings collection genre (*Gattungsgeschichte*) from its roots in Jewish wisdom literature via Q to its later bifurcation, one branch leading to the biographical narrative gospels, Matthew and Luke, the other to gnostic revelation dialogues such as the *Book of Thomas*. The tendency of the genre to associate sayings with a sage meant that 'it could easily be swept into the christological development moving from personified Wisdom to the gnostic redeemer' (Robinson 1971: 105).

The presence of wisdom sayings among Jesus' words (as illustrated by Q) must undoubtedly have led to their organization into the *Gattung 'logoi sophon'*, and the tendency of the *Gattung* was co-ordinated with Q's association of Jesus with heavenly Wisdom. *Thomas* suggests the gnosticizing distortion that readily took place in this *Gattung*, as the target of such a trajectory, of which the process of embedding Q into the Markan outline by Matthew and Luke in the alternative genre 'gospel' represented an orthodox criticism and counter. But this meant that the genre was short-lived in Christianity. On the one hand, the oral tradition of Jesus' sayings, the essential context of the genre, died out and was replaced among the 'orthodox' by the canonical gospels, while, on the other, gnostics came to prefer the genre of dialogues of the risen Christ with his disciples as a more flexible form for their speculations.

Other scholars have enthusiastically taken up and developed this position. Helmut Koester, in particular, has accepted the genre *logoi sophon*, but preferred to characterize Q and *Thomas* as 'wisdom gospels', in that not only are they sapiential, but they actually represent a form of kerygma independent of the cross and resurrection form of the canonical gospels. In wisdom gospels what is authoritative is the presence of the teacher ('Jesus, the Living One') in his word; what crystallized the sayings into a 'gospel' was 'the view that the kingdom is uniquely present in Jesus' eschatological preaching and that eternal wisdom about man's true self is disclosed in his words' (Koester 1971: 186).

Koester argues from the character of the sayings as of Jesus, and the absence of features typical of post-resurrection secret revelations, that 'Jesus, the Living One' is the earthly Jesus, and that the sayings themselves as our only sure guides require form-critical analysis of their distinct categories. Such an analysis reveals types and forms similar to those used by Jesus in his proclamation. Most typical are parables, revelatory 'I' sayings, wisdom sayings and rules for the community. Least typical are prophetic and apocalyptic sayings, especially apocalyptic Son of Man sayings, which are lacking in *Thomas*. Thus for Koester the basis of *Thomas* is a sayings collection more primitive than the canonical gospels, of which Q was a secondary version, into which the apocalyptic Son of Man eschatology had been introduced to check the gnosticizing tendencies of the former. The suggestion that Paul's opponents in Corinth had such a wisdom theology (Paul quotes a saying found in *Thomas*[8]) confirms the antiquity of such a sayings collection (Koester 1971: 186f.).

More recently John Kloppenborg in his work on Q has analysed in detail the range of ancient sayings collections, criticizing Robinson for largely limiting his discussion of the genre to Jewish examples. Thus he points to Hellenistic sayings collections, the *gnomologium* and the *chreia*,[9] confirming the fluidity and dynamism of the genre, suggesting in relation to the former category the instructional character of *Thomas* and its esoteric hermeneutic of investigation resulting in salvation, with 'the Living Jesus' as a kind of divine figure akin to Sophia, according to some of the sayings (Kloppenborg 1987: 289f., 301, 305). He also points to the educational character of *chreiae* and their looseness of structure, with self-contained units, often with clusters of *gnomai*, but no consistent theme, unlike the instruction or *gnomologium* and the fluidity of the boundary between them and biography (311, 315f.).

Now, as already noted, Koester's definition of 'gospel' involving sapiential sayings collections has been criticized, on the grounds that 'gospel' must be defined in terms of the four canonical gospels, that is, narratives 'of the words and deeds of Jesus of Nazareth, necessarily culminating in his death and resurrection' (Meier 1991: 143), but the understanding of *Thomas* as belonging to the well-attested genre of *logoi sophon*, as illuminated by the work of Kloppenborg and others, seems generally accepted. But the question still remains where on the trajectory of that genre *Thomas* is to be situated. More light may be cast on this by the following discussion of the relation between *Thomas* and the canonical gospels, but in this section on genre, some consideration of why it might have been composed and for whom, as well as its attraction for gnostics (and Manichees) might be in order. However ancient and primitive some of its contents may be, it was collected (or at least redacted) as an esoteric document, the words of 'Jesus, the Living One', presented as a divine Wisdom figure. The Greek fragments preseve the present tense, reinforcing the authoritative, timeless character of the statements of a Jesus who, if not presented as the usual post-resurrection Lord of the gnostic dialogues, is nevertheless no mere earthly figure. That authoritative status is further guaranteed by the claim that Judas Thomas was the recipient and recorder, as special confidant of Jesus (see saying 13), a feature characteristic of a later stage in the formation of the gospel tradition when the need for authentication became ever more pressing (Dunderberg 1998b: 8off.). Further, despite the oral background of the sayings, they are presented in written form, in Greek and reflecting contemporary literary categories, Jewish and pagan. And if the evidence suggests a fluidity of order, as we have seen, it also suggests fixity in the vital opening thematic statements.

Thus *Thomas* might be more readily situated in the context of late first- and early second-century interest in collecting the sayings of Jesus as authoritative. Robinson and Koester both allude to sections of the *Didache* and *1 Clement* as evidence for such collections, and indeed the evidence of the former is instructive. As with *Thomas*, the work derives from a Syrian milieu, is presented as instructional and maintains the 'authorial fiction' of apostolic transmission, in this case the teaching of the Lord via the apostles to the heathen. Then follows a collection of Jesus' sayings involving prophetic sayings, parenesis and community rules, mainly from the Sermon on the Mount, combining Matthew and Luke (or Q?: *Did.* 1.3–5), with later citation of sapiential material.[10] There is also the evidence of Papias about the value of apostolic preservation of the sayings of Jesus. Further the Naassene and gnostic use of *Thomas* might support the hypothesis of its gnostic character from the start. In this light, Koester's attempt to understand *Thomas* as the best example of a primitive 'wisdom gospel', of which the hypothetical Q is the only other example, seems an inadequate basis for establishing such a genre, while Robinson's suggestion of the inevitability of – or even inbuilt tendency towards – a gnosticizing development of the sapiential sayings collection genre seems equally debatable. Thus it has been argued that *Thomas* contains many secondary compositions artificially put together, and that it is more than a mere collection of sayings, with evidence of dialogue structure and larger complexes of sayings, and thus more like the gnostic dialogues (Dehandschutter 1982, 1992).

This brings us to consider the question of *Thomas*'s relation to the canonical gospels, and the synoptics in particular. What is so striking about the text is not only the large number of sayings that are very similar to the synoptics',[11] but also those that are so different. The former, moreover, seem to divide into those that are versions of synoptic sayings at a pre-synoptic (e.g. sayings 8–10, 21, 31, 44, 47, 57, 63, 68, 76, 89, 91, 95) or post-synoptic (e.g. sayings 32, 39, 45, 104) stage, and those that clearly modify the synoptic versions, often in a gnosticizing way (e.g. sayings 2–5, 11, 12–14, 16, 19, 22–5, 27, 46). Now one or two of those quite independent of the synoptic tradition may preserve authentic sayings of Jesus (e.g. saying 82), but many others again seem to reflect a more gnosticizing strain (e.g. sayings 7, 11, 15, 18, 23, 28–30, 37, 42, 49–52, 56, 59–60, 62, 67, 70, 75, 77, 80, 83–5, 87–8, 106, 108, 110–112, 114).

Earlier scholarship tended to assume that *Thomas* was dependent on the synoptics,[12] but the only detailed attempt to demonstrate that by appeal to the Coptic versions of the New Testament (Schrage 1964) has been judged by many critics as flawed, particularly as regards its methodology. The present text of *Thomas* clearly represents a later stage of what was a fluid tradition, with transpositions, additions and likely scribal assimilations to the Coptic New Testament versions. And, as already indicated, a considerable body of scholars nowadays seems more convinced by the case for the independence of *Thomas*, accounting for the sayings that betray awareness of the synoptic tradition as later insertions and modifications. Their arguments for the autonomy of the *Thomas* material seem to consist, first and primarily, of an appeal to the lack of any consistent pattern of borrowing by *Thomas* from the synoptics. Second, they appeal to *Thomas*'s apparent lack of links with synoptic redactional material, and third they appeal to the general lack of characteristic synoptic features such as a narrative structure, or the kerygma of cross and resurrection, or apocalyptic features and titles. Conversely they stress the sapiential colouring of *Thomas* and the many instances where *Thomas*'s version of a saying or parable is demonstrably earlier and more original than the synoptic one. But, as Tuckett has observed, defenders of *Thomas*'s ultimate dependence on the synoptic tradition continue to appear, among whom he is a notable figure.

On the consistency issue Tuckett has suggested that such a criterion has been drawn up too narrowly, implying the kind of dependence shown by Matthew and Luke on Mark, or a 'scissors-and-paste' approach involving direct use of the actual gospel texts. It may be that the author/redactor of *Thomas* was using a harmonized version of the gospels (like Tatian, another Syrian). Tuckett has concentrated on sayings that he argues depend on redactional elements in all three synoptics, and insisted that the number of cases of synoptic dependence on the part of redactor(s) of *Thomas* is too great to be accounted for by later casual assimilation. But as he himself admits, there is a danger of stalemate on the whole issue of the relation between *Thomas* and the synoptics, with both sides becoming polarized and no really new lines of approach or arguments being advanced (Tuckett 1988: 132). More recent scholarship on *Thomas* has perhaps opened up new lines of approach to the issue. Thus one scholar has argued for the likelihood of an *indirect* use, appealing to an oral tradition and interpretation, building not on the supposed original oral traditions underlying *Thomas*, but on the written synoptic tradition (a kind of 'secondary orality': Uro 1998a). However, as Tuckett also admits, the question may ultimately be insoluble given the present state of the evidence (1988: 157).

More recently attention has turned to the relation, if any, between *Thomas* and the Fourth Gospel. Although *Thomas* appears at first sight closer to the synoptics not only in terms of verbal parallels, but also in terms of literary forms, there are enough similarities, particularly in terms of the symbolic world they both inhabit and the concern both have with the divine origin of Jesus and the believer, with the promise of immortality and a kind of 'realized eschatology', and with criticism of 'the Jews', to have given rise to two main explanations of their relationship. The first, which was developed by Raymond Brown in the early 1960s, was that *Thomas* was dependent on John (Brown 1963: 155–77). Brown focused on the close parallels as alone significant and noted their accumulation in two Johannine passages (John 7:37–8:59; 13–17). From their dispersal in these passages and the fact that the passages are composite, Brown deduced that *Thomas* must have been dependent on John. However, since there are no direct quotations, Brown suggested that the traces of Johannine influence could be attributed to the second source of *Thomas*, for him a gnostic document exhibiting tendentious modifications of synoptic sayings, whose author may have known the Fourth Gospel (Brown 1963: 177). Others have followed Brown's approach, although it has been criticized for its methodology and too ready assumption that *Thomas* is a gnostic document (Dunderberg 1998a: 36).

The second main theory regarding the relationship is that both share a common sayings tradition, whether it be found within the Johannine community, with *Thomas* as a pre-Johannine form (Davies 1983: 107–16), or as distinctively Palestinian (Quispel 1991: 137–55). Koester too sees *Thomas* as influencing the development of the distinctive Johannine Gospel tradition, with its developed discourses. He argues that *Thomas* and the *Dialogue of the Saviour* can help us trace the tradition history of those discourses in that, while the former demonstrates the first stage of transition from sayings collection to dialogue, the latter shows the beginnings of larger compositions. Indeed, he even argues on the basis of John 8: 12–59 for a tension between the pre-Johannine traditions of *Thomas* and the Johannine, whereby the former reflect a gnostic view of salvation which the Johannine author attempted to refute (Koester 1980: 253; 1990: 263, etc.).

However, perhaps none of these hypotheses is entirely convincing; what is required is careful, detailed analysis of the two texts as well as their contexts to establish whether there is any real evidence of dependence in either direction. Here the recent studies of Dunderberg (1998a, 1998b) and Marjanen (1998) help illuminate the contexts of *Thomas* and the Fourth Gospel and the question of the gnostic character of the former. Thus Dunderberg notes the methodological problems raised by the relationship question: that there is no way of knowing which antedates the other; that the differences in genre can equally allow *Thomas*'s use of John and vice versa, as also their entire independence, and that no agreement has been reached regarding the redaction history of each. Thus an essentially literary approach needs to be completed by a broader analysis of the conceptual relationship of both.

Dunderberg focuses his analysis on the I-sayings in *Thomas* as forming a relatively cohesive group expressing Jesus' self-definition and as having significant Johannine parallels in some cases. He concludes that there are no certain indicators of any literary dependence, nor did the two communities seem to have had any contact. On the other hand, a number of conceptual affinities suggest a similar context in early Christianity for both, but in the period from 70 CE to the turn of the first century rather than earlier (1998a: 63f.). His following study of *Thomas* and the Beloved Disciple focuses on the questions that arise from the similarities between the two figures. These include the importance of 'authorial fiction' in both, the way both are intended to be read, the way the claims for authorship in both are related to other early Christian writings claimed to be the work of disciples of Jesus, and the contexts of such claims (1998b: 67).

In his conclusions Dunderberg is led to repeat his earlier finding that there is no clear literary relation between the two texts, and that one cannot assume that similarities between the two figures can best be explained by assuming that *Thomas* was dependent on John (1998b: 71). Further, neither claim, that Thomas was the model for the Beloved Disciple or that the two were identical, seems justified: both characters are represented entirely differently, apart from their alleged close relationship with Jesus and the claims of authorship connected with them. Finally, Dunderberg deals with the phenomenon of 'authorial fiction' so prominent in the two texts, as in a wide variety of contemporary literary genres. The most obvious function of such a fiction is authentication, and the use of Jesus' disciples as figures of authentication is found in various early Christian writings, in increasingly concrete forms. Thus 'authorial fiction' can help to locate writings such as John and *Thomas* within early Christianity. On this basis, the latter represents a less concrete stage than the former. But both find their best context within the broad tendency of claiming apostolic authority, attested particularly in the later generations of early Christianity. This for Dunderberg supports the view that neither John nor *Thomas*, at least in their extant forms, can be dated very early in the first century CE (1998b: 82ff.).

Finally, we might note the way Marjanen treats the claim that *Thomas* is a gnostic document and Uro that it is encratite. The former, after dealing with the debate about the character of *Thomas* and the still unresolved question of the definition of gnosticism, again suggests a new perspective: how *Thomas* views the world, as compared to the Wisdom of Solomon, the Gospel of John, the *Gospel of Philip* and the *Apocryphon of John* (1998: 107ff.). He concludes that, unlike the Wisdom of Solomon, *Thomas* sees the world as a worthless and even threatening entity, while not considering it an error, the work of a perishable demiurge, as do the *Gospel of Philip* and the *Apocryphon of John*. Overall its view of the cosmos comes closest to that of John, while not going so far as to posit his ruler of this world. *Thomas*'s and John's attitude to the world is gnostic if they are the touchstone, but not, if the *Gospel of Philip* and *Apocryphon of John* are.

Uro sets his discussion of the encratite character of *Thomas*, stressed by many scholars and Quispel in particular, but denied by others, in the context of the recent more developed understanding of asceticism in the ancient world. He focuses on sexual asceticism in *Thomas* and its three main themes: anti-familial sayings, sayings on 'becoming one' and sayings about the 'solitary'. He is led to conclude that the ambiguity in *Thomas* over a number of issues, not just marriage versus celibacy, may reflect a development towards a more encratite communal situation (1998b: 162).

Thus the various strands of interpretation can be seen to converge on certain tentative conclusions about *Thomas*, its origins, milieu, character and relation to the New Testament gospels. It would seem best to see it as a sayings collection combining early, pre-synoptic, material with synoptic and later, from a similar period and milieu and sharing similar concepts with John, developing in a more gnostic and encratite direction, and intended by its 'authorial fiction' to be considered authoritative. No wonder it proved so attractive to the Naassenes and the compilers of the Nag Hammadi library.

Gospel of Mary

The *Gospel of Mary* is the first of the three gnostic documents in Sahidic found in the Berlin Gnostic papyrus, known since 1896 but not published until 1955 (Till 1955: Till and Schenke 1972). A Greek fragment from Oxyrhynchus with considerable textual variants was found in the Rylands Collection (P. Ryl. 463: Roberts 1938: 18–23). The Coptic MS has been dated to the early fifth century and the Greek fragment to the early third century. Unfortunately pages 1–6 and 11–14 of the Coptic text are missing and the Greek fragment, which is quite lacunous, only covers parts of pages 17–19. The Coptic text, as with the other works in the codex, has the title at the end, and there is space for a title at the end of the Greek fragment, but it is not clear whether there was a title at the beginning of the Coptic, as there is in the case of the third work, the *Sophia of Jesus Christ*.

Whether the title 'gospel' is original or not, the work is clearly a composite of two parts, probably dating from the late second century. The first part consists of a typical gnostic revelation discouse of the risen Lord to his disciples, in which Mary (Magdalene, as in other gnostic texts) plays a minor role, encouraging the downcast disciples by recalling the Saviour's grace and their elect status. The missing opening section probably dealt with cosmology, as is suggested by the discussion of the various natures and their roots in the surviving text. In the second part, in response to Peter's request that she recount the words of the Saviour that she alone knows, Mary describes a vision of the Lord and the experience of the ascending soul as it is interrogated by hostile powers. Levi defends Mary from the disciples' criticism, which may reflect mainstream Christian objections, as fully worthy and loved by the Saviour even more than them.[13] They then go forth to preach the gospel.

There are clear allusions to the canonical gospels, clustered around the transition (Wilson 1957: 236–43), and their influence on the frame story is evident. Furthermore, there are several references to 'the gospel' as meaning the message the disciples have to proclaim, and the usage 'gospel of the kingdom' suggests a fairly fixed formula reminiscent of Matthew (Koester 1990: 22). This raises the question of the significance of the work's title. Mary Magdalene was evidently a significant figure for gnostic groups. As already noted, she plays a central role in several texts, and according to the Naassene gnostics was their source as recipient of the voluminous secret revelations of James, the Lord's brother.[14] Applying Williams's 'history of revelation' hypothesis to the Berlin Gnostic codex, one could classify the *Gospel of Mary* as a primal revelation dealing with the origins and destiny of the various natures, particularly the soul. That Mary should feature so prominently perhaps suggests that the key to the selection process of BG lies in its editor's interest in the role of female figures in gnostic myth and history. Thus the *Apocryphon of John* with its fully developed gnostic myth of Sophia and fuller details of the fates of various souls comes next, followed by the *Sophia of Jesus Christ* with its concern with Sophia as the cause of the visible world, described in the Saviour's final response–to Mary! The final work, *The Act of Peter*, which seems more encratite than gnostic, may have been included because of its concern with the fate of its virgin heroine and capacity for gnostic allegorization.

Gospel of Philip

The *Gospel of Philip* is the third text in codex II from Nag Hammadi, but it is not the same as the libertine gnostic work under that title from which Epiphanius quotes (*Panarion* 26.13.2–3). The Coptic MS of the mid-fourth century probably goes back to a Greek original of the second or third century, perhaps from Antioch or its neighbourhood, as is suggested by certain details such as the use of Syriac words. As noted above, it has been variously described, most recently as an example of the genre 'collection' (Turner 1996: 240ff.). It is clearly not a gospel either in the sense of the canonical gospels, or in the sense of a sayings collection like *Thomas* (although it quotes some sayings of Jesus, both from the canonical gospels and from *Thomas*); or even in the sense of a gnostic 'gospel', a revelation dialogue like the *Gospel of Mary*. Nor does it proclaim a message of salvation, as in Paul's sense of the term or that of the *Gospel of Truth*. The title only occurs in the scribal colophon at the end and may be secondary. Philip may have been chosen as the only disciple mentioned by name (II 73.8–15), but the choice may be no accident since he is a privileged recipient of the Lord's revelation according to the *Pistis Sophia*, and is prominent in the *Sophia of Jesus Christ*.[15] The title 'gospel' would appear to have been based on knowledge of the canonical gospels,[16] perhaps another attempt at authentication by 'authorial fiction'.

If Turner's proposed classification is correct, then one need not seek a coherent structure in the work, and one is spared the problem of identifying it as a whole with any particular gnostic sect. Most commentators would classify it as Valentinian on the basis of the striking similarities in concepts and terminology, particularly as regards sacraments. But Turner's analysis suggests a collection of sources of varying origin. Thus she identifies (1) a source linked to the early Thomas tradition; (2) an early or conservative Valentinian tradition (including a section very similar to the *Gospel of Truth*); and (3) passages very different from the first two involving 'Sethian' material about an ignorant creator and a fallen Sophia (1996: 234f.). Turner usefully compares it with the *Excerpta ex Theodoto*, but the latter is limited to Valentinian sources and reveals Clement's main motive of disagreement and refutation. She rightly stresses the positive attitude of the collector of *Philip* for whom each excerpt is of value. And here reference to the main themes of true God/inferior creator and procreating/creating coupled with her allusion to the anti-sacramental approach shared by the *Gospel of Philip* and the *Gospel of Truth* is instructive. The former does indeed centre on the key theme of gnostic sacramental rebirth and its proper understanding. If the Nag Hammadi texts do, as I have argued, represent libraries of the gnostic cult movement based on their Christ-centred myth and rite of initiation and are widely attested by the fathers and beyond (Celsus, Plotinus, Porphyry), then the *Gospel of Philip* would fit well into this scenario. It can be seen as another testimony to the gnostic understanding of sacraments, particularly initiation, collected by a member of the cult from relevant evidence, Valentinian in particular. Thus it may be no accident that the texts involving Philip do tend to come from groups associated with this gnostic movement.[17] As the gnostic 'spiritual gospel' equivalent to John, the *Gospel of Philip* comes appropriately after the gnostic Genesis (the *Apocryphon of John*) and the gnostic sayings gospel (*Thomas*).

Gospel of Truth

The *Gospel of Truth* is the third of five writings in the Subachmimic dialect of Coptic from codex I from Nag Hammadi, and the text also occurs in Sahidic in rather different but very fragmentary form as the second treatise in codex XII. The general consensus is that it was translated from a Greek original. Whether it is identical with the 'Gospel of Truth' mentioned by Irenaeus as recently composed by Valentinians and entirely unlike the canonical gospels is debated. Certainly it is unlike the latter, just as it is unlike any of the gnostic gospels discussed so far. It is a homily or meditation on the gospel, with the term 'gospel' occurring in the incipit and twice more in the text, always in the sense of the message of salvation (Koester 1990: 22f.). It has been understood as a confirmation homily, although it may be a purely literary text.

Some scholars have even suggested that it was written by Valentinus himself, perhaps in Rome, alluding to its sophisticated rhetorical style and certain echoes of his fragments (van Unnik 1955; Standaert 1976). However, there are enough significant differences between its themes and those found within the body of Valentinian literature to make some reject a Valentinian provenance. Thus it begins with God as monad, has very little to say about the fall in the Godhead, and almost none of the characteristic Valentinian speculation about the three anthropological categories, pneumatic, psychic and hylic. The discrepancies might be due to the work reflecting the earlier views of Valentinus, or being a much later product of Valentinian *rapprochement* with Catholic Christianity. However, the Nag Hammadi monograph series editors plausibly explain them by suggesting that the *Gospel of Truth* should be considered an exoteric work, directed, like the Valentinian Ptolemy's *Letter to Flora*, to the general membership of the church in Rome or Alexandria. This would explain its – typically allusive – use of various New Testament themes and its apparent knowledge of most of the contemporary Church's New Testament canon, including the synoptics and John, most of the Pauline letters, Hebrews and Revelation (Attridge 1985: 76–81).

Although van Unnik's bold claim that the *Gospel of Truth* thereby attests an authoritative collection at Rome around 140–50 CE virtually identical with our New Testament has been criticized (von Campenhausen 1972: 140f.), the researches of Wilson and Tuckett further illuminate the nature and extent of the author's knowledge. Thus Tuckett would see the finished Gospel of Matthew as the sole source of the synoptic material in the *Gospel of Truth*, thereby adding an argument for its early date (1986: 57–68). Acknowledgment of the authority of John and of Paul would not be surprising for a Valentinian (including Valentinus): Valentinians seem among the first to regard John as scripture, and Pauline themes of grace and election have been argued to underpin their theology. The work's rich allusive style and concern with salvation involving anointing and naming make its inclusion in a library of the gnostic cult perfectly understandable.

Gospel of the Egyptians

This text appears at first sight to have even less claim to the title 'gospel' than the others. It is, according to its editors and translators, 'an esoteric tractate representing mythological gnosticism . . . a work in which Sethian gnostics portrayed their salvation history' (Robinson 1977: 195). Indeed, the formal title is 'The Holy Book of the Great Invisible Spirit', and the title 'Gospel of the Egyptians' occurs at the beginning of the colophon which ends with that formal title.[18] Although there are only a few New Testament echoes, the editors argue for the appropriateness of the title 'gospel' from the way that the work presents the life of Seth, from his prehistory to his saving work in the world, in a manner analogous to the canonical gospels' presentation of the life of Jesus. The author of the colophon has completed the Christianization of a non- or only marginally Christian work by explaining it as a gospel on the basis of the identification of Seth with Jesus. The reference to the Egyptians might be because of a transformation of Egyptian Seth into biblical Seth (Böhlig and Wisse 1975: 18–22).

I would only disagree with the description of the work as marginally Christian and Christianized on the basis of my interpretation of the Sethians as Christian gnostics (Logan 1996), with their distinct myth and ritual of initiation as reflected – if allusively – in the *Gospel of the Egyptians*. I wholeheartedly endorse their point that all the Nag Hammadi texts entitled 'gospel' are only understandable on the basis of a real gnostic-cosmic view, or in other words a gnostic myth (Böhlig and Wisse 1975: 22). The same could be said of the *Gospel of Mary*.

CONCLUSION

This survey of the gnostic texts entitled 'gospel' and their relation to the canonical gospels has suggested, first, that all of them, apart from the earlier strata of *Thomas*, betray some awareness of the canonical gospels and a desire to appropriate their title and authority for their own purposes. Second, despite their varied provenance and genres, they can be classed as 'gospel' in the original sense of message of salvation interpreted in a typically gnostic way to imply a universal myth of restoration. This would help to explain their presence and status within the Nag Hammadi and Berlin codices as library collections of the gnostic cult.

NOTES

1 *Refutatio omnium haeresium* 5.7.20. The context seems to allude to sayings 2–4, and 5.8.32 echoes saying 11. On the self-designation cf. 5.6.4. On authorship and date see Brent 1995.
2 Cf. Ps.-Hipp. *Refutatio* 5.9.7: Epiph. *Panarion* 39.5.1; 40.2.1f.
3 BG would seem to break the pattern, with a 'gospel' first, but it does include a general revelation, which the *Apocryphon of John* and *Sophia of Jesus Christ* then expand.

4 See Williams 1996: 249, on a deliberate scribal procedure in codex I, and 253–60 on the order of the other codices. The scribal note (NHC VI 65,8–14) implies a particular rationale in the selection of Hermetic treatises.

5 In codex V, *Eugnostos* acts as the primal revelation or ancient testimony about the heavenly world, followed by a series of apocalypses involving apostolic ascents. See Williams 1996: 256f.

6 NHC II 32.10–12, preserved in Greek in POxy 654.

7 Cf. *Ref.* 5.7.20, with the allusions to saying 2 (seeking) and 3 (heaven within man), as well as 4.

8 Cf. 1 Cor. 2:9 and *Gospel of Thomas* 17.

9 The *gnome* is essentially a saying, the *chreia* a story.

10 See the recurring refrain 'my child. . .' in 3.1,3–6; 4.1; 5.2.

11 Koester 1990: 87 speaks of 79 sayings with synoptic gospel parallels.

12 See e.g. Haenchen 1961: 147–78, 306–38; Grant 1959: 170–80.

13 For a similar defence of Mary Magdalene's status cf. *Pistis Sophia* (e.g. ch. 61); *Gospel of Philip* 63.34–64.10; *Dialogue of the Saviour* 139.12f. See Marjanen 1996.

14 See Ps.-Hipp. *Ref* 5.7.1.

15 Cf. *Pistis Sophia* ch. 42.; *Sophia of Jesus Christ* NHC III 92.4ff. (the opening response!).

16 Cf. Wilson 1962: 7; 1963: 291 and Tuckett 1986: 72–81.

17 E.g. Epiphanius's libertine gnostics (*Pan.* 26.13.2–3), the *Sophia of Jesus Christ* and the *Pistis Sophia*.

18 Cf. *Gospel of the Egyptians* NHC III 69.6f., 16–20. The version in IV probably had no colophon (Böhlig and Wisse 1975: 8f.). The work is not identical with that mentioned in Clement of Alexandria, *Stromateis* 3 or Ps.-Hipp. *Ref.* 5.7.8f.

BIBLIOGRAPHY

Arnal, W. E. (1995) 'The Rhetoric of Marginality: Apocalypticism, Gnosticism and Sayings Gospels', *Harvard Theological Review* 88: 471–94.

Attridge, H. W. (ed.) (1985) *Nag Hammadi Codex I (The Jung Codex): Introductions, Texts, Translations, Indices* (NHS 22), Leiden: Brill.

Böhlig, A. and Wisse, F. (1975) *Nag Nammadi Codices III,2 and IV,2: The Gospel of the Egyptians* (NHS 4), Leiden: Brill.

Brent, A. (1995) *Hippolytus and the Roman Church in the Third Century*, Leiden: Brill.

Brown, R. E. (1963) 'The Gospel of Thomas and St John's Gospel', *New Testament Studies* 9: 155–77.

Campenhausen, H. von (1972) *The Formation of the Christian Bible*, London: A. & C. Black.

Davies, S. L. (1983) *The Gospel of Thomas and Christian Wisdom*, New York: Seabury.

Dehandschutter, B. (1982) 'L'Évangile de Thomas comme collection de paroles de Jésus', in J. Delobel (ed.) *LOGIA: Les Paroles de Jésus – The sayings of Jesus* (BETL 59), Leuven: Leuven University Press, 507–15.

—— (1992) 'Recent Research on the Gospel of Thomas', in F. van Segbroeck et al. (eds) *The Four Gospels* (BETL 100), Leuven: Leuven University Press, 2257–62.

Dunderberg, I. (1998a) '*Thomas*' I-Sayings and the Gospel of John', in Uro 1998, 33–64.

—— (1998b) '*Thomas* and the Beloved Disciple', in Uro 1998, 65–88.

Grant, R. M. (1959) 'Notes on the Gospel of Thomas', *Vigiliae Christianae* 13: 170–80.

Haenchen, E. (1961) 'Literatur zur Thomasevangelium', *Theologische Rundschau* 27: 147–78, 306–38.

Helderman, J. (1988) 'Das Evangelium Veritatis in der neueren Forschung', in H. Temporini and W. Haase (eds) *Aufstieg und Niedergang der römischen Welt* 2, 25.5, Berlin: de Gruyter, 4054–106.

Kloppenborg, J. S. (1987) *The Formation of Q: Trajectories in Ancient Wisdom Collections*, Philadelphia: Fortress.

Koester, H. (1971) 'One Jesus and Four Primitive Gospels', in Robinson and Koester 1971, 158–204.

—— (1980) 'Gnostic Writings as Witnesses for the Development of the Sayings Tradition', in B. Layton (ed.) *The Rediscovery of Gnosticism*. Vol. 1. *The School of Valentinus*, Leiden: Brill, 238–61.

—— (1984) 'Frühchristliche Evangelienliteratur', in H. Temporini and W. Haase (eds) *Aufstieg und Niedergang der römischen Welt* 2, 25.2, Berlin: de Gruyter, 1463–1542.

—— (1990) *Ancient Christian Gospels: Their History and Development*, London: SCM/Philadelphia: Trinity Press International.

Layton, B. (1987) *The Gnostic Scriptures*, Garden City: Doubleday.

Logan, A. H. B. (1996) *Gnostic Truth and Christian Heresy*, Edinburgh: T. & T. Clark.

—— (1997) 'The Mystery of the Five Seals: Gnostic Initiation Reconsidered', *Vigiliae Christianae* 51: 188–206.

Marjanen, A. (1996) *The Woman Jesus Loved: Mary Magdalene in the Nag Hammadi Library and Related Documents* (NHMS 40), Leiden: Brill.

—— (1998) 'Is *Thomas* a Gnostic Gospel?' in Uro 1998, 107–39.

Meier, J. E. (1991) *A Marginal Jew: Rethinking the Historical Jesus*, New York: Doubleday.

Perkins, P. (1980) *The Gnostic Dialogue: The Early Church and the Crisis of Gnosticism*, New York: Paulist Press.

Quispel, G. (1991) 'Qumran, John and Jewish Christianity', in J. Charlesworth (ed.) *John and the Dead Sea Scrolls*, New York: Crossroad, 137–55.

Roberts, C. H. (1938) *Catalogue of the Greek Papyri in the John Rylands Library*, Vol. 3, Manchester: Manchester University Press.

Robinson, J. M. (1971) 'LOGOI SOPHON: On the Gattung of Q', in Robinson and Koester 1971, 71–113.

Robinson, J. M. (ed.) (1977) *The Nag Hammadi Library in English*, Leiden: Brill.

Robinson, J. M. and Koester, H. (1971) *Trajectories through Early Christianity*, Philadelphia: Fortress.

Schrage, W. (1964) *Das Verhältnis des Thomas-Evangeliums zur synoptischen Tradition und den koptischen Evangelienübersetzungen: Zugleich ein Beitrag zur gnostischen Synoptikerdeutung* (BZNW 29), Berlin: Töpelmann.

Standaert, B. (1976) 'L'Évangile de Verité: critique et lecture', *New Testament Studies* 22: 243–75.

Till, W. C. (ed.) (1955) *Die gnostischen Schriften des koptischen Papyrus Berolinensis 8502* (TU 60), Berlin: Akademie.

Till, W. C. and Schenke, H.-M. (eds) (1972) *Die gnostischen Schriften des koptischen Papyrus Berolinensis 8502* (TU 60^2), Berlin: Akademie.

Tuckett, C. M. (1986) *Nag Hammadi and the Gospel Tradition: Synoptic Tradition in the Nag Hammadi Library*, Edinburgh: T. & T. Clark.

—— (1988) 'Thomas and the Synoptics', *Novum Testamentum* 30: 132–57.

Turner, M. L. (1996) *The Gospel according to Philip: The Sources and Coherence of an Early Christian Collection* (NHMS 38), Leiden: Brill.

Unnik, W. C. van (1955) 'The "Gospel of Truth" and the New Testament', in F. L. Cross (ed.) *The Jung Codex*, London: Mowbray, 79–129.

Uro, R. (ed.) (1998) *Thomas at the Crossroads: Essays on the Gospel of Thomas*, Edinburgh: T. & T. Clark.

—— (1998a) '*Thomas* and Oral Gospel Tradition', in Uro 1998, 8–32.

—— (1998b) 'Is *Thomas* an Encratite Gospel?' in Uro 1998, 140–62.

Vorster, W. S. (1992) 'Gospel Genre', in D. N. Freedman (ed.) *The Anchor Bible Dictionary*, Vol. 2, London: Doubleday, 1077–9.

Williams, M. A. (1996) *Rethinking 'Gnosticism'*, Princeton: Princeton University Press.

Wilson, R. McL. (1957) 'The New Testament in the Gnostic Gospel of Mary', *New Testament Studies* 3: 236–43.

—— (1962) *The Gospel of Philip*, London: Mowbray.

—— (1963) 'The New Testament in the Nag Hammadi Gospel of Philip', *New Testament Studies* 9: 291–4.

—— (1976) 'Philip, Gospel of', in *The Interpreter's Dictionary of the Bible*, Supplement Vol., Nashville: Abingdon, 664–5.

Wisse, F. (1971) 'The Nag Hammadi Library and the Heresiologists', *Vigiliae Christianae* 25: 205–23.

—— (1978) 'Gnosticism and Early Monasticism in Egypt', in B. Aland (ed.) *Gnosis FS für H. Jonas*, Göttingen: Vandenhoeck & Ruprecht, 431–40.

EARLY JEWISH BIBLICAL INTERPRETATION

—·•·—

Alison Salvesen

The practice of commentary and interpretation in a faith community implies at the very least the acceptance of writings that have become normative in some way for the life and beliefs of that community even before a final canonization as 'Holy Scripture'. Interpreters were influenced by a variety of factors, such as the need to explain the Scriptures to later generations unfamiliar with the language or attitudes of the original works, and the desire to harmonize both apparent discrepancies between Scripture and contemporary custom or teaching, and also inconsistencies within Scripture itself.

INNER-BIBLICAL INTERPRETATION

In the case of Judaism, this practice of interpretation goes back a long way, even into the Hebrew Bible itself, and is sometimes termed *Inner-biblical Interpretation*. For instance, the writer responsible for the book of Chronicles ('the Chronicler') based his work on material found in what we know as the books of Samuel and Kings. He emphasized certain aspects of these accounts while diminishing others in accordance with his own particular aims. For instance there is a much greater focus on the Temple in Jerusalem, the cult, and the Davidic monarchy, but no mention of David's gradual rise to kingship over Israel and Judah, Absalom's revolt, or the less creditable episodes of David's life such as his adultery with Bathsheba and his part in Uriah's death. It is hard to be certain of the date of the Chronicler, but the fourth century BCE is likely. The book of Chronicles was eventually accepted as part of Scripture, though in Jewish tradition it is considered part of the 'Writings', and does not appear among the Former Prophets with the other historical books which it parallels.

REWRITTEN BIBLE

As the biblical books became more widely known and authoritative among Jews, the stories could be reinterpreted in different ways, from a variety of perspectives. This genre is often known as the 'Rewritten Bible', and many examples can be found in the early period (up to the end of the first century CE) especially among the

Apocrypha and Pseudepigrapha and the Dead Sea Scrolls found at Qumran, though in the latter case many of the texts are so fragmentary that it is difficult to say much about their treatment of Scripture. Flavius Josephus and Philo Judaeus are also notable exponents of the genre.

Jubilees

The apocryphal book of *Jubilees* survives in its entirety only in Ethiopic, but Hebrew fragments of the work have been found at Qumran and Masada, and small portions are known in Greek and Latin translation. *Jubilees* is a version of Genesis 1–Exodus 20 dictated at God's command by an angel (*Jub* 1.27) to Moses on Mount Sinai. Its treatment of the biblical story includes folkloric additions such as the young Abraham's defiance of his father's idolatry; the eternal character of the Mosaic Law, which the ancients observed even before its actual promulgation at Sinai; and, most notably, a great interest in calendars and chronology. *Jubilees* promotes the idea of the year consisting of 364 days, so that religious festivals will always fall on the same day of the week, and also divides world history into periods of forty-nine years, each equal to one 'jubilee'. Presenting this book as if it were a kind of second revelation of the Law from Sinai is an obvious attempt to promote the views of the writer and the group to which he belonged. From the interest in the festivals and calendar it is thought that he was a priest, and that the work dates from the mid-second century BCE.

Genesis Apocryphon

The *Genesis Apocryphon* found in Cave 1 at Qumran (1QapGen) is another interpretation of the Genesis narrative, this time in a more popular style. Though fragmentary, we have enough of the text to see that it renders the patriarchal narratives of the Bible into a literary Aramaic better understood by Palestinian Jews than the original classical Hebrew. The work probably dates from sometime in the first century BCE. The writer introduces new elements: for instance, Noah's birth is out of the ordinary and therefore his father suspects his wife of infidelity with one of the angels, and Pharaoh's messengers are given a speech in which they praise Sarah's beauty at length. The *Genesis Apocryphon* omits some of the original details, and conflates episodes such as the abductions of Sarah by a king in Genesis 12 and 20. Harmonizing chapters 12 and 20 also serves to remove any dubious behaviour on the part of Abraham: in the biblical account of Genesis 12 he is open to charges of greed and cowardice for letting Sarah be taken away in return for cattle and slaves (Gen 12.15–16). In the *Genesis Apocryphon*, however, Sarah is taken away by force, and Abraham is given an anguished prayer in which he begs God for justice and asks him to prevent Sarah's defilement. God sends an evil spirit upon Pharaoh's household, and it is only when Abraham has prayed for Pharaoh to be healed and Sarah is restored to her husband that Abraham is enriched. Pharaoh gives Sarah gold, silver and fine clothes in reparation for his abduction of her, which reflects Genesis 20 rather than chapter 12.

First Enoch

The composite pseudepigraphical work known as *1 Enoch* is preserved in its entirety only in Ethiopic, though fragments of five Aramaic copies have been found at Qumran. Within it *1 Enoch* 6–11 appears to be a separate document that develops and expands Genesis 6–9. Genesis 6 briefly presents a myth concerning a descent of the sons of God to the daughters of men, the Nephilim who result from these unions, and the Lord's determination to bring the Flood in order to blot out humans and their wickedness. *Enoch* 6–11 interprets the sons of God as 'angels, the sons of heaven', giving them names, and describing how they teach the women magic. Their offspring are giants who ravage the earth, while the angels teach humans astrology and how to make weapons, jewellery, cosmetics, and dye. This leads to all kinds of corruption in the world. The souls of the dead cry out for justice, and the archangels respond by petitioning the Lord, who decrees a flood to cleanse the earth but promises peace and eternity for the future. The aim of *1 Enoch* 6–11 appears to be the explanation of a difficult biblical passage and a justification of God's action in sending the Flood by emphasizing the enormity of the corruption that preceded it. Thus an ancient legend in the Hebrew Genesis has been converted into criticism of contemporary civilization and a promise of resolution by divine judgment in the end times.

Pseudo-Philo

The *Biblical Antiquities* of Pseudo-Philo, written around the turn of the first millennium, reinterprets the history of Israel from Adam to David in a selective manner. Genesis 1–3 and Leviticus are omitted, yet the very minor character Kenaz (known only as brother of Caleb and father of Othniel in Judg 3.9, 11) has chapters 25–8 of the *Biblical Antiquities* devoted to him as the first judge of Israel. Some traditions reappear later in rabbinic interpretations; for instance that Job married Jacob's daughter Dinah. The theology is that of the book of Deuteronomy, that is, sin has led to punishment, but God will one day bring restoration. The original work must have been composed in Hebrew and then translated into Greek, but the only version to survive is in Latin.

Other Works

Those writings that rework biblical passages with a legal and juridical content arguably belong to a separate genre from those in the category of 'Rewritten Bible'. However, often they too reflect an accommodation of Scripture to the beliefs of a particular group. For instance, at Qumran, the *Temple Scroll* (11Q19 and 11Q20) uses Deuteronomy as its base but brings in many other biblical texts to support the authority of the teachings presented. The style has been described as a mosaic, but this ignores the care taken with the structure of the *Temple Scroll*, and some prefer the term 'anthological', which emphasizes the careful coordination of the different verses used to justify a new legal approach to problems of, say, kingship or festival laws. The methodology of reconciling different texts is similar to later rabbinic techniques of interpretation. It is noteworthy that the laws in the *Temple Scroll* are uttered directly by God in the first person, not relayed through Moses. As with *Jubilees*, the contents are presented as direct revelation to Israel at Sinai, not as interpretation on Scripture.

Josephus

A later example of the genre of 'Rewritten Bible' is the *Jewish Antiquities* of Flavius Josephus, who was a Jewish writer living in Rome in c. 90 CE. Josephus's motive is primarily apologetic, and the work is primarily addressed to non-Jews with the intention of combating Graeco-Roman anti-Semitism, especially in the wake of the Jewish struggle against Rome in 66–70 CE, which had ended in the destruction of the Jerusalem Temple. As in the case of the *Genesis Apocryphon*, Josephus renders the narrative of the Hebrew Bible into the literary language of his audience: Greek. He also Hellenizes the Jewish Bible by making it part of a twenty-volume historical work on the Jews, deriving the last books from non-biblical historical sources. The model is evidently the *Roman Antiquities* of Dionysius of Halicarnassus. In this way Josephus provides his people with a national history like that of the Greeks and Romans. He also demonstrates the antiquity and rationality of Jewish religious customs and thus their legitimacy.

Josephus's Hellenistic treatment extends to many details, such as the description of major characters who take on the qualities of Greek heroes and heroines, such as good birth, wisdom, piety, courage, beauty, hospitality, generosity, justice. Episodes that do not reflect well on Israel and its leaders for reasons of idolatry or immorality tend to be omitted by Josephus; for instance the Golden Calf (Exod 32) and the Brazen Serpent (Num 21.4–9), and Tamar's seduction of her father-in-law Judah (Gen 38). Others are retained with extenuating circumstances, such as when Abram sends the pregnant Hagar away in Genesis 16: her banishment is said to be the will of God (*J.Ant* I.217). Other Hellenistic features are the introduction of speeches and the heightening of dramatic or erotic elements: there is rather more passion in Josephus's account than in the Hebrew Bible.

Josephus plays down the role of the magical and miraculous in his account, perhaps in view of his sophisticated audience, though sometimes he tries to provide rational explanations, as in *Jewish Antiquities* I.107–8 when he says that the patriarchs' enormous lifespans were attributable to their good diet, religious merit, and the need to be able to observe the movements of the heavenly bodies over a long period in order to develop the sciences of astronomy and geometry for posterity. A combination of personal and Hellenistic misogyny is probably responsible for Josephus's lack of interest in the prominent women of the Hebrew Bible, such as Moses' mother in Exodus 1–2 (*J.Ant* II.210–23), almost completely eclipsed by her husband (who is hardly mentioned in the biblical account), and also Ruth the Moabite, the ancestress of King David. Josephus has no interest in Ruth's personality, or even in her exemplary fidelity to her widowed mother-in-law, and tells her story only to draw the lesson that God can raise up ordinary folk to greatness (*J.Ant* V.318–37).

Minor Hellenistic Jewish writers

Josephus's retelling of the Bible from historical and literary perspectives was not the first attempt to present Jewish Scripture in a Hellenistic guise. He was preceded by several Jewish writers, including the historians Demetrius, Artapanus, and Eupolemus, and the poets Ezekiel and Philo, but their work is much less well preserved than the *Jewish Antiquities*. Nevertheless we have enough material to see that all presented apologetic views of Jewish history and Scripture that glorified the great figures of Israel's past and tried to combat contemporary anti-Semitism, though the relationship of their works to the text of Scripture is often tenuous. Ezekiel the tragedian rewrote the Exodus story as a Hellenistic drama, called the *Exagoge*. Certain aspects of the original could give non-Jews the wrong impression, and so Ezekiel modified them. Zipporah, Moses' wife in Exodus 4, is identified in the *Exagoge* with the Ethiopian woman that he marries in Numbers 12.1, to avoid the suggestion that Moses was polygamous. Exodus 3.22, 11.2–3, 12.35–6 says that the Israelites borrowed Egyptian property and then took it away with them at the Exodus: thus they 'plundered the Egyptians', according to the biblical text. In common with later interpretations, Ezekiel says that this property was given as payment for the Israelites' work, and was not stolen from the Egyptians (*Exag* 165–6; cf. Philo *de Mosis* I.141).

Philo

Another major but very different Hellenistic Jewish interpreter of the Bible is Josephus's older contemporary Philo Judaeus. Philo, a member of the Alexandrian Jewish community, was strongly influenced by Stoicism, Pythagoreanism and Platonism while remaining an observant Jew. He probably knew no Hebrew and depended on the Greek translation of Scripture, which he regarded as equally inspired. There are apologetic aspects to his interpretation of Scripture, and he also tried to show that the Jewish Law revealed in the Pentateuch was absolute and perfect Truth in a philosophical sense.

Philo's biblical interpretation can be divided into three categories:

1. In the *Allegorical Commentaries* he explains Scripture on two levels, the plain meaning and the more elaborate allegorical sense pointing to the eternal reality behind the words. For instance, though he seems to regard the major figures of the Bible as historical personalities, he is much more interested in the spiritual types they represent: typically, in Philo's treatise *de Congressu*, Sarah is 'virtue', while Hagar is 'education'. He portrays Mosaic Law as philosophy rather than lawcode, though he is at pains to stress that the allegorical interpretation never invalidates the full observance of Jewish Law.
2. His systematic presentation of Jewish Law and his biographies of major biblical figures are given in free paraphrase in his *Exposition of the Law*, and so can be considered as belonging to the genre of 'Rewritten Bible'. However, his retelling of Scripture is less dramatic than that of Josephus, and he adds fewer speeches. For example, his version of Genesis 22 in *de Abrahamo* 167–77 has fewer additions to the story. The two levels of interpretation appear in this group of works

as well: there is the 'natural' meaning for the 'multitude', and the 'hidden' meaning for the 'few' (e.g. *de Abrahamo* 147).

3. The third genre Philo employs is that of 'Question and Answer', a running commentary in biblical sequence, giving the relevant text of Scripture and supplying an explanation. For instance, 'Why does God say "I will send fear to go before you"? The literal meaning is clear, for a strong force to terrify the enemy is fear . . . But as for the deeper meaning, there are two reasons why men honour the Deity, love and fear . . .' (*Questions and Answers* on Exodus II *21). Thus the answers cover both plain and allegorical senses.

Philo's striking use of allegory, seen throughout his works, is heavily indebted to the methods of the Homeric allegorists developed in his home city of Alexandria. These scholars regarded Homer as the perfect poet and philosopher and, to overcome the problem of the unedifying behaviour of gods and men, they employed allegorical explanations. Such methods seem strange to modern eyes, but were very popular in the early and medieval Church, which preserved Philo's works when they fell out of favour among Jews.

Philo's interpretations presuppose a widely known standard text form of Scripture in Greek, which he quotes frequently; and the actual wording is important for his exegesis, in contrast to the approach of Josephus, who, though thoroughly conversant with the text of Scripture in Hebrew, Greek and possibly Aramaic, converts the wording into literary Greek.

PESHER

Unlike the genre of 'Rewritten Bible', which does not necessarily depend on a standard form of Scripture, biblical interpretation in the form of commentary does assume an accepted (if not fully standardized) text. The genre of *commentary*, which is a very familiar form of biblical interpretation today, is found at Qumran as *Pesher*, literally 'interpretation'. Pesharim on the prophetic books of Hosea, Nahum, Micah, and Habakkuk and also on Psalm 37 take the form of lemma (quotation of a verse or phrase from the bible) plus comment, and they proceed in biblical order. They are products of the sectarian milieu, however, and use Scripture to legitimate the authority of the community's founder, the Teacher of Righteousness, to find allusions in the text of Scripture to contemporary events concerning the sect, and (especially) to predict what will happen in the end times. So the emphasis is on Scripture as proof-text for present doctrine, rather than on interpretation *per se*. An example would be the comment on Habakkuk 2.8b ('Because of the blood of men and the violence done to the land, to the city, and to all its inhabitants'), which runs, 'The interpretation of it concerns the Wicked Priest, whom God delivered into the hand of his enemies because of the iniquity committed against the Teacher of Righteousness and the men of his council, that he might be humbled by means of a destroying scourge, in bitterness of soul, because he had done wickedly to his elect' (1QpHab 9.8–12). The author has connected the biblical verse with the struggle between the High Priest and the sect's founder, the so-called 'Teacher of Righteousness'.

TRANSLATION

Biblical interpretation can also take the form of *translation*. Like commentary, it presupposes some sort of standard text.

Septuagint

The earliest rendering of the Hebrew Bible was of the Pentateuch, that is, the Torah consisting of Genesis, Exodus, Leviticus, Numbers and Deuteronomy, central to Jewish life. It was probably produced in Alexandria in the third century BCE for the benefit of the large Greek-speaking Jewish community there. Legend attributes it to the work of seventy or seventy-two Palestinian Jewish translators, hence the name Septuagint, 'seventy'. Greek translations of other books followed, to which the name Septuagint (LXX) was also attached. On the whole, the interpretative element of LXX is minimal since the translators attempted to produce a fairly literal rendering in order to be faithful to the Hebrew text, especially in its cultic and legal sections. However, the poetic books, for example Psalms, Proverbs, Job, the Prophets, diverge more from the plain meaning of the Hebrew largely because the translators found the original text difficult to understand and had to fall back on their own intuition for the particular context, thus unintentionally introducing their own theology and attitudes. Later revisions of the LXX, for instance those of the school of Theodotion (turn of the era) and then of Aquila (c. 130 CE), attempted to bring the Greek translation closer to the Hebrew text form that was becoming standardized in Palestine. The more literal these revisions were, the less room there was for apparent interpretation, although a particular line of thinking can often be found in a single word. The Greek revision of Symmachus at the end of the second century CE is less literal and reflects contemporary rabbinic interpretation of the Hebrew text.

Targum

The loss of the knowledge of classical Hebrew among the Jews of Palestine and Babylonia was addressed in a similar manner as in Alexandria. It is not known at what stage the Aramaic translations known as Targumim (sing. Targum) emerged. Although fragments of written Targumim of the books of Job and Leviticus were discovered at Qumran, it seems that synagogue readings from the Hebrew Scripture (Torah and Haftorah) were rendered orally into Aramaic for some time, and were not written down until much later. Presumably the reluctance to give the Targumim a literary form relates to the desire to maintain the primacy and authority of the Hebrew text, which had already been superseded by the LXX in Greek-speaking communities. But in contrast to the LXX, which rendered the Hebrew quite closely, many Targumim are paraphrastic and incorporate a good deal of interpretation, though every word of the Hebrew is represented in translation. Consigning the Targumim to writing may have been a way of controlling the content of interpretative renderings as well as providing a crib or study tool. Common features of the many and varied Targumim would include a dislike of anthropomorphism (i.e. of God being described in human terms, such as having hands or eyes) and an avoidance of ambiguity (for instance, rhetorical questions are converted into statements). Targum also develops themes already present in parts of the Bible; for instance, that sin has led to exile and Diaspora, that observing the Torah will lead to national and religious restoration, and that the Lord will one day send his Messiah to reign over his people.

THE ROLE OF TEXT AND CANON, RABBINIC MIDRASH

The practice of biblical interpretation takes on a new dimension when Hebrew Scripture is fully canonized. This means that a particular list (canon) of holy books gradually became normative for the Jewish community, and exclusive in that no other writings carried the same religious authority. The text itself became fixed, with a standard consonantal text circulating by the second century CE, and an authoritative reading of vowels was established in rabbinic tradition, leading to a fully vocalized text by the eighth century. The process of canonization and standardization, which was well under way by the first century CE, was given further impetus by the destruction of the Temple and its aftermath. The loss of the sacrifical cult and the end of the authority of the priests and political leaders meant that the study of Scripture and religious tradition became more central in Jewish life, under the leadership of the nascent rabbinic movement. Interpretation became less concerned with rewriting the narratives or translating the Hebrew. Instead, the focus for rabbinic interpretation was the fixed Hebrew text in all its details, and these details are often the basis of interpretation.

The term most generally used of biblical interpretation by the rabbis is *midrash*, which loosely translated means 'investigation'. However, there is much debate concerning the exact definition and scope of midrash. It is clear, however, that the Hebrew text is the foundation and focus of the exegetical activity: there is no rewriting, only exposition and reconciliation where necessary. It is also generally agreed that midrash can be divided into two main types: (a) *haggadic midrash*, which concerns narrative material and often involves folkloric expansions of the text that develop the story in some way, link different episodes, or reconcile differences; (b) *halakhic midrash*, which seeks to extrapolate principles from biblical examples *or* to justify existing practice from the biblical text. Halakhic interpretations can also explain difficulties or apparent contradictions between different rulings or between ancient and current practice. Some freedom is possible with haggadic midrash (= haggadah), since different versions of a story do not affect religious observance. But in the case of halakhic midrash there is much less flexibility and the details of the Hebrew text assume great importance, as with any modern legal document, since the interpretations would provide guidance and authority for everyday life. In fact, the rabbis often had differences of opinion over legal interpretation, recorded in literature, but it was important to demonstrate that the correct methodology had been used to arrive at any ruling.

The corpus of literature containing rabbinic interpretation of Scripture is vast, partly because the latter underpinned almost everything they discussed. So although there are *midrashim* (effectively commentaries) to most of the biblical books, with material dating from the second century onwards, interpretations of Scripture are also found scattered throughout the texts that encode rabbinic legal discussions: the Mishnah, the Palestinian and Babylonian Talmuds, and the Tosefta.

The earliest midrashim naturally cover the first five books of the Hebrew Bible, the Torah or Pentateuch, which are fundamental to Judaism. They vary in content according to the nature of the contents of each scriptural book. *Bereshith Rabbah* is a haggadic commentary on Genesis, the *Mekhilta of Rabbi Ishmael* is a mixture of haggadah and halakhah on most of Exodus, while *Sifra Leviticus* and *Sifrei Numbers* and *Deuteronomy* are halakhic. Most verses receive some sort of comment. It should be stressed that all these have the nature of compendiums of interpretations, ordered according to biblical sequence. Later, commentaries were produced for other books of the Bible. There are also the homiletic midrashim, such as *Pesikta de Rab Kahana* and *Pesikta Rabbati*, which are collections of discourses on the Scriptural readings for the Sabbaths and festivals. In the midrashim, though individual opinions may be attributed to particular rabbis, they are not necessarily the origin of those ideas, which are often traceable to earlier sources. But the transmission of an older tradition by a famous rabbi demonstrated its authority.

The methodology used by the rabbis in biblical interpretation is rarely explicit and different techniques are often used by different rabbis on the same verse. Some methods and traditions go back centuries and can be seen at work in some of the texts mentioned earlier, such as the pesharim and Pseudepigrapha. Certainly there are similarities between Philo's literal and allegorical interpretations, and the plain (*peshat*) and metaphorical (*derash*) meanings given by the rabbis. Peshat involved an examination of the general context of the word or verse, its philology, and similar uses elsewhere in Scripture. Thus R. Berekiah in *Genesis Rabbah* II.1 connects Genesis 1.2, 'the earth was a formless void', with the very similar wording of Jeremiah 4.23 to illustrate its meaning. But shortly after the same Hebrew words are interpreted symbolically (i.e. as *derash*), as referring to the 'nothingness' of Adam and of Cain (*Gen Rabbah* II.3–4). *Derash* could be used even when the literal interpretation seems obvious. Thus the biblical law on retribution in Exodus 21.24, 'an eye for an eye, a tooth for a tooth', is not understood literally but metaphorically, as referring to the worth of the eye or tooth, and therefore to monetary compensation (*Mekhilta of R. Ishmael, Nezikin* 8). However, the same passage in the *Mekhilta* brings in other parallels to support this legal principle. One suspects that because payment for physical injury had become the current custom, the rabbis needed to justify this contemporary practice that appeared to contradict the plain sense of a particular verse. To do this they employed accepted methods of interpretation in order to show that the principle was in harmony with Scripture.

Allegory was also employed where the literal meaning of Scripture seemed too commonplace, as in Ecclesiastes 9.8, 'let your garments always be white': R. Jochanan ben Zakkai in *Ecclesiastes Rabbah* understood this to mean that one should always be 'clothed' with good deeds. Metaphor also avoided the difficulties of literal interpretation as with Song of Songs, the canonicity of which was debated because of its apparent lack of interest in religion and its highly erotic content. In this case the entire book was read as an allegory of God's love for Israel. However, the rabbis did not use typology as Philo had, such as identifying biblical characters with spiritual types. To them Abraham, Moses, David, and so on, were fully historical figures, heroes and exemplars to contemporary Jews.

One of the most basic principles of their interpretation was that Scripture was God-given, eternally valid, and could not contain contradictions or redundancies. So conflicting statements were reconciled, and every detail was significant, including grammatical particles such as 'also', 'this', 'with', 'only'. Unusual words are explained by turning their consonants into acronyms, a technique known as *notarikon*: for instance the word *lāšād*, used to describe the flavour of manna in Numbers 11.8, is understood as a combination of dough (*layiš*), oil (*šemen*), and honey (*d^ebaš*) (*Sifre Num* 89). Because Hebrew letters were used to represent numbers in antiquity, each had a numerical value, and by totalling up the numbers of the individual letters in a word it was possible to arrive at interesting interpretations. This was called *gematria*. A notable example of this occurs in a widespread interpretation of Genesis 14.14, where 318 servants are said to accompany Abraham in his pursuit of his nephew's captors. Since Abraham had a servant named Eliezer, the letters of whose name added up to 318, it was understood that Abraham was accompanied by Eliezer alone (*Gen Rabbah* 43.2). This makes the success of Abraham's mission all the more miraculous. As with 'Rewritten Bible', midrash could extend and update scriptural principles. In this way the biblical prohibition of the cult of the god Molech (Lev 18.21), no longer practised in rabbinic times, was taken to cover all idolatry (*Mekhilta de Rabbi Ishmael, Bahodesh* 6, and Exod 20.3). It is hard to do justice to the wealth and variety of rabbinic midrash. Though it has a clear practical function in clarifying Scripture and making it relevant, at times the rabbis appear to be merely demonstrating their skill in applying the complex techniques of midrashic interpretation, to produce some surprising or entertaining results.

BIBLIOGRAPHY

Fishbane, M. (ed.) (1985) *Biblical Interpretation in Ancient Israel*. Oxford: Oxford University Press.

Jacobson, H. (1996) *A Commentary on Pseudo-Philo's Liber Antiquitatum Biblicarum, with Latin Text and Translation*. 2 vols. Leiden: E. J. Brill.

Josephus, Flavius (repr. 1995) *Jewish Antiquities*. Books 1–4, trans. H. St. J. Thackeray. Loeb Classical Library 242. Cambridge, Mass./London: Heinemann.

—— (repr. 1988) Books 5–8, trans. H. St. J. Thackeray and R. A. Marcus. Loeb Classical Library 281. Cambridge, Mass./London: Heinemann.

Mulder, M. J. (ed.) (1988) *Mikra: Text, Translation, Reading and Interpretation of the Hebrew Bible in Ancient Judaism and Early Christianity*. Assen/Philadelphia: Van Gorcum/Fortress.

Nickelsburg, G. W. E. (1984) 'The Bible Rewritten and Expanded', *Jewish Writings of the Second Temple Period: Apocrypha, Pseudepigrapha, Qumran Sectarian Writings, Philo, Josephus*, ed. M. E. Stone. Assen/Philadelphia: van Gorcum/Fortress, 89–156.

Philo, Judaeus (1929–62), *Philo with an English Translation*. Vols 1–12, trans F. H. Colson and G. H. Whitaker. Loeb Classical Library 226. Cambridge, Mass./London: Heinemann.

Sæbø, M. (ed.) (1996) *Hebrew Bible/Old Testament: The History of its Interpretation*. Vol. 1: *From the Beginnings to the Middle Ages (until 1300)*. Göttingen: Vandenhoeck & Ruprecht.

Sparks, H. F. D. (ed.) (1984) *The Apocryphal Old Testament*. Oxford: Clarendon.

Trebolle Barrera, J. C. (1998) *The Jewish Bible and the Christian Bible: An Introduction to the History of the Bible*. Leiden/Grand Rapids: E. J. Brill/Eerdmans.

Vermes, G. (1997) *The Complete Dead Sea Scrolls in English*. London: Penguin.

CHAPTER NINETEEN

EARLY CHRISTIAN BIBLICAL INTERPRETATION

──── ·◆· ────

Mark Edwards

The history of early Christian exegesis is inseparable from that of the New Testament. Presenting the work and death of Christ as the key to Jewish prophecy, the Gospels and Epistles offered specimens of exegetic practice, while later portions justified the ascription of a comparable authority and density to these 'apostolic' writings. The canon shaped the doctrine of its readers, and this doctrine curbed additions to the canon; opacity of style or a profusion of new matter could outweigh the reputation of the author to entail the degradation or exclusion of a text. By the end of the second century, not only had the Ignatian, Clementine and Petrine documents been excluded, but even the composition of works professing to elucidate the sacred corpus seems to have been regarded with suspicion.[1] For Churchmen of this age, commentary on scriptures, old or new, was incidental to the refutation of errors that opponents had derived from them; thus the exegesis or redaction of Christian literature was at first a heterodox monopoly.

The first great figure (c. 140) was Marcion of Pontus, who collated (and occasionally abridged) the letters of Paul, composing prefaces to these and to the Gospel of Luke, which he also abbreviated. Tatian of Edessa, the founder of the world-denying Encratites, produced the *Diatessaron*, or harmony of the Gospels around 170 AD, thus bearing witness to the fourfold canon. The myths in Gnostic documents are expansions, imitations or revisions of the narratives in Genesis, while those of their more Christian successors, the Valentinians, seem to have aimed at simultaneous paraphrase of themes in Johannine and Pauline literature.[2] Their disparagement of the body and its Creator could be justified by appeal to 1 Corinthians 15.62, but allegory yielded a crop of fanciful confirmations to Heracleon in his *Commentary on John*.[3] While Gnostic myth shows certain traits of midrash, this, the earliest treatise on an apostolic book, has more in common with Philo's exposition of the Pentateuch,[4] which treats both law and history as a syllabus of virtues for the soul. In spite of Philo, only a limited value was accorded to the Old Testament by Valentinian exegetes, who declared that both the Law and the Legislator were defective emanations of the Spirit. The Church's tool for preserving the integrity of scripture was not allegory but typology, which interpreted the narratives and ceremonial precepts in the Old Testament as foreshadowings of the more transparent mysteries of the New. The first extensive essays on this subject are the Epistle to the Hebrews, which sees Joshua and Melchizedek as forerunners of Christ, and the letter ascribed to Barnabas, which argues that the new covenant restores the original tables of the law that Moses shattered when he saw the golden calf. Setting a rule for others, he discerned the highest mysteries in the least possible commandments: circumcision and dietary laws have lapsed, but the enigmatic sacrifice of the red heifer is a symbol of the Passion (ch. 8). Some knowledge of the Paschal rite helped Melito of Sardis to demonstrate in his Easter homily (c. 170) that Christ is the minister of that redemption which the Exodus foretold.

In Justin Martyr's *Dialogue with Trypho* (c. 160), the angels who communicated the will of God to the patriarchs are identified with a personal agent, the Word of God, who is one with yet distinct from him, his power being also visible in the fabric of the universe, the inspiration of the Hebrew prophets and even in the words of some who lived outside the Jewish dispensation. This, with all its burdens, was transitional, a shadow of the work to be accomplished when the Author of the prophecies became the Nazarene Jesus of the Gospels. His strange nativity and shameful death were anticipated in his own utterances to Israel, as was the unbelief of the Jews, whose punishment by exclusion from the kingdom was prefigured in circumcision.[5] Recondite and unconsummated prophecies are the strongest proof that the Church has now become the second Israel: this is true above all of certain verses now found only in the Septuagint, which, Justin claims, were present in the Hebrew copies also until they were culled by Jewish teachers. The Septuagint, now proved to be such a useful reservoir of testimonia, held its own again the Hebrew in the West until the time of Jerome, and in the Eastern Church to the present day. But when, in the early third century, Tertullian (c. 160–c. 240) made a similar compilation against the Marcionites, the Old Testament itself was on trial, and with it not the divinity of Christ, but his Incarnation. Following Irenaeus (c. 180), Tertullian held that exegetes must conform to the 'rule of faith' that was handed down from the apostles and is sustained by the unanimity of the churches. When a text, read literally, conflicts with the rule, a figurative construction may be warranted: thus, because the Resurrection teaches us that flesh and blood can enter heaven, 1 Corinthians 15.50 must be applied, not to the substance, but to the works of flesh and blood, and more specifically to the Jews (*On the Resurrection* 50). This could be deemed an instance of metonymy, the trope of reference by association. Northrop Frye's assimilation of typology to metonymy,[6] though questionable, is true in so far as both provided antidotes to the poison left in pious veins by metaphor and myth.

Heretics and Greeks defended myth on the grounds that its lewd veneer concealed the secrets of philosophy; Clement of Alexandria (fl. 200) rejoined in his *Protrepticus* that there was no cause to keep them secret, least of all in such a form. Yet were there not, as the pagan Celsus argued, numerous passages in scripture, and especially the Old Testament, that compromised the goodness, the omnipotence or the majesty of God?[7] Clement's first reply, for which he will have found a precedent in Philo, is that God is so much higher than our thoughts that words can never do justice to him. His second is that if there were no difficulties in scripture, we should have no opportunity to increase our faith through knowledge. The wisdom thus acquired by the 'gnostic' Christian teaches him to regard philanthropy, not vigour of body or intellect, as the test of moral progress. Thus, as he argues in *The Rich Man's Salvation*, the 'noetic' sense of Matthew allows the body to retain its goods so long as there is no avarice in the soul. This passage intimates that Clement posited different levels of understanding for the exegete; some have reckoned three or even four, in correspondence with the conventional divisions of philosophy.[8] No trace of such a scheme is found, however, in what remains of Clement's writing on the New Testament Epistles; theories of multiple meaning are discernible in the *Excerpts from Theodotus* and *Prophetic Extracts*[9] but not in the parts that represent the opinion of Clement. Alexandria did not yet possess a true discipline of exegesis, though Clement would appear to have been acquainted with contemporary thought on the application of Pythagorean maxims (*Stromateis* 5.27). True commentary began with the next generation, in the West as in the East. Hippolytus (d. 235), a dissident, Greek-speaking member of the Roman clergy, produced commentaries on Revelation, the Song of Songs and the book of Daniel. None of these afforded rich materials for a creed or moral homily; it is clear that they were chosen simply because they were arcane enough to require elucidation. The book of Revelation (undisputedly canonical until the mid-third century) had given rise to rumours of an imminent Second Coming; Hippolytus taught the Church to read the work through different lenses by observing that the Beast whose crimes will usher in the end is not so much a single person as a typological parody of Christ (*On Antichrist* 6). The authorship of this book was still debated, long after that of the Gospels had been settled. The antiquity of Daniel does not seem to have been impugned by any Christian,[10] but Hippolytus appears to have at least a premonition of the modern view when, noting that the fanciful chronology of the last part supervenes on a more accurate account of the Maccabean age, he tells us that in the latter case the prophet was recounting 'what had happened in his own time' (*On Daniel* 4.48).

It was Origen (185–254) who bequeathed to the Church a theory of exegesis, philosophical in its premises and compendious in its scope. Still more theologian than scholar, he continued to employ the Greek Bible, even though he seems to have mastered Hebrew. The purpose of his *Hexapla* – a synopsis of the Hebrew text, a Greek transliteration and four translations – was not to displace the Septuagint, but to clarify its obscurities and adjudicate between divergent readings. Notwithstanding his attempt to demonstrate against Julius Africanus that the story of Susanna could have been part of the original book of Daniel (Eusebius, *Church History* 6.31), he knew that another of his favourite texts, the Wisdom of Solomon, had no place in the Jewish canon. This did not deter him from appealing to it on doctrinal questions, any more than his doubts as to the authorship of Hebrews made him scruple to rest a case on its authenticity. None the less, he restricts himself to the primitive 'books of Solomon' when he argues that they are so arranged as to lead us through the stages of philosophy: Proverbs imparts morality, Ecclesiastes knowledge of the natural world, and the Canticle *theoria*, or the vision of the truth in God.[11] Origen and his followers applied this scheme to the progress of the soul, as it acquires first bodily discipline, then a deeper understanding of God's purposes, and finally the theological insight that belongs to a perfect spirit. In Origen's longest exercise in Biblical criticism, each of these three elements in the human person answers to one of the coinherent senses that can be distinguished in the Word of God.

335

One is often told that these three senses are the literal, the moral and the enoptic.[12] But the last term has no status in Greek or English, there is no equivalent to the first in Origen, and the moral sense is surely the literal one if the text itself is a command. The one that Origen styles the body of scripture is the easiest to define: it is the narrative or *historia* where the language is indicative, and the literal application where the language is imperative. But for a handful of stumbling-blocks, which God puts there to arouse the higher faculties, the bodily sense is always true and sufficient for the faithful.[13] The third, which Origen calls the mystical, we call typological: in every word of scripture it leads us back to the one ubiquitous and undivided Word. Scripture, as he tells Celsus, is a continual descent of Christ, who 'becomes flesh, as it were, and speaks to us with literal voice' (*Against Celsus* 4.15). The second sense is frequently subsumed in the other two, as soul is often subsumed in flesh or spirit in a Christian anthropology: but taking the Apostle's question 'Does God care for oxen?' (1 Cor 9.9) as his paradigm, Origen implies that the 'soul' of scripture assigns each work of God to its due place in the cosmic order (*First Principles* 4.2). If the soul and spirit, then, are respectively cosmology and theology, Origen's higher senses correspond to the two degrees of allegorical interpretation recognized by students of mythology in his era;[14] and this triple scheme was adopted in the next century, with little change, by Gregory of Elvira and his fellow-Origenist Ambrose of Milan.[15]

Origen wrote commentaries and homilies on almost the whole of scripture, speculating freely in the commentaries, though seldom drawing all three senses from a single text. The 'bodily' sense was rejected only when it seemed offensive, insignificant or at odds with other passages. The literal sense, as we should call it, is not suppressed but redeemed and purified in his exegesis, just as the body is not suppressed but redeemed and purified in his eschatology. It was in fact a literal construction of Genesis 1–2 that made him espouse a theory of two creations, one of the inner and one of the outer man (*Genesis Homily* 1). Conversely, it was Origen's literal belief that flesh and spirit were reconciled in the Incarnation that enabled him to harmonize John and Matthew by describing one as a parabolic, the other as a historical account of the same events (*Commentary on John* 10.5). His fame as an interpreter survived the first complaints against his doctrines, but fell in the wake of the Arian controversy (318–25), when Marcellus of Ancyra, a would-be orthodox theologian, denounced his predilection for the enigmatic texts (Eusebius, *Against Marcellus* 1.4.3). Even his ardent champion Eusebius of Caesarea (c. 260–339) pursued a more philological, less speculative method. The most important fruits of this were a chronography, a concordance of the Gospels, some notes on the evolution of the canon in his *Church History*, and a small gift to the allegorist in his *Onomasticon*, or key to topographic names.[16]

The great heresiologist Epiphanius of Salamis (c. 315–403) maintained that God's design in human history implied a first man and a first transgression, both of which, he said, had been denied in Origen's arbitrary treatment of the Fall (*Ancoratus* 55–62). Admitting, for his own part, that the book of Revelation is enigmatic, that a title claimed by Christ can be metaphorical and that the Bible uses types of things to come, he none the less gives voice to the ruling spirit of his century, which, without defining allegory, compelled Greek-speaking Christians to disclaim the use of it.

Basil of Caesarea (c. 330–79) applied the literal rule to Genesis, but his younger brother, Gregory of Nyssa (c. 335–95), coined a new term, *cheiragogia* (leading by the hand), and thus baptized the classical principle of looking for the *skopos*, or intention, of the text.[17] Origen had not neglected this, but it was frequently in conflict with his customary practice of interpreting texts in the light of distant parallels. Gregory had learned, no doubt from the Platonists,[18] that the *skopos* demands a certain tone or ethos, which is suited to a particular intellectual disposition in the reader. Having learned both his penmanship and his preaching in the schools of rhetoric, Gregory could not deny that a text requires an audience; yet he argued that the addressees of a sacred text are not secular but spiritual contemporaries of its prophetic author. Nothing proves this more clearly than the Song of Songs, whose *skopos*, as Origen knew already, must be something better than mortal love. In reading it, we need the Spirit to take us by the hand through paths of deepening obscurity, until, with the mortification of the senses and the extinction of every appetite, whether physical or mental, the inner man achieves sublime and peaceable communion with God. Gregory practised similar meditations on the Psalms, Ecclesiastes and the *Life of Moses* – the last in emulation of a famous work by Philo – but over the next millennium the supreme resource of mysticism was the Song of Songs.

In the late fourth century, however, other mystics quoted scripture in the old, desultory fashion; and, while some Desert Fathers might possess no other volume than a Bible, it served chiefly as an oracle for instruction and reproof.[19] Scholarship passed into the hands of Antiochene theologians, for whom allegory was simply a falsification of the text. In his commentaries on the Pauline letters, John Chrysostom (c. 354–407), Bishop of Antioch, drew attention to historical circumstances, modes of argument, and the eloquent devices by which Paul secured the interest, the obedience or the sympathy of his audience. He does not scruple to draw upon the technical vocabulary of rhetoric,[20] though, unlike some modern exponents of 'rhetorical criticism', he does not conclude that Paul had undergone a formal training in this discipline. On the contrary, Paul's bursts of anger, sorrow and solicitude are ascribed to virtue rather than technique, and the distance between his Greek and the classical idiom is freely, though euphemistically, exposed. Each of Chrysostom's homilies concludes with a discourse that goads the audience to its duty, but in a pure and copious style that spares the dignity of a cultivated ear. In the fifth century many of his comments found their way into the sparser annotations of Theodoret (c. 393–466) on the Pauline corpus, together with a coda at the end of every letter saying where it was believed to have been composed. Not all of these are credible, but Theodoret was evidently a scholar who approached the New Testament in a modern spirit. Comparison with Gregory of Nyssa shows how differently the two Testaments had fared in Christian study. Knowing or caring little about the situation dramatized in the Song of Songs, Gregory traced its 'cheiragogic' action on the spirit of the reader; Theodoret, whose eyes are fixed on Paul and his correspondents, is not afraid to attribute to him a 'psychagogic' action on their feelings, even if this entails that certain passages had nothing to contribute to the future edification of the Church.

Hence it is that the work of Theodore of Mopsuestia (d. 428) is a landmark in the Christian exegesis of the Old Testament. In his expositions on the Psalms, he urged that the best interpretation is not the one that conveys the largest body of doctrinal truth, but the one most faithful to the purpose of the author and the occasion for which he wrote. He argued that the Psalms had many purposes – to praise the Lord, to edify through personal experience and to prophesy the future[21] – and that only when the New Testament demanded it should we look in them for presages of Christ. Galatians 4.24, where Paul had stated that some stories in the Old Testament were allegories, had been dashed aside by Chrysostom with the statement that allegory means typology; but Theodore, who was almost equally hostile to the latter method, made this verse the occasion of a vigorous polemic against the allegorists, which he seems to have expanded to the dimensions of a book. He was not a fundamentalist, since he sometimes treated Adam as a symbolic figure; nor was he a liberal theolgian, as he did not deny the plenary inspiration of the scriptures, or the authenticity of the Davidic Psalms. Nevertheless, no other ancient critic worked so hard to prove that the faculties and perceptions of the author remain intact in their co-operation with the Holy Spirit. In this, as in his teaching on free will and on the integral humanity of Christ, he was pressing common principles to exceptional conclusions – a fact that may explain why little of his exegesis survives in Greek. Tradition favoured the commentaries on John and on the prophets by his posthumous destroyer Cyril (d. 444), who, like all Alexandrians, held that an allegory is tenable wherever it serves to vindicate the doctrine of the Church.

Cyril proved himself a true Alexandrian in his adherence to the Septuagint, the authority of which, as a dispensation to the Gentiles, had been upheld in Epiphanius's tract *On Weights and Measures*. Himself a Palestinian and a poor scholar in five languages, Epiphanius feared that Symmachus, Aquila and Theodotion would betray their readers into Judaism. In the neighbourhood of Antioch, however, the Syrian version or Peshitta, based on the Hebrew, enjoyed wide currency, giving rise to homiletic paraphrases by Aphrahat and the poet Ephrem. Greek-speaking Antiochenes, such as Diodore of Tarsus and Eusebius of Emesa, turned to both the Hebrew and the Syriac in order to correct or elucidate the Septuagint.[22] The results of their researches took the form of topical questions (*Quaestiones*) in the manner of those compiled by Philo on Genesis and Exodus. When Jerome (c. 347–420), the only Latin speaker known to have been an admirer of Epiphanius, joined this scholarly tradition with his *Questions on Genesis*, he found himself unable to sustain his mentor's preference for the Septuagint. He embarked on a new translation of the scriptures, using only Hebrew sources for the Old Testament and thus accepting only the Hebrew canon. The project aroused hostility, and some detected errors in the translation; he replied that even apostolic writers were not always faithful in their quotations either to the Hebrew or to the Greek (Letter 57). For all that, he admitted that the Greek portions of the Old Testament had a certain inspiration, and revealed the conservative tendency of his own thought when he argued that apparent misquotations in the New Testament could be justified by consultation of Hebrew manuscripts. He maintained that even the Hebrew of Isaiah 7.14 sufficed to prophesy the Virgin Birth,[23] and his cultivation of the 'Hebrew truth' (*Hebraica veritas*) did not make him a literalist. On the contrary, he commended tropological readings even of the New Testament where the literal sense was useless to the reader. While censuring the theology of Origen, he borrowed from him constantly and openly in his commentary on Ephesians, though occasionally declining to pursue him to the end of his speculations. Whether he or Origen was the better Hebraist remains a question in dispute.

Only with the addition of the Greek or 'apocryphal' books, did Jerome's Bible become the Vulgate of the Latin Church. Yet even in the Greek world of the fourth century it was no rare thing to endorse the Hebrew canon, as we see from the thirty-ninth of Athanasius's Festal Letters[24] and the Fourth Catechetical Homily by Cyril of Jerusalem. On the other hand, African codes from 393 to 419 continued to insist that the apocrypha be included in the canon, and this was the position of Augustine (354–40) in his essay *On Christian Doctrine*, though he was well aware that Solomon did not write all the books that bear his name (2.12). Not authorship but the consensus of the churches was his test of canonicity, and the same logic that had sanctified the Greek Old Testament guaranteed the inspiration of the Latin versions. In difficulties, one might collate translations or resort to those who knew the ancient languages, but even in that case Greek was as good as Hebrew. While Jerome seems to have sought some compensation in the Hebrew for the poor style of the Septuagint, Augustine is content to inveigh against the love of eloquence, with the eloquence of Jerome's own apology for the barbarous Greek of Paul. He did not, however, allow the same latitude in exegesis: in a mild rebuke to his predecessor Optatus, he maintains that in using scripture against schismatics, we should not develop fanciful applications of the Old Testament, but vindicate the catholic understanding of the Church from the clear intention of the text.[25] Charity, which constitutes the inner man, is the test of Christian purity, and charity is the rule that guides the interpreter of scripture (*On Christian Doctrine* 3.14–15, etc.). The spirit of the sacred text, which emancipates us from the carnal reading, is not allegory but a literal and perfect reverence for the law of love.

Augustine waived his objection to allegory when the reader would otherwise have been misled into repeating an immoral act reported in the Old Testament (*On Christian Doctrine* 3.24, etc.). For allegory we should strictly say typology: the Christian will be less inclined to imitate the mendacity of Rahab if he knows that these things signify in the higher dispensation (*On Lying* 33). The literal truth of the narrative was not denied, for when Augustine called a reading allegorical, he meant that, however orthodox and fruitful, it was subsidiary to the primary one 'according to the letter'. This becomes apparent in his huge dissertation *On Genesis according to the Letter*, where he toyed with the notion that the opening chapter is a parable of redemption, only to say that it was an allegory and therefore not germane to his present purpose (1.33–4). His master Ambrose (c. 340–97) had mingled the allegorical and the literal in his treatises *On the Six Days* (*Hexaemeron*) and *On Paradise*, and in a previous work, *On Genesis against the Manichaeans*, Augustine had built upon this precedent, arguing that Eden and its rivers are a parable for the Spirit's irrigation of the soul. Even the sense 'according to the letter' was not always the superficial one: if it were, one would be bound to construe the six days of creation as extended intervals, thereby compromising the omnipotence of God. Augustine proposed instead that the 'evening and morning', unintelligible without the sun and moon, betokened the instantaneous conversion of the potential to the actual, or a transition in the angelic mind from ignorance to knowledge (4.40–56). This 'physiological' reading, far from literal as it is, does more justice to the *skopos* of the text than that of Barnabas (15.4), who suggested that the days are archetypes of the six millennia that will measure the whole duration of the world.

Augustine would appear to have been the first exegete who felt the need for a comprehensive theory of the sign.[26] In the works *On Christian Doctrine* and *On Genesis according to the Letter* he distinguished the written characters from the image that they engender in the 'spirit', and this in turn from the imageless idea by which the mind interprets it. Body, spirit and intellect thus supplanted the old trichotomy of body, soul and spirit, and were harnessed not to discrete senses of scripture, but to three concurrent factors in the understanding of it. The unity of the person and the unity of scripture thus gave mutual guarantees, but the consequences for hermeneutic practice were even slighter than those of Origen's triple scheme. Nor did he give much play to the seven rules of the contemporary sectarian Tyconius, except when he commended them to readers of *On Christian Doctrine* (3.44–56). These required the reader (1) to distinguish between the body and the head of Christ in typological sayings about his person; (2) to recognize that what is true of Christ is not yet wholly true of his earthly body; (3) to perceive the promise within the law; (4) sometimes to read generically what is said of a single subject; (5) to reconcile dissonant computations of the same time by mastering the numerical conventions; (6) to be aware that Hebrew is prone to duplication of 'recapitulaion' of previous matter; (7) to distinguish between the devil and his body on earth, as we do with that of Christ. Augustine himself, like all great critics, was better than his theories, showing all the versatility of an able and systematic theologian who is determined to make the Bible speak for him. Thus, while he has been frequently upbraided for his florid, obscure and labyrinthine readings, he is just as often brief, perspicuous and rectilinear. Once he had decided that his business was to demonstrate the unity and pervasive inspiration of a corpus so diverse in style, in audience, in content and in time of composition, he quickly came to see that no one tool is omnicompetent, and that even the most unwieldy sometimes works where others fail.[27]

NOTES

1 G. Hahnemann, *The Muratorian Fragment and the Development of the Canon* (Oxford 1992), has not convinced me that this Roman canon is later than one would deduce from its allusion to Hermas as a near-contemporary.

2 On Valentinus (fl. 140) and his Alexandrian precursors see D. Dawson, *Allegorical Readers and Cultural Revision in Ancient Alexandria* (Berkeley 1992).

3 E. Pagels, *The Johannine Gospel in Gnostic Exegesis* (Nashville 1973).

4 On Philo (c. 40 BC - c. 40 AD) see D. Runia, *Philo and Early Christian Literature* (Assen 1993).

5 *Trypho* 24ff. See further O. Skarsaune, *Justin and the Proof from Prophecy* (Leiden 1979).

6 N. Frye, *The Great Code* (London 1982), 85.

7 Origen, *Against Celsus* 4.45. Celsus's polemic seems to date from c. 170.

8 P. Hadot, 'La division des parties de la philosophie dans l'antiquite', *Museum Helveticum* 35 (1979), 201–23.

9 Both indebted to Valentinian authors: *Extracts from Theodotus* 66 (typical/mystical; parabolic/enigmatic; plain/naked); *Prophetic Extracts* 5–9.

10 On the pagan Porphyry, and his possible debt to Syriac commentators, see P. M. Casey, 'Porphyry and the Origin of the Book of Daniel', *Journal of Theological Studies* 26 (1976), 15–33.

11 *Proem to Song of Songs*, p. 75 in edition of W. Baehrens (Leipzig 1925).

12 H. De Lubac, *L'Exégèse Medievale*, part 1, vol. 1 (Paris 1959), 205.

13 *First Principles* 4.2.9. Cf. Iamblichus, *On the Mysteries* 1.11, and Julian the Apostate, *Hymn* 5, 22.

14 Eusebius, *Preparation for the Gospel* 3.9, on physiological and theological approaches.

15 Gregory, *Tractate* 5.1; Ambrose, *On Isaac* 68.

16 T. D. Barnes, *Constantine and Eusebius* (Berkeley 1981), 106–25.

17 R. A. Heine, *Gregory of Nyssa on the Inscriptions to the Psalms* (Oxford 1995), 20–9.

18 See proem to Proclus, *On the Timaeus*, etc.

19 L. Burton-Christie, *The Word in the Desert* (Oxford 1994).

20 On rhetorical practice and Christian hermeneutics see F. M. Young, *Biblical Exegesis and the Formation of Christian Culture* (Cambridge 1997).

21 D. Zaharopoulos, *Theodore of Mopsuestia on the Bible* (New York 1989), 83–4.

22 A. Kamessar, *Jerome, Greek Scholarship and the Hebrew Bible* (Oxford 1993), 34–40. For a different view of Jerome's purpose see C. T. Hayward, *Jerome's Quaestiones in Genesim* (Oxford 1995).

23 A. Kamessar, 'The Virgin of Isaiah 7.14', *Journal of Theological Studies* 41 (1990), 51–76.

24 Though omitting Esther and including Baruch. The practice of Athansius (298–373) may have influenced later theories of the *skopos*.

25 *Letter to Catholics* 42, on Optatus, *Against the Donatists* 3.3.

26 R. Markus, 'Augustine on Signs', *Phronesis* 2 (1957), 60–83, and especially *On Genesis according to the Letter* 12.23, on the commandment to love; this follows a division of perception into corporal, spiritual and intellectual. The roots of the theory may be Platonic or 'Pythagorean': see Porphyry on Aristotle, *Categories* 16a, cited in Boethius, *On Interpretation* 2.33.

27 I am grateful to the British Academy for a postdoctoral Fellowship that made possible much of my research for this chapter.

PART IV

HISTORY

CHAPTER TWENTY

BIBLICAL ARCHAEOLOGY

———·◆·———

Felicity J. Cobbing

INTRODUCTION

'Biblical archaeology' is a term often applied to the archaeology of the ancient Levant and embraces a number of perspectives, ranging from the broad to the more specific.

At the broader end of the scale, 'biblical archaeology' can be taken to mean the archaeology of the region in which the biblical narratives of the Hebrew Bible, the Old Testament, were set.

Narrowing the definition somewhat, the term has also been used to mean the archaeology not only of the land in which the biblical narratives were set but of the time during which the events narrated took place.

At its most extreme, biblical archaeology is the archaeology of the ancient Levant, using the Hebrew Bible (the books of the Old Testament) as the primary source of information and motivation for exploration. Under this definition, biblical archaeology is often seen as having the aim of finding material, solid evidence for the places, people, and events of the biblical narratives, as a journey of faith, or a theological construct. This last definition characterized the development of Levantine archaeology by chiefly American scholars during the middle part of the twentieth century. The American contribution to biblical archaeology as defined above therefore forms the basis of this discussion.

THE HISTORY AND DEVELOPMENT OF BIBLICAL ARCHAEOLOGY

The eighteenth and early nineteenth centuries

The roots of 'biblical archaeology' are to be found in the mid-nineteenth century, with the rediscovery of the splendid civilizations of ancient Egypt and Mesopotamia. As a near neighbour of these two ancient giants, and the home of the most profoundly significant influence on Western thought, religion and civilization, the Bible, Syro-Palestine and the Levant held obvious attractions for Western explorers and scholars.

In addition to the physical application of the infant subject of archaeology, the discipline of biblical criticism (analysing the biblical texts from a historical and/or literary perspective) was being developed at this time. Thus it was thought that by excavating sites connected with the Bible, archaeology, together with geography, might provide solid physical proof of biblical places, events, and possibly even people, thereby cementing the biblical narratives in historical fact.

Initially Europeans – the French, Germans and British – were most active in the field. The Americans, although very much involved in the academic scholarship of biblical studies, were slower to approach the subject of biblical research from the more practical angles of archaeology and historical geography. This reticence might have been due to lack of funds and practical know-how, but it was perhaps also due to a less clearly defined political incentive. It must be remembered that at this time the European powers were all watching the slow but inexorable demise of the Ottoman Empire with considerable interest, and academic missions involving the physical surveying of the country, as well as establishing ideological and religious links with its past, might well have had less esoteric uses than the publication of worthy articles in obscure journals.

Having said this, one of the earliest scholars of distinction to make a significant contribution to the development of the physical study of the Holy Land was an American, Edward Robinson (1794–1863). Robinson was a Congregationalist minister, a biblical scholar, a linguist of considerable talents, and an able explorer. He combined an understanding of European, particularly German, academic methodologies relating to historical and linguistic studies with a deep conviction in the essential historicity of the biblical texts.

Robinson was highly sceptical of the traditional associations of biblical events with places that existed at this time. Through his field survey in Palestine and the Sinai in 1838, and later in Palestine in 1852, and his development of a set of rules for the linguistic comparative analysis of ancient Hebrew geographical terminology with modern Arabic, he established the study of biblical geography as a serious academic pursuit as opposed to a rather haphazard combination of local traditions and superficial, untested observations by Western travellers.

One of the most important organizations during the formative years of archaeology and exploration in Palestine and the Levant was the British Palestine Exploration Fund (PEF), founded in 1865. The Fund was responsible for the groundbreaking *Survey of Western Palestine*, published between 1881 and 1884, the first accurate geographical survey of the whole of Palestine west of the Jordan River. The PEF continues to publish its academic journal, the *Palestine Exploration Quarterly* (PEQ), and an occasional monograph series.

On behalf of the PEF, Sir William Flinders Petrie, the distinguished Egyptologist and archaeologist, began excavations at Tell el-Hesi in southern Palestine with a six-week season in 1890. At the time of Petrie's work, Tell el-Hesi was thought to be the site of ancient Lachish. This was subsequently shown to be erroneous by the positive identification of Lachish with Tell ed-Duweir. Biblical Eglon has since been suggested as a candidate for Tell el-Hesi, but the location of the site does not fit the biblical description, and it is slightly ironical, therefore, that Tell el-Hesi remains a site of no known biblical significance.

Sir Flinders Petrie is often regarded as the founder of modern Near Eastern archaeology, developing as he did the principles of archaeological stratigraphic excavation, and ceramic typology. The basic principles of stratigraphy were, in fact, first developed by geologists who noticed that in cases where the natural rock was exposed over a large area (a cliff face, for example), different layers were visible, suggesting that the different components were formed at different times, and deposited one on top of another in sequence. Clearly, in such a circumstance, the lowest layer represented the earliest deposition, and the top represented the latest.

Following the work of Heinrich Schliemann at Hissarlik in Anatolia in 1870, Petrie adapted these principles and applied them to archaeological excavations in Egypt and then the Levant. With the development of ceramic typology and seriation (the observation of gradual changes in pottery styles, and the arrangement of them in developmental sequences) it was possible to add chronological and cultural definition to the observed stratigraphy.

At Tell el-Hesi Petrie was the first archaeologist to apply these principles of stratigraphy and ceramic chronology to a Palestinian site, identifying three periods of occupation, which he termed 'Amorite' (c. 1700 BC), 'Phoenician' (1350–850 BC), and 'Jewish' (up to 450 BC). Although the terminology and dating of the material has since been put aside, Petrie's excavations at Tell el-Hesi established a strategy that has come to dominate the development of archaeological excavation in Palestine; that is, the stratigraphic excavation of large multiperiod tell (occupation mound) sites.

A second season at Tell el-Hesi was conducted on behalf of the PEF by Frederick Jones Bliss in 1893, and this represented the first significant involvement of an American in the archaeology of Palestine. Born in Lebanon, the son of missionaries, Bliss refined further the stratigraphic methodology employed by Petrie, but because of the time-consuming nature of his work, he was eventually dismissed by the Fund. The value of his work, however, was certainly recognized by some future key players, most notably William Foxwell Albright (below).

In 1903 Bliss delivered the Ely Lectures at Union Theological Seminary in New York City (Robinson's old school). These lectures were published under the title *The Development of Palestine Exploration* (1906), and this was to become a central work of scholarship in the field of biblical studies and biblical archaeology. In this volume the combination of Bible and archaeology is much in evidence, as was to be the case throughout the development of American archaeology in Palestine. Indeed, during this formative period most scholars, including Petrie and the Palestine Exploration Fund, as well as Bliss, were principally interested in undertaking work that could, in some way be related to the Bible, and little consideration was given to the pursuit of archaeological discovery in the region for its own sake.

In 1900 the American Schools of Oriental Research (ASOR) were founded. A pledge of annual financial support from the Archaeological Institute of America (AIA) enabled the new body to open its first research centre in Jerusalem itself in the same year. ASOR was the archaeological 'wing' of the Society for Biblical Literature (SBL), which had been established fifteen years before in 1880. At the beginning of its life, the school in Jerusalem was hindered by political instability in the region, but it was to play an important role in the development of American archaeology in the Levant in later years.

Initially, ASOR existed as a society to facilitate field research in Palestine itself, for the purposes of exploring the biblical geography, and conducting when possible excavations to illuminate the biblical past. Although ASOR's interests soon broadened out to include areas of interest not necessarily connected with biblical studies, but falling under the wider umbrella of 'Orientalism', the geographical and cultural biases expressed by the founding fathers of SBL were to shape much of the research carried out by its affiliates.

It has been suggested that biblical archaeology as a tool for realizing biblical truth developed to a much greater degree in the United States than in Britain and Europe. The reasons for this difference in focus undoubtedly lay in the differences in the professional backgrounds of those involved in the subject at the end of the nineteenth and the beginning of the twentieth century. Many of the pioneers of European, and especially British, field archaeology, were military men, with a talent (most of the time) for organization and method. In America, on the other hand, most of the practitioners of Syro-Palestinian archaeology came from seminary colleges with a personal and communal faith to strengthen and uphold. Although American archaeologists were no strangers to organization and method, and British and European archaeologists cherished their own biblical heritage, the evangelical nature of much American Christianity must also be taken into account.

In the early part of the twentieth century, Christian religious life in America underwent something of a re-evaluation of itself. Many Americans, lay people, clerics, and scholars alike, from all denominations redefined what seemed to some to be a slowly dwindling faith, and injected it with new enthusiasm.

The publication of the six-volume series of evangelical theology, entitled *The Fundamentals*, was a major catalyst for this religious wind-change, and affected not only American religious and social life, but also its academic life. As a part of this phenomenon, archaeology came to be seen increasingly as a useful and valid tool for the physical exploration of the biblical past, almost in the manner of a modern pilgrimage of discovery.

The rise of 'biblical archeology' and the Albrightian School (1920s–1960s)

Throughout the period of the Great War of 1914–18, which saw the demise of the Ottoman Empire, archaeological work in Palestine was halted. Activities were resumed in 1919 under the British Mandate. Under the Ottoman administration excavators had been required to obtain a permit (or *firman*), but antiquities laws specific to Palestine were not formalized until the post-war era with the establishment of a Department of Antiquities.

In 1919, largely through the the efforts of the American Egyptologist J. H. Breasted, and with a generous donation from J. D. Rockefeller Jr, the highly influential Oriental Institute of the University of Chicago was founded. The aims of the Oriental Institute were initially far more wide reaching than those of ASOR, as it was intended to be a repository for information collected by all disciplines working in Egypt and the Near East, and not just those directly concerned with biblical studies and biblical archaeology. Great rivalry developed between the Oriental Institute and ASOR, which to some extent still exists to this day. Among the many research and field projects undertaken by the Oriental Institute in its early years was the excavation of Megiddo. Beginning in 1925, the project was overambitious, aiming to expose the remains of this very large site completely, layer by layer, rather than targeting specific areas. The project ended with the outbreak of World War II in 1939.

Also in 1919 the PEF, together with the Jerusalem Literary Society (JLS) and the British Academy, founded the British School of Archaeology in Jerusalem (BSAJ), modelled on its sister organizations in Athens and Rome. The BSAJ enjoyed very close relations with ASOR, even sharing the same accommodation in Jerusalem for some time. After initially publishing its quarterly reports in the *Palestine Exploration Quarterly*, the BSAJ's own journal *Levant* was launched in 1969. Over the years the BSAJ was to play a major role in British and collaborative research and field projects in Palestine, nurturing some of the most important archaeological talents of the day, including J. W. Crowfoot, Dame Kathleen M. Kenyon, Basil Hennessey and Crystal M. Bennett. The consistent philosophy of the BSAJ has been to promote solid field methodology, focusing on the training of the excavators and the accurate publication of their results.

William Foxwell Albright (1891–1971)

One of the most influential, if not the most influential, Orientalists of the period between 1920 and 1970 was William Foxwell Albright, the son of self-supporting Methodist missionary parents. Albright was raised in Chile, but his family moved to Iowa in 1903, and he graduated from Upper Iowa University in 1912. A brilliant natural linguist, he knew Spanish, French, German, Latin, and Greek, and, during his time at college, he taught himself Akkadian and Hebrew. While a high school teacher, he sent the proofs of an article he had written concerning an Akkadian word, which had been accepted by a German scholarly journal, to the Assyriologist Paul Haupt at Johns Hopkins University in Baltimore, Maryland. On the basis of this article, Albright was granted a four-year scholarship to Johns Hopkins. He won the Thayer Fellowship for study in Jerusalem, but was unable to use it until the end of World War I. He gained his PhD in 1916, after which he taught in Haupt's Oriental Seminary at Johns Hopkins. It was Haupt who introduced Albright to biblical criticism. Haupt himself was sceptical about the historical truth of the biblical accounts, a position that very probably influenced Albright during the early part of his career, despite the conclusions he was to draw later on in life.

Albright arrived in Jerusalem in 1920, becoming the director of the American School of Oriental Research (ASOR) in Jerusalem (today known as the William Foxwell Albright Institute of Archaeological Research). During his ten-year directorship, the Jerusalem school began to flourish. Within a month, he had launched the *Bulletin of the American Schools of Oriental Research* (*BASOR*), which he used as a vehicle in which to publish much material from his early excavations, and was its editor from 1930 to 1968.

The physical reality of the 'Holy Land' had a major impact on Albright, to such an extent that, according to his own statements, he became convinced of the Bible's fundamental historicity. This led to the establishment of the theory of Albrightian biblical archaeology – the cementing of biblical narratives in physical and historical reality through archaeological exploration.

In 1929 Albright became chairman of the Oriental Seminary at Johns Hopkins, a position he held until his retirement in 1958. It was during this period of tutorship that he developed the so-called Albrightian School of biblical archaeology, which was to dominate much of the field, producing a number of talented, dedicated, and faithful young students. The strength of his personality and ideology, and his undeniable scholarship, proved to have an enduring effect on his students. It would not be out of place to describe his relationship with his students as patriarchal. Outstandingly prolific, Albright published a huge quantity of work, amounting to over 1100 books and articles. The range of his scholarly abilities was exceptional, covering all areas of ancient Near Eastern studies, from linguistics and literary criticism, through to historical research and archaeology.

As an archaeologist, Albright possessed a particular talent for the detailed typological study of ceramic material, or 'pottery reading' as it is known. What made him an exceptional scholar, however, was his ability to see the results of his archaeological research in the broader context of the ancient Near East as a whole.

Albright excavated at Tell el-Fûl (biblical Gibeah) in 1922, and at Tell Beit Mirsim from 1926 to 1932. Between 1929 and 1935 he conducted low-budget excavations at Bethel and Beth-Zur. Albright's excavations at Tell Beit Mirsim, however, perhaps provide the clearest example of his practical fieldwork, and of the contribution he made to the discipline of Syro-Palestinian archaeology as a whole.

The site of Tell Beit Mirsim lies 20 km (12 miles) south-west of Hebron, and 13.5 km (8 miles) south-east of Lachish (Tell ed-Duweir) in the chalk foothills of the region known in the biblical texts, and in the present day, as the Shephelah of Judah.

The procedure of excavation employed by Albright at the site was the 'Broad-Site' method, initially developed by George Andrew Reisner and Clarence Fisher during their excavations at Samaria in 1909. Using this method, excavations were conducted over a large area in an attempt to uncover as much of the plan of any given phase as possible, placing an emphasis on the architecture and spatial relationships between buildings and features within any particular phase. The nature of the excavations were therefore horizontal rather than vertical, in other words, across the site rather than down into it. Photographs of all features exposed were taken, producing a pictorial record of the entire excavated site, a first in archaeology in the region. In addition, plans, section plans, and notes of all excavated remains were required. Thus, a system of excavation was developed that appeared to fulfil the complex needs of the archaeologist working on tell sites in Palestine.

At Tell Beit Mirsim, Albright excavated two main areas. The first, a broad exposure on the south-eastern end of the tell, was also excavated vertically, sometimes down to bedrock. Here the chronological sequence was established. On the other side of the tell, in the north-western area, a large exposure of the uppermost occupation level (stratum A) only was cleared. Overall, ten major strata (occupation levels) were excavated (some of them subdivided). These were given letter designations, from the latest, 'A' (nearest the surface and hence the first to be uncovered and identified), to the earliest, 'J' (the deepest level of occupation).

The material excavated by Albright seemed to represent a nearly continuous sequence of occupation stretching over many centuries. Albright's interpretation of the stratigraphy was based on the architectural remains, together with the numerous destruction levels that appeared to separate the periods of occupation clearly. Beyond this, however, there was little reference to the internal and external depositional layers of occupation debris that might or might not have related to the various buildings. The published section drawings from Tell Beit Mirsim illustrate this approach, showing architectural remains surrounded by undefined space.

Although the stratigraphic understanding was, in retrospect, not what one would expect of an archaeologist today, it was within the framework of successive destruction levels that Albright formulated a coherent typology and chronology of the pottery from the site, defining therefore periods of culture using the ceramic material, and developing a terminology far more appropriate to the material than had been used before. This had major implications for the development of Palestinian archaeology. Prior to Albright's excavations at Tell Beit Mirsim, the terminology of divisions of phases of settlement or culture used by scholars varied from person to person, and from site to site. One scholar might use the term 'Late Canaanite', another, 'Early Semitic', without a clear understanding of what, culturally or chronologically, the terminology was attempting to define. This obviously created problems for interpretation, and showed a lack of familiarity with the material on the part of the early archaeologists, for the simple reason that archaeological exploration in the region was still fairly new, and the material was therefore scattered, patchy, and unfamiliar.

Through systematic excavation and careful reading of the ceramic material, Albright developed a terminology that has formed the basis of chronological interpretation ever since, namely, the definition of broad cultural phases, based on the European 'Three Age' system, with Early Bronze Age (around 3000–1900 BC, by modern reckonings), Middle Bronze Age (around 1900–1540 BC), Late Bronze Age (around 1540–1120 BC), and Iron Age (around 1120–587/6 BC, the date of the start of the Neo-Babylonian period). Albright also laid down the foundations for the internal subdivisions of these phases, producing terms such as EB (Early Bronze) I, II, III, and IV; MB (Middle Bronze) IIA, B, and C; LB (Late Bronze) I, IIA, and IIB; and Iron Age I and II; and so on. While debate as to where the divisions should be applied in relation to the material remains an endless source of amusement for archaeologists, the framework and terminology are fundamentally Albright's, creating a unity of understanding within the subject and making it possible for proper and useful discourse and research to take place. For the first time all archaeologists of the region could recognize what it was they were agreeing or disagreeing about!

Among the remains excavated by Albright at Tell Beit Mirsim, the Middle Bronze Age levels (strata I to D) produced a number of buildings, structures, and artefacts. This was the period Albright came to associate with the Patriarchs of the Old Testament – Abraham, Isaac, Jacob, and Joseph – of whose existence in historical reality he was convinced.

One of these structures was the 'Patrician's House' (stratum D, MB IIB, about 1550 BC). This spacious and well-constructed villa (about 15 by 15 m) was built in the traditional Canaanite manner, employing sun-dried mud bricks for the superstructure on stone foundations. Floors and walls were coated with lime-plaster. The house consisted of a large rectangular walled courtyard, open to the sky, with six smaller rooms adjoining one of its long sides, of which four were concentrated in a square in one corner. According to Albright, the rooms had a second storey, and while he does not produce substantive archaeological evidence for this, it is a reasonable suggestion given the scale of the plan and the quality of the construction. This was obviously the house of a person or a family of some wealth, and possibly importance.

Some of the contents of the 'Patrician's House' are worthy of mention, and confirm the residence as that of a notable individual or family: in particular, a broken limestone 'stela' depicting what Albright described as a 'serpent goddess', but which has subsequently been identified as a Canaanite dignitary. An ivory gaming board consisting of twenty squares and playing pieces also came from this house, together with a quantity of ceramic vessels (principally for storage), stone vessels, metal knives, jewellery, and scarabs. Although these finds seem rather mundane in comparison to some of the spectacular discoveries in Egypt and Mesopotamia, Tell Beit Mirsim became one of the most important excavated sites in Syro-Palestine, not because of its individual artefacts, but due to the methodology of Albright's approach. In this sense, he took archaeology a step further away from its treasure-seeking past, and revealed some of its true potential as an academic discipline.

Albright published the results of his excavations at Tell Beit Mirsim in four volumes of the Annual of the American Schools of Oriental Research (AASOR – see Bibliography for details). These reports represented for many years a breakthrough in archaeological excavation, recording, and publication. Although they may not be of the same standard as would be expected of today's archaeologists, the significant advance in methodology they represent is central to the modern discipline.

It must be remembered that Albright was not solely an archaeologist. Although he is often referred to as the greatest biblical archaeologist of all time, especially in the United States, his practical archaeological career as such was relatively brief. He was also a critical textual scholar, with a special interest in the historical and theological development of the monotheism of Judaism, and its literary traditions. As a literary scholar, Albright was keenly interested in the archaeological discoveries of textual clay tablets at ancient Mari on the Euphrates in eastern Syria (suggested by Albright to be Tell Hariri, an identification proved to be correct by excavation), Nuzi (Yorghan Tepe) in northern Iraq and Ugarit (Ras Shamra) on the Syrian coast. His particular interest in defining a cultural and historical setting for the Hebrew Bible led to his exploration of the light these extraordinary finds might shed on the biblical narratives. Albright, together with Mari's excavator, the French archaeologist André Parrot, interpreted the texts in such a way as to illuminate the world of the biblical Patriarchs in their journeys from Mesopotamia to the Levant. The linguistic importance of the tablet archives from Ras Shamra was, if anything, even more significant than the language of the Mari tablets. The close relationship between 'Ugaritic', as the language of the Ras Shamra archive became known, and the Hebrew of the Old Testament, in linguistic, grammatical, and literary terms, is undeniable, and, for Albright, they were a key in arguing for the authenticity of the early biblical narratives.

Whatever the final judgement on Albright as an archaeologist and ideologist, his significant contribution to the field cannot be overlooked. His unflagging energy for research, study, and publication resulted in a maintenance and development of lasting interest in the area of biblical archaeology. The huge body of material he produced marks him out as one of the most energetic and scholarly figures not only in the history of biblical archaeology, but in the history of the study of the ancient Near East. He must be credited with providing a solid cornerstone from which the American Schools of Oriental Research in Jerusalem have gone from strength to strength, and for establishing an enduringly high-quality academic journal in *BASOR*. Finally, his most valuable contribution to the discipline of archaeology in the Levant itself is undoubtedly the chronological terminology he developed at his excavations at Tell Beit Mirsim, and which has become the subsequent basis of all archaeological chronological understanding in the region.

Albright's domination of the field of Near Eastern studies and archaeology in America led in part to the development there of 'biblical archaeology' as opposed to 'archaeology of the ancient Levant'. Under his influence and direct involvement, sites were chosen for excavation based primarily on their significance in the biblical texts, and Christian organizations were often targeted for funds and support. Field staff were frequently enlisted from seminaries, and included members of the clergy (or those studying for clerical degrees), and other biblical scholars. Therefore, the majority of those involved in American archaeology in Syro-Palestine at this time came from a primarily Christian (mainly Protestant) background, with this interest fundamental to their involvement in archaeological fieldwork. Apart from Albright's own excavations at Tell el-Fûl, Tell Beit Mirsim and Bethel, fieldwork conducted by other American archaeologists and biblical scholars (some of them Albright's students) during this period include Tell en-Nasbeh (F. Badé, Pacific School of Religion, 1926–35); Beth-Shemesh (E. Grant, Haverford College, Pennsylvania, 1928–33); Shechem (G. E. Wright, Drew–McCormick Expedition, seven seasons, 1956–1968); Ai (J. A. Callaway, ASOR, 1964–76); Gibeon (J. B. Pritchard, University of Pennsylvania, 1957–62); and Bab edh-Dhraʾ (P. Lapp, ASOR, 1965–7)

G. Ernest Wright (1909–1974)

One of Albright's protégés, G. Ernest Wright, was to become synonymous with developments in biblical archaeology and Christian religious thought in America in the 1950s. As a progression from the rebirth of Christian life in America in the 1920s, the 1950s saw theological thought develop into a form of orthodoxy or fundamentalism. It would appear that at this time, some American Christians felt the need to justify their faith with proof of the events, people, and places portrayed in the biblical narratives. A protagonist of this new direction, Wright made a direct link between faith, history, and developments in Syro-Palestinian archaeology. In this sense, biblical archaeology as typified by scholars like Wright was attempting to provide a service for which there was an increasingly large demand in clerical, scholarly, and lay populations throughout America.

George Ernest Wright was the son of a Presbyterian minister in Ohio. He was educated at the College of Wooster, whence he received his BA in 1931. He graduated as a Bachelor of Divinity in 1934 from the McCormick Theological Seminary, going on to study under Albright at Johns Hopkins University. There, he specialized in the ceramics of the Neolithic, Chalcolithic, and Early Bronze Ages in the ancient Near East. Like Albright, he combined archaeological scholarship with textual studies, particularly the biblical texts and their theological content. He joined Albright on his excavations at Bethel in 1934, and developed a keen interest in the topographical study of the area, an interest that led to his conducting a survey of the region around the site.

Albright himself said of Wright that of all his students, it was he who understood best the principles and practice of the ceramic chronology and typology that had so recently been developed. Wright put these skills in pottery reading to good use in 1937, working with Elihu Grant of Haverford College to organize the ceramic material of ʿAin Shems/Beth Shemesh. In 1938 he became field secretary for ASOR, and launched the *Biblical Archaeologist*, a periodical designed to present Palestinian archaeology to a popular audience. He was the publications editor for twenty-five years, presenting many of his own articles, reviews, and editorials in its pages.

From 1939 to 1959 Wright taught the Hebrew Bible at McCormick Theological Seminary, and it was during this time that he cultivated an interest in social and environmental history to add to the more traditional avenues of research of the biblical scholar. This interdisciplinary approach in a traditional theological setting was a defining characteristic of Wright's own brand of scholarship, and is evident in three biblical monographs he published during his time at McCormick: *The Challenge of Israel's Faith* (1944), *The Old Testament against its Environment* (1950), and *God Who Acts: Biblical Theology as Recital* (1952).

The combination of the physical with the religious, and Wright's interest in the interface between the two, can be seen again in the *Westminster Historical Atlas to the Bible* (1945), which he co-authored with the New Testament scholar Floyd V. Filson. However, for Wright, as with Albright before him, the physical was always in the service of the textual, whether this was theological or historical. Thus, as a subject that relies on physical evidence, archaeology was considered to be very much the servant of biblical history and theology, rather than a discipline and approach in its own right. Wright's perception of the relationship between the disciplines is apparent in many of his archaeological publications, notably *Biblical Archaeology* (1957), and *Shechem: The Biography of a Biblical City* (1965)

Wright's position in the academic community grew consistently throughout the 1950s, and in 1959 he was appointed to the Parkman Chair of Divinity at Harvard University, a position that reflected his influence in all fields of biblical scholarship in the United States at this time. In 1966 he was made president of ASOR, increasing his domination of the American scene still further.

Wright was an active field archaeologist, and conducted excavations that, as in the case of Albright's work at Tell Beit Mirsim, represented, in terms of methodology and technique, an advance on what had gone before. Together with Bernhard W. Anderson, Wright established the Drew–McCormick Expedition to Tell Balatah/Shechem (see below), conducting excavation seasons in 1956, 1957, 1960, 1962, 1964, 1966 and 1968. These excavations became a training ground for many of Wright's students, some of whom would direct excavations in their own right at sites such as Gezer, Heshbon (Hesban), Tell el-Hesi, Taʾanach, Caesarea, and Ai.

In 1964 he handed over the excavation of Shechem to his colleagues and, with Nelson Glueck (another of Albright's students), he began excavations at Gezer, which he staffed with his Harvard students. As with Shechem, the role of scientists and social scientists in archaeological excavation of Gezer was developed further, a trend he continued in the excavations at Idalion, in Cyprus (1971–4)

The excavations at Shechem provide an example of Wright's archaeological field-work in the context of biblical studies. The 6-acre mound of Tell Balatah, identified as the biblical Shechem, is situated in the hill country of north-central Israel, 10 km (6 miles) south-east of Samaria/Sebaste. The site occupies a strategically commanding position, controlling as it does the eastern entrance to a pass that runs transversely between the mountains of Ebal to the north and Gerizim to the south, and overlooks the Plain of Askar to the east.

The site was first formally investigated by the German scholar Ernst Sellin in a series of campaign seasons, interrupted by World War I, from 1913 to 1914, and again from 1926 to 1929 when he was joined by the architect Gabriel Welter, with a final season in 1934. Tragically, many of the field records and final reports from these excavations were destroyed in the Allied bombing of Germany in World War II.

The Drew–McCormick expedition, under the direction of Wright, set out to reinvestigate the site and the findings of the German expedition, employing a multidisciplinary methodology and sophisticated excavation techniques based largely on the highly refined stratigraphical approach demonstrated by Kathleen Kenyon in her excavations at Jericho and Jerusalem. Known as the 'Wheeler–Kenyon method', this system involved the excavation of squares, perhaps 4 or 5 metres in size, divided by unexcavated areas known as 'baulks' ('balks' in the USA), the purpose of which was to provide a record of the layers removed. Kenyon paid particular attention to the information in the baulks, concentrating on their maintenance (keeping them clean of dust, sharply cut and clearly labelled), and their detailed recording in the excavation notebooks, in drawings and in photographs. Relating the excavated material and finds to the strata visible in the unexcavated baulks enabled her to build up an enormously complex picture of the chronological development of the site, an archaeological time-line detailing every phase of human occupation excavated. This approach to excavation revolutionized digging in the Levant, making it possible to realize a level of stratigraphical and chronological control over the information that had previously been impossible.

G. Ernest Wright was one of the first archaeologists in the region to employ the Wheeler–Kenyon method, adapting it for the purposes of his excavations at Shechem. Twenty-four occupation strata were identified on the main tell (strata XXIV–I), dating from the Chalcolithic period (c. 3500 BC) through to the Maccabaean period in the second century BC with the destruction of the city by John Hyrcanus in 107 BC.

Shechem was not occupied continuously throughout these millennia: several periods show an absence of occupation, most notably throughout the whole of the Early Bronze Age (third millennium BC).

Wright excavated much of significance at Shechem, such as massive defensive systems and walls from several periods, and numerous public buildings, including the so-called Fortress–Temple of El-Berith (named after the temple mentioned in the Bible – Judg. 9:4, 46), one of the first of its kind to be excavated in the Levant.

This structure belongs to a type now known as *migdal* (tower or fortress) temples, which were often closely associated physically with the defensive walls of the city, were very sturdily built, and were dedicated to warlike Canaanite gods such as Baal or El. They became common in the Middle Bronze Age IIC period (c. 1650–1550 BC), a time when many sites underwent massive fortification. Examples of these fortress–temples have been found or identified throughout the Levant: from Ebla in north-central Syria, and Byblos on the coast, through to the Canaanite heartland at sites like Hazor, Megiddo, and Shechem, and as far south as Tell ed-Dab'a, the Hyksos capital in the Nile Delta in northern Egypt.

The structure identified by Wright as the Temple of El-Berith at Shechem consisted of two main building phases (1a and 2a), each with an intermediate phase (1b and 2b). Phases 1a and 1b (strata XVI–XV) cover the period of the Middle Bronze Age IIC. Wright and his team excavated a large, carefully constructed, and massively built structure, 26.3 m long by 21.2 m wide, with stone foundation walls more than 5 m in thickness. The thickness of the walls seemed to indicate a substantial mud-brick superstructure, perhaps with several storeys. The temple was orientated lengthways on a north-west to south-east axis, with two massive towers, both with stairwells at the south-eastern entrance. These towers flanked an entrance hall with a central column that led directly to the interior pillared hall or *cella*. An altar located in the forecourt was approached by a ramp.

During the second building phase (1b) of this temple the entrance was altered from a central-axis to a bent-axis access point, or dogleg approach, and two stelae were erected outside on either side of the entrance.

Roughly a century after Shechem's destruction at the hands of the Egyptians in the mid-sixteenth century BC, the city was rebuilt (now in the Late Bronze Age) and a new temple (strata XIII–XI, c. 1450–1125 BC; phases 2a and 2b) was erected on the site of the old *migdal* temple. This later structure, rather than that of the Middle Bronze Age, is more plausibly identified as the temple of Baal/El-Berith mentioned in the biblical texts.

The axis of the new temple was north–south, with the entrance located on one of the long walls, creating a typical Canaanite *broad-room* temple plan. The Late Bronze Age temple was not as large, or as well built as its predecessor, but the huge *masseba* (a biblical term for a sacred standing stone) erected in the courtyard, along with a stone altar, indicate the continued importance of the site as a religious centre.

G. Ernest Wright is generally acknowledged as a fine archaeologist who adopted with enthusiasm new stratigraphic excavation techniques and scientific methods. As with Albright before him, what distinguishes him as a biblical, as opposed to a Levantine, archaeologist was not so much his archaeological practice, but his *interpretation* of the excavated material. An assumption in his writing of the implicit historicity of the biblical narratives drove him to relate the excavated results to his understanding of the biblical stories. The historical existence of characters such as Abraham, Jacob and Moses was never questioned, and the narratives relating to them were seen as accurate historical accounts. In the foreword to *Shechem: The Biography of a Biblical City*, Wright expresses the view that for people seriously concerned with religious matters (those linked with the Bible), the historical nature of the Bible should be of the utmost importance. The historicity of the biblical narratives was somehow directly linked to the validity of biblical religion and faith. In an attempt to counteract the challenge to the fundamental validity of the Bible, presented, for example, by the popular understanding and acceptance of evolutionary theory, clerics such as Wright employed the scholarly, even scientific, tools of historical and archaeological research to bring confirmation of historical truth as proof for people's faith. In this way, any demonstration of the historical reality of biblical events, places, and people would be seen as having a direct bearing on the reality of the Bible's spiritual and theological content. It is this direct conflation of archaeology and biblical theology that has become primarily associated with 'biblical archaeology' in its most specific (and perhaps, extreme) sense, and that has led many scholars to question the motives and rationales of those associated with biblical archaeology in even its broadest and most secular sense.

Wright was certainly motivated by the Bible in much of his work in the Levant. His interpretations of the archaeological evidence from sites such as Shechem do give great emphasis to the relationship with biblical tradition. However, as with Albright, the excavation process itself was well observed and well recorded, allowing other scholars considerable latitude to disagree objectively with Wright's own biblically focused interpretations.

American contemporaries of G. Ernest Wright

Wright was not the only student of Albright to achieve great things. Nelson Glueck (1900–71) was Albright's successor as director of ASOR in Jerusalem, and was responsible for the first systematic archaeological surveys of the Negev (see *Rivers in the Desert: A History of the Negev*, 1959) and Transjordan – published as *Explorations in Eastern Palestine* (1934–51). Glueck, too, was convinced of the underlying historical truth of the biblical narratives, but did not support the notion that this was somehow proof of the Bible's theological and spiritual content. He saw the two as separate issues, a view he expressed in the journal *Biblical Archaeologist* (1959: 106).

Another of Albright's students to make a major contribution to Palestinian archaeology was J. B. Pritchard (1910–97), Professor of Religious Thought and director of the University Museum of the University of Pennsylvania. Like Wright, he was a keen exponent of the Wheeler–Kenyon method. He excavated several sites on both sides of the Jordan River, including Herodian Jericho in 1951 (Tulul Abu el-ʿAlaiq), Gibeon (el-Jib) from 1956 to 1962, and Tell es-Saʿidiyeh from 1964 to 1967. After the 1967 Arab–Israeli war, Pritchard excavated the Phoenician city of Sarepta on the Lebanese coast. All of the results of these excavations have been fully, and objectively published. Like Albright, Pritchard was a fine textual scholar as well as an archaeologist. His seminal edited work *Ancient Near Eastern Texts Relating to the Old Testament* (1969) remains a key source book today. Like others, Pritchard was very much concerned with biblical studies, but by no means exclusively so. El-Jib has been positively identified as biblical Gibeon, and Tell es-Saʿidiyeh may be biblical Zarethan. But neither Tell es-Saʿidiyeh nor Sarepta are major biblical sites.

The foundation of the State of Israel, Yigael Yadin
(1917–1984) and Israeli biblical archaeology

If Albright and his disciples have been fundamental to the development of biblical archaeology from an American and Protestant Christian tradition, there have certainly been other contributors from different religious and ideological backgrounds, the most influential of whom must surely be the Israeli school of archaeologists. Since the birth in 1948 of the modern State of Israel, Israeli archaeologists have brought their own perspectives to the field, creating an alternative definition of biblical archaeology, or, as many Israeli archaeologists prefer, the archaeology of Eretz-Israel (the Land of Israel). For many Israeli archaeologists, particularly in the early days of the modern State, the archaeology of their new country was of fundamental importance in establishing their identity. Unlike the Albrightian School this was neither a religious nor a theological position, but a social and political one; and indeed, much of Israeli archaeology was refreshingly secular from the outset.

Yigael Yadin (born Yigael Sukenik) can be regarded as the father of Israeli biblical archaeology. Very much a child of the Zionist movement which culminated in the creation of the modern State of Israel, Yadin was a scholar, soldier, politician, and hero of Israel. During the 1930s and 1940s his academic studies in archaeology were interrupted by his joining the Haganah, the Zionist underground. He became chief of operations at the outbreak of the Arab–Israeli war of 1948. It is here that he acquired the code-name 'Yadin' ('he will judge', Gen. 49:16), which he later adopted as his surname. In 1949 Yadin became chief of staff of the Israel Defence Forces (IDF).

Yadin's academic career took precedence after his retirement from military life. In 1955 he completed his PhD thesis on the Qumran 'Scroll of the War of the Sons of Light Against the Sons of Darkness', and joined the staff of the Hebrew University. Almost immediately he began the excavations at the major Canaanite and Israelite site of Hazor in Upper Galilee, directing the James A. de Rothschild Expedition. Excavations continued until 1958, and were to become the 'flagship' of Israeli archaeology. Vast quantities of material from the Bronze and Iron Ages were uncovered, including the Late Bronze Age destruction levels that Yadin associated with a unified Israelite conquest of Canaan under Joshua in about 1250 BC. This association has since been questioned, both in terms of date, and in terms of the cause of the city's destruction. The significance of Yadin's excavations at Hazor lay in the architectural stratigraphic approach he developed with the expedition's architect Immanuel Dunayevsky, the active way in which he solicited funding for the expedition, and the use of Hazor as a training excavation for a new generation of Israeli field archaeologists.

Yadin's most famous archaeological excavations were at Masada (1963–5), the cliff-top palace of Herod the Great, and the scene of the Zealots' famous stand against Rome, which ended in AD 74 with the suicide of the Jewish defenders. The excavation of the extraordinary Herodian palaces, the administrative and textual material, and the skeletons, apparently those of the ill-fated Zealots, caused much discussion in scholarly and popular circles, and made both Masada and Yigael Yadin household names.

Other excavations include the expeditions to the Judean Desert, particularly in the area of Nahal Hever, which revealed many artefacts and contemporary documents relating to the Bar Kokhba Revolt, including military dispatches and legal documents left by the refugees.

During the Arab–Israeli war of 1967 Yadin served as security adviser to the Israeli Prime Minister Levi Eskhol. He obtained IDF assistance in confiscating and ultimately purchasing an illegally removed ancient scroll, which he named the *Temple Scroll*. The material it contained related to the religious law, or halakhah of the Qumran Essenes.

After the 1973 Arab–Israeli war, Yadin entered public life, eventually becoming deputy prime minister of Israel in the Begin administration from 1977 to 1981. He returned to academic life in 1981, and remained an active archaeologist and textual scholar until his sudden death in 1984.

Like Albright, Yadin was both an archaeologist and a textual scholar, commanding a wide range of material. In one sense his interests were quite wide, ranging from discussions on the archaeological evidence for warfare, through to the transcription of religious textual material. In another sense, however, Yadin focused his attention primarily on material, both textual and archaeological, that appeared to relate in some way to previous periods of Hebrew nationalistic struggle, such as the biblical Conquest, the Maccabaean Revolt of the second century BC, the First Jewish War (AD 66–74) and the Bar Kokhba Revolt (AD 132–5).

Certainly from Yadin's perspective, the identity of modern Israel was connected directly to the Jewish people's biblical and revolutionary past. This was not so much a religious as a nationalistic perspective. It was not the religious identity of the Jewish people that was of concern to Yadin, but their national identity: their laws, customs, and history (as expressed in the Bible) were seen as being of fundamental importance to the development of the identity and character of the modern State of Israel. Archaeology and biblical studies were highly effective and emotive tools in the realization and articulation of this past identity.

As the pioneer of the Israeli school of archaeology, and as a most significant political and military leader in the new Israeli State, Yadin's position was at the extreme end of what was to characterize Israeli archaeology in the future. His own students very quickly distanced themselves from his overtly nationalistic approach, adopting less political language and objectives, and Israeli archaeologists in general, have subsequently acquired a reputation for objectivity and clarity of purpose, and have made a significant contribution to Syro-Palestinian archaeology and to the advancement of the subject as a whole.

1970s–1980s, and to the present day

By the 1970s the interpretative position of biblical archaeology as typified by the work of Albright and Wright was beginning to be undermined by developments within Syro-Palestinian archaeology itself, and other branches of academia and science. Israeli archaeologists had begun to make significant contributions to the archaeology of the Levant, within their own territory. Together with the Americans, they now represent the largest group of archaeologists working in the field in Israel itself. Since the mid-1960s there have been a great number of Israeli and American excavations, many of which are ongoing. These include Gezer (William G. Dever, Joe D. Seger and others, 1964–74, 1984, and 1990); Tell el-Hesi (Lawrence E. Stager, John E. Worrell and others, 1971–83); Sepphoris (Eric M. Meyers and Carol Meyers, 1970–81, and James F. Strange, 1984–); Lahav (Joe D. Seger and Dan P. Cole, 1976–); Tel Miqne-Ekron (Seymour Gitin and Trude Dothan 1981–); Ashkelon (Lawrence E. Stager and others 1985–); Caesarea (Robert J. Bull and Lawrence E. Toombs, 1971–); Tel Anafa (Saul S. Weinberg and Sharon Herbert, 1968–81); Tel Jemmeh (Gus Van Beek, 1970–82).

More recent American and Israeli archaeologists have employed the stratigraphic techniques of the Wheeler–Kenyon method and have adapted them to the individual needs of their own excavations. Following the example of Wright's excavations, there has been an increasing use of professionals and students with specific expertise, such as human and animal bone specialists, archaeobotanists, geophysicists, technology specialists, and so on, depending on the nature of the excavated material.

The involvement of professionals from less Bible-orientated backgrounds has had the effect of 'secularizing' the subject somewhat, providing new emphases in excavation strategies, and in the final published reports, not just in terms of content, but in terms of approach.

In many respects, this natural evolution in Syro-Palestinian archaeology (as well as in other areas of archaeology) towards a more scientific approach to the material, initially mirrored the so-called 'New Archaeology' in the USA, a theoretical development which followed anthropological models looking at 'cultures' rather than 'history'. The 'New Archaeology' emphasized the scientific, was multidisciplinary, and, as was the case with the sciences, required a clear 'mission statement' on the part of the researchers and excavators outlining their method, and their project's purpose.

Since the 1980s, however, the emphasis in archaeology in general, including Syro-Palestinian archaeology, has changed somewhat. Today Syro-Palestinian archaeologists tend to pay greater attention to the historical and textual material, which forms a significant part of the material culture of the ancient Levant, than the New Archaeology models would have allowed them to do. Nevertheless, the contribution of scientific expertise and technology to Syro-Palestinian archaeology has grown consistently since the end of World War II, throughout the 1970s and 1980s, and continues to do so.

Greater attention to detail requires longer excavation projects, and longer publication times. Specialist equipment can be prohibitively expensive. The growing cost of archaeological excavation has undoubtedly led to the increased deployment of large numbers of student volunteers, often willing to support themselves in order to gain access to the academic stage. Such students do not necessarily come from religious colleges, seminaries, or departments of biblical studies or even archaeology, but from such diverse academic backgrounds that their presence has been a further factor in the secularization of American Syro-Palestinian archaeology.

With this broadening of the source of staff for excavation projects it is hardly surprising that the range of issues raised by the archaeological data, and indeed the nature of the questions for which resolution is sought, has similarly broadened, causing a shift in the discipline away from a bibliocentric perspective. Issues such as demography, trade, or agricultural practices, have become valid areas of research in their own rights, and not because they could necessarily illuminate the world of the Bible. In this respect Syro-Palestinian archaeology has begun to achieve a new balance, as has existed in other geographical regions for some time.

The Americans and Israelis have never been and are still not, of course, the only nations conducting active fieldwork in Syro-Palestine. The British and Europeans too have continued to excavate sites and conduct fieldwork and research in the area. Many of these projects have been in Arab countries, primarily Jordan and Syria, and to a lesser extent, perhaps, in Lebanon. Since the 1970s the most significant British excavations include Tell Nebi Mend (Qadesh), Syria (P. J. Parr, Institute of Archaeology, University of London, 1975–); Tell Iktanu, Jordan (K. Prag, University of Manchester, 1987, 1989, 1990); and Tell es-Sa'idiyeh, Jordan (J. N. Tubb, British Museum, 1985–).

Other European projects of note include the Italian excavations at Tell Mardikh (Ebla) and Tell Meskene (Emar) in Syria, the continuing French involvement with Ras Shamra (Ugarit) in Syria and their excavations at Tel Yarmut in Israel, the German excavations at Tel Masos (Israel), and the Dutch excavations at Tell Deir 'Alla in Jordan.

Arab scholars, too, have added a vigorous new element to Syro-Palestinian archaeology. National schools were established during the 1960s after the creation of the independent Arab states. Overall, and understandably, they have tended to avoid both biblical studies, with the implicit connections to the nationhood of Israel and Israel's ancient history, as well as the search for Western cultural and theological roots in the Holy Land, and instead have concentrated on their own perspectives, which have generally, although by no means exclusively, been orientated towards Islamic archaeology. As such, nationalistically or religiously motivated concerns have on occasion provided a focus for research, but this tendency has, in recent years been less pronounced, with a general broadening of the scope of research to embrace all of the cultures represented within their borders.

Since the Peace Agreement of 1996 a long-awaited period of academic exchange between Israel and the Arab world has begun to be possible. Israeli and Jordanian archaeologists have for the first time in many years been able to visit each other's countries and archaeological sites, to invite each other to conferences and to embark upon joint projects and publications. Developments such as these may well move the archaeology of the region still further away from nationalistic concerns towards a more reasonable and meaningful academic dialogue.

At the present time Syro-Palestinian archaeology encompasses many different areas of specialization, including certainly those areas concerned in one way or another with the Bible. Biblical archaeology, defined as the archaeology of sites associated with the Bible, clearly forms a large element of the modern discipline. The Bible is, and always will be, a major textual product of the region, and as such it is not, nor should it be, ignored. However, other aspects of scholarship have come to be seen to be as important for an understanding of the region's past as biblical studies. Biblical archaeology, therefore, in the sense defined above, has become more relaxed. Links between archaeology and the biblical texts are no longer sought out to the same degree, but are accepted where they occur. In no way does the modern discipline of biblical archaeology attempt to 'prove' the Bible as might have been the case during the days of Albright and Wright. In these terms biblical archaeology no longer represents an ideological position, but instead can be seen as an area of interest or specialization as valid as any other.

BIBLIOGRAPHY

Albright, W. F. (1932) *The Archaeology of Palestine and the Bible*. New York.

—— (1932–43) *The Excavation of Tell Beit Mirsim*. Vol. 1: *The Pottery of the First Three Campaigns*; Vol. 1A: *The Bronze Age Pottery of the Fourth Campaign*; Vol. 2: *The Bronze Age*; Vol. 3: *The Iron Age*; Annual of the American Schools of Oriental Research, 12, 13, 17, 21/22. New Haven.

—— (1954) *The Archaeology of Palestine*. London.

—— (1969) 'The Impact of Archaeology on Biblical Research', in David Noel Freedman and Jonas C. Greenfield (eds) *New Directions in Biblical Archaeology*. Garden City, NY, 1–16.

Bliss, F. J. (1906) *The Development of Palestinian Exploration*. New York.

Dever, W. G. (1990) *Recent Archaeological Discoveries and Biblical Research*. Seattle.

Glueck, N. (1934–51) *Explorations in Eastern Palestine*. 4 vols. Annual of the American Schools of Oriental Research, 14, 15, 18/19, 25/28. New Haven.

—— (1959) *Rivers in the Desert: A History of the Negev*. New York.

Long, B. O. (1997) *Planting and Reaping Albright – Politics, Ideology, and Interpreting the Bible*. Philadelphia.

Moorey, P. R. S. (1991) *A Century of Biblical Archaeology*. Cambridge.

Pritchard, J. B. (ed.) (1969) *Ancient Near Eastern Texts Relating to the Old Testament*. 3rd edn. Princeton.

Silberman, N. A. (1982) *Digging for God and Country: Exploration, Archaeology, and the Secret Struggle for the Holy Land, 1799–1917*. New York.

Wright, G. E. (1944) *The Challenge of Israel's Faith*. Chicago.

—— (1950) *The Old Testament against its Environment*. Chicago.

—— (1952) *God Who Acts: Biblical Theology as Recital*. London.

—— (1957) *Biblical Archaeology*. Philadelphia (rev. edn 1962).

—— (1965) *Shechem: The Biography of a Biblical City*. New York.

—— (1969) 'Biblical Archaeology Today', in David Noel Freedman and Jonas C. Greenfield (eds) *New Directions in Biblical Archaeology*. Garden City, NY, 149–65.

Wright, G. E. and Filson, F. V. (1945) *Westminster Historical Atlas to the Bible*. Philadelphia.

Yadin, Y. (1966) *Masada: Herod's Fortress and the Zealots' Last Stand*. New York.

—— (1975) *Hazor: The Rediscovery of a Great Citadel of the Bible*. New York.

PALESTINE DURING THE BRONZE AGE

——·◆·——

J. Maxwell Miller

BEFORE THE BRONZE AGE (PREHISTORIC TIMES)

The origins of the human species are hidden in the distant past, and most of our existence on the earth falls within what historians traditionally have called 'prehistoric times' – that is, within the long silent millennia before humans learned to write. Paleontologists and archeologists can chart some of the important developments that occurred during prehistoric times. It appears, for example, that humans mastered the use of fire some 400,000 years ago. *Homo sapiens sapiens*, the subspecies to which modern humans belong, began to appear on the scene approximately 100,000 years ago. The Pleistocene epoch (popularly known as 'the Ice Age') drew to a close approximately 16,000 years ago. There followed, approximately 10,000 years ago, the 'Neolithic revolution.' The latter was characterized by early forms of agriculture, domesticated animals and small permanent settlements (i.e., the earliest villages). Palestine[1] shared in these prehistoric developments and offers some important prehistoric sites. Especially noteworthy are the Nahal 'Amud caves and the Qafzeh cave representing the Middle Paleolithic Age, the Mount Carmel caves representing Middle and Upper Paleolithic, and Tell es-Sultan (Jericho) one of the early Neolithic villages.[2]

Geologists and archeologists employ different but overlapping chronological schemes for dealing with prehistoric times. Geologists, attentive to gradual changes in the physical features of the earth's surface and to the fossil record of all life forms, divide time into four major eras, which they subdivide then into epochs. Archeologists, on the other hand, more attentive to developments in human material culture and thus concerned with only the latest epochs of geological time, recognize four major prehistoric ages: Paleolithic ('Old Stone'), Epi-Paleolithic (sometimes called Mesolithic or 'Middle Stone'), Neolithic ('New Stone'), and Chalcolithic ('Copper–Stone').[3] As will be apparent from Figure 21.1, the Paleolithic and Epi-Paleolithic Ages fall chronologically within the geologists' Pleistocene epoch, while the Neolithic and Chalcolithic Ages take us into the Holocene epoch.

The dates indicated in Figure 21.1 should be understood as broad approximations for geological and archeological changes that will have occurred gradually over the

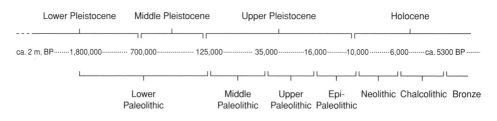

Figure 21.1 Comparison of geological and archeological chronologies.

millennia. Keep in mind also that the changes in human culture to which the archeo-logical dates refer did not occur everywhere at the same time. The dates given for the Chalcolithic and Bronze Ages pertain specifically to developments in Palestine. Note that Chalcolithic covers approximately the sixth millennium BP ('before the present'), which would be the fourth millennium BC (or BCE, 'before the common era'). This millennium saw striking innovations in human society, such as the begin-nings of metallurgy, and set the stage for the even more spectacular developments of the subsequent Bronze Age. Palestine's Chalcolithic Age corresponds roughly to Egypt's early Predynastic Period (Naqada I and II), and to the Halaf, 'Ubaid and Uruk Periods in Mesopotamia.

THE FIRST THREE THOUSAND YEARS OF RECORDED HISTORY (BRONZE AND IRON AGES)

By the closing centuries of the fourth millennium BCE urban centers large enough to be regarded as cities were emerging in the Middle East, especially in the Nile, Euphrates, and Tigris River valleys. The earliest known experimentation with writing occurred about the same time, and these two developments signaled that humankind was entering a new phase of existence. Other features of the new phase included the rise of urban-centered political and religious structures, the accumula-tion of wealth, and occupational diversity (rulers, scribes, priests, craftsmen, and so on). Urban society would flourish during some periods and decline during others over the next three thousand years that composed the Bronze and Iron Ages, and in fact most of the population probably continued to live in small villages and hamlets or to follow a nomadic existence. Most of our information for this first three thou-sand years of recorded history derives from and pertains to the cities, however, and the cities naturally dominated the surrounding villages and hamlets.

Cities located in especially favorable agricultural settings, on important trade routes, and blessed with easily defendable positions grew particularly strong. The resulting 'city-states' often went to war with each other, which called for fortifica-tions, and occasionally a city would manage to extend its authority far afield. Among the cities that became seats of extended kingdoms or empires at one time or another during this first three thousand years of recorded history were Memphis and Thebes in the Nile River valley, Qatna and Aleppo in the Levant, Hattusha in central Anatolia, and Ur, Babylon, Assur, and Mari in the Mesopotamian valley. Among

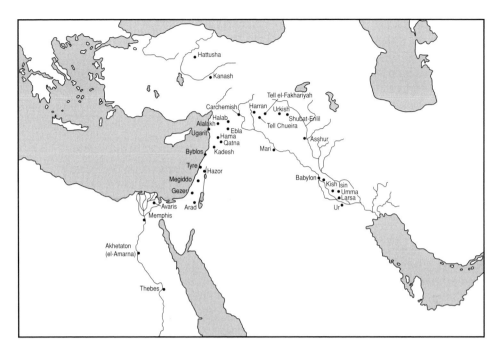

Figure 21.2   Map – Bronze Age cities in the ancient Middle East.

the ancient empires that emerged from these cities were Egypt's Old, Middle, and New Kingdoms, Hammurabi's Babylonian empire, and the later Neo-Assyrian, Neo-Babylonian, and Persian empires. Alexander's conquest of the East in 334–323 BCE represents another major watershed in Middle Eastern history. For approximately the next thousand years after Alexander, the Middle East would be dominated politically by Greek- and Latin-speaking peoples and be heavily influenced by their cultural traditions.

The written materials available from this first three thousand years of recorded history are in different languages (principally Sumerian, Akkadian, Egyptian, Hittite, Canaanite, and Aramaic) and of various sorts (royal inscriptions and correspondence, temple records, domestic and commercial documents, literary compositions including mythical and religious texts, tomb inscriptions, seals, seal impressions, and so on). Particularly useful for the historian's purposes are royal archives discovered by archeologists among the ruins of several key cities. Unfortunately the available written materials tend to be sporadic and uneven in coverage. Thus historical developments in some areas and during certain periods are fairly well documented, while other areas and periods remain largely unknown. Most of the surviving written materials from the first three millennia of recorded history in the Middle East derive from Egypt and Mesopotamia, for example, with Syria and Anatolia somewhat less well represented, and Palestine hardly represented at all. Notable exceptions for Syria are the archives discovered at Ebla (Tell Mardikh), Mari (Tell Hariri), and Ugarit (Ras Shamra).

One might think of Palestine as a land bridge connecting Syria, Anatolia, and Mesopotamia with Africa and Arabia. The peoples of Palestine often were caught up in international conflicts, therefore, and were influenced culturally from different directions. The strongest cultural ties (language, architectural and ceramic styles, religious imagery, and so on) were with Syria and Mesopotamia. Palestine lay more within Egypt's zone of political influence during the Bronze Age, however, and consequently most of the available written information pertaining specifically to Palestine during the Bronze Age comes from Egyptian sources.

Because even the Egyptian sources provide very limited information about Palestine, and there is virtually no written evidence available from Palestine itself during the Bronze Age, historians must depend heavily upon what can be learned from silent archeological remains. Here again, the most spectacular remains from the Bronze and Iron Ages are to be seen in Egypt and Mesopotamia (such as the pyramids and ziggurats). Perhaps the most characteristic archeological feature from these three millennia, however, are the stratified city ruins or 'tells' ('tel' in Hebrew) scattered throughout the Middle East. Generally the Palestinian tells are of more modest size than those of Syria and Mesopotamia. This is indicative of the fact that Palestine, offering less favorable agricultural conditions and being less strategically situated with respect to important trade routes, was marginal to the major urban centers of the ancient world. It was a region of modest cities, villages and small hamlets.

Archeologists divide the first three millennia of urban civilization in Palestine into four major ages: Early Bronze Age (ca. 3300–2000 BCE), Middle Bronze Age (ca. 2000–1550 BCE), Late Bronze Age (ca. 1550–1200), and Iron Age (ca. 1200–323 BCE). Israeli archeologists sometimes use the rubrics Canaanite Period and Israelite Period for the Bronze Age and Iron Age respectively. Archeologists working in Syria generally prefer the rubrics Old Syrian Period, Middle Syrian Period, and New Syrian Period for archeological phases that correspond roughly to the Middle Bronze, Late Bronze, and Iron Ages respectively.

As explained above, archeological chronology and terminology have to do with trends in material culture; and these trends, besides occurring gradually over time, involved other features in addition to metal technology. Thus the names 'Bronze Age' and 'Iron Age' should not be taken too literally, and the dates assigned by archeologists to these ages and their subphases are only approximations. When assigning dates, moreover, archeologists usually depend heavily on written sources – that is, they attempt to coordinate trends observed in the material culture with historical periods as reconstructed from written sources. This is not always a simple matter. The written evidence itself often is unclear for one thing, and human history does not divide easily into discrete periods. Not surprisingly, therefore, archeologists sometimes disagree on the dates they assign to archeological periods. In fact, all dates for the first two and a half millennia of recorded history, even those calculated by historians from written sources, are uncertain to some degree.[4]

Note in Figure 21.3 that the Bronze Age as a whole (Early, Middle, and Late Bronze combined) represents approximately the first two thousand years of recorded history, and that the Iron Age represents approximately the next thousand years. Ancient Israel enters the picture at the end of the Bronze Age as we shall see, and

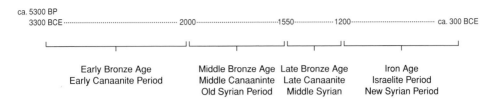

Figure 21.3   The Bronze and Iron Ages in Syria–Palestine.

Israel's history unfolded during the Iron Age. Accordingly, the Israelites were heirs of Bronze Age civilization rather than participants in it.

THE EARLY BRONZE AGE
(ca. 3300–2000 BCE)

The dates given above for the Early Bronze Age include a period at the end (ca. 2300/2250–2000 BCE) that in some aspects represents a continuation of Early Bronze but probably should be thought of as a separate interim period between the Early Bronze and Middle Bronze Ages. Thus Palestine's Early Bronze Age proper, excluding the interim period, spanned almost a thousand years. It overlaps Egypt's Early Dynastic (or Archaic) and Old Kingdom Periods. In Mesopotamia, this was the time of the early Sumerian city-states. Written records from Egypt and southern Mesopotamia enable historians to reconstruct the overall contours of historical developments in those two areas, and the Ebla archive allows us to look in briefly on a major city-state that flourished in western Syria. Palestine, however, is essentially beyond the horizon of written sources during the Early Bronze Age (see Figure 21.4[5]).

Excavations at Palestinian tells indicate that villages began to emerge in the land on the eve of the third millennium BCE; some of them grew into cities that flourished for several centuries (not always simultaneously or without interruptions); and then, after about 2300 BCE, the cities began to decline, and in most cases disappeared. Archeologists recognize four subphases of the Early Bronze Age: Early Bronze I (ca. 3300–3050 BCE), Early Bronze II (ca. 3050–2700 BCE), Early Bronze III (ca. 2700–2300 BCE), and the interim period at the end (ca. 2300/2250–2000 BCE) during which the cities disappeared.[6]

Early Bronze I (ca. 3300–3050 BCE)

EB I was a proto-urban period with village settlements based on Mediterranean economy – sheep and goat herding, olive, vine, and fruit trees – beginning to appear in the Palestinian highlands and inner valleys. This represented a demographic shift, most of the small camps and settlements of the Chalcolithic Age having been situated in the agriculturally marginal steppes and arid zones. Some of the villages grew to be respectable towns during EB I, but it is doubtful that any of them could be regarded as cities. Most if not all remained unfortified, for example, and modest temples seem to have been the only public buildings. Sumerian cities (Eridu, 'Ubaid,

- Pyramid and tomb texts (in hieroglyphics) from Egypt, especially from the vicinity of ancient Memphis.

- Sumerian texts (cuneiform on clay tablets) from the Sumerian city-states in southern Mesopotamia (Nippur, Lagash, Ur, Erech, Larsa, Shurrupak, Isin). It was the Sumerians who first developed cuneiform writing. Their writings include administrative documents, letters, myths, and so on.

- Akkadian texts (cuneiform on clay tablets) from cities situated in the vicinity of Baghdad (Kish, Babylon, Eshnunna). These are similar in content to the Sumerian texts, but Akkadian is a different language, a Semitic language, for which the cuneiform method of writing was adapted.

- Ebla archive (cuneiform on clay tablets) discovered in 1974–5 at Tell Mardikh approximately 40 miles south of Aleppo. The Ebla texts are mostly royal administrative documents covering approximately 40 years prior to a destruction of the city ca. 2300 BCE. Eblite was an early Semitic language akin to both Akkadian and Canaanite.

Figure 21.4 Important literary sources from the Early Bronze Age.

Ur, Uruk, Nippur, Lagash, Umma) were emerging in southern Mesopotamia at the same time – that is EB I corresponds roughly to the Uruk IV–Jemdet Nasr (Early Sumerian) period in southern Mesopotamia. Settlements were appearing in Syria as well. Some of them, such as Habiba-Kabira, may have been Sumerian colonies. One would expect Mesopotamian and Syrian influences on Palestine during EB I, and this is confirmed by the material culture associated with Palestine's EB I settlements (some of the pottery forms for example, and the appearance of cylinder seals). In southern Palestine, however, the closest ties were with Egypt. This is indicated by numerous small finds, especially seal impressions of Egyptian officials and *serekhs* (a pharaoh's name inscribed within a rectangular border). Two *serekhs*, one from Arad (Tell Arad) and the other from Tel Erani,[7] identify Narmer, the first pharaoh of Dynasty I. Thus it can be established that EB I overlapped chronologically the first part of Egypt's Early Dynastic Period.

Early Bronze II (ca. 3050–2700)

By the early centuries of the third millennium BCE urbanization was intensifying throughout the Fertile Crescent. The Sumerian cities were in their Early Dynastic Period (Early Dynastic I) for example, and Memphis was emerging under the pharaohs of Dynasties I and II as the capital of a unified Egypt. Palestine, no doubt stimulated and influenced from both directions, participated in the trend. We may now speak of proper cities in Palestine with fortifications and public buildings, although these were modest cities compared to those of Egypt, Mesopotamia, and Syria. Most of Palestine's population probably continued to live apart from the cities, either in surrounding hamlets or as seminomads. There are indications that the cities

Figure 21.5 Map – Bronze Age sites in Palestine (all of them were not necessarily occupied at the same time).

Figure 21.6 Excavations under way at Et-Tell. Photo J. Maxwell Miller.

were destroyed from time to time during the course of EB II – probably the result of local warfare.

Among the settlements that emerged as fortified cities during EB II were some that would figure prominently, off and on, throughout the remainder of the Bronze and Iron Ages: Hazor (Tell el-Qadeh), Beth-Shan (Tell el-Husn), Megiddo (Tell el-Mutesellim), Jericho (Tell es-Sultan), Lachish (Tell ed-Duweir), and others. Abydos ware, discovered first in Egypt (late Dynasty I contexts) but probably originating in Syria–Palestine, serves as a chronological cross-reference with Egypt and likewise counts as evidence of continued contact between Egypt and Palestine during EB II. Also from this period archeologists have discovered what appear to be caravan way stations along the route between Egypt and southern Palestine.

Three sites that have been particularly important for understanding EB II are Tell el-Far'ah and 'Ai (et-Tell) in the north-central hill country, and Arad between Beersheba and the Dead Sea. Because much of Arad's 25-acre site was not reoccupied during later periods and the EB II remains thus lay immediately beneath the surface of the ground, excavators were able to expose a large portion of the city plan. The city was surrounded by a massive stone wall (2 to 2.5 m thick) strengthened at intervals with round towers. At the center of the city was a water catchment system and deep reservoir. The domestic houses, also of stone (at least the lower courses), were rectangular and entered by a door on the broad side. At the door, one stepped down from ground level into the broad room. Typically there was a bench

Figure 21.7   Foundations of an Early Bronze II house at Tel 'Arad (ancient Arad). Photo J. Maxwell Miller.

surrounding the room at the base of its walls. Larger structures, which the excavators interpreted as a palace and two sets of 'twin temples,' followed similar plans.

Early Bronze III (ca. 2700–2300 BCE)

The beginning of EB III is marked by the appearance of a distinctive new pottery style, Khirbet Kerak ware, but there was no break or sudden change in the material culture. Basically it may be said that Palestine's Early Bronze Age phase of urbanization that had begun during EB I reached its zenith in EB III. Some of the EB II cities were abandoned (such as Tell el-Far'ah North and Arad), other new settlements were founded (such as Beth-Shemesh and Numeira), and on the whole there may have been somewhat fewer cities in EB III than in EB II. But those that flourished during EB III tended to be larger and to present more impressive architecture than their predecessors. Among the largest were Beth-Yerah (over 50 acres), Yarmuth (40 a.), Tell el-Hesi and 'Ai (both about 25 a.). Other settlements reached 10 to 15 acres, but most were still smaller.[8] Palestine's urban population at the time may have reached 150,000.[9] The main public buildings were temples, some of them rather impressive (e.g., at Megiddo, 'Ai and Yarmuth). In Palestine, no doubt, as in the contemporary Sumerian cities of southern Mesopotamia, the temples were at the center of economic and political power.

Southern Mesopotamia, now in its Early Dynastic II and III Periods, was intensely urbanized. It has been estimated that more than 80 percent of the population lived in and around the cities.[10] Kish had emerged as the dominant Sumerian city by Early Dynastic II, and Lugalzaggesi from Umma was a powerful ruler at the close of Early Dynastic III. Semitic names, first for scribes and then for rulers, turn up increasingly in the Sumerian documents during these two periods, and there is also some representation of the Akkadian language. Syria likewise experienced a period of rich urban development during EB III, cities in the upper Euphrates region having

Figure 21.8   Early Bronze III altar at Megiddo (upper right-hand).
Photo J. Maxwell Miller.

developed a dry farming agriculture paralleling the irrigation methods of southern
Mesopotamia. Representative Syrian cites of this period are Mari (Tell Hariri), Tell
Taya, Shubat-Enlil (Tell Leilan), Tell Chuiera, and especially Ebla (Tell Mardikh).[11]
   Ebla, which emerged as a regional power in western Syria near the end of EB III,
is particularly important for our understanding of the period because of the more
than 1,700 cuneiform documents discovered there. These documents cover a span of
about 40 years and pertain mostly to the reigns of two Eblite kings, Irkab-Damu
and Ishtar-Damu.[12] We learn that Ebla exerted political and commercial influence
as far south as Hama on the Orontes River, north to the vicinity of Carchemish on
the Euphrates, and even east of the Euphrates where Ebla's interests conflicted with

those of Mari. Although none of the Palestinian cities was comparable in size to Ebla, and Palestine is beyond the horizon of the Ebla documents, we may suppose that the sociopolitical circumstances reflected in these documents will have existed in Palestine as well – that is, cities ruled by local dynasties, some of them able to exert regional power.

Egypt meanwhile had entered its Old Kingdom Period, during which the pharaohs of Dynasties III and IV constructed the famous pyramids of Sakkara, Dashur, and Giza. During the Old Kingdom, Egypt established maritime relations with cities along the Levantine coast further north than Palestine, especially with Byblos. This probably explains why Egyptian artifacts largely disappear from Palestine during EB III; Egyptian commerce was bypassing Palestine.

From Early Bronze to Middle Bronze
(ca. 2300/2250–2000 BCE)

Palestinian cities began to decline and disappear after about 2350 BCE, until virtually all of the population seems to have reverted to a nonurban lifestyle. This situation was to continue until about 2000 BCE, the beginning of the Middle Bronze Age, when cities gradually begin to reemerge. Archeologists have not been able to agree on what to call this nonurban period between Early Bronze and Middle Bronze. Some, noting a degree of continuity between the pottery of this period and that of the preceding Early Bronze III, prefer to call it Early Bronze IV. Others, more impressed with characteristics that seem to anticipate the Middle Bronze Age prefer to call it (or at least the latter part of it) Middle Bronze I. Still others search for terminology that labels it as a truly interim period – 'Intermediate Early Bronze/Middle Bronze' or simply 'Intermediate Bronze Age.'

The cause of the breakdown and decline in city life at the end of EB III is unclear. Earlier archeologists generally attributed it to turmoil created by population movements, and a popular theory supposed Amorite migrations (see below). There was a related theory that Abraham and his family entered Palestine in connection with the Amorite movements. But neither of these theories has much following today. Contemporary archeologists tend to think more in terms of internal sociopolitical developments or of climatic factors. For example, long periods of drought could have destroyed the agricultural economy that supported the EB II–III cities. Whatever the cause, the urban decline were not limited to Palestine. Egypt also entered a phase of decentralization and urban decline at this time – that is, the First Intermediate Period. Egypt's First Intermediate Period generally is understood to begin with Dynasty VII (ca. 2170–2131), but the decline set in already under the pharaohs of Dynasty VI (ca. 2350–2170). At least one of the Dynasty VI pharaohs, Pepi I (ca. 2332–2283), is known to have conducted a military campaign into Syria–Palestine.

Mesopotamia, meanwhile, entered its Akkadian period (ca. 2350–2193 BCE) associated with Sargon and his descendants. Sargon rose to power in Kish, established a new capital at Agade (location still unknown) and began the conquest of an extensive empire. His grandson, Naram-Sin, extended the realm still further. They spoke a Semitic language that has come to be called Akkadian (after the name of their capital city Agad). Gutian invasions contributed to the collapse of Akkadian hegemony, after which the Gudians dominated southern Mesopotamia for approximately a half century. This was followed by a brief Sumerian revival centered at Ur under a dynasty founded by Ur-Nammu (Ur Dynasty III; ca. 2112–2004). Probably it was either Sargon or Naram-Sin that destroyed Ebla about 2350 BCE. Ebla was rebuilt and continued on as an important city, but overshadowed by the kingdoms of Yamkhad centered at Halab (Aleppo) and Qatna (Tell Mishrifeh), east of present-day Homs. Palestine would have been hinterland to these strong Syrian cities.

There continued to be some small settlements in Palestine during the Interim Period. Because these were such small settlements, however, and usually one-period sites that did not produce conspicuous tells, they are difficult to find. Much of our information comes from isolated cemeteries, moreover, and from what appear to be seminomadic settlements situated in areas marginal to the agricultural lands that had supported the EB cities and towns. Many such settlements have been found in the Jordan Valley, for example, and in the central Negeb. Possibly the Negeb settlements belonged to pastoralists who ranged annually with their flocks between the southern hill country, the Shephelah, and the Negeb. The typical pottery from this Interim Period represents a departure from EB traditions. Exceptional to all of the above, however, are a few sites in the region east and northeast of the Dead Sea (Iktanu, Khirbet Iskander, 'Aroer). Although quite small, these Transjordanian settlements continued EB III pottery traditions and one of them (Iskander) was fortified. Some archeologists see these Transjordanian settlements as atypical of the Interim Period, apparently surviving remnants of the EB III urban population.[13] Others think that they may have been more characteristic of the Interim Period, and accordingly prefer to call the period EB IV.[14]

THE MIDDLE BRONZE AGE
(ca. 2000–1550 BCE)

Cities began to reemerge in Palestine around 2000 BCE signaling the beginning of a new phase of urbanization – the Middle Bronze Age. This age spanned approximately four and a half centuries, and toward the end of the age Palestine was blanketed with heavily fortified cities surrounded by small towns and hamlets. This was the peak of urbanization in ancient Palestine. The cities were larger and more massively fortified than ever before or after. Middle Bronze Age pottery reflects superior craftsmanship, and for the first time in Palestine there is evidence of the technology for producing bronze. Similarities between Palestine's Middle Bronze Age fortification systems, public architecture, and other aspects of material culture indicate strong cultural ties with Syria and Mesopotamia where Amorite dynasties ruled. Indeed it is appropriate to think of Middle Bronze Age Palestine as an extension of Syrian civilization.

Archives discovered at Mari and Alalakh (Tell el-ʿAtshanah) provide information about circumstances in Syria. A few scattered bits of writing in Akkadian cuneiform have been discovered at Palestinian sites (Hazor and Gezer). Also certain Egyptian documents, such as the execration texts, offer indirect information about circumstances in Palestine. But otherwise Palestine remains on the outskirts of recorded history during the Middle Bronze Age (see Figure 21.9).

- More pyramid, tomb, and literary texts from Egypt. The *Story of Sinuhe* and two groups of Execration Texts are particularly noteworthy.

- More Akkadian cuneiform texts from Mesopotamian cities, many of these cities dominated now by Amorite dynasties. Two important epics, the *Gilgamesh Epic* and the *Atrakhasis Epic*, probably originated during this period. More than 20,000 documents discovered at Mari (Tell Hariri) in 1934 and following are especially important for understanding the history and culture of the Upper Euphrates and Syria during the eighteenth century BCE.

- Kültepe texts (Old Assyrian dialect of Akkadian) from an Assyrian trade colony residing at Kültepe (ancient Kanesh) in Anatolia during the twentieth to eighteenth centuries BCE.

- Alalakh archive and Idrimi Inscription (in Akkadian) excavated 1937–9 and 1946–9 at Tell el-ʿAtshanah in present-day Turkey. These cuneiform documents date from the late eighteenth and early seventeenth centuries BCE, thus slightly later than the main group of Mari texts. Other texts from Alalakh date from the fifteenth century.

Figure 21.9   Important literary sources from the Middle Bronze Age.

Four population groups need to be introduced at this point – Amorites, Hurrians, Hittites, and Canaanites. Although their presence was not limited to the Middle Bronze Age, it was during that age that these peoples began to figure prominently in written sources. Exactly what role each of these groups played in Palestinian affairs is unclear, but all four clearly had a role, including contributing to the population mix. A fifth group, the Hyksos, is to be associated specifically with the last phase of Middle Bronze and will be discussed below. A word of caution is in order before attempting to explain who these peoples were. Even today we often mix terms of different sorts when referring to population groups, and a term may take on different meanings depending on the context. Depending on the context, for example, 'Irish,' 'American,' or 'Arab' may be intended as primarily geographical, nationalistic, or ethnic–cultural designations. No doubt the ancients did the same thing, which means that even back then it probably would have been difficult to explain what exactly was an Amorite, Hurrian, Hittite, or Canaanite.

Amorites

The term 'Amorite' (Akkadian *Amurru*) originally meant something like 'westerner' and began to turn up in Akkadian texts near the end of the third millennium BCE. The Amorites spoke a Semitic language and probably are best defined as the indigenous population of the Syrian interior. No Amorite texts have been discovered, so the character of the language is known only from Amorite names mentioned in primarily Akkadian documents. The earliest references to Amorites suggest that they were a largely pastoral and nomadic people. By the beginning of the second millennium, however, a new ruling elite with Amorite names began to make their presence felt in key Mesopotamian cities such as Isin, Larsa, Mari, and Babylon. While our information about Amorites during the Middle Bronze Age derives from Mesopotamian sources, we may assume that they were making their presence felt in western Syria and Palestine as well. In fact, it probably is appropriate to think of the core population of Middle Bronze Age Syria–Palestine as basically Amorite. During the Late Bronze Age, as we shall see, a particular region in Syria (upper Orontes and Lebanese coast north of Byblos) was known as Amurru. Also, of course, the biblical writers remembered the Amorites as part of the indigenous population of Palestine.

Hurrians

Although concentrated in the region of the upper Khabur (one of the main tributaries of the Euphrates), Hurrians were to be found throughout the Fertile Crescent. Only a few Hurrian texts have been discovered. These are written with the Sumerian–Akkadian cuneiform script, but the language itself is difficult to classify. Neither Semitic nor Indo-European, Hurrian may have been related to the language spoken by the people of Urartu (in the Lake Van area). Hurrians were making their presence felt in cities well outside of the Khabur region already during the Middle Bronze Age. But the Hurrians were particularly strong during the early part of the Late Bronze Age when a Hurrian confederation known as Mitanni exerted political influence deep into Syria. Washukanni, the Mitanni capital, has not yet been located. Tell el-Fakhariyah, situated near where the Khabur crosses the present-day Syrian–Turkish border, is a contender. Tell Mozan in the Khabur plain east of Tell el-Fakhariyah has been identified as the Hurrian city Urkesh. The presence of Hurrian elements in Palestine during the Middle Bronze Age is indicated by two Hurrian names inscribed in cuneiform on a clay envelope discovered at Gezer (Tell Jezer). The name of the earliest known king of Jerusalem, 'Abdu-Heba (see below), is Hurrian. The Hivites (or Horites) whom the biblical writers counted among the population of Canaan may have been Hurrians.

Hittites

From their chief city Hattusha (present-day Boghazköy in central Turkey), the Hittites carved out an extensive empire. Like the Hurrians, they figure more prominently in Syro-Palestinian affairs during the Late Bronze Age; but already during the seventeenth century BCE they expanded their domain into northern Syria, sacked Yamkhad, and conquered Babylon around 1595. Their capture of Babylon brought to a close the Amorite dynasty to which Hammurabi belonged and that had ruled Babylon for three centuries.[15] The Hittites spoke an Indo-European language, and an archive of Hittite documents has been discovered at Hattusha. These documents are written in a cuneiform script apparently adapted from the Sumerian–Akkadian script. Also, a uniquely Hittite hieroglyphic script was developed to write Luwian, another dialect of Hittite. While Palestine itself seems to have remained beyond the range of Hittite political authority, people of Hittite stock no doubt found their way into Palestine. This is assumed by the biblical writers in any case. Hittites

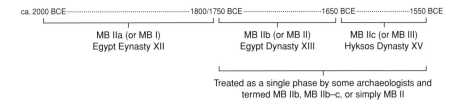

Figure 21.10   The Middle Bronze Age.

always are mentioned along with the Amorites and Canaanites as composing the indigenous peoples of the land. And Abraham is said to have purchased the cave of Machpelah from a Hittite.

Canaanites

References to Canaan and Canaanites in ancient sources (Mari, Alalakh, Ugarit, Amarna Letters) all point toward the Levantine coast. Late Bronze Age Egyptian sources recognize Canaan as an administrative district that included coastal cities such as Tyre and Byblos, for example, while Iron Age and classical sources treat Canaan as roughly equivalent to Phoenicia. The biblical writers often use the term 'Canaan' broadly as in 'land of Canaan,' but in other instances speak of the Canaanites as if they were a particular element of the population of the land, not always but usually associated with the coastal region. In short, 'Canaanite' seems to have been a loose designation for the settlements and population along the Levantine coast and its immediate hinterland. The people in this area spoke a distinctive Semitic language that scholars call 'Canaanite.' Most of the Late Bronze Age texts discovered at Ugarit on the Syrian coast were written in a local dialect of Canaanite. Other Canaanite dialects known from Iron Age sources include Hebrew, Ammonite, Moabite, and Edomite.

Contemporary archeologists are not in full agreement regarding either the subphasing of the Middle Bronze Age or what to call the subphases.[16] As explained above, earlier archeologists used the designation MB I in connection with the interim period between Early Bronze and Middle Bronze. Thus the main part of the Middle Bronze Age came to be called MB II and subdivided into MB IIa, MB IIb, and MB IIc. In view of the difficulty of distinguishing between MB IIb and MB IIc on purely archeological grounds, however, some archeologists treat MB IIb and MB IIc as a single phase. This is complicated further by the fact that some archeologists prefer now to dispense with the old MB II a-b-c terminology and rename these phases MB I, MB II, and MB III (see Figure 21.10).

Middle Bronze IIa (ca. 2000–1800/1750 BCE)

MB IIa witnessed the revival of urban centers in Palestine. These were small unfortified settlements at first, found mostly along the coast and adjacent valleys. Representative sites include Tel Kabri, Tell el-Fukhar/Tel Akko, Megiddo and Aphek (Tell Ras el-ʿAin). As MB IIa drew to a close, settlements began to appear deeper in the Palestinian interior – for example, Dan (Tell el-Qadi/Tel Dan), Hazor, Shechem (Tell el-Balatah), and Tell el-Far'ah north. Also some of the settlements began to be fortified, enhanced with public buildings, and hamlets sprang up around them. Aphek is an especially important site for understanding MB IIa because it provides a good stratified sequence for the period. Both the location of the MB IIa settlements and MB IIa ceramic forms represent a break from the preceding Interim Period. Instead, the ceramic forms suggest connections with the Lebanese coast and Orontes region where the Early Bronze Age urban momentum had not been interrupted. Probably the new Palestinian settlements were stimulated by population expansion from Lebanon and Syria.

The *Story of Sinuhe* is an Egyptian literary composition relevant to the early stage of the MB IIa reurbanization process.[17] Dating from early in Dynasty XII, the story tells of an Egyptian official's exile to Upper Retenu. Upper Retenu would have been somewhere in the Levant, and the story confirms that the region was largely rural and pastoral. Several stela inscriptions discovered in Egypt witness to occasional Egyptian military campaigns into Palestine by later pharaohs of Dynasty XII – that is, during the latter half of MB IIa. One inscription reports an attack on Shechem. Egyptian presence in Palestine is suggested also by numerous small finds at MB IIa sites and by a statue of an Egyptian official discovered at Megiddo. Yet we need not conclude that Egypt actually ruled Palestine at any time during the Middle Kingdom. Moreover, there was two-way traffic between Egypt and Palestine, as illustrated by the Beni Hassan tomb painting. This painting dates from early in Dynasty XII and depicts a band of Asiatics who had journeyed to Egypt from Syria–Palestine. Thus it provides clues regarding the appearance and dress of the people who inhabited Palestine during MB IIa, at least from an Egyptian perspective.

Perhaps the most intriguing Egyptian documents relevant to MB IIa Palestine are the so-called execration texts. These are magical texts intended to insure control over local settlements and rulers in lands along Egypt's frontiers. Accordingly, they contain incantations and curses directed toward specific places and rulers. Of the numerous execration texts from different periods that have been discovered in Egypt, two groups (Berlin group and Brussels group) contain names of Palestinian places and rulers. Exact dating is uncertain, but the Berlin group probably derives from middle or late Dynasty XII, and the Brussels group a generation or so later.[18] Most of the place names mentioned in the Berlin group that can be identified were settlements along the Palestinian and Lebanese coast (e.g., Ashkelon, Rehob, and Byblos). Those of the Brussels group were scattered in the interior of Palestine as well (e.g., Hazor, Shechem, and Pella). It is interesting that the Berlin group usually associates three or four rulers with each settlement, while the Brussels group normally names only one ruler for each place. Some scholars have interpreted this as indicative that a shift was underway from tribal society to more centralized government. Be that as it may, it is noteworthy that the personal names mentioned in both groups are west Semitic – that is, similar to the Amorite names known from other sources.

The Mari archives shed light on circumstances in Syria and Mesopotamia during the eighteenth century[19] – that is, at approximately the transition from MB IIa to MB IIb. Amorite rulers are now in place in the major cities of Syria and Mesopotamia. One of the powerful rulers of Amorite stock was Shamshi-Adad (ca. 1830–1776) who united northern Mesopotamia. He delegated territories to his two sons, the important city of Mari falling to the younger, Yasmakh-Adad. Zimri-Lim, of the previously ruling Amorite dynasty of Mari, took refuge in Yamkhad until Shamshi-Adad died, and then recovered Mari. Zimri-Lim's reign (ca. 1776–1761) marked the high point of Mari's history; but his reign was eclipsed when Hammurabi of Babylon, also of Amorite stock, turned on him and conquered Mari. Babylon then reached its first zenith under Hammurabi (dated ca. 1792–1750) who gradually conquered all of southern Mesopotamia and parts of Assyria. The Mari archives are particularly rich for Yasmakh-Adad's last 6 years and Zimri-Lim's 14-year reign. Especially the royal correspondence preserved in these archives allows us to identify the major cities of Mesopotamia and Syria, learn the names of some of their rulers, and catch a glimpse of political and commercial patterns. Among the important cities of the Levant were Carchemish (Kargamiṣ/Jerablus, where the Euphrates crosses from Turkey into Syria), Halab (present-day Aleppo, chief city of Yamkhad), Ugarit, Qatna, Kadesh (Tell Nebi Mend near the source of the Orontes River), and Hazor. Hazor in northern Palestine is the southernmost city mentioned. We learn about shipments of tin to Hazor, whose king at the time was named Ibni-Adad.[20]

Middle Bronze IIb–c (ca. 1800/1750–1550 BCE)

There were no sudden changes in the material culture between MB IIa and MB IIb, so any date given for the beginning of MB IIb must understood as very approximate. Whether to place the beginning of MB IIb nearer to 1800 BCE or nearer to 1750 involves, among other things, the excavations at Hazor, the Mari archives, and Hammurabi. Excavations at Hazor have revealed that it was a relatively insignificant settlement during MB IIa, but then expanded into a major city during MB IIb. The references to Hazor in the Mari correspondence seem to presuppose a city of some consequence and thus probably have to do with the MB IIb phase. The correspondence in which these references occur must be dated before Mari was destroyed by Hammurabi during the thirty-sixth year of his reign, an event usually dated to 1761 BCE. In short, it seems that Hazor's expanded MB IIb city must be dated before 1761, and if we consider that the MB IIb expansion may have occurred several decades before Hazor began to turn up in the Mari correspondence, then the date is pushed further back toward 1800. However, the dates for Hammurabi's reign are not entirely secure; some historians have dated him earlier and others later. Likewise it has been suggested that the expanded city at Hazor might be characterized as transitional between MB IIa and MB IIb rather than fully mature MB IIb.[21]

As explained above, there also is difference of opinion as to whether MB IIb and MB IIc should be treated separately. Changes in material culture from one to the next were gradual and have to do largely with the subtleties of ceramic typology. Basically there was a continued trend toward urbanization that reached a peak toward the end. Yet the surrounding historical circumstances were different for the early part of MB IIb–c than for the latter part, and in that regard it is useful for our purposes to treat them separately.

MB IIb (ca.1800/1750–1650 BCE) covered approximately the next hundred years after Mari's destruction and corresponds roughly to Egypt's Dynasty XIII (from ca.1759 to 1630 BCE or later). Dynasty XIII is regarded as a continuation of the Middle Kingdom, yet decline had set in. A rapid turnover of pharaohs resulted in increasingly powerful viziers. A few inscriptions from Byblos are the only written evidence pertaining to Egyptian presence in the Levant during Dynasty XIII. Small finds at Palestinian sites indicate that there was continued contact of some sort, however, while excavations in Egypt's eastern delta, especially at Tell ed-Dabʻa, suggest the beginnings of infiltration into the area by people with Syro-Palestinian cultural heritage. Probably we have to do here with the early stages of 'Hyksos' immigration into Egypt. Texts discovered at Alalakh dating from the late eighteenth and early seventeenth centuries BCE fill in the picture somewhat for Syria toward the end of MB IIb and the beginning of MB IIc. We learn from the Alalakh materials, for example, that Yamkhad and Qatna had emerged as widely influential cities in western Syria.

MB IIc (ca. 1650–1550 BCE) corresponds to Egypt's Second Intermediate Period (ca. 1630–1539/23) during which Egypt was dominated by the Hyksos (Dynasty XV). 'Hyksos' is a Greek name derived from an Egyptian phrase that meant 'foreign rulers.' According to Manetho, an Egyptian historian who wrote during the third century BCE, they invaded Egypt and ruled the land from Avaris (Tell ed-Dabʻa). Apparently the Hyksos dominated Egypt throughout the Second Intermediate Period, although Dynasties XIV and XVI–XVII (the latter two ruled at Thebes) overlapped chronologically and must have maintained some degree of autonomy. Little written evidence is available regarding the Hyksos, but archeological remains at Tell ed-Dabʻa and other Hyksos sites in the eastern delta strongly suggest that they were of Syro-Palestinian origin. This is especially evident from their temple architecture and burial customs, but their material culture in general has been described as a blending of Levantine and Egyptian elements. Hyksos scarabs and small finds discovered as far afield as Nubia and Cyprus probably reflect commercial activity. An abundance of Hyksos scarabs and Egyptian import items found at southern Palestinian sites indicate especially close ties between Egypt and southern Palestine.[22] Whether this is to be attributed to commerce also, or whether the Hyksos exercised political hegemony over southern Palestine, is unclear.

Urbanization of ancient Palestine reached its zenith during the Hyksos period – that is, toward the end of MB IIb–c. By that time Palestine was strewn with well-fortified cities surrounded by smaller towns and hamlets. The fortification systems typically consisted of massive walls that were augmented by ramparts or glacis and towers, and were pierced by monumental direct-access gates. Among the Palestinian sites where excavations have produced significant MB IIb–c remains are Dan, Hazor, Megiddo, Tell el-Farʻah (north), Shechem, Aphek, Jericho, Gezer, and Sharuhen (Tell el-ʻAjjul). But this is only a partial list of sites that have produced MB IIb–c remains. Jerusalem also was a walled settlement during MB IIb–c, for example, although relatively small.

Hazor became Palestine's premier city.[23] Covering almost 200 acres, it approached in size some of the prominent Syrian cities of the day. Hazor's massive defensive system also calls to mind Syrian parallels (e.g., Carchemish, Ebla, and Qatna). The system consisted of a moat and huge earthen rampart on the western and northern sides of the city, a city wall lifted high by the rampart and rendered more difficult to approach with siege equipment, and at least two imposing city gates. The gates were protected by towers and offered direct entry into the city between three pairs of pilasters that formed two chambers on each side. Two temples and a corner of a palace also call to mind Syrian parallels and remind us again of the close cultural ties between MB Palestine and the lands to the north.

Gezer serves as an example of a MB IIb–c city that, although not in Hazor's league, was impressive enough. Gezer's walls with a glacis at the base enclosed a city of approximately 30 acres. One entered the city through a monumental three entryway gate, and there was an impressive citadel on the acropolis. But perhaps the most notable feature of MB IIb–c Gezer was its open-air cultic center. This featured a row of ten standing stones (*masseboth*), some almost ten feet high.[24] Although it was not one of the more imposing gates of the period, the one at Dan deserves mention also because it has been preserved to roof level. It was constructed of mud brick and had an arched entryway and two pairs of pilasters. Apparently this mud-brick gate was considered inadequate, however, because later it was blocked, covered by an earthen embankment, and replaced with a stone gate. These heavily fortified cities imply a high degree of centralization of power, accumulation of wealth, and intercity warfare.

An Egyptian inscription reports that Ahmose, founder of Dynasty XVIII, conquered Avaris (Tell ed-Dab'a), chased the Hyksos to Sharuhen (Tell el-'Ajjul) in southwestern Palestine, and destroyed Sharuhen as well. This event would have occurred somewhere around 1550 BCE, and archeological evidence from Tell ed-Dab'a and Tell el-'Ajjul indicates that both sites were destroyed about that time. Moreover, there appears to have been a wave of city destructions especially in southern Palestine that many archeologists attribute to Egyptian armies who may have pursued the Hyksos beyond Sharuhen. Whatever the explanation for this wave of destructions, archeologists recognize it as the close of the Middle Bronze Age and the beginning of the Late Bronze Age.

THE LATE BRONZE AGE (ca. 1550–1200)

With the expulsion of the Hyksos, Egypt entered its New Kingdom Period that was to last approximately two and a half centuries. This was Egypt's empire age during which the pharaohs of Dynasties XVIII–XIX ruled from Thebes and expanded Egypt's frontiers from Nubia to Syria. Palestine's Late Bronze Age corresponds to this New Kingdom Period, and a crucial point to keep in mind is that Late Bronze Palestine was essentially Egyptian territory.[25] Egypt's imperial interests met with more resistance in Syria, however, where the Hurrians and Hittites had interests as well. Mycenaean civilization also reached its heyday during the Late Bronze Age. Centered on the Greek mainland, Mycenaean hegemony spread to the islands and impacted the whole eastern Mediterranean world. Mesopotamia, on the other hand, dominated now by Kassites, entered a dark age.

Egypt's New Kingdom left relatively abundant written records, and because Palestine was an Egyptian domain these New Kingdom/Late Bronze Age records are considerably more revealing about local circumstances in Palestine than are Early and Middle Bronze Age sources. Accounts of Egyptian campaigns into Syria–Palestine provide extensive lists of Palestinian cities, for example, while Egyptian inscriptions

---

- Extensive hieroglyphic inscriptions and literary texts from Egypt's New Kingdom Period, especially from Thebes (Karnak and Luxor).

- Amarna Letters (Akkadian cuneiform on clay tablets). Correspondence from foreign lands including Syro-Palestinian vassals to Amenhotep III and IV. These were discovered in 1887 and later at the site of the Amenhotep IV/Akhenaten's capital city Akhetaten in the el-Amarna district of Egypt.

- Hittite archive (Hittite language written in cuneiform script) discovered in 1906 and following at the site of the Hittite capital Hattusha (Boghazköy) in central Turkey.

- Ugaritic archives (a Canaanite dialect written with a cuneiform–alphabetic script) discovered at the site of ancient Ugarit (Ras Shamra) on the Syrian coast, excavated 1929 and following. These archives include royal correspondence and other documents of various sorts including religious texts pertaining to Baal and other gods of the Canaanite pantheon.

- Nuzi (Some 4,000 Akkadian tablets with Hurrian influence) excavated 1925–31 at Yorghun Tepe in northern Iraq and dating to approximately the fifteenth century BCE.

Figure 21.11 Important literary sources from the Late Bronze Age.

and other Egypt-related finds in Palestine enable archeologists to correlate the archeological data fairly closely with Egyptian history. The Amarna Letters, described below, provide for the first time a close-up look at sociopolitical circumstances in Syria–Palestine, including the names and intrigues of local Egyptian vassals. Archives of texts discovered at Ugarit on the Syrian coast, while not from Palestine itself, introduce the gods of Canaan along with basic religious themes and cultic practices.

Ugarit managed to survive under the shadow of the Hittite and Egyptian empires without succumbing completely to the imperial agenda of either. As a port city, moreover, it was a meeting place between Mycenaean and Levantine civilization. The hundreds of literary documents discovered at Ugarit date for the most part around 1400 BCE and witness to the pluralistic character of the city. These documents include texts in various languages – Sumerian, Akkadian, Hurrian, Hittite, Egyptian, and Minoan – but most of them are in a local Canaanite dialect that scholars call Ugaritic. Ugaritic was written in cuneiform script, but the cuneiform characters were used alphabetically. Alphabetic writing was an important new development in human history, and soon a noncuneiform alphabetic script was developed for writing the Canaanite language.

As explained above, the end of the Middle Bronze Age and beginning of the Late Bronze Age is marked by a wave of city destructions that was especially devastating in southern Palestine.[26] Probably this is to be interpreted as Egyptian actions against cities that had been allied with the Hyksos and may have remained under Hyksos control after the fall of Avaris and Sharuhen. Most of the cities in northern Palestine were destroyed during the latter half of the sixteenth century also, but it is less clear that this occurred as a single wave or that it was the work of Egyptian armies. Possibly the northern cities were victims of the general disorder and violence that would have accompanied the breakdown of Middle Bronze Age political structures.

Some of the cities, especially in northern Palestine, seem to have been rebuilt relatively soon after they were destroyed; and ceramic traditions continued, although generally of poorer quality. But Palestine's urban society never fully recovered. Many cities remained abandoned, and those that continued occupation during the Late Bronze Age were much more modest than their Middle Bronze predecessors. It has been estimated that the number of settlements in western Palestine dropped by 30 to 40 percent, and that the total settled area was reduced by a third.[27] Most of the surviving Late Bronze Age cities were situated in the lowlands. There were exceptions, such as Shechem, Jerusalem, and Hebron, but these were scattered far apart leaving most of the hill country sparsely settled. Typically the Late Bronze Age cities remained unfortified or repaired and reused their Middle Bronze Age defensive systems. All of the above fits the pattern of Egyptian imperial rule. The Egyptians would hardly have encouraged and may not have permitted the cities to refortify. Instead, they supported petty vassal rulers who used the declining cities as a base to exploit the land in Egypt's behalf. Economic decline exacerbated by Egyptian taxation would have encouraged people to withdraw from the cities and beyond the reach of Egyptian administration.

While the Palestinian cities deteriorated during the Late Bronze Age, however, their material remains reflect an international character. The pottery is a good example. Along with local wares that continued Middle Bronze traditions, Late Bronze Age pottery includes a broad representation of Mycenaean and Cypriot styles. Naturally there is an abundance of Egypt-related items in Late Bronze Age contexts, and the Egyptian connection also explains the overall international character of Late Bronze Age Palestine. Egypt was concerned not only to exploit Palestine itself, but also to reap the benefits of international trade; and Palestine was part of Egypt's international trade network. Arts and crafts, such as ivory carving, were highly developed in the Levant during the Late Bronze Age, and some of this will have been produced locally in Palestine.

Hazor, for some reason, managed to stand apart from the pattern of urban decline described above. Middle Bronze Age Hazor met with a catastrophic destruction that left a thick layer of ash, but the city recovered quickly and continued to flourish during the Late Bronze Age at about the same size and presumably with about the same level of population. The Late Bronze Age city was well fortified with a defensive system that partially reused the massive Middle Bronze Age system. Two of Hazor's Late Bronze Age temples are particularly noteworthy. One of these was discovered on the inner slope of the rampart that protected the western side of the city (the rampart constructed during MB but serving still as part of the LB defensive system). Placed in a niche in the western wall of this temple were several small stelae and a small statue of a seated figure. Depicted on one of the stelae were two hands raised as if in worship before a crescent and full moon. The seated man had a moon crescent on his chest and was holding a cup in his right hand. The other temple, the so-called Orthostat Temple, was situated at the north end of the city and showed evidence of having gone through four building phases during the Late Bronze Age. It consisted of three parts in approximately south–north alignment: a porch, a main hall, and a broad room along the north side of the hall. The plan is similar to roughly contemporary temples at Alalakh and also calls to mind Solomon's temple as described in 1 Kings 6–8. Presumably this broad room was the inner shrine or 'holy of holies.'

There were no sudden changes in Palestine's material culture during the Late Bronze Age, so the archeological subphasing is a matter of coordinating gradual changes, mostly in the pottery, with Egyptian history. Egypt-related items discovered in Palestinian contexts play a crucial role in this endeavor, as does the presence of Mycenaean and Cypriot pottery. Archeologists agree on three main subphases, but sometimes differ slightly on the dates and do not always use the same terminology:

> LB I (ca.1550–1400 BCE) Some archeologists subdivide LB I further into
> > LB Ia (ca. 1550–1470 BCE – before Thutmose III's victory at Megiddo)
> > LB Ib (ca. 1470–1400 BCE – from Thutmose III to the Amarna age)
> LB IIa (ca. 1400–1300 BCE) The so-called Amarna age. Some archeological manuals may refer to it simply as LB II.
> LB IIb (ca. 1300–1200 BCE) The time of the early pharaohs of Dynasty XIX. Some archeologists refer to it as LB III. Also, for reasons to be explained below, there is some inclination to date the end of LB IIb (= LB III) ca. 1150 rather than 1200 BCE.

Regardless of one's views on the finer points of archeological terminology and dating, it is possible and useful for our purposes to distinguish four historical phases that correspond essentially to the archeological divisions outlined above.

The early years of Dynasty XVIII
(LB Ia, ca. 1550–1470 BCE)

Ahmose, recognized as the first pharaoh of Dynasty XVIII, expelled the Hyksos from Egypt and destroyed Sharuhen in southwestern Palestine. A wave of city destructions in southern Palestine about the same time probably is to be attributed to Egyptian armies intent on crushing Hyksos power once and for all. It is not clear whether or to what extent Ahmose and his immediate successors contributed to the demise of MB cities in northern Palestine. Probably Amenhotep I and certainly Thutmose I campaigned deep into Syria; Thutmose I (ca. 1493–1479) reached the Euphrates in fact and erected a stela there. Yet the early pharaohs of Dynasty XVIII did not establish any sort of permanent military presence in Syria–Palestine, and during the reigns of Thutmose II and Hatshepsut the Hurrian kingdom of Mitanni gained the upper hand in northern Syria. Also, possibly in alliance with Mitanni, the cities Tunip and Kadesh emerged as regional powers in central Syria.

From Thutmose III's victory at Megiddo to the Amarna age (LB Ib, ca. 1470–1400 BCE)

When Thutmose III (ca. 1458–1425) finally gained the throne at Hatshepsut's death, one of his first moves was to march against the king of Kadesh whose political influence now extended into northern Palestine. The latter chose to make a stand at Megiddo where he was joined by a host of rulers and princes from southern Syria and northern Palestine.[28] Thutmose managed to catch them off guard, however, defeated them in open battle, and when they retreated behind the walls of Megiddo laid siege to the city. When Megiddo fell to Thutmose some months later he became the undisputed master of the region. Unlike his predecessors who had conducted only sporadic campaigns, Thutmose set about to establish permanent military and political authority in Syria–Palestine. Rather than executing the defeated rulers for example (the king of Kadesh had managed to escape), he extracted oaths of loyalty from them, left garrisons of Egyptian soldiers at strategic places, and followed up with military campaigns throughout his reign. In these later campaigns Thutmose subdued Kadesh and Tunip, reached the Euphrates where he defied a Mitanni army (the king of Mitanni chose to withdraw rather than fight), and erected a stela near that of his grandfather Thutmose I. While Thutmose campaigned freely throughout Syria–Palestine, however, he managed to bring only Palestine and southern Syria under permanent Egyptian control. His successors maintained the grip on Palestine, and Amenhotep II (1426–1400) claimed spectacular victories in Syria. Eventually it was clear that Egypt would not be able to annex Syria to its empire, however, and Mitanni was beginning to recognize that the Hittites posed a more serious and immediate threat than the Egyptians. Thus Egypt and Mitanni concluded a treaty by which they recognized each other's zone of political influence. Palestine remained undisputed Egyptian territory.

The Amarna age (LB IIa/LB II, ca. 1400–1300 BCE)

When Amenhotep III ascended the throne shortly after 1400, Egypt's New Kingdom was in its heyday with a firm grip on Nubia, Palestine, and southern Syria, and reaping the benefits of these territories. Then his son and successor Amenhotep IV (ca. 1353–1336) instigated a religious reform that favored the sun god Aten over Amun of Thebes. In addition to changing his own name from Amenhotep to Akhenaten, this pharaoh built a new capital city in what is now the Amarna district of Egypt. The reform was unsuccessful in the end, and destabilized Egypt while the Hittites under Shuppiluliuma I (ca. 1380–1340) managed to expand deep into Syria and conquer Mitanni. The so-called Amarna Letters (discovered at the site of Akhenaten's capital) shed light on local circumstances in Palestine at this crucial time. These letters are correspondence from the rulers of various surrounding lands to Amenhotep III and Akhenaten. Although most of them were sent from largely Canaanite- or Amorite-speaking regions and addressed to the Egyptian court, they are written in Akkadian, the international language of the day. For Palestine they present a scene of petty Egyptian vassals residing in the declining cities, squabbling with each other, and unable to police disruptive elements in the countryside.

Examples are 'Abdu-Heba, Egypt's vassal king of Jerusalem, and Shuwardata the vassal king of a city south of Jerusalem (possibly Gath or Hebron). Two letters from Shuwardata accuse 'Abdu-Heba of disloyalty. Five letters from 'Abdu-Heba, whose name is of Hurrian origin, insist that it is not he but others who are disloyal to Egypt and urge the pharaoh to send him military support. We learn from the Amarna Letters that Shechem, under Lab'ayu and his sons, managed to achieve a degree of independence for a time and to exert some regional influence in central Palestine. Amurru, on Egypt's Syrian frontier and taking advantage of Hittite advance, also emerged as a semi-independent state. In their letters to the Egyptian court, the local rulers occasionally refer to those who flout Egyptian authority, or who are disruptive to the social order in one way or another, as *'Apiru*. *'Apiru* probably is related to the biblical term 'Hebrew,' but clearly was not intended as an ethnic designation. A proper translation would be 'rebel,' 'outcast,' 'bandit', or something of the sort.

Sety I, Ramesses II and Merneptah
(LB IIb/LB III, ca. 1300–1200 BCE)

The early pharaohs of Dynasty XIX, particularly Sety I (ca. 1290–1279) and Ramesses II (ca. 1279–1213), restored stability in Egypt and set about to reaffirm Egyptian authority in Syria–Palestine. By this time, however, the Hittites were deeply embedded as far south as Kadesh and Damascus. Kadesh was the scene of a crucial battle between Ramesses II and Muwattalli I about 1275 BCE. The Hittite army seems to have won the day. But it was not a decisive victory and the two powers, finding themselves at a stalemate, concluded a treaty a few years later that reaffirmed Hittite control in Syria and Egyptian control in Palestine. Merneptah (ca. 1213–1204) ascended the throne late in life, after Ramesses II's unusually long and prosperous reign, and his most important military achievement was a victory over Libyans who were threatening the western delta. Yet Merneptah also conducted at least one campaign into Palestine, and at the end of an inscription commemorating the Libyan victory claims:

> The princes are prostrate, saying, 'Mercy!'
>   Not one raises his head among the Nine Bows.
> Desolation is for Tehenu: Hatti is pacified;
>   Plundered is the Canaan with every evil;
> Carried off is Ashkelon; seized upon is Gezer;
>   Yanoam is made as that which does not exist;
> Israel is laid waste, his seed is not;
>   Hurru is become as a widow for Egypt!
> All lands together, they are pacified;
>   Everyone who was restless, he has been bound.[29]

This text has received a great deal of attention because it includes the earliest reference to Israel in surviving written sources from ancient times. The earliest references to Moab and Edom also appear about this time. Many scholars question whether the Israelite exodus from Egypt described in the Bible was a historical event.[30] Those who are confident that it was a historical event generally identify Ramesses II or Merneptah as the pharaoh of the exodus. Be that as it may, it is clear from the Palestinian archeological evidence as well as from Egyptian records that Palestine was more thoroughly controlled and influenced by Egypt during this last century of the Late Bronze Age than ever before.

THE END OF THE BRONZE AGE

Widespread disturbances and population upheavals underway approximately 1200 BCE mark the end of the Late Bronze Age. Mycenaean civilization collapsed, the Hittite empire came to an end, and Egypt entered another period of decentralization – the Third Intermediate Period. Ugarit, Alalakh, and other major cities throughout the ancient world were destroyed. Among the peoples on the move who may have contributed to the collapse of the Egyptian and Hittite empires, were the so-called Sea Peoples. Ramesses III (ca. 1187–1156 BCE) of Dynasty XX defended Egypt's frontiers against the Sea Peoples and mounted a last-ditch effort to reassert Egyptian authority in Palestine. His efforts are reflected in the archeological evidence – namely, there appears to have been a brief revival of Egyptian administration in Palestine that lasted through the reign of Ramesses VI (ca. 1145–1137). Realistically, therefore, it may be appropriate to date the end of the Late Bronze Age in Palestine a half century or so after 1200 BCE.[31]

Then Syria–Palestine, and indeed most of the Middle East, entered a 'dark age' that would last through the first three centuries or so of the Iron Age. These opening centuries of the Iron Age may be regarded as dark-age centuries both in the sense that it was a time of urban fragmentation and decline, and in the sense that we know so little about what was going on. Contemporary written records are scarce and archeological remains are meager. Late Bronze Age pottery traditions continued, however, and the social, political, and religious patterns that characterized the Bronze Age must have remained deeply embedded in Palestinian society. Israel's origins are to be sought in these dark-age centuries.

NOTES

1 The regional name 'Palestine' is of course anachronistic for prehistoric times and the Bronze Age. It derives from the Philistines who did not settle in the region until the early Iron Age.
2 See especially Bar-Yosef (1984: 3–16) and Ben-Tor (1984: 17–23).
3 Neolithic and Chalcolithic sometimes are referred to as periods rather than ages.
4 In this chapter I have followed the historical chronology from Sasson (1995) and the archeological chronology from Mazar (1990). As an example of how archeologists occasionally disagree on dates, Mazar places the beginning of the Bronze Age in Palestine ca. 3300 BCE, Dever (1992: 109–14) favors 3400 BCE, and Ben-Tor (1992: 95–6) favors 3200 BCE.
5 Selections from many of the written sources listed here and below are translated in anthologies edited by J. B. Pritchard (1955, 1968).
6 For detailed treatments of the archeology of Early Bronze Palestine, see Broshi and Gophna (1984), Richard (1987), Mazar (1990: 91–150), and Ben-Tor (1992).
7 I have used the ancient names for cities in this essay when they are known, and given the present-day names of the corresponding archeological sites in parentheses – e.g., Arad (Tell Arad). In many cases the ancient name is unknown – e.g., Tel Erani.

8 Broshi and Gophna (1984) provide a full listing of EB II–III sites with estimation of their sizes.
9 Broshi and Gophna (1984: 45).
10 Robert Adams, *Heartland of Cities* (Chicago: University of Chicago Press, 1981), cited by Weiss (1985b: 123).
11 Weiss (1985a); Dornemann (1992).
12 Milano (1995).
13 E.g., Mazar (1990: 158).
14 E.g., Richard (1987).
15 Sasson (1995: 913).
16 For detailed treatments of the archeology of Middle Bronze Age Palestine, see Dever (1987), Mazar (1990: 174–231) and Kempinski (1992).
17 For a detailed treatment of Egyptian sources pertaining to Palestine during the Bronze Age, see Redford (1992a).
18 Redford (1992b).
19 Durand (1992, 4: 529–36) and Margueron (1992, 4: 525–38).
20 Malamat (1983).
21 Mazar (1990: 194).
22 See especially Weinstein (1981).
23 Ben-Tor (1993).
24 William Dever (1997), who excavated Gezer, dates the beginning of this high place to MB IIa.
25 For detailed treatments of Egypt's relations with Palestine during the New Kingdom Period see Weinstein (1981) and Redford (1992a: 125–280).
26 For detailed treatments of the archeology of the Late Bronze Age see Weinstein (1981), Gonen (1984, 1992), Leonard (1989), and Mazar (1990: 232–94).
27 Gonen (1984: 63–9).
28 Redford (1992a: 156–8) emphasizes the king of Kadesh's role as leader of the coalition.
29 Pritchard (1955: 378).
30 E.g., Miller and Hayes (1986).
31 As does Gonen (1992: 216).

BIBLIOGRAPHY

Bar-Yosef, Ofer. 1984. 'Research on Stone Age Archaeology in Israel Since 1948.' In *Recent Archaeology in Israel*, ed. Benjamin Mazar (Hebrew edn) and Hershel Shanks (English edn). Jerusalem and Washington, D.C.: Israel Exploration Society and Biblical Archaeological Society, 3–16.

Ben-Tor, Amnon. 1984. 'At the Dawn of History – The Chalcolithic Period and the Early Bronze Age.' In *Recent Archaeology in Israel*, ed. Benjamin Mazar (Hebrew edn) and Hershel Shanks (English edn). Jerusalem and Washington, D.C.: Israel Exploration Society and Biblical Archaeological Society, 17–23.

—— 1992. 'The Early Bronze Age.' In *The Archaeology of Ancient Israel*, ed. A. Ben-Tor; trans. R. Greenberg. New Haven: Yale University Press, 81–125.

—— 1993. 'Hazor,' *New Encyclopedia of Archaeological Excavations in the Holy Land*, ed. E. Stern. Jerusalem: Israel Exploration Society, 2: 594–606 (includes a section by Y. Yadin, 'Excavation Results: First Four Seasons (1955–1958),' 593–606).

Ben-Tor, Amnon, ed. 1992. *The Archaeology of Ancient Israel*, trans. R. Greenberg. New Haven: Yale University Press.

Broshi, M. and Gophna, R. 1984. 'The Settlements and Population of Palestine during the Early Bronze Age II–III.' *Bulletin of the American Schools of Oriental Research* 253: 41–53.

Dever, W. G. 1987. 'The Middle Bronze Age: The Zenith of the Urban Canaanite Era.' *Biblical Archaeologist* 50: 148–77.

—— 1992. 'Archaeology of Palestine (Bronze Iron Ages).' In *The Anchor Bible Dictionary*, ed. D. N. Freedman. New York: Doubleday, 5: 109–14.

—— 1997. 'Gezer.' In *The Oxford Encyclopedia of Archaeology in the Near East*, ed. E. M. Meyers. Oxford: Oxford University Press, 2: 396–400.

Dornemann, Rudolph H. 1992. 'Bronze and Iron Age Syria.' In *The Anchor Bible Dictionary*, ed. D. N. Freedman. New York: Doubleday, 6: 275–81.

Durand, J.-M. 1992. 'Mari (Texts).' In *Anchor Bible Dictionary*, ed. D. N. Freedman. New York: Doubleday, 4: 529–36.

Gonen, Rivka. 1984. 'Urban Canaan in the Late Bronze Period.' *Bulletin of the American Schools of Oriental Research* 253: 49–59.

—— 1992. 'The Late Bronze Age.' In *The Archaeology of Ancient Israel*, ed. A. Ben-Tor; trans. R. Greenberg. New Haven: Yale University Press, 211–57.

Gophna, Ram. 1992. 'The Intermediate Bronze Age.' In *The Archaeology of Ancient Israel*, ed. A. Ben-Tor; trans. R. Greenberg. New Haven: Yale University Press, 126–58.

Kempinski, Aharon. 1992. 'The Middle Bronze Age.' In *The Archaeology of Ancient Israel*, ed. A. Ben-Tor; trans. R. Greenberg. New Haven: Yale University Press, 159–210.

Leonard, Albert, Jr. 1989. 'The Late Bronze Age.' *Biblical Archaeologist* 52: 4–39.

Malamat, A. 1983. *Das davidische und salomonische Königsreich und seine Beziehungen zu Ägypten und Syrien: Zur Entstehung eines Großreichs.* Vienna: Verlag der österreichischen Akademie der Wissenschaften.

Margueron, J.-C. 1992. 'Mari (Archaeology).' In *Anchor Bible Dictionary*, ed. D. N. Freedman. New York: Doubleday, 4: 525–9.

Mazar, Amihai. 1990. *Archaeology of the Land of the Bible: 10,000–586 bce* New York: Doubleday.

Milano, Lucio. 1995. 'Ebla: A Third-Millennium City-State in Ancient Syria.' In *Civilizations of the Ancient Near East*, ed. Jack Sasson. New York: Charles Scribner's Sons, 1219–30.

Miller, J. M. and Hayes, J. H. 1986. *A History of Ancient Israel and Judah*. Philadelphia: Westminster Press.

Pritchard, J. B., ed. 1955. *Ancient Near Eastern Texts Relating to the Old Testament*. Princeton: Princeton University Press.

—— 1968. *The Ancient Near East: Supplementary Texts and Pictures Relating to the Old Testament*. Princeton: Princeton University Press.

Redford, Donald B. 1979. 'A Gate Inscription from Karnak and Egyptian Involvement in Western Asia During the Early 18th Dynasty.' *Journal of the American Oriental Society* 99: 270–89.

—— 1992a. *Egypt, Canaan, and Israel in Ancient Times*. Princeton: Princeton University Press.

—— 1992b. 'Execration and Execration Texts.' In *The Anchor Bible Dictionary*, ed. D. N. Freeman. New York: Doubleday, 2: 681–2.

Richard, Susanne 1987. 'The Early Bronze Age: The Rise and Collapse of Urbanism.' *Biblical Archaeologist* 50: 22–43.

Sasson, Jack M. 1995. 'King Hammurabi of Babylon.' In *Civilizations of the Ancient Near East*, ed. Jack Sasson. New York: Charles Scribner's Sons, 901–15.

Sasson, Jack M., ed. 1995. *Civilizations of the Ancient Near East*. New York: Charles Scribner's Sons.

Yadin, Yigael and Ben-Tor, Amnon. 1993. 'Hazor.' In *The New Encyclopedia of Archaeological Excavations in the Holy Land*, ed. E. Stern. Jerusalem: Israel Exploration Society, 2: 594–606.

Weinstein, James M. 1981. 'The Egyptian Empire in Palestine: A Reassessment.' *Bulletin of the American Schools of Oriental Research* 241: 1–28.

Weiss, Harvey. 1985a. 'Protohistoric Syria and the Origins of Cities and Civilization.' In *Ebla to Damascus: Art and Archaeology of Ancient Syria*, ed. Harvey Weiss. Washington, D.C.: Smithsonian Institution Traveling Exhibition Service, 77–120.

——— 1985b. 'Third Millennium Settlement and Subsistence.' In *Ebla to Damascus: Art and Archaeology of Ancient Syria*, ed. Harvey Weiss. Washington, D.C.: Smithsonian Institution Traveling Exhibition Service, 123–33.

Weiss, Harvey, ed. 1985. *Ebla to Damascus: Art and Archaeology of Ancient Syria*. Washington, D.C.: Smithsonian Institution Traveling Exhibition Service.

CHAPTER TWENTY-TWO

PALESTINE DURING THE IRON AGE

———·◆·———

Keith W. Whitelam

INTRODUCTION

Palestine in the Iron Age forms part of a rich and intricate historical tapestry whose threads, woven deep in the past, continue into the present. Its geographical and climatic diversity has produced a mosaic of landscapes that have an important bearing upon its history. Yet, equally, it forms part of an ancient world from which it cannot easily be separated as though it were a self-contained, autonomous domain. The concentrated attention of countless biblical specialists, historians, and archaeologists has helped to elucidate many separate pieces of this rich mosaic. However, the inevitable consequence of such specialization, vital as it is to scholarship, is the intimation that Palestine in the Iron Age represents a discrete entity, both geographically and chronologically, that can be understood apart from the many currents that tie it to its wider world.[1] Its geographical boundaries are fluid, particularly the southern, arid zones where settlement is not only at the mercy of variable rainfall but is intricately linked to the political situation throughout the region as a whole. Equally, the numerous schemes that have been devised by historians and archaeologists to define its chronological limits tend to suggest to the unsuspecting reader that this is a discrete period in time estranged from the chronological links that precede and follow.

This has been reinforced by the peculiar interest of biblical specialists, including historians and archaeologists among its ranks, in this period of the region's history because of the long-held belief that it represents the 'biblical period' *par excellence*.[2] According to the biblical traditions, this was the period of Israel's conquest of the land after miraculous escape from captivity in Egypt, the period of the struggle for survival against the Philistines, encapsulated in the traditions about Samson and David, and the period of great kings with the founding of the Davidic dynasty, the building of the temple by Solomon, culminating in the devastation of Jerusalem by the Babylonians. As such, for biblical scholarship it has come to represent the period when Israel emerged fully into the light of history at the end of the Late Bronze Age, the period of its development into a major power in the region under David and Solomon, before the devastation of the northern and southern kingdoms by the Assyrians and Babylonians culminating in the destruction of Jerusalem and the

Davidic dynasty in 586/7 BCE (Noth 1960; Bright 1981; Soggin 1984; Miller and Hayes 1986).

Biblical scholars have long thought that many of the biblical traditions were crystallized and committed to writing during this period, particularly within the Davidic court, and that many of the historical traditions, particularly in the books of Samuel and Kings, provide a sound basis for a historical description of the period. Thus, scholarly investment over a century or more has been dominated by attempts to correlate archaeological discoveries with the events and personalities of the biblical traditions. The Iron Age in Palestine has been dominated by, in effect seen to be coterminous with, the history of ancient Israel. Thus for the Judaeo-Christian tradition it has come to be regarded as fundamental for Western history in particular and so for world history in general. According to Hallo (1992: 1–6), the opening of the period marks a 'watershed' in human history comparable to the agricultural and urban revolutions. Such an assessment reinforces the perception that this is a discrete, even unique, period of human history.[3] The traditional understanding of this period as dominated by the history of ancient Israel is now a matter of considerable debate following radically changed perceptions on how the biblical traditions developed and how they relate to history. At the same time, the increasing body of archaeological data has added considerably to our knowledge of Palestine in the Iron Age, providing a radically different picture of the history of the region from those based primarily on the biblical traditions.[4] How far it represents a 'watershed' or discrete, even unique, period in human history, rather than a continuation of important trends in the history of the region is now a matter of considerable contest.

The myriad of competing and confusing schemes devised by different archaeologists, which define the limits and internal relations of this period, only serve to illustrate how far scholarly convention and convenience hide assumptions that colour the way in which history is understood and represented. Such chronological schemes are determined by an understanding of political events, largely on assumptions drawn from the biblical traditions, rather than a primarily archaeological understanding of material culture. The very name for the period, the Iron Age, is misleading in that iron did not become the dominant metal in the region until the tenth century, nearly two centuries after the opening of the period (Mazar 1992: 298; Muhly 1992: 18).[5] Muhly (1992: 18) points out that there was no metal shortage either side of 1200 BCE so that 'whatever the underlying causes of this important historical and cultural transition . . . they do not seem to have anything to do with shortages of metal'. Equally, iron was not replaced as the dominant metal at the close of this period in 586/7 BCE. The delimitation of the period has been determined more by political events and an understanding of history based upon the biblical traditions than on archaeological considerations. The danger is that such precise archaeological phases tend to suggest discrete periods, representing identifiable breaks, by emphasizing discontinuities and overlooking or playing down equally important continuities.[6] This has been encouraged further by the search for ancient Israel and its physical manifestations. For much of biblical scholarship until very recently, the beginning of the Iron Age was defined by the destruction and decline of urban centres in Palestine in association with the emergence of Israel, while its closure was marked by the destruction of Jerusalem and its temple by the Babylonians. The seemingly objective material determinants of the chronological limits of this period were determined by a prior understanding of political events – the appearance of Israel in Palestine and the downfall of the Davidic monarchy in 586/7 BCE. Such a history of events, *l'histoire événementielle* as Paul Lacombe and François Simiand termed it, was largely dependent upon a reading of the biblical traditions. It is variously referred to as comprising 'the period of the Judges', 'the settlement period', 'the monarchic period', or even 'the Israelite period' (Aharoni 1982; Mazar 1992: 258).[7] Thus the history of ancient Israel has dominated the history of the region as traditionally presented for much of this century. The extent of our knowledge of Israel's origins or emergence within Palestine is one of the most controversial and contentious issues within biblical studies, generating considerable passion and rancour. Similarly, the question of the origins, extent, and nature of an Israelite monarchy founded by David, the search for a historical David, has become a site for scholarly debate, denunciation, and personal accusations.

The conventional portrait of this period is of the emergence and rise to dominance in the region of ancient Israel following an initial catastrophic collapse throughout the eastern Mediterranean. It closes with a similar catastrophic defeat of the southern kingdom of Judah in 586/7 BCE including the destruction of the temple in Jerusalem and the end of the Davidic dynasty. Viewed in this way, Palestine in the Iron Age appears to be a period of dramatic flux moving from the trough of depression to the crest of political and economic resurgence in the Iron II, as a result of a new and distinct ethnic entity in the region, only to be plunged again into political and economic crisis at the end of the period. Our texts, including the biblical traditions, encourage this sense of the dramatic by concentrating on the dominant personalities and the most dramatic events of the period. These events that shine so brightly, thereby catching and holding the attention of historians, are surface events, 'surface disturbances, crests of foam that the tides of history carry on their strong backs. A history of brief, rapid, nervous fluctuations, by definition ultra-sensitive; the least tremor sets all its antennae quivering' (Braudel 1972: 21).[8] Yet within this range of movement over centuries there is 'immense inertia' where routine predominates: a routine that helps to define the boundaries between 'possibility and impossibility' (Braudel 1974: xi). To set the beginnings of the Iron Age at 1200 BCE provides a starting point that explains little and raises a series of very important questions, which have underpinned the debates on Israelite history during the second half of this century. These chronological boundary markers should be treated for what they are, scholarly conveniences in order to concentrate attention upon a particular period in the history of the region. It is essential to look carefully at the processes and trends that precede and follow, and which provide the threads that bind the historical tapestry of Palestine through the centuries (Coote and Whitelam 1987; Finkelstein 1995, 1998; Levy and Holl 1995).

While our texts direct our gaze to the dominant personalities, archaeologists have increasingly made us evermore aware of the lives and struggles of the vast majority of the population, hidden and anonymous, against the environment; their responses to famine, piracy, brigandage, exploitation, and shifting political alliances. It is archaeology above all that has opened this world to us, what Schama (Vulliamy 1999: 3) has called, in a different context, 'the hinges between private and public life'. A world that has been neglected by our earlier standard biblical histories, which, by concentrating on religious and political developments in the search for ancient Israel, remain unaware of the lives of at least 90 per cent of the population of ancient Palestine. Broad movements when viewed over centuries help to explain the surface movements that are the concern of chroniclers and many contemporary historians. It was these fluctuations, the peaks and troughs of demographic growth, that, as of all ancient societies, characterized Palestine in the Iron Age. It was not always a continuous rise but the settlement shifts and demographic changes helped to transform and revitalize Iron Age Palestine. Within the six centuries traditionally assigned to this period there is also an almost unobservable inertia of the repeated and regular, which characterizes all periods prior to the present and demands greater attention if we are to understand the Iron Age in Palestine.

THE TRANSFORMATION AND REINVIGORATION OF IRON AGE PALESTINE

For most of its history Palestine lacked the infrastructure and weight of numbers to compete with the neighbouring riverine civilizations of Egypt and Mesopotamia. However, its position on the land routes and sea lanes of the eastern Mediterranean world economy often allowed it to exploit its favoured position. This had its drawbacks, of course, since it was constantly at the attention of world powers who needed to control these lucrative trade and military routes, either by proxy or directly. The Late Bronze Age is indicative of both the benefits and drawbacks of this situation, with evidence of material prosperity, international trade and exchange, and cosmopolitan culture, but also of direct imperial control in the form of Egyptian garrisons.[9] Any disruption within the Mediterranean economic system reverberated throughout the region, affecting the fortunes of Palestine and its people. The Late Bronze Age was marked by extensive international trade, although it must be emphasized that the agrarian economy remained dominant: this economy was the locus of the revival of Palestine's fortunes in the early Iron Age following the disruptions of the end of the Late Bronze Age. Palestinian produce, including grain, wine, oil, linen, dyed textiles, and timber, was widely distributed throughout the Mediterranean system from Egypt through the Aegean as far as Italy (Liverani 1987: 68; Cline 1994: 50).[10] Such open trade routes around the Mediterranean during the Late Bronze Age directly benefited Palestine, given its strategic position within the trade nexus.[11]

The disruption and dislocation of this international system at the end of the Late Bronze Age reverberated throughout the eastern Mediterranean with significant consequences for Palestine and its inhabitants. This dislocation has frequently been represented as a sudden cataclysmic collapse throughout the eastern Mediterranean ushering in 'a dark age' that represents a significant break with what had gone before. Such views encouraged searches for monocausal explanations for the collapse, ranging from dramatic changes in the climate or volcanic eruptions to foreign invasions by new ethnic groups.[12] However, re-evaluations of the complex data now available have led to a significant shift in understandings of the events of the Late Bronze to Iron Age transition throughout the region.[13] Earlier portraits of dramatic collapse stressed the widespread destruction of urban centres throughout the Mediterranean world: ranging from the destruction of the coastal cities of Cyprus (Karageorghis 1990, 1992; Stager 1995: 337), the collapse of the Hittite empire in Anatolia (Singer 1987), to the destruction or abandonment of urban centres along the Syria–Palestine littoral.[14] The effects within Palestine appeared all too evident with the destruction of many of its major towns: Hazor, Aphek, Beth Shemesh, Gezer, Tell Beit Mirsim, Tell Abu Hawam, and Lachish, among others (Mazar 1992: 260).[15] Pottery imports from Cyprus and Greece disappeared, suggesting a disruption and dislocation of international trade leading to catastrophic collapse throughout the region. In addition, considerable population displacements, like today's, accompanied such widespread destruction. The movement of groups of 'Sea Peoples', still one of the most intriguing and disputed questions in the history of the region, illustrated movements throughout the whole of the Mediterranean basin from its western extremities to the coast of Palestine and Egypt (Na'aman 1994: 239).[16] Hallo (1992: 2) cites such population displacements as one of the major characteristics of the period. The documentary evidence points to population movements into Palestine by various groups, including the Sea Peoples and Syro-Anatolian groups (Na'aman 1994: 239). The collapse was invariably explained in ethnic terms. For Palestine it was seen to be the result of the invasion of the Sea Peoples along the Palestinian littoral in combination with the invasion or infiltration of Israelite tribes from Transjordan. Such historical reconstructions were determined by a reading of the biblical traditions with extra-biblical evidence, from excavations or textual materials, being used to illustrate the biblically based accounts.

However, it has become increasingly clear that the destruction of towns throughout the eastern Mediterranean, including within Palestine, was not synchronous but took place over a century or more. The complexity of the situation in Cyprus, where not all towns suffered the same fate or at the same time, is illustrative of the wider situation (Karageorghis 1992: 80). Dever (1992: 101) notes that a number of Palestinian sites suffered only minor disruptions, with a continuing Egyptian presence down to the time of Rameses VI (c. 1143–1136 BCE). The dating of the destruction layers of these Late Bronze Age centres is controversial and constantly being revised (Fritz 1987: 86–9). Mazar (1992: 285) warns that the precise dating of such destruction levels is based on 'relatively flimsy evidence'. Thus the idea that this was a rapid and dramatic collapse marking a distinct cultural change has tended to obscure the protracted nature of the disruption and dislocation throughout the region. Hazor was destroyed in the middle of the thirteenth century BCE, whereas Lachish survived until the second half of the twelfth century BCE (Na'aman 1994: 223; Fritz 1995: 43). This evidence, along with recent data from surface surveys and excavations illustrating that new rural villages in the highlands and steppes were largely indigenous, rapidly undermined the biblically derived assumption that many of the Palestinian towns were destroyed by invading Israelites (see Lemche 1985; Ahlström 1986; Coote and Whitelam 1987; Finkelstein 1988; Thompson 1992).

The fact that the decline and disruption was spread over a century or more, and that it was uneven throughout the region, suggests that it was the result of a complex set of circumstances. It illustrates the rhythms and patterns of Palestinian history, rather than representing some defining moment.[17] Any protracted process of disruption and dislocation invariably encompasses a combination of factors, where it is difficult to distinguish between cause and effect. However, it is now evident that the system as a whole did not collapse to be replaced by something new, but was able to adapt and generate recovery from within itself. Although the end of the Late Bronze Age has often been thought of as a 'dark age', with much of its history hidden from the historian's view, the increasing body of data suggests that the foundations for revival, demographic expansion, and economic growth emerged from the countryside. It was here that the seeds of the revival and transformation, which gathered pace throughout the Iron Age, were to be found. Thus it can be said that the beginnings of the Iron Age in Palestine were founded on the Late Bronze Age rather than representing a major cultural and ethnic break.

Despite the focus on the disruption and destruction of towns and interregional trade, the regeneration and transformation of Iron Age Palestine was dependent upon the countryside. This was a rural world, populated by peasants and pastoralists, in which agricultural production was critical. The size of population, and so the growth and development of towns, were dependent upon agricultural produce and food supplies. Demography and economics present us with the most obvious and easily appreciated signs of these deep-seated movements: the surface events force attention upon political events, the roles of individuals, the destruction or abandonment of towns, but it is the rural population and its produce that silently guide and underpin the history of the region. Thus it is becoming clear that the opening of the Iron Age was not a response to a sudden and dramatic collapse, as it has usually been understood, but was a protracted process of dislocation in which there are signs of health and revival, which led to a transformation that gathered momentum throughout the period. The low-water mark at its opening was followed by a dramatic shift in settlement and a striking rise in population, resulting eventually in a series of small statelike structures throughout the region that survived until the re-establishment of imperial power in the shape of the Assyrians and Babylonians.

REVIVAL IN THE COUNTRYSIDE: THE WEIGHT OF NUMBERS

The weight of numbers in any agrarian economy is vital: demography, it might be said, is the engine of ancient history. Although famine and drought were constant threats throughout the history of Palestine, naturally limiting the size of population – particularly when the carrying capacity of the land had been reached, 'the limits of the possible' as Braudel termed it – this was not the case at the end of the Late Bronze Age. The disruptions and dislocations that engulfed the eastern Mediterranean at the end of the Late Bronze Age had profound, often catastrophic, effects on the indigenous population of Palestine. Yet, as Braudel (1974: 3) notes, 'every recession solves a certain number of problems, removes pressures and benefits the survivors'. The transformation of Palestinian society in the Iron Age, which gathered momentum throughout the period, eventually leading to the revival of the towns with increasing fortification at some sites, began in the countryside as a response to the recession. The revival of the towns in the Iron II period is often attributed to the reawakening of long-distance trade throughout the eastern Mediterranean.

However, the roots of the transformation are to be found in the realignment and demographic changes within Palestinian society, which followed the disruptions at the beginning of the period. The transformation of Iron Age Palestine was based on gradual population growth: as villages and towns increased and expanded, so the exchange of goods increased. But this was not a massive tidal wave of population sweeping across the Palestinian landscape from outside, as earlier explanations based on the biblical traditions always assumed.[18] How far it was the result of internal population displacement, external movements, or internal demographic growth is a matter for considerable debate, which is difficult to resolve due to the paucity and ambiguity of some data.[19] However, it is a process that needs to be viewed over two to three centuries in order to reveal the significant realignment and transformation of Palestinian society that had been underway since the beginning of the Iron Age.

The reordering of the countryside has been spectacularly revealed by a series of regional surveys conducted by Israeli archaeologists in recent years. These surveys have revolutionized the study of the history of Palestine in the Iron Age and have undermined previous biblically based reconstructions.[20] Change did not happen overnight, nor did the movement occur at the same pace everywhere as Weippert (1988: 26–7) and Dothan (1989: 1–14; 1992: 93–8) have emphasized. Regional variations ensured different rates of development across Palestine, and were characterized by a complex process in which indigenous, Philistine, and Egyptian cultures overlapped and interacted (Mazar 1992: 260).[21] Thus, this transformation needs to be viewed in regional perspective, as Finkelstein and Na'aman (1994: 13) have noted, since the particular ecological, economic, and demographic background of different regions, including the mountains of the Galilee, the fertile intermontane valleys of the northern hill country, the semi-arid Beersheba valley, or the arid Judaean desert, profoundly affected the rate and nature of development.

The response to the disruption and dislocations of the Late Bronze Age was a sweeping shift in settlement location into the highlands and steppes with the growth of hundreds of small rural villages in those regions that had been sparsely populated in the Late Bronze Age and were removed from the direct control of the major towns. The countryside became dotted with hundreds of small unwalled villages, most newly established in the twelfth century, arranged in a variety of patterns, with many located on hilltops near arable lands.[22] The appearance and use of pillared buildings, silos, cisterns, terracing, and utilitarian pottery forms, such as the distinctive collared-rim ware, are explicable in terms of the topographical and environmental conditions facing the inhabitants of highland and marginal settlements in the context of the disruption of local and regional economies (Whitelam 1994; Finkelstein 1995; see also Dever 1991: 83–4). Importantly, such material features also indicate that the distinctive demographic and settlement response to the disruptions at the end of the Late Bronze Age were largely indigenous rather than primarily the result of ethnic changes in the region. The attempt has long been to explain the settlement shift and revival in ethnic terms, attributing the resurgence to Israelites. Although the Merneptah stele indicates that some entity called Israel was in the region during the Late Bronze to Iron Age transition, its precise nature, location, and contribution to the settlement shift is impossible to gauge on the basis of available evidence (Whitelam 1994; Finkelstein 1998: 15).[23] Recent scholarship has recognized that the archaeological data confirm that the settlement shift was a largely indigenous response to the strains at the end of the Late Bronze Age rather than the result of some new ethnic entity coming from outside Palestine's boundaries. As Finkelstein (1995: 359) notes, 'what has been said above clearly indicates that the material culture of the Iron Age I sites in the highlands should not be viewed in terms of ethnic perspectives (contra Dever 1993). It rather reflects the ecological background, the subsistence economy and the social frameworks of these highland communities . . .'.

Such a view is further confirmed by the fact that many different regions from southern Europe, through Greece, Anatolia, and Syria–Palestine witnessed similar settlement shifts as a response to the disruption of the Mediterranean basin. Central and south-eastern Europe in the twelfth century witnessed a proliferation of small rural settlements, comprising a few buildings with silos for grain storage, situated on good agricultural land and devoted to farming and herding (Wells 1992: 33). The shift in settlement away from the exposed lowlands to the protection of the highlands is similarly reported from Greece to Syria (Desborough 1972: 19–20, 82, 88; Caubert 1992; McClellan 1992: 164; Sader 1992: 161; Yon 1992: 111–20). The revival of early Iron Age Palestine in the countryside appears to have been part of a wider regional response by rural pastoral groups to the decline or disruption of towns and their associated regional and interregional economies. As such, it reveals the rhythms and patterns of Palestinian history throughout centuries borne on the backs of the peasantry and their produce rather than representing the emergence of a new ethnic group and a radical break with the past (see Coote and Whitelam 1987; Finkelstein 1995; Levy and Holl 1995).

The survey data have revealed that the reordering of the countryside began in those areas easiest to colonize, which provided good agricultural land and conditions most suited to herding and grain growing.[24] The greatest density of settlement was to be found in the northern hill country with its fertile intermontane valleys decreasing significantly as it approached the steeper, more rugged western flanks of the southern hills. Similarly, the eastern desert fringes provided much greater settlement potential compared with the less hospitable western slopes. Significantly, the less hospitable southern hill country and the western slopes that required considerable investment in the opening of new land, and was most suited to long-term cultivation of olives and vines, did not experience similar density of settlement until the Iron II period. The increasing pressure of numbers required new land and the opportunities offered by the development of more specialized agricultural strategies such as fruit and olive production. These ecological frontier zones have always been highly sensitive, often being the first to suffer in times of settlement crisis and the last to be repopulated when the economy revives (Finkelstein 1995: 353–4). The fact that such a response is not the result of new ethnic groups in the area, particularly understood in the past as the result of Israelites coming from outside, is revealed in that similar patterns of settlement as a response to the dislocations of the Late Bronze Age, exhibiting a remarkably similar material culture, are also found in Transjordan, with settlement focused in the north and decreasing towards the ecologically more sensitive south.[25]

The pattern of settlement, however, does not reveal the direction from which the inhabitants of these villages came, but indicates that it was a response to the limits of the possible as part of the realignment of Iron Age Palestine (see Ofer 1994: 107–9). Furthermore, such settlement shifts are not unique in the history of Palestine, but reveal the patterns and rhythms of its history over many centuries (Coote and Whitelam 1987). Many of the Iron I villages in the hill country, such as Tell en-Nasbeh, Khirbet Rabud, and Khirbet Raddanah, had been occupied in the Early Bronze Age, with 116 of the 254 Iron I sites of the central hill country having been occupied in the Middle Bronze period, but abandoned in the Late Bronze Age: 'It is, therefore, more reasonable to explain these settlement fluctuations in terms of socio-economic change, that is shifts towards a more sedentary or a more pastoral society, in accordance with political, economic and social transformations' (Finkelstein 1995: 355; see also Whitelam 1994). The direction of settlement emerging from the analyses of recent survey and excavation data appears to have been dictated much more by the possibilities offered by the most opportune agricultural land in the north and eastern desert fringes and the location of springs and gullies rather than the movement of groups across the boundaries of Palestine.[26] The spread of settlement to the south and west followed later as the weight of numbers created a more pressing need for access to ecologically sensitive areas.

The important point is that the realignment and reinvigoration of Iron Age Palestine began in the countryside. Although the response was not uniform throughout the country, the pattern revealed by regional surveys is reasonably clear. The reordering of the countryside began in those regions most suited to agriculture and grazing and gradually expanded towards the ecological frontiers. The reshaping of Palestine emerged from this process of internal colonization, the need for crop cultivation and animal grazing, in which formerly abandoned villages and their territories were reclaimed, while the old boundaries were pushed back to open up more ecologically sensitive regions and those that required long-term investment in the production of olives and vines. Although the surveys have revealed considerable regional variation, it was from within the delicate balance and continuum between peasants and pastoral groups that the revival began, leading over centuries to the transformation and realignment of Iron Age Palestine.[27] This continuum between town, countryside, and pastoralism, a constant in the history of Palestine through the ages – part of the inertia of the past – hides the dynamic shifting political, economic, and social relationships that carry along the history of the region. The increasing archaeological data have revealed a past, significantly different from that presented by the biblical traditions and reconstructions that rely on them, of a system adapting and gradually responding over centuries to the threats and disruption that reverberated through the Mediterranean basin at the end of the Late Bronze Age. The drastic reduction of the world of the towns in the Late Bronze Age must have exerted enormous economic pressure on agricultural and pastoral groups, which led to the reordering of the countryside. Yet it was from this world, the world of peasants and pastoralists, that towns would be revived and repopulated later in the period.

The fortunes of towns at the end of the Late Bronze Age, the destruction or abandonment of many towns mainly in the lowlands and coastal plain, alongside the disappearance of Mycenaean and Cypriot pottery, was seen as evidence that trade, the very lifeblood of the towns as Braudel termed it, had ceased. Yet, beside the evidence of severe dislocation of the eastern Mediterranean system, there are still some signs of vitality in the economy and life of the towns during the Late Bronze to Iron Age transition and beyond. It is clear that the extensive trade networks of the Late Bronze Age were disrupted: as Mazar (1992: 300) notes, finds from Iron I sites reflect isolation and interruption of international relations. But all signs of life and vitality were not erased. Muhly (1992: 19) argues that Mediterranean trade, especially the economy of Cyprus, expanded around 1250–1150 BCE: 'Not a world dominated by sea raiders, pirates, and freebooting mercenaries, living off booty and plunder, but a world of enterprising merchants and traders, exploiting new economic opportunities, new markets, and new sources of raw materials. A world taking the first tentative steps that were to lead, in the centuries ahead, to the great Greek and Phoenician expansion of the Orientalizing period.'[28] Sader (1992: 161) too claims that internal trade is also evident with the discovery of Phoenician bichrome ware at Megiddo, Tel Qasile, Philistia, and Tel Masos in the northern Negev, as well as lower Egypt, suggesting continuing contacts, particularly along the Phoenician coast (Mazar 1992: 300). The distribution of Philistine ware at Beersheba and Tel Masos in northern Negev, Megiddo and Tell Qiri in the Jezreel Valley, and as far north as Tel Dan, as well as 'Midianite' ware and Cypriot pottery at Megiddo and Tel Qasile, indicate that not all internal trade links had been severed.

The disruption occupies a century or more and is reflected in the varying fortunes of different towns over an extended period testifying to the rhythms of Palestine history. The rebuilding of a number of the towns destroyed towards the end of the Late Bronze Age, albeit in reduced circumstances, suggests that not all vitality had been extinguished. While the destruction and impoverishment of a major town such as Hazor, or the abandonment of Taanach and Lachish, illustrates the problems, the survival or recovery of Megiddo and Bethshan in the lowlands and coastal plain, or Tel Sera and Tell el-Farah South in the northern Negev, suggests important signs of vitality within the system (Mazar 1992: 261). Similarly, Weinstein (1992: 142; see also Bunimowitz 1994: 201–2) reports that archaeology has revealed an extensive Egyptian presence in southern Palestine and the Jezreel Valley, suggesting continued economic vigour. Similar signs of vitality are indicated by the founding of sites on the southern coastal plain, traditionally associated with Philistine settlement and control. The development of Tel Qasile, or the recovery and growth of such sites as Tel Miqne, Ashdod, Ashkelon, Gaza, and Dor, suggests a continuation or at least revival of shipping and trade, albeit drastically reduced from its height during the Late Bronze Age.

Thus, although the revival of Palestine began in the countryside, this should not be taken to suggest that the towns of the region and their economies had collapsed completely and were moribund. The archaeological surveys and excavations have revealed a complex picture showing wide regional variation to the stresses and strains placed upon Palestine at the end of the Late Bronze Age and the beginning of the Iron Age. These signs of vitality were to grow stronger as the period progressed.

THE REORDERING OF THE COUNTRYSIDE: THE GROWTH OF TOWNS IN IRON II

Only with the increasing weight of numbers throughout the early Iron Age were the limits of the possible approached. It was the increasing population in Iron I, rather than technological innovations, as thought by earlier scholars, that allowed the colonization of the highlands and steppes.[29] As noted above, settlement in Iron I took place in the areas easiest to master for subsistence, and only as numbers increased were the less hospitable zones tackled. The space had always been there but the weight of numbers called for its utilization (cf. Braudel 1974: 18). The end of Iron I, with its expansion of agricultural settlements throughout the highlands and steppes of Palestine, and the beginning of Iron II saw a growth in towns, many with fortifications, testifying to the result of the weight of numbers. The reordering of the countryside led to the revival and growth of towns throughout the region, which once again began to reclaim the hinterland and its produce. Thus it is commonplace to characterize the Iron II as an 'urban period' (Barkay 1992: 304; Mazar 1990: 371–5; Finkelstein 1994: 149). The phrase is misleading if it suggests a comparison with modern urban phenomena since the majority of the towns in Palestine were relatively small, catering for only a few hundred to a few thousand inhabitants, and dependent largely upon agricultural produce from the immediate vicinity (see Hopkins 1997: 301–4; Lemche 1997: 329–30).

The increasing population placed pressure on existing space and resources and with the revival of the towns pushed Palestine towards critical thresholds. The balance of power between town and countryside changed throughout the period, resulting eventually in the dramatic increase in the size of a number of sites such as Samaria, Jerusalem, Ekron, and Ashdod. Such demographic pressures inevitably increase and exaggerate social stratification and this, alongside the increasing dominance of such highland settlements as Samaria and Jerusalem, resulted in the development of a series of small statelike structures throughout the region. Traditionally, this has been seen as the period of the Judaean and Israelite monarchies following the development of a major state under David and Solomon centred on Jerusalem in the tenth century BCE. How early such state structures formed, their nature, and extent is now one of the most contested areas between biblical specialists, archaeologists, and historians.

The survey data once again reveal important regional patterns in the rhythms of Palestinian history in the Iron II period. Finkelstein (1998: 32; 1995: 355) notes that a dramatic expansion in settlement took place in Iron II in the central hill country with a doubling of sites from 254 in Iron I to 520, accompanied by a tripling of occupied area.[30] Just as the less hospitable Judaean hills south of Jerusalem provided an important barometer of settlement in the early Iron Age, so its transformation in the Iron II period illustrates the effects of the increasing weight of numbers. Jerusalem, supposedly the capital of an Israelite state in the early tenth century under David according to biblically based reconstructions, was little more than a small isolated town in the tenth century BCE, reflecting the lack of population in the immediate vicinity. However, by the end of the Iron II period it had grown significantly, covering around 150 acres. Judah became dotted with dozens of rural towns and villages, in close proximity. During the last two centuries of the Iron II period Judah, the Judaean desert, and the northern Negev had gone some way to reaching their carrying capacity. Though some Iron I sites were abandoned in the eleventh century – Izbet Sartah, Giloh, Khirbet Raddana, and Ai – the majority of the Iron I sites in the hill country continued to be occupied throughout the Iron Age. Ofer (1994: 106) reports that the hill country of Judah in the Iron II saw an increase in settlement into all parts of the Judaean hills: settlement increased from 86 small or very small sites in the ninth century BCE to 122 sites, with a built-up area of 92.6 hectares, in the eighth century. In the eighth to seventh centuries BCE settlement in Judah reached its peak with settlement in the arid zones and the number of towns in the Judaean hills and Shephelah at an unprecedented level, surpassed only in the Byzantine period when the region enjoyed its greatest density of settlement prior to the modern period.[31] Similarly, sites in the northern Negev – Tel Ira, Aroer, Tel Masos, Tel Mulhata, and Beersheba – prospered, particularly in the seventh century BCE (Herzog 1994: 143–4; Holladay 1995: 386), while the Palestinian littoral and lowlands continued to experience an expansion of settlement and the revival of its towns with the rebuilding of Tel Qasile, Dor, Ashdod, Ashkelon, and Gaza in the coastal plain, Betshan and Megiddo in the Jezreel Valley, and Gezer and Lachish in the Shephelah (Mazar 1990: 389).

The Iron II expansion is traditionally attributed to the development of an Israelite monarchy by David and Solomon, particularly at the end of Iron I, followed by the competing states of Judah and Israel centred on Jerusalem and Samaria respectively. Barkay is typical in describing the tenth century as 'the period of the United Monarchy' (1992: 305) or 'a high point in Israelite history, a period of economic and cultural prosperity, of peace, fondly remembered in later times' (1992: 305).[32] Similarly, Fritz (1994: 149) equates the destruction or abandonment of various sites at the end of Iron I with increasing centralization under David.[33] Such standard presentations of a golden age of the 'United Monarchy' under David and Solomon rest upon the correlation and interpretation of archaeological results with the biblical traditions. The discovery of monumental architecture, fortified gate complexes, and casemate walls at Hazor, Megiddo, and Gezer was dated to the Solomonic period on the basis of the description in 1 Kings 9:15 of Solomon's building programme. The debate on the dating of remains from the tenth century BCE, including such structures, is now one of the most critical problems facing archaeologists, and thereby historians, and has profound inplications for understanding the history of Iron Age Palestine.

The idea of a major state, let alone an empire, centred on Jerusalem in the tenth century BCE, and the biblically based reconstruction of the reigns of David and Solomon, have been increasingly disputed in recent years as each element of a once seemingly interlocking network of ideas has been re-examined.[34] What began as a critique from within biblical studies, marginalized at first as a radical movement, has now been strengthened by serious questions raised by archaeological specialists (see Jamieson-Duke 1991; Davies 1992; Gelinas 1995; Finkelstein 1996, 1998; Prag 1998: 158). The view that the gate-complexes were built to 'a single blueprint', thereby suggesting the existence of centralized state planning, has been undermined by questions of their dating and differences in the size, construction, and type of wall to which they are bonded (Barkay 1992: 307; Hopkins 1997: 303). Thus Hopkins (1997: 303) concludes that 'there is precious little indication of regional integration in the archaeological record' for the Solomonic period.[35] While the dating and interpretation of the so-called 'Solomonic' gates at Megiddo, Hazor, and Gezer has become the area of most spectacular disagreement, the interpretation of Pharaoh Shishaq's campaign into Palestine, central to the tenth-century dating of destruction layers at particular sites, has also been challenged (Davies 1992: 42–73; Thompson 1992: 306–7; Gelinas 1995: 230–3). Barkay, for example, argues that it has not been proven that any sites were destroyed by Shishaq in 925 BCE and that 'the attribution of destruction levels to the end of the tenth century at many sites is mere conjecture' (1992: 307).[36] Furthermore, sites in the Negev previously thought to represent part of a network of royal fortifications are now the subject of re-evaluation (Barkay 1992: 323–5).[37]

The existence of a significant state in the early Iron Age, which has long been at the very heart of biblically based reconstructions of Iron Age Palestine, is now in serious question. There is a growing recognition that Jerusalem in the tenth century, far from being the capital of an extensive united monarchy, or even an 'empire' on some accounts, was little more than a small highland town.[38] Not until the later Iron II did its fortunes change significantly. The growing consensus is that state structures developed first in northern Israel around Samaria in the ninth century and only later in southern Judah around Jerusalem in the eighth century, as reflected in the revival of towns and the increasing growth of first Samaria and then Jerusalem as the Iron II period progresses (Jamieson-Drake 1991; Thompson 1992; Finkelstein 1998). Yet, even arguments for the existence of Judahite and Israelite states in these later periods must be tempered by questions about the nature and degree of centralization they achieved. As Hopkins (1997: 304) notes, these 'replicated the city-states of the Bronze Age to a far greater extent than they anticipated the nations of the European Industrial Age. The nationalist ideology of the biblical literature projects a unity that simply did not exist economically or sociologically.'[39] He makes the important point that ancient Israel and Judah were not a society 'so much as a constellation of "plural societies"' and that its nature and structure was inherited from the Bronze Age urban centres ('city-states') with a small elite 'sustained by an agricultural and pastoral hinterland' (Hopkins 1997: 304). In this sense, the position of Samaria and Jerusalem in the ninth and eighth centuries as they took advantage of the reordering and revitalization of the countryside ought to be compared more closely with the so-called 'city-states' of the Middle Bronze II period rather than seen as some revolutionary development in the history of the region.[40]

The degree of centralization and the extent of the development of statelike structures is a question that is only now beginning to be addressed in the light of the collapse of the previous paradigm, which assumed the existence, and so continuity with, a major centralized state in the region from the tenth century BCE onwards. The reappraisal of biblically based reconstructions, which has raised serious questions about the Late Bronze to Iron Age transition and the nature of the tenth century BCE, or the full implications of the redating Finkelstein has proposed, has not fully impacted upon the study of the Iron II period. The focus of attention of our standard histories of the region, 'the period of the divided monarchy', as it is traditionally termed in biblically based histories, is fixed upon the events and characters – Omri, Ahab, Josiah, and so on – named in the biblical traditions, as well as in Assyrian and Babylonian inscriptions. But it is the rhythms of Palestinian history, the revival of the countryside, and its produce and labour, on which the exploits of such named individuals are borne. The emergence of highland powers in Samaria, and later Jerusalem, form part of the general process of the reordering of the countryside and the pressures and changes that invariably take place as carrying capacity is approached.

The fortunes of these and other towns, of course, varied with inevitable periods of expansion or contraction. Towns began to thrive due to surplus production from the countryside, whether as the centre of regional markets or through redistribution and taxation. The Samaria and Arad ostraca, and the famous royal-jar handle stamps, testify to the redistribution of flour, oil, and wine during the Iron II and hence the vitality of the economy. The pressure of the weight of numbers to open and clear new land, the investment in terracing, and the growing markets of the towns and reviving economy witnessed an increasing commitment to large-scale horticulture, which is revealed in the development of the olive oil industry in Iron II Palestine. The growth of olive oil production is one of the most spectacular illustrations of the revival and reinvigoration of Iron Age Palestine.[41] Olive presses have been found in Judah and the Shephelah and at small farms on the western slopes of the mountains of Ephraim. The way in which the revitalization of the countryside benefited towns is illustrated most spectacularly at Tel Miqne where over 100 olive presses have been found throughout the houses at the site. By the seventh century BCE Tel Miqne had expanded almost fivefold, from around 4 to 20 hectares, as a result of its central importance in this lucrative industry. Similarly, nearby Tel Batash was able to benefit from the vitality of horticulture. The discovery of 'industrial' and residential quarters at both sites, along with Ashdod, is a further pointer to the continuing vitality of the economy. Leaving aside the disputed dating of their fortifications, the importance of Hazor, Megiddo, and Gezer was that they controlled vital trade routes to Syria or through the Esdraelon Valley and northern Shephelah. The revival of international trade is indicated by the small amounts of Cypriot imports at a few Palestinian sites from the mid-eleventh century BCE onwards, with increasing evidence of imported materials as the period progresses.

Such economic vitality and growth inevitably brought the attention of Assyria from the ninth century BCE onwards, and later Babylonia, as trade revived throughout the Mediterranean basin. This was a reimposition of imperial control over Palestine given its strategic location within the trade nexus. Traditional biblically based reconstructions tell the political history of ancient Israel for this period, and the struggle of the small state structures and their rulers in the region with the imperial powers of Mesopotamia (see Noth 1960; Bright 1981; Miller and Hayes 1986). The destruction of Samaria and Lachish by the Assyrians in the late eighth century BCE appears to have resulted in the rise to prominence of Ekron and Jerusalem. However, despite the concentration of biblically based reconstructions on the subjugation of Samaria and northern Israel and the constriction of Jerusalem and Judah, Assyrian economic and political interests led to the development of trade contacts between Edom, Judah, and the coast through the Negev, and continued later.[42]

404

As has been noted, Judah experienced a major expansion from 900–700 BCE, particularly in the seventh century.

Similarly, Mazar (1990) notes that Transjordan experienced prosperity and economic growth during the Assyrian and Babylonian periods because of the need to protect the trade route through Transjordan to Arabia: most of the Iron Age sites in the region relate to the prosperous period of the Assyrian and Babylonian domination from the late eighth to the early sixth century BCE. The situation towards the end of the Iron Age is less clear, with the defeat of Judah by the Babylonians. Again, biblically based reconstructions have tended to focus upon the plight of Jerusalem and its immediate environs as well as the theological and political effects of the ending of the Davidic dynasty, the loss of the temple, and the loss of political autonomy. Barkay (1992: 372) acknowledges that the effects, however, were localized, with material continuity in many areas of Palestine outside the confines of Jerusalem and its immediate vicinity. The fact that such regional variation has only relatively recently become apparent again illustrates the concentration of attention on a small subregion due to the overwhelming interest in the Hebrew Bible. Hoglund (1991) reports that there was a dramatic drop in the number of settlements from Iron II to the Persian period, reflecting a process of urbanization or depopulation. The Judaean territory was an exception to this pattern with a 25 per cent increase in the number of sites, the vast majority of which were small unwalled settlements.[43]

Once again it is possible to see important regional variation in response to the events of the sixth century with a reordering of the countryside, particularly in Judah. Ofer (1994: 105–6) reports that at the end of the Iron Age, during the seventh and early sixth centuries, there were 133 settlements with 71.5 hectares of built-up area in the southern hill country. Again the southern border of the region retreated during a time of political instability as settlement almost died out during the transition to the Persian period and was considerably weakened in the central region, but increased by 65 per cent in the north compared with the preceding period. Site location, as in earlier periods of instability, appears to have been determined by access to good agricultural land, water sources, and main routes. The location of small sites on higher places tends to suggest a concern for security in response to regional circumstances. However, the continued vitality of sites along the Phoenician coast and in the lowlands, such as at Tell Keisan in the valley of Acre, suggests that the reinvigoration of trade throughout the Babylonian and Persian empires benefited Palestinian sites able to exploit the trade routes through their strategic location.

Thus the end of the Iron Age in Palestine again illustrates the rhythms and patterns of its history, the differing responses of its fragmented landscape and its inhabitants to the deep-seated movements of history. While biblically based constructions focus upon the glare of political events in and around Jerusalem and the theological and political consequences of the Babylonian capture of the city, increasing archaeological data reveal the silent world that guides the history of the region. What is beginning to emerge is a greater understanding of the complex responses of the inhabitants of Palestine throughout the Iron Age to the economic and political realities of this ancient world – a picture significantly different from the priorities that govern the way in which the biblical writers, and modern 'biblical historians' who rely almost exclusively on these accounts, present this world.

CONCLUSION

Viewed from a wider perspective, freed from the constraints of biblical history, the Iron Age in Palestine represents an integral part of the complex history of the region, as archaeologists have increasingly demonstrated.[44] The simplistic representation of the Iron Age in Palestine as encircled, at its beginning and end, by catastrophic collapse and decline represents, in Schama's terms, a distraction caused by concentration on such 'sudden moments of realization'. These periods of dislocation at the transition points into and from the Iron Age do not define some discrete period in the history Palestine but are integrally connected to the oscillations in settlement that precede and follow. The processes that contribute to and emerge from these seemingly sudden moments, the complex regional variations, are gradually being uncovered and appreciated by archaeologists and historians. As scholars have come to appreciate increasingly the cyclical nature of Palestinian history (Coote and Whitelam 1987; Finkelstein 1995, 1998; Levy and Holl 1995), so perceptions of Iron Age Palestine have begun to change quite significantly. These six centuries or so illustrate the rhythms and patterns of Palestinian history in general. Within these rhythms, history is never completely static despite the massive inertia of the ancient past: 'It has gentle slopes along which the whole mechanism slides' (Braudel 1974: xi). As Braudel (1974: x) has remarked of Europe, 'the frontier zone between possibility and impossibility barely moved in any significant way, from the fifteenth to the eighteenth century. It was only successfully crossed in the last years of the eighteenth century, and then only at a few points. It was the following century that saw a violent breakthrough, revolution, total upheaval of the world.' This is even more applicable to Palestine in the Iron Age when the boundaries of possibility were even more rigidly defined. The physical boundaries of the arid and semi-arid zones were sensitive barometers in the history of the region. The revival and reinvigoration of Palestine that emerged from the disruption and dislocations of the late Bronze Age pushed back these boundaries as the weight of numbers opened up and reclaimed the less hospitable subregions, but the limits of the possible were able to reassert themselves in other periods of political and economic uncertainty.

The end of the period brought renewed interest from the demographically more dominant powers in Mesopotamia due to the increasing prosperity through the revived international and interregional trade. The pattern, which is common throughout the history of Palestine, reasserts itself. Again the close of the period has traditionally been presented as one of decline after the defeat of the southern kingdom of Judah by the Babylonians. However, recent surveys have begun to reveal important regional differences that undermine the myopia of standard accounts based solely on the biblical traditions. The transformation and reinvigoration of Palestine throughout the Iron Age bears witness to the ebb and flow of the tides of history to which this region has always been sensitive, given its strategic location in the geopolitical scheme of things. Once again at the end of the period, historians and archaeologists are beginning to appreciate the differing regional responses to the political and economic crisis of the Babylonian period, including a reordering of the Judaean countryside in response to the decline of Jerusalem.

NOTES

1 See Whitelam (1996: 37–70) for an introduction to some of the problems of defining chronological and geographical boundaries in Palestinian history. Gordon (1992: 192), for example, notes the artificial separation of Phoenician coast and its towns from the history of Palestine.

2 Davies (1992: 24) points out that the term 'the biblical period' should be reserved for the period when the biblical literature was composed in the Second Temple period rather than for the Iron Age as the time to which much of the literature refers. He contrasts 'the biblical period' with the 'classical' age of the Israelite and Judaean monarchies (1998: 3).

3 Drews (1993: 3) is illustrative of this approach in his categorization of the end of the Bronze Age in the eastern Mediterranean as 'one of history's most frightful turning points', which he terms 'the Catastrophe', a beginning rather than an end, yet signalling a radical break with what had gone before. Hallo (1992: 1) similarly points to changes in writing systems, political organization, and increasing urbanization as representing a significant break with the past. The classic statement of Israelite history as 'the pinnacle of biological evolution' can be found in Albright (1957: esp. 121–2).

4 The most recent and comprehensive statement of the difficulties in trying to use the biblical traditions for historical reconstruction can be found in Thompson (1999). See also the collection of essays in Grabbe (1997).

5 Hallo (1992: 2, 6) asks the question of whether or not Bronze and Iron are merely labels of convenience rather than the crucial components of tools and weapons. However, he goes on to add that the shift in metal use was fairly rapid: 'we can therefore justify the use of the term Iron Age as a label of convenience for a period whose characteristics – whether metallurgical or otherwise – do not fully come into their own until two centuries after its beginning'.

6 The scheme for subdividing the Iron Age was proposed by Aharoni and Amiran following excavations at Hazor (Tell el-Qedar) in 1958 (see Mazar 1992: 258–301). The absolute chronology of Iron Age Palestine is dependent upon Egyptian chronology (see Mazar 1992: 259 for high and low Egyptian chronologies). Amiran divided the period into two phases: Iron I (1200–1000 BCE) and Iron II (1000–586 BCE), while Aharoni and Amiran subsequently subdivided Iron II into Iron II (1000–840 BCE) and Iron III (840–586 BCE). However, in Avi-Yonah (1975) there is a further refinement, with Iron IIa (1000–900 BCE), Iron IIb (900–800 BCE), and Iron IIc (800–586 BCE). Barkay (1992: 305) has recently suggested a further refinement into Iron IIa (1000–800 BCE), Iron IIb (800–700 BCE), Iron IIIa (700–586 BCE) and Iron IIIb (586–late sixth century BCE). Finkelstein and Na'aman (1994: 16) emphasize the fluidity of the chronological divisions in their designation of the Late Bronze Age as ranging from 1550 to 1200/1150 BCE, thus providing a half-century 'overlap' between the Late Bronze Age and the Iron Age. Such terminology is confusing and subject to considerable debate. This has been brought out most clearly in recent years with the intense debate on the dating of tenth-century remains and their relationship to the biblical traditions. The controversial attempts by Israel Finkelstein (1996, 1998) to redefine the period from an archaeological perspective, and the response by Mazar (1997), illustrate how biblical presuppositions have been built into standard representations of the Iron Age in Palestine. Finkelstein (1998: 167) characterizes the disputes as 'much more than a dispute over the dating of strata and pottery assemblages in the main mounds of Palestine; it is part of a quest to emancipate Iron Age archaeology from Bible archaeology'. No chronological scheme can ever hope to achieve the amount of precision suggested by the standard representations of Iron Age Palestine: the risk is that such precision, however qualified, distracts from the continuities and seeming inertia of vast sweeps of time in the history of the region.

7 Barkay (1992: 302), for instance, considers the Iron II–III to be 'a historical era in the fullest sense of the word' with the Bible providing the 'principal historical source': it is appropriate to use the term 'biblical archaeology'. The chronology of the Iron II–III is based on synchronisms between references in the Bible and other sources to the destruction and construction of cities and excavations of foundation phases and destruction layers at these cities (Barkay 1992: 304). Barkay terms the 460 years between the establishment of the monarchy of David

and the conquest by the Persians as Iron Age II–III, or 'the Late Israelite period' (1992: 304). Although he recognizes that the Israelites were not the 'sole ethnic entity' in the land, the term is used to subsume the history of the region. Contrast the statements in Finkelstein (1996, 1998).

8 Braudel (1972: 21) goes on to warn that 'resounding events are often only momentary outbursts, surface manifestations of these larger movements and explicable only in terms of them'.

9 Weinstein (1981; see also Bunimowitz 1994: 195) has demonstrated that Egypt tried to maintain its interest in and control of Palestine into the twelfth century BCE, probably until the time of Rameses VI (c. 1143–1136 BCE). Singer (1994: 284–94) describes the final stages of Egyptian control of Canaan, noting that during the reign of Rameses III the archaeological evidence points to the fact that it strengthened its control of the southern trade routes through the lowlands.

10 The Canaanite jar, which was used for transporting much of the produce, is found in Greece, while Egyptian wall paintings depict the unloading of such jars and produce (Gonen 1992: 246–9).

11 Cline (1994: xvii–xviii) notes that during the Late Bronze period there is no clear domination of Aegean trade routes by any one foreign power. Objects from Egypt, Syria, Palestine, Cyprus, and Italy are found in approximately equal quantities. Cline (1994: 100–1) argues that the Ulu Burun (Kas) shipwreck illustrates the international nature of cargoes carried by merchant ships in the Late Bronze Age and represents a microcosm of trade in the Aegean, Egypt, and the Near East. Similarly, Bass (1986, 1987) maintains that the cargo reflects the international world of the ancient Near East illustrated in the Amarna Letters.

12 Thompson (1992: 215; 1999: 155–61) has revived the argument that climatic change was an important factor in the transformation of Palestine at the end of the Late Bronze Age. Hallo (1992: 2) points out that all such theories rely upon the chance recording of essentially perennial factors: earthquakes, volcanic eruptions, global warming or cooling, endemic pestilence, famine, and flooding. Famine is well documented throughout the region from the biblical traditions to documents from Hattusha, Ugarit, and Egypt which indicate that there were extreme food shortages (Na'aman 1994: 243). It should be noted that famine has multiple causes, often the consequence of human action, rather than simply being a direct result of inclement weather conditions.

13 Muhly (1992: 10–11) discusses how perceptions of this so-called 'Dark Age' have changed. See the wide-ranging essays in Ward and Joukowsky (1992) for a re-evaluation of the period throughout the region, including southern Europe and Mesopotamia.

14 Na'aman (1994: 235–9) provides a good description, based on inscriptional evidence from Mesopotamia, of the dislocation throughout Syria and southern Anatolia.

15 See Dever (1992: 99–101) for questions about which sites demonstrate evidence of destruction.

16 The definition and interpretation of Philistine culture has become an important issue in understanding the transition from the Late Bronze into the Iron Age in Palestine in recent years. Bunimowitz (1990), Bunimowitz and Yasur-Landau (1996), and Singer (1994: 300–1) highlight the problems in trying to define Philisitine culture, particularly in ethnic terms.

17 The same is true of the Middle Bronze to Late Bronze transition, where the major sites of the region and periphery were not devastated contemporaneously but during a process that lasted from the end of the seventeenth to the middle/end of the sixteenth century BCE (Bunimowitz 1994: 184–5). As Bunimowitz (1994: 186) notes, 'the repeated disintegration of the social fabric of the hill country during the Bronze Age is of special interest due to the fact that it happened under similar environmental and demographic conditions'.

18 Convenient surveys of older approaches can be found in Miller (1977), Ramsey (1982), Chaney (1988), H. and M. Weippert (1991), and Thompson (1992).

19 Finkelstein (1994: 158–9) argues that the pace of growth in the total built-up area in all sites in the northern hill country for early Iron I to late Iron I cannot be explained by natural population growth. Rather it shows that new elements either came from outside the region or were from a pastoral background, continuing to settle during the twelfth to eleventh

centuries BCE. Finkelstein argues for the latter on the grounds that in the Late Bronze Age a large number of pastoral groups were active in the hill country.

20 Davies (1992) and Brettler (1995) review the convergence of factors, such as new literary studies and increasing interest in social history, that have contributed to the paradigm shift within biblical studies.

21 T. Dothan (1992) argues that the complex process and cultural changes that took place were not applicable to all sites. Although Dothan (1992: 93) tries to tie the changes to ethnic explanations, she demonstrates the complexity of the social dislocation in citing the juxta-position of continuity at some sites of facets of Canaanite culture, the signs at other sites of temporarily intensified Egyptian presence, the appearance and expansion of hill country, which she and many others attribute to the Israelites, and the establishment of Philistine and other Sea Peoples' enclaves along the coast, indicating that the cultural coherence of Late Bronze Age Canaanite society had broken down. The fact that at 'Philistine' sites Philistine pottery was only a small percentage of the overall repertoire that showed clear continuities with Late Bronze Age material culture suggests that such changes cannot easily be reduced to simple ethnic differences and the influx of foreign populations.

22 Dever (1992: 104) provides a convenient description of these settlements, while Mazar (1992: 287–92) outlines the material culture of these villages and some of the regional variations. See also Finkelstein (1988) and Fritz (1995: 68–72) for the arrangement of these villages.

23 One of the most striking shifts in scholarly perceptions in recent years is the acceptance that the rural settlements were largely indigenous rather than the result of external infiltration or invasion by Israelite tribes. The discussion on much of this material has been sidetracked by attempts to correlate the archaeological data with ethnic groups, particularly in the search for ancient Israel. The question of whether or not the inhabitants of these rural settlements were Israelites or 'proto-Israelites' has become a matter of considerable debate (see Whitelam 1994, 1996; Finkelstein 1995; Dever 1996; among many others). Finkelstein (1995: 365) suggests that the absence of pig bones in Iron I hill country settlements, although they are found in significant numbers in the Bronze Age and in the lowlands and Transjordan in Iron I, may point to a pig taboo and thus may indicate that the villagers were Israelites. However, compare the cautious remarks of Hesse (1990), Hesse and Wapnish (1997), and Prag (1998) on the many factors affecting pig production. What is important for understanding the history of the region are the processes at work, the continuities and discontinuities, in the settlement shift. The question of self-identification is important but difficult to resolve given the current level of information.

24 For the results and analysis of the surveys by Finkelstein, Gal, Ofer, Herzog, and Zertal, see the essays in Finkelstein and Na'aman (1994), and particularly Finkelstein's synthetic treatments (1995, 1998).

25 See Bienkowski (1992: 1–12; 1998: 164) for a useful overview of the problems of ceramic dating and the identification of Iron I settlement in Transjordan.

26 For details on the distribution of settlement, and some differences of opinion, see Finkelstein (1994, 1995, 1998), Gal (1994), Ofer (1994), Zertal (1994), Herzog (1994), and Frankel (1994).

27 See Lemche (1985) and Coote and Whitelam (1987) for the complexities of the social continuum in ancient Palestine and the complex interrelationships between pastoral and agricultural communities. The pastoral sector never disappears completely, since the economy of urban and nomad populations is interconnected and the two coexist at all times (Na'aman 1994: 233).

28 Rutter (1992: 61) also argues that 'in terms of its forms of material cultural expression, the post-palatial Aegean world is clearly anything but moribund. Much of the disparagement of the post-palatial era as a period of cultural decline results from what amounts to the decisive and permanent abandonment in that period of those forms of earlier material culture which were concentrated with the social and economic order maintained through the royal citadels.' Wells (1992: 38) sees the changes taking place in central and south-eastern Europe and the eastern Mediterranean as part of the general process of economic transformation in the Late Bronze Age and the reorientation of trade routes. Mazar (1992: 297) describes the vitality of

Tel Abu Hawam, Tell Keisan, and Akhziv along the Phoenician coast, particularly in the eleventh century BCE.

29 The transformation of the Iron Age has often been explained in terms of innovations such as the introduction of iron, slaked-lime plaster cisterns, terracing, or even particular types of architecture or pottery, as though these were on a par with the agricultural revolution. However, the use of terracing or cisterns in earlier periods indicates that these were appropriate responses to prevailing socio-environmental conditions, rather than technological breakthroughs in the Iron I period or Israelite innovations, as thought earlier (see Finkelstein 1995: 364–5).

30 Finkelstein and Na'aman (1994: 11) report that over 80 per cent of the Iron I sites in southern Samaria continued to be occupied in Iron II.

31 The growth of towns also includes a series of around 50 sites generally refered to as 'forts' or 'fortresses'. These sites vary in shape – circular, oval, rectangular, amorphic – and usually follow the contours of hills on which they are built; they vary in size from 25 to 70 m, often with isolated houses or at some distance. Mazar (1990: 390) follows Cohen in arguing that they are designed to control the Negev and its inhabitants and secure the trade routes crossing the Negev through Kadesh-Barnea towards the Red Sea and the commercial ties with Arabia.

32 Finkelstein (1998: 8), for instance, has reiterated the view that 'the genuine change – the ground breaking transformation in the history of Palestine – came with the rise of the territorial national states in the first millennium BCE'. However, he argues also that fully blown statehood was not achieved until later: the ninth century BCE in Israel, and not until the eighth century BCE in Judah (Finkelstein 1995: 362; 1998: 32).

33 Mazar (1990: 374) attributes the destruction of Megiddo (Str. VIA) and Tel Qasile (Str. X) to the time of David. Again this reflects the urge to try to reconstruct the history of the region with reference to the biblical traditions even though there is no mention in the traditions associated with David of such destructions. Herzog (1994: 143–4) notes that there was a shift from a wide spread of settlements in the Beersheba valley and more arid zones to the south in the eleventh century to fewer sites of the tenth century located in a restricted area along the valley. The total area in the tenth century was similar if not smaller than the agricultural sites of the eleventh century – with fortified, non-residential units and a smaller overall population. Herzog argues that the changes in settlement pattern are not due to the transition to the monarchy, but to climatic factors that led to the abandonment of most of the agricultural villages. He also argues that the spatial distribution of the Negev highland sites, the large variety of their shapes, and the fact that in many cases houses and animal pens are found outside the confines of the main settlement, support the view that this was a local settlement process rather than a state initiative (1994: 145).

34 See Knoppers (1997) for a comprehensive review of opposing positions, and the essays in Handy (1997) and Fritz and Davies (1996).

35 Similarly, Barkay (1992: 307) is forced to conclude that the 'glorified picture' emerging from the biblical traditions does not correspond to 'the reality reflected in the archaeological findings'.

36 Barkay (1992: 306) concludes a recent survey of the Iron II period with the words that 'the precise dating of settlement strata and find assemblages of the tenth and ninth centuries is fraught with difficulties'.

37 Knoppers (1997) provides a review and assessment of the various interpretations of the so-called Negev 'forts'.

38 Knauf (1997: 81-2) concludes that the archaeological record for the tenth century has 'no room for a Solomonic empire, not even a state of Judah of [*sic*] Israel'. As Hopkins (1997: 309) notes, it is difficult to see how Jerusalem of the tenth century could have been the centre of a bureaucratic centralized state or empire when it was 'barely the center of its contiguous domain'.

39 Dever (1995: 72) argues that material continuity from the twelfth to the sixth centuries BCE points to a 'national Israelite material culture' deriving from the monarchic period and is evidence of increasing centralization. However, Hopkins (1997: 304), by contrast, refers to 'a degree of homogenous material culture', and questions the degree of centralization involved.

40 Bienkowski (1998: 165) points out that there are huge regional variations in Iron II pottery in Transjordan with significant differences from north to south and within regions. The marked changes every 30 km or so, he argues, reflect the relative isolation of settlements, which, despite being regarded as parts of unified kingdoms, may have had little contact with one another and in which so-called 'centralized control' may have been superficial. See also Knauf (1992) and Miller (1992) for influential challenges to traditional arguments about state formations in Iron Age Transjordan.

41 Rosen (1994: 345) notes that there is no evidence of utensils or structures for the production of oil or wine in the subsistence economy of Iron I. He believes that the beginning of large-scale horticulture marks the transition from pre-monarchic to monarchic Israel. However, what it signifies is that the shift to large-scale horticulture took place as the revival continued in the countryside. Wine and oil production demanded long-term stability and settlement given the time it takes for vines and olive trees to reach maturity. The initial shift was towards the areas that offered the quickest return in subsistence. As the revival continued, horticulture once again became a viable option and advanced significantly in the Iron II period.

42 Thompson (1999: 184–5) points out that traditional histories fail to deal with the continued existence of Samaria and the northern hill country in the history of Palestine, because of their reliance on the biblical narratives in which the northern kingdom and its major towns disappear from the account on theological grounds.

43 See Hoglund (1991: 57) for some of the problems involved in the ceramic chronology for the Persian period.

44 This has been largely unwitting since many archaeologists have pursued the goal of correlating archaeological results with the biblical traditions in the search for ancient Israel without asking these wider questions. Only recently, as it has become apparent that the archaeological data cannot be related easily to the biblical traditions or the events portrayed within them, have these questions been pursued in earnest.

BIBLIOGRAPHY

Aharoni, Y. (1982) *The archaeology of the land of Israel: from the prehistoric beginnings to the end of the First Temple period*, London: SCM Press.

Ahlström, G. W. (1986) *Who were the Israelites?* Winona Lake: Eisenbrauns.

Albright, W. F. (1957) *From the Stone Age to Christianity: monotheism and the historical process*, Doubleday: New York.

Avi-Yonah, M. (ed.) (1975) *Encyclopedia of archaeological excavations in the Holy Land*, 4 vols, London: Oxford University Press.

Barkay, G. (1992) 'The Iron Age II–III', in A. Ben-Tor (ed.) *The archaeology of ancient Israel*, New Haven: Yale University Press, 302–73.

Bass, G. F. (1986) 'A Bronze Age shipwreck at Ulu Burun (Kas): 1984 campaign', *AJA* 90: 269–96.

—— (1987) 'Oldest known shipwreck reveals splendors of the Bronze Age', *National Geographic* 20: 692–733.

Bienkowski, P. (ed.) (1992) *Early Edom and Moab: the beginning of the Iron Age in southern Jordan*, Sheffield: Sheffield Academic Press.

—— (1998) 'Comments on the papers of Kitchen, Whitelam and Finkelstein', in S. Ahituv and E. D. Oren (eds) *The origin of early Israel – current debate: biblical, historical and archaeological perspectives*, Beersheva: Ben-Gurion University of the Negev Press, 163–5.

Braudel, F. (1972) *The Mediterranean and the Mediterranean world in the age of Philip II*, vols 1–2, London: Collins.

—— (1974) *Capitalism and material life 1400–1800*, London: Fontana.

Brettler, M. (1995) *The creation of history in ancient Israel*, London: Routledge.

Bright, J. (1981) *A history of Israel*, 3rd rev. edn, London: SCM Press.

Bunimowitz, S. (1990) 'Problems in the 'ethnic' identification of Philistine material culture', *TA* 17: 210–22.

—— (1994) 'Socio-political transformations in the central hill country in the Late Bronze–Iron Age transition', in I. Finkelstein and N. Na'aman (eds) *From nomadism to monarchy: archaeological and historical aspects of early Israel*, Jerusalem: Israel Exploration Society, 179–202.

Bunimowitz, S. and Yasur-Landau, A. (1996) 'Philistine and Israelite pottery: a comparative approach to the question of pots and people', *TA* 23: 88–101.

Caubert, A. (1992) 'Reoccupation of the Syrian coast after the destruction of the "crisis years",' in W.A. Ward and M.S. Joukowsky (eds) *The crisis years: the 12th century B.C. from beyond the Danube to the Tigris*, Dubuque: Kendall/Hunt Publishing, 102–131.

Chaney, M. (1983) 'Ancient Palestinian peasant movements and the formation of premonarchic Israel', in D. N. Freedman and D. F. Graf (eds) *Palestine in transition: the emergence of ancient Israel*, Sheffield: Almond Press.

Cline, E. (1994) *Sailing the wine-dark sea: international trade and the Late Bronze Age Aegean*, Oxford: Tempus Reparatum.

Coote, R. B. and Whitelam, K. W. (1987) *The emergence of Israel in historical perspective*. Sheffield: Almond Press.

Davies, P. R. (1992) *In search of 'ancient Israel'*, Sheffield: JSOT Press.

—— (1998) *Scribes and schools: the canonization of the Hebrew Scriptures*, Louisville: Westminster John Knox Press.

Desborough, V. R. (1972) *The Greek dark ages*, London: Benn.

Dever, W. G. (1991) 'Archaeological data on the Israelite settlement: a review of two recent works', *BASOR* 284: 77–90.

—— (1992) 'The Late Bronze–Early Iron I horizon in Syria–Palestine: Egyptians, Canaanites, 'Sea Peoples,' and proto-Israelites', in W. A. Ward and M. S. Joukowsky (eds), *The crisis years: the 12th century B.C. from beyond the Danube to the Tigris*, Dubuque: Kendall/Hunt Publishing, 99–110.

—— (1993) 'Cultural continuity, ethnicity in the archaeological record, and the question of Israelite origins', *EI* 24: 22*–33*.

—— (1995) 'Will the real Israel stand up? Archaeology and Israelite historiography: part I', *BASOR* 297: 61–80.

—— (1996) 'The identity of early Israel: a rejoinder to Keith W. Whitelam', *JSOT* 72: 3–24.

Dothan, T. (1989) 'The arrival of the Sea Peoples: cultural diversity in Early Iron Age Canaan', in S. Gitin and W. G. Dever (eds) *Recent excavations in Israel: studies in Iron Age archaeology*, Winona Lake: ASOR/Eisenbrauns, 1–14.

—— (1992) 'Social dislocation and cultural change in the twelfth century BCE', in W. A. Ward and M. S. Joukowsky (eds) *The crisis years: the 12th century B.C. from beyond the Danube to the Tigris*, Dubuque: Kendall/Hunt Publishing, 93–8.

—— (1997) 'Tel Miqne-Ekron: an Iron Age I Philistine settlement in Canaan', in N. A. Silberman and D. B. Small (eds) *The archaeology of Israel: constructing the past, interpreting the present*, Sheffield: Sheffield Academic Press, 96–106.

Drews, R. (1993) *The end of the Bronze Age: changes in warfare and the catastrophe ca. 1200*, Princeton: Princeton University Press.

Finkelstein, I. (1988) *The archaeology of the Israelite settlement*, Jerusalem: Israel Exploration Society.

—— (1994) 'The emergence of Israel: a phase in the cyclic history of Canaan in the third and second millennia BCE', in I. Finkelstein and N. Na'aman (eds) *From nomadism to monarchy: archaeological and historical aspects of early Israel*, Jerusalem: Israel Exploration Society, 150–78.

—— (1995) 'The great transformation: the 'conquest' of the highland frontiers and the rise of the territorial states', in T. E. Levy (ed.) *The archaeology of society in the Holy Land*, Leicester: Leicester University Press, 349–60.

—— (1996) 'The archaeology of the united monarchy: an alternative view', *Levant* 28: 177–87.

—— (1998) 'Bible archaeology or archaeology of Palestine in the Iron Age? A rejoinder', *Levant* 30: 167–74.

Finkelstein, I. and Na'aman, N. (eds) (1994) *From nomadism to monarchy: archaeological and historical aspects of early Israel*, Jerusalem: Israel Exploration Society.

Frankel, R. (1994) 'Upper Galilee in the Late Bronze–Iron I transition', in I. Finkelstein and N. Na'aman (eds) *From nomadism to monarchy: archaeological and historical aspects of early Israel*, Jerusalem: Israel Exploration Society, 18–34.

Fritz, V. (1987) 'Conquest of settlement? The Early Iron Age in Palestine', *BA* 50: 84–100.

—— (1994) *An introduction to biblical archaeology*, Sheffield: JSOT Press.

—— (1995) *The city in ancient Israel*, Sheffield: Sheffield Academic Press.

Fritz, V. and Davies, P. R. (1996) *The origins of the ancient Israelite states*, Sheffield: JSOT Press.

Gal, Z. (1994) 'Iron I in lower Galilee and the margins of the Jezreel valley', in I. Finkelstein and N. Na'aman (eds) *From nomadism to monarchy: archaeological and historical aspects of early Israel*, Jerusalem: Israel Exploration Society, 35–46.

Gelinas, M. M. (1995) 'United monarchy–divided monarchy: fact or fiction?' in S. W. Holladay and L. Handy (eds) *The pitcher is broken: memorial essays for Gösta W. Ahlström*, Sheffield: Sheffield Academic Press, 225–37.

Gonen, R. (1992) 'The Late Bronze Age', in A. Ben-Tor (ed.) *The archaeology of ancient Israel*, New Haven: Yale University Press, 211–57.

Gordon, C. H. (1992) 'The Mediterranean synthesis', in W.A. Ward and M. S. Joukowsky (eds) *The crisis years: the 12th century B.C. from beyond the Danube to the Tigris*, Dubuque: Kendall/Hunt Publishing, 188–96.

Grabbe, L. (1997) *Can a 'history of Israel' be written?*, Sheffield: Sheffield Academic Press.

Hallo, W. W. (1992) 'From Bronze Age to Iron Age in western Asia: defining the problem', in W. A. Ward and M. S. Joukowsky (eds) *The crisis years: the 12th century B.C. from beyond the Danube to the Tigris*, Dubuque: Kendall/Hunt Publishing, 1–9.

Handy, L. K. (1997) *The age of Solomon: scholarship at the turn of the century*, Leiden: E. J. Brill.

Herzog, Z. (1994) 'The Beer-Sheba Valley: from nomadism to monarchy', in I. Finkelstein and N. Na'aman (eds) *From nomadism to monarchy: archaeological and historical aspects of early Israel*, Jerusalem: Israel Exploration Society, 122–49.

Hesse, B. (1990) 'Pig lovers and pig haters: patterns of Palestinian pig production', *Journal of Ethnobiology* 10: 195–225.

Hesse, B. and Wapnish, P. (1997) 'Can pig remains be used for ethnic diagnosis in the ancient Near East?' in N. A. Silberman and D. B. Small (eds) *The archaeology of Israel: constructing the past, interpreting the present*, Sheffield: Sheffield Academic Press, 238–70.

Hoglund, K. (1991) 'The Achaemenid context', in P. R. Davies (ed.) *Second Temple studies: 1. Persian period*, Sheffield: JSOT Press, 54–72.

Holladay, J. S. (1995) 'The kingdoms of Israel and Judah: political and economic centralization in the Iron IIA–B (ca. 1000–750 BCE)', in T. E. Levy (ed.) *The archaeology of society in the Holy Land*, Leicester: Leicester University Press, 368–74.

Hopkins, D, (1997) 'The weight of the bronze could not be calculated: Solomon and economic reconstruction', in K. L. Handy (ed.) *The age of Solomon: scholarship at the turn of the millennium*, Leiden: E.J. Brill, 300–11.

Jamieson-Duke, D. W. (1991) *Scribes and schools in monarchic Judah: a socio-archaeological approach*, Sheffield: Almond Press.

Karageorghis, V. (1990) *The end of the Late Bronze Age in Cyprus*, Nicosia: Pieridis Foundation.

—— (1992) 'The crisis years: Cyprus', in W. A. Ward and M. S. Joukowsky (eds) *The crisis years: the 12th century B.C. from beyond the Danube to the Tigris*, Dubuque: Kendall/Hunt Publishing, 79–86.

Knauf, A. (1992) 'The cultural impact of secondary state formation: the case of the Edomites and Moabites', in P. Bienkowski (ed.) *Early Edom and Moab: the beginning of the Iron Age in southern Jordan*, Sheffield: Sheffield Academic Press, 47–54.

—— (1997) 'Le roi et mort, vive le roi! A biblical argument for the historicity of Solomon', in K. L. Handy (ed.) *The age of Solomon: scholarship at the turn of the millennium*, Leiden: E. J. Brill, 81–95.

Knoppers, G. N. (1997) 'The vanishing Solomon: the disappearance of the united monarchy from recent histories of ancient Israel', *JBL* 116: 19–44.

Lemche, N. P. (1985) *Early Israel: anthropological and historical studies on the Israelite society before the monarchy*, Leiden: E. J. Brill.

—— (1997) 'On doing sociology with Solomon', in K. L. Handy (ed.) *The age of Solomon: scholarship at the turn of the millennium*, Leiden: E. J. Brill, 312–35.

Levy, T. E. (ed.) (1995) *The archaeology of society in the Holy Land*, Leicester: Leicester University Press.

Levy, T. E. and Holl, A. F. C. (1995) 'Social change and the archaeology of the Holy Land', in T. E. Levy (ed.) *The archaeology of society in the Holy Land*, Leicester: Leicester University Press, 2–8.

Liverani, M. (1987) 'The collapse of the Near Eastern regional system at the end of the Bronze Age: the case of Syria', in M. Rowland, M. Larsen and K. Kristiansen (eds) *Centre and periphery in the ancient world*, Cambridge: Cambridge University Press, 66–73.

—— (1990) *Prestige and interest: international relations in the Near East ca. 1600–1100 B.C.*, Padova: Sargon.

Mazar, A. (1990) *Archaeology of the land of the Bible: 10,000–586 B.C.E.*, London: Doubleday.

—— (1992) 'The Iron Age I', in A. Ben-Tor (ed.) *The archaeology of ancient Israel*, New Haven: Yale University Press, 258–301.

—— (1994) 'Jerusalem and its vicinity in Iron Age I,' in I. Finkelstein and N. Na'aman (eds) *From nomadism to monarchy: archaeological and historical aspects of early Israel*, Jerusalem: Israel Exploration Society, 70–91.

—— (1997) 'Iron Age chronology: a reply to I. Finkelstein', *Levant* 29: 157–67.

Miller, J. M. (1977) 'The Israelite occupation of Canaan', in J. Hayes and J. M. Miller (eds) *Israelite and Judaean history*, London: SCM Press.

—— (1992) 'Early monarchy in Moab?' in P. Bienkowski (ed.) *Early Edom and Moab: the beginning of the Iron Age in southern Jordan*, Sheffield: Sheffield Academic Press, 77–92.

McClellan, T. L. (1992) '12th century BC in Syria: comments on Sader's paper', in W. A. Ward and M. S. Joukowsky (eds), *The crisis years: the 12th century B.C. from beyond the Danube to the Tigris*, Dubuque: Kendall/Hunt Publishing, 164–73.

Miller, J. M. and Hayes, J. (1986) *A history of ancient Israel and Judah*, London: SCM Press.

Muhly, J. D. (1992) 'The crisis years in the Mediterranean world: transition or cultural disintegration?' in W. A. Ward and M. S. Joukowsky (eds), *The crisis years: the 12th century B.C. from beyond the Danube to the Tigris*, Dubuque: Kendall/Hunt Publishing, 10–26.

Na'aman, N. (1994) ' "The conquest of Canaan" in the book of Joshua and in history', in I. Finkelstein and N. Na'aman (eds) *From nomadism to monarchy: archaeological and historical aspects of early Israel*, Jerusalem: Israel Exploration Society, 218–81.

Noth, M. (1960) *The history of Israel*, London: A. & C. Black.

Ofer, A. (1994) ' "All the Hill Country of Judah": from settlement fringe to a prosperous monarchy', in I. Finkelstein and N. Na'aman (eds) *From nomadism to monarchy: archaeological and historical aspects of early Israel*, Jerusalem: Israel Exploration Society, 92–121.

Prag, K. (1998) 'A response from the "Plains of Moab"', in S. Ahituv and E. D. Oren (eds) *The origin of early Israel – current debate: biblical, historical and archaeological perspectives*, Beersheva: Ben-Gurion University of the Negev Press, 153–61.

Ramsay, G. W. (1982) *The quest for the historical Israel: reconstructing Israel's early history*, London: SCM Press.

Rosen, B. (1994) 'Subsistence economy in Iron I', in I. Finkelstein and N. Na'aman (eds) *From nomadism to monarchy: archaeological and historical aspects of early Israel*, Jerusalem: Israel Exploration Society, 339–51.

Rutter, J. (1992) 'Cultural novelties in the post-palatial Aegean world: indices of vitality and decline', in W. A. Ward and M. S. Joukowsky, (eds) *The crisis years: the twelfth century B.C. from beyond the Danube to the Tigris*, Dubuque: Kendall/Hunt Publishing Company, 61–78.

Sader, H. (1992) 'The 12th century in Syria: the problem of the rise of the Aramaeans', in W. A. Ward and M. S. Joukowsky (eds), *The crisis years: the 12th century B.C. from beyond the Danube to the Tigris*, Dubuque: Kendall/Hunt Publishing, 157–63.

Singer, I. (1987) 'Dating the end of the Hittite empire', *Hethitica* 8: 413–21.

—— (1994) 'Egyptians, Canaanites, and Philistines in the period of the emergence of Israel', in I. Finkelstein and N. Na'aman (eds) *From nomadism to monarchy: archaeological and historical aspects of early Israel*, Jerusalem: Israel Exploration Society, 282–338.

Soggin, J. A. (1984) *A history of Israel: from the beginnings to the Bar Kochba Revolt, AD 135*, London: SCM Press.

Stager, L. E. (1995) 'The impact of the Sea Peoples in Canaan (1185–1050 BCE)', in T. E. Levy (ed.) *The archaeology of society in the Holy Land*, Leicester: Leicester University Press, 333–48.

Thompson, T. L. (1992) *The early history of the Israelite people: from the written and archaeological sources*, Leiden: E. J. Brill (1992).

—— (1999) *The Bible in history: how writers create a past*, London: Jonathan Cape.

Vulliamy, E. (1999) 'Simon Schama, dilettante don', *Guardian*, 2 January, 1–3.

Ward, W. A. and Joukowsky, M. S. (eds) (1992) *The crisis years: the 12th century B.C. from beyond the Danube to the Tigris*, Dubuque: Kendall/Hunt Publishing.

Weinstein, J. (1981) 'The Egyptian empire in Palestine: a reassessment', *BASOR* 241: 1–28.

—— (1992) 'The collapse of the Egyptian empire in the southern Levant', in W. A. Ward and M. S. Joukowsky (eds), *The crisis years: the 12th century B.C. from beyond the Danube to the Tigris*, Dubuque: Kendall/Hunt Publishing, 142–50.

Weippert, H. (1988) *Palästina in vorhellenistischer Zeit: Handbuch der Archäologie*. Vorderasian 2/Band 1, Munich: C. H. Beck'sche Verlagsbuchhandlung.

Weippert, H. and M. (1991) 'Die Vorgeschichte Israels in neuem Licht', *TRu* 56: 341–90 .

Wells, P. S. (1992) 'Crisis years? The 12th century BC in central and southeastern Europe', in W.A. Ward and M.S. Joukowsky (eds) *The crisis years: the 12th century B.C. from beyond the Danube to the Tigris*, Dubuque: Kendall/Hunt Publishing, 31–9.

Whitelam, K. W. (1994) 'The identity of early Israel: the realignment and transformation of Late Bronze–Iron Age Palestine', *JSOT* 63: 57–87.

—— (1996) *The invention of ancient Israel: the silencing of Palestinian history*, London: Routledge.

Yon, M. (1992) 'The end of the kingdom of Ugarit', in W. A. Ward and M. S. Joukowsky (eds) *The crisis years: the 12th century B.C. from beyond the Danube to the Tigris*, Dubuque: Kendall/Hunt Publishing, 111–22.

Zertal, A. (1994) '"To the land of the Perizzites and the giants": on the Israelite settlement in the hill country of Manasseh', in I. Finkelstein and N. Na'aman (eds) *From nomadism to monarchy: archaeological and historical aspects of early Israel*, Jerusalem: Israel Exploration Society, 47–69.

CHAPTER TWENTY-THREE

THE AGE OF THE EXILE

—— ·◆· ——

Joseph Blenkinsopp

DEPORTATIONS AND DEMOGRAPHY

The period from the first deportation by Nebuchadrezzar (597 BC) to the restoration of an imperially backed local cult in Jerusalem in the sixth year of the Achaemenid Darius (515) is among the most important, and at the same time one of the most misunderstood, in the entire history of Israel and emergent Judaism. It begins with the extinction by the Babylonian armies of Judaean independence after an existence of some four centuries. The biblical texts refer to three successive deportations to Babylon in the early sixth century BC, but the Deuteronomistic historian (hereafter Dtr) provides figures only for the first of the three following on the surrender of Jerusalem to the Babylonians in 597 BC. At this point of the history we have a conflation of two reports, with the same classes of military personnel, craftsmen and smiths mentioned in both, one of which gives the figure of 10,000, the other 8,000, though in neither case is it clear whether these figures refer to just one category or the totality of deportees (2 Kgs 24:14–17). After the sack of Jerusalem eleven years later we are told that all of the people left in the city, those who had deserted to the Babylonians earlier and the rest of the skilled workers (reading *'āmmān* with Jer. 52:15) were deported, leaving only some of the peasantry (*dallat hā'āreṣ*) to till the land (2 Kgs 25:11–12 = Jer. 52:15–16; cf. 39:9–10). That the author, in defiance of historical verisimilitude, informs us at *both* junctures that only peasants were left (2 Kgs 24:14; 25:12) provides the first of several clues to the ideological slant of this account of the deportations.

A quite different version of what happened, without parallel in either the Hebrew text of Kings or the Old Greek version, is recorded in Jeremiah 52:28–30. Here the statistics are 3,023 for the first of three deportations in the seventh year of Nebuchadrezzar (597),[1] 832 for that of the eighteenth year (586[2]),and 745 for the twenty-third year (582), therefore 4,600 in all. Those deported on the first and third of these occasions were Judaeans, and the 832 deported after the sack of the city in the year 586 were Jerusalemites. That the author of this notice refers to the deportees with the collective term *nepeš* (living soul, human being) might suggest that these figures are inclusive rather than limited to adult males. In any case, it is agreed that they inspire greater confidence than the Dtr statistics. They are not rounded out and they do not square with the ideology either of the history or of the editors of the book of Jeremiah according to which the deportations emptied the land of any significant population (Jer.13:19b; 40:11).[3]

The key explanatory role played by *the idea of exile* in Dtr is not difficult to detect. Beginning with the valedictory address of Joshua after the conquest of Canaan (Josh. 23:13, 15–16), the historian punctuates the narrative with frequent predictions of banishment from the land as the inevitable consequence of non-observance of the (Deuteronomic) law, and more specifically for violation of its cultic demands. The same message is conveyed in Solomon's prayer at the dedication of the temple which, with its clear allusion to diasporic Judaeans (1 Kgs 8:46–53), could not have been composed before the sixth century BC. The point begins to be made more insistently as we come to the Assyrian deportations subsequent to the conquest of the Galilee (15:29), Damascus (16:9), and of course the Kingdom of Israel itself (17:6). The entire people is to blame, and therefore the entire people is deported. The historian anticipates the fall of Judah by concluding the account of the fall of Samaria with a similar formula – 'Israel went into exile from its land' (2 Kgs 17:23; cf. 25:21; cf. Jer. 52:27), with the clear implication of a *total* deportation and depopulation. The ideological rationale for this reading of the history of the kingdoms is to be sought in those passages of Deuteronomy in which banishment or exile is the working out of a curse incurred for violation of the covenant relationship between the national deity and the people as a whole (Deut. 4:26–8; 28:36, 41, 63–8; 29:28). In this respect, as students of Deuteronomy have long been aware, the authors were following the lead of those Assyrian scribes who drafted treaties with vassal states. The prospect and threat of being uprooted from their own land is one of the curses serving to encourage vassals to observe the stipulations of these treaties; the *reality* of exile is of course well attested in Assyrian inscriptions and iconography.[4] In view of the statements about exile in Dtr, the practice in Assyrian inscriptions of speaking in terms of totality – all the men, all great and small are exiled – is also worth noting. Tiglat-pileser III, for example, claims to have deported all the men (*puḫur niŝeŝu*) of the house of Omri (Oded 1979). And where statistics are given we generally have reason to be sceptical. It would be imprudent, for example, to calculate the population of eighth or seventh century Judah *exclusively* on the basis of the 200,150 Judaeans whom Sennacherib claims to have deported in 701 BC.[5]

The documentary evidence for the existence of ethnic minorities in southern Mesopotamia during the Neo-Babylonian and early Achaemenid periods includes a considerable number of Judaeo-Babylonians filling various occupational niches. As interesting and important as they are, these data (to be discussed shortly) do not help us to decide on the actual number of deportees. We cannot even be sure that individuals bearing Judaean names belonged to the families and descendants of Judaeans deported by the Babylonians. Nor can we use for this purpose the various lists in Ezra–Nehemiah, especially the master census of Ezra 2:1–69 (= Neh. 7:6–68). This list purports to contain the names, affiliations or destinations of about 50,000 immigrants from Babylonia at the beginning of the Achaemenid period, but it is tolerably clear that it originated much later and for a different purpose.[6] We are therefore left without a definite statistical outcome with respect to Judaean deportees in the first two decades of the sixth century, but it seems that the weight of evidence favours the lower total of Jeremiah 52:28–30 rather than the Dtr statistics. If the Jeremian figure counts only adult males, heads of families averaging four or five individuals each, the figure would still not exceed 20,000, somewhat lower than the 27,290 whom Sargon II claims to have deported after the fall of Samaria (*ANET* 284–5). This is an unsatisfactory result, but it seems to be the best we can do with the available data.[7]

Estimating the number of deportees is not particularly helpful, however, unless calculated as a percentage of the total population of Judah. Biblical scholars are only beginning to pay attention to the methodological issues involved in calculating the population of ancient settlements. To be successful, such calculations require an array of different sorts of data including the carrying capacity of the environment in question, human skeletal remains, floor space, the number of habitations in the settlement, and the average size of families.[8] Needless to say these data are not always available; in fact they are generally not available, and the situation for ancient Palestinian sites is not improved by the frequent failure of archaeologists working in that region to publish scientific reports on their excavations and surveys, resulting in a severe shortage of usable settlement plans.

But even where data are available, it will not always be easy to come up with reliable results. Estimating the availability of resources, especially water and cereals, allows us to determine only the *maximum* amount, not the actual amount, consumed at the site. Human remains will, under ideal conditions, give us information on health and life expectancy, but it will not always be possible to determine that a particular collection (typically a cemetery) is chronologically homogeneous and representative of the population during the period in question. For example, infant bones are often underrepresented or mistaken for animal remains. Moreover, religious opposition to excavating human remains has gravely inhibited the work of the very few physical anthropologists associated with excavations in the State of Israel. The most promising approach is to work from living space and family size in those cases where an adequate floor plan of the site is available. But even here there are problems, for we cannot always be sure that non-residential space (e.g. administrative buildings, storage areas) has been factored out and non-permanent residence factored in. Assessment of family size is also problematic (estimates in the literature are anywhere from 3.5 to 8 individuals) and the minimum individual *roofed* floor space requirement (anywhere between 5.3 sq. m and 10 sq. m per individual) must also be taken into account.

The prospects for determining even approximately the population of Judah during the Neo-Babylonian period are not, therefore, very promising, even if we were quite clear about the extent of the province at that time. Though the tendency is to assume a drastic drop in population after disasters such as were visited on the region between 597 and 582 BC we should not underestimate the resilience of a population afflicted in this way and its ability to restore some semblance of normality in a remarkably short time. During and in the aftermath of military conquest population levels can fluctuate significantly. As the Babylonian army approached, many would have taken refuge in one or other of the inaccessible places of refuge with which southern Palestine and the Jordan Valley are liberally provided, to emerge thence once the worst was over. This is precisely what happened much later during Macedonian and

Roman campaigns in Syria–Palestine. We are in fact told that military units that had taken refuge 'in the open country' (*baśśadeh*) re-emerged after the appointment of Gedaliah (Jer. 40:7; cf. 2 Kgs 25:23), and when things had settled down somewhat many others came back from the Tranjordanian kingdoms and perhaps from as far away as Egypt (Jer. 40:11–12). It is also quite likely that a significant part of the population at that time became semi-nomadic or lived for a time in impermanent and improvised dwellings that would have left no signature on the archaeological record.

One noteworthy statistic provided by Dtr occurs in the account of the tribute imposed on Menahem by the Assyrians in the final decades of the Kingdom of Samaria (2 Kgs 15:19–20). Assuming that Menahem did not draw to a significant extent on other sources of revenue to buy off Tiglat-pileser, the 60,000 men of substance or property holders from whom the enormous indemnity was recovered would imply a total population of around 200,000. This total would be more or less compatible with the 27,290 deported by Sargon II from Samaria after the city fell (*ANET* 284–5). It is also within the range of the 200,150 whom Sennacherib claimed to have driven out (not necessarily deported) from forty-six provincial fortified cities, forts and villages in Judah (*ANET* 288). To many this statistic of the Taylor Prism will look like a typical exaggeration, but we cannot exclude the possibility that it represents a more or less accurate estimate, but perhaps an estimate of the total population of the Kingdom of Judah at that time (701 BC). At any rate, settlement patterns towards the end of Iron II in most parts of Judah, inclusive of the northern regions incorporated into the Kingdom of Judah by Josiah, suggest a fairly high population density level. Allowing for textual corruption and duplication, the settlements in Judah, Simeon and Benjamin listed in the book of Joshua (15:1–63; 18:11–28; 19:1–9), most if not all of which would have been in existence in the Neo-Babylonian period,[9] amount to more than 150, only very few of which have been identified archaeologically. Moreover, several sites which have been excavated are fairly major, in the range of 2 to 3 ha, with an estimated minimum population of 500 to 1,000,[10] and Jerusalem and Lachish at least were much larger and more populous. Further indications are provided by the survey of the Judaean hill region carried out by A. Ofer over an area of about 900 sq. km south of Jerusalem. Ofer lists 235 inhabited sites of 1,000 sq. km or more, and estimates their total population at about 23,000 in Iron IIC (eighth century).[11] As Ofer points out, the Judaean hill region has the lowest population density of the Central Massif. It would therefore presumably have been much less densely populated than the Shephelah (Lowlands) and the coastal region, and in fact most of the major sites in the province lie outside the region surveyed. An earlier survey reported by M. Kochavi shows a 25 per cent increase of settlements, mostly small unwalled villages, in Judah exclusive of the Judaean wilderness and Benjamin territory between Iron II and the Persian period.[12] While we obviously cannot draw from these surveys any *precise* conclusions for the province as a whole prior to the deportations, they are consistent with indications noted earlier, which (allowing for a reasonable margin of error) suggest a total population in the last decades of Judaean independence of about 200,000.

We therefore arrive, tentatively, at the conclusion that the deportations reduced the total population of the province by 10 per cent at the most. Even if we add a considerable death toll as a result of Babylonian and Edomite incursions there is no reason to conclude, from the point of view of demography at any rate, that civic, cultural and religious life came to a standstill in the province in the half-century from the sack of Jerusalem to the fall of Babylon.[13]

THE ARCHAEOLOGY OF JUDAH IN THE EXILIC AGE

Can this conclusion claim support from the archaeological data available for Judah during the same half-century? The questions are easy to formulate but not so easy to answer: Was the territory of Judah completely devastated in the course of the Babylonian conquest? Does the evidence support the thesis of a major depopulation, and thus make it less likely that the infrastructure essential for cultural, intellectual and cultic activity could have survived? Is the evidence of destruction evenly distributed or is it concentrated in certain regions? And where there does seem to be clear physical evidence for destruction, can we be sure that the Babylonians were the perpetrators? The task of providing answers to these questions is complicated by the dubious practice of using the Babylonian conquest of 589–586 as the terminus for Iron II, often with nothing between this point and the Persian period. This conventional method of periodizing archaeologically has the disadvantage of focusing exclusively on one quantitatively minor part of the Syro-Palestinian region. It also has the effect not only of insinuating a cultural hiatus in that area, which may or may not have been the case, or may have been the case to a greater or lesser extent, but of leaving most of the Neo-Babylonian period in a kind of limbo. Needless to say, it is not always possible to give as precise a date for material evidence for destruction (typically, a layer of ash) as 586 BC.[14] We should therefore not be surprised that many of the claims advanced for destruction by the Babylonians have been called into question or rejected outright; in which respect we are witnessing a shrinking of the database reminiscent of the old debates about Israelite cities devastated in the wake of Joshua's army. We can hardly avoid a feeling of *déjà vu* (or *déjà lu*) on rereading such confident statements as the following apropos of the Babylonian conquest: 'all, or virtually all, of the fortified towns in Judah had been razed to the ground' or 'there is not a single known case where a town of Judah proper was continuously occupied through the exilic period'.[15]

The need for caution in making such claims on archaeological grounds can be illustrated without much difficulty. The most recent excavation of Beth-shemesh came up with neither architectural remains nor pottery datable to the seventh century BC. The re-excavators therefore quite reasonably called into question the final destruction of the site (stratum IIC) in 586 proposed by Elihu Grant and George Ernest Wright and since then widely accepted.[16] Another instance of misdating in which it seems that the preference should be for 701 BC rather than 586 BC is Tell Beit Mirsim. The site was excavated in 1926–32 by W. F. Albright who identified it with biblical Debir (Kiriath-Sepher) and dated its destruction (stratum A2) to 586 BC largely on the basis of a seal impression that appears to mention the exiled king Jehoiachin (*l'lyqm n'r ywkn*). Though his conclusions were, once again, widely accepted, and this site is on most lists of cities destroyed by the Babylonians, more recent stratigraphic and epigraphic studies have come up with poor attestation for settlement in the seventh and early sixth centuries and have called into question both Albright's identification of the site and his date for its destruction.[17]

An equally controversial site excavated by Albright in the 1920s and 1930s (and re-excavated by P. W. Lapp in 1964) is Tell el-Fūl about 5 km north of the Damascus Gate. Both excavators identified the site with Gibeah, city of Saul, and Lapp dated its destruction in Period III to Nebuchadrezzar's campaign.

Here, too, both conclusions have been questioned, and in fact the stratigraphy remains so unclear even after several revisions by the excavators that no solid conclusions can be drawn from it.[18] Albright was also involved in an advisory capacity in the excavation of Khirbet et-Tubeiqah, generally identified with Beth-Zur about 30 km south of Jerusalem, which was carried out in 1931 and 1957 under the direction of O. R. Sellers. The architectural and ceramic data from Iron II were in general very scarce, and evidence alleged in 1931 for a violent destruction by the Babylonians was not confirmed when the excavator returned to the site twenty-six years later.[19] Nevertheless, Beth-Zur still features occasionally in lists of Judaean sites destroyed during the Babylonian punitive campaign ending with the sack of Jerusalem in 586 BC.[20]

These case histories illustrate the need for caution in correlating archaeological data with biblical dates. The situation is also rendered more complex by well-documented Edomite encroachment on southern Judah both before and after the Neo-Babylonian conquest. The principal excavator of Beersheba, Y. Aharoni, dated the latest destruction phase at the site (stratum II) to Sennacherib's campaign in 701. Some have since rejected this conclusion in favour of a later date, with the result that the ceramic evidence has so far proved insufficient to decide the issue one way or the other.[21] Even greater uncertainty surrounds the interpretation of the data at Arad in the eastern Negev. Traces of burning on the floors of the citadel in stratum VI (Iron IIC, early sixth century), if dated correctly, would more likely have resulted from an Edomite than a Babylonian attack, a conclusion reinforced by the ostraca found in situ, which testify to hostile Edomite presence in the region. But there are so many unsolved and probably insoluble problems with the stratigraphy of this site that no reliable conclusions for its history in the Neo-Babylonian period are at present possible.[22] Biblical tradition connects Hormah with Arad (Num. 21:1–3), and it therefore made sense to associate this biblical toponym with that area of the eastern Negev. Among excavated sites the major candidates seem to be Kh. Ghara – Tel Ira and Tell el-Milḥ – Tel Malḥata. Whatever their biblical connections may or may not be, both sites show signs of destruction by fire in late seventh to early sixth century BC and Edomite pottery has turned up at both. The probable conclusion, therefore, is that the destruction or damage at both sites occurred in the course of Edomite infiltration into southern Judah, for which there is no lack of evidence, both biblical and archaeological.[23] Since the time of Edward Robinson, Judean Aroer has been identified with ʿArarah about 20 km south-east of Beersheba, which in its turn has been identified with the Adadah of Joshua 15:22 (LXX[B] Arouel). The identification is possible but by no means assured, especially since Aroer features in the biblical account of David's career (1 Sam. 30:28), and yet evidence of settlement on the excavated site prior to the seventh century BC is lacking. The principal excavator, A. Biran, states that Aroer ceased to exist with the Babylonian conquest but offers no evidence for destruction. The presence of significant Edomite pottery and an Edomite seal suggest, however, that it too was occupied at least temporarily by Edomites no later than the Neo-Babylonian period.[24] Finally, Tell Abu Hureireh (Tel Haror), about 20 km west of Beersheba, by some identified with biblical Gerar, seems to have been destroyed about the middle of the seventh century, possibly in an Assyrian or Egyptian attack, but at any rate not by the Babylonians.[25]

The growing body of evidence for Edomite expansion into the eastern Negev and Edomite occupation of Israelite strong points in that region (Horvat ʿUza, Horvat Radum, Horvat ʿAnim, Horvat Tov) makes it unlikely that the Babylonians penetrated so far south; and the survival of the chain of forts or lookout points in the southern approaches to Jerusalem in the Hebron hill country points to the same conclusion.[26] One of these Iron II sites without a biblical identification is the fortress excavated at Khirbet Abu Tuwein in the early 1970s. On the basis of debris and ash in one of the rooms it was at first claimed that the fortress had been burnt at the end of Iron II, but a few years later the evidence was reinterpreted to indicate desertion by its inhabitants rather than destruction.[27]

In central Judah, consisting of the Shephelah, the hill country and the Arabah, destruction would have been more extensive, but also selective. It was hardly in Babylonian imperial interests, and not at all in accord with what we know of Babylonian policy, to wreak indiscriminate destruction on subject countries, and in fact Jeremiah 34:7 speaks of the Babylonians concentrating their attack on the fortified cities. Jerusalem was, of course, the primary target of the punitive campaign, and we have reason to believe that it suffered more severely than provincial towns. The evidence is well known: thick layers of ash, burnt houses and arrowheads uncovered in recent decades in the course of excavations in different parts of Jerusalem bear witness to the fate of the city at the hands of the Babylonians, and there are indications that nearby Khirbet Salih – Ramat Rahel may have suffered the same fate.[28] No site apart from Jerusalem has clearer attestation of destruction than Tell ed-Duweir – Lachish, doubtless because of its situation on the route from the coast to Jerusalem taken by invading armies (Mic. 1:10–16). Partially restored after the Assyrian assault of 701 BC, the city was again destroyed and remained buried under destruction debris until well into the Persian period (see Jer. 34:7 and the ostraca found in one of the gate annexes[29]). The fate of Azekah (Tell Zakariya) is commonly linked with that of Lachish on account of its mention in Jeremiah 34:7 and Lachish ostracon 4. This may be correct, though Jeremiah 34:7 simply says that Azekah had not fallen at the time of writing, and the failure of Hoshaiah and his people to see the signals of Azekah is susceptible of more than one explanation. It should also be noted that the report of the excavation of Tell Zakariya, now a century old, said nothing about a destruction level datable to that time.[30]

Destruction levels have been identified at a few other sites in the heartland of Judah. The gate and some domestic houses at Tell Jezer – Gezer stratum V (late eighth to seventh century BC) show signs of burning, perhaps in 586 according to the excavator W. G. Dever, though a somewhat earlier date can hardly be excluded.[31] A similar claim has been made for stratum VIIa at Tell el-Hesi, by some identified with biblical Eglon, but given its situation we can hardly exclude destruction by

Edomites.[32] At the extreme eastern edge of the province Engedi (Tell el-Jurn – Tel Goren) provides a striking example of both the possibilities and problems involved in using archaeological data for historical reconstruction. The principal excavator, B. Mazar, reported that stratum V (c.630–582) was completely destroyed by fire. I noted earlier that the terminal date for stratum V, that is, 582 BC, was chosen not on archaeological grounds, at least not on any made available in the reports, but on the basis of Jeremiah 52:30 listing a third deportation in the twenty-third year of Nebuchadrezzar. Another problem is the gap between c.582 and c.500, the latter designated as the beginning of stratum IV corresponding roughly to the Persian period, a time when Engedi went through a period of expansion and prosperity with flourishing industrial installations, at least down to the end of the fifth century. We therefore have practically no information on the settlement during the Neo-Babylonian period, no assurance that it was destroyed in the year indicated, and no proof that the Babylonians rather than Edomites were the destroyers.[33]

For our understanding about what was going on in Judah during the obscure period from Nebuchadrezzar to Cyrus the most interesting aspect of this survey is to be sought north of Jerusalem, in the erstwhile territory of Benjamin. To date, no evidence of destruction in late Iron II strata has come to light in any of the sites excavated. None was discovered at el-Jîb (Gibeon), a major centre for wine production, and it now seems that the late Iron Age cemetery continued in use after the fall of Jerusalem, presumably for the inhabitants of the town.[34] Badè's excavation of Tell en-Naṣbeh (identified with biblical Mizpah) in the 1920s and 1930s uncovered evidence consistent with a change from border fortress to provincial capital of the province following the sack of Jerusalem.[35] J. L. Kelso's excavation of Beitin (Bethel), in close proximity to Mizpah, uncovered evidence for a destruction in the late Neo-Babylonian or early Persian period but not during the campaign that led to the destruction of Jerusalem.[36] I recall, finally, the premature and almost certainly mistaken identification of a destruction layer in Period III of Tell el-Ful, by some identified with Gibeah of Benjamin.

The situation in Benjaminite territory suggested by the archaeological data is confirmed by the census list at Ezra 2:1–67 (= Neh. 7:6–68), which includes the names of about twenty towns or villages in which the first immigrants settled on their return from Babylon (Ezra 2:20–35 = Neh. 7:25–38). Allowing for the occasional error in transmission and uncertainty of location, twelve or thirteen of these towns are in Benjamin, and only two (Bethlehem and Netophah) are located south of Jerusalem. This is exactly what we would expect if the band of territory north of Jerusalem, corresponding to land originally assigned to Benjamin, was spared the attentions of the Babylonian army. The absence of Mizpah from the census list is also understandable in view of its status as provincial administrative centre under Babylonian rule, about which more will be said later.

It seems impossible to explain this situation without assuming either that the territory of Benjamin north of Jerusalem surrendered to the Babylonians at an early stage of the campaign, or that these 'Benjaminites' belonged to the anti-war or appeasement party after the Neo-Babylonian takeover of the entire region. Interesting in this respect is the treatment of Jeremiah when he attempted to leave the city by the Benjamin Gate during the siege in order to take possession of a plot of land in

Benjaminite territory (Jer. 32:1–15; 37:11–15): in spite of his protests he was arrested as a *deserter* (37:13) and barely escaped with his life. The revival at that time of a distinctive tribal identity of Benjaminites *vis-à-vis* Judaeans is a puzzling phenomenon. Perhaps the collapse of the state apparatus in the final decades of Judah's quasi-independence led to a kind of retribalization reflected in an addiction to genealogies (1 Chr. 7:6–12; 8:1–40 for Benjamin), classification by ancestral houses (the distinctive *bēt 'ābôt*, ancestral 'house', of Persian period texts) and the use of Judah and Benjamin as personal names (e.g. Neh. 12:34). The description of the Persian province of Judah *from within* as 'Judah and Benjamin' (Ezra 1:5; 4:1; 10:9; Neh. 11:4 and often in Chronicles) is also significant in this respect. We may sum up by saying that destruction during the Babylonian conquest was selective, limited to the region south of Jerusalem, and in that region to a few specific centres of resistance. It is on this basis that any reconstruction of the political, cultural and religious situation of Judah as a province of the Neo-Babylonian empire (597–539 BC) must be grounded.

POLITICS AND RELIGION IN NEO-BABYLONIAN JUDAH

According to the biblical record of events, following the Babylonian conquest Mizpah (Tell en-Naṣbeh), situated about 12 km north of Jerusalem, replaced Jerusalem as the administrative centre of the province and was chosen as the residence of the Babylonian-appointed governor (2 Kgs 25:22–6; Jer. 40:6–41:18). The appointee was Gedaliah, member of a distinguished Judaean family and grandson of Shaphan the public official who played a prominent role in public affairs during the reign of Josiah. If the seal bearing the name Gedaliah discovered at Lachish is genuine and belonged to him, he may also have served as major-domo of the palace during Zedekiah's reign.[37] The relevant biblical texts (2 Kgs 25:22–3; Jer. 40:5, 7, 11; 41:2, 18) are not forthcoming about Gedaliah's official status, but leave room to suspect that he was installed at Mizpah as a puppet king. This was fairly standard procedure followed by Babylonians and, before them, Assyrians (e.g. Sennacherib set up Bel-ibni as puppet king in Babylon and Nebuchadrezzar did the same in Judah with Mattaniah, 2 Kgs 24:17). The rather odd absence of a title – supplied gratuitously in several modern versions – may in fact be due to embarrassment or vexation at the appointment of a non-Davidic king. Pointing in the same direction is the description of Gedaliah's eventual assassin Ishmael as a chief officer of the king (*rab hammelek*, Jer. 41:1), certainly not the Babylonian king. Ishmael *was* a Davidide (Jer. 41:1), which of course helps to explain why he carried out his terrorist act, probably in 582 BC, with the connivance of the Ammonite king Baalis who opposed the policy of accommodation pursued by Gedaliah (Jer. 40:9–10, 14; 2 Kings 25:24). (Hostility between Ammon and Judah will continue into the Achaemenid period in the persons of Tobiah and Nehemiah.) Of possible relevance is also the seal discovered at Tell en-Nasbeh, during Badè's excavation, belonging to one Jaazaniah, a royal official (*ly'znyhw 'bd hmlk*), the same name as the one borne by a member of Gedaliah's court at Mizpah (2 Kgs 25:23; cf. Jezaniah, Jer. 40:8).[38] Finally, the king whose daughters were taken captive by Ishmael at Mizpah (Jer. 41:10) may be Gedaliah, though the author could also have been thinking of the exiled and by now possibly defunct Zedekiah.[39]

Mizpah retained its importance after the province of Judah (Yehud) passed under Iranian control about half a century later, at which time it served as the official residence of the satrap on visits to the province (Neh. 3:7). The results of excavation at Tell en-Naṣbeh are consistent with the important political role assigned to this city during the Neo-Babylonian and early Achaemenid periods. Badè uncovered one of the stronger defensive perimeters in the country, the buildings of stratum 2 (Neo-Babylonian period) were larger, better constructed, and on a different grid from those in the earlier Iron II level, and there appear to be traces of a large public building at the northern end of the site.[40] One reason for the choice of Mizpah as the capital of the Babylonian province was its situation in Benjaminite territory, the population of which, as noted earlier, seems to have been prepared to accept Babylonian rule, at least as a *faute de mieux* and a prudent alternative to open rebellion. The political and therefore also the religious centre of gravity shifted during this period from the centre and south of the province to the north. It is difficult for us in retrospect to imagine that Jerusalem could ever have been eclipsed, yet it must have appeared by no means inevitable at that time that 'this rebellious city hurtful to kings and provinces' (Ezra 4:15) would be restored to its former position. It was certainly not inevitable for Nebuchadrezzar and his successors. That it was restored was due to a combination of circumstances, principally the initiative of enthusiastic Judaeo-Babylonians supported by imperial policy-makers in distant Susa with a special interest in this small western province, especially after the conquest of Egypt by Cambyses (525 BC). That its restoration was bitterly resisted is apparent from the sustained opposition to it, both internal and external, attested in Ezra–Nehemiah and prophetic texts from the early Persian period.

A further consideration relevant to the political status of the province is Josiah's annexation of territory belonging to provinces of the Assyrian empire a few miles north of Jerusalem. The biblical historian records Josiah's activity in Bethel and the cities of Samaria (2 Kgs 23:15–20), and his fatal encounter with Pharaoh Neco took place at Megiddo (23:29). To what extent he succeeded in annexing territory belonging to the Assyrian provinces we do not know.[41] In the relative absence of information on imperial administration in Syria–Palestine it has generally been assumed that the Babylonian overlords left existing arrangements in place.[42] If this was the case, the strategically advantageous position of Mizpah on the main south–north route suggests that it may have served as administrative centre for territory well beyond the northern boundary of the former Kingdom of Judah.

As the administrative centre of the Babylonian province of Judah and the residence at least for a time of a royal court, Mizpah would presumably have had a sanctuary of however modest dimensions attached to it. Local cults and their personnel were a normal part of the apparatus of imperial control in the Near East. After the conquest of Samaria, for example, the Assyrians insisted on setting up a cultic installation at Bethel to teach the immigrant population 'the law of the god of the land' (2 Kgs 17:24–8). The Babylonian commander Nebuzaradan had seen to it that the Jerusalem temple and its personnel were no longer available to provide religious legitimation for further resistance, and even if the altar had survived it would have been corpse-contaminated (e.g. Lam. 2:20) and therefore ritually inaccessible. Lamentations may have been composed for use on the site of the ruined temple, but if so its recital would no more have amounted to a regular liturgy than prayers offered at the *kotel* (the Western Wall) by pious Jews today. Jeremiah 41:4–10 reports that a delegation of eighty individuals from the north was on its way to 'the temple of Yahweh' with offerings when they were slaughtered by Ishmael the day after the bloody coup in Mizpah (Jer. 41:4–10). Most commentators have assumed that they were intercepted and massacred while on their way to Jerusalem, but since the Jerusalem temple was in ruins and its altar desecrated it seems more likely that their destination was the designated provincial sanctuary at or near Mizpah. The likelihood that this was the case is increased by allusions to Mizpah as an important political and religious centre in narratives set in the early period of Israelite history but originating no earlier than the Neo-Babylonian period (Judg. 20–1; 1 Sam. 7:5–6, 9–10; 10:17). In this connection the proximity of the ancient and prestigious sanctuary of Bethel (Beitin) to Mizpah should also be borne in mind.[43]

Any attempt to put together the textual *disiecta membra* at our disposal into a convincing reconstruction of the political and religious situation in Neo-Babylonian Judah will necessarily be provisional. Two conclusions, however, seem to be reasonably assured. First, the infrastructure of the province was not destroyed, and thus a certain level of cultural activity including writing remained possible. Second, the polarity in the province between south and north, between rebellious Jerusalem gutted by the Babylonians and the administrative complex at Mizpah, between the abandoned cult centre in Jerusalem and its replacement in or near Mizpah, was a decisive feature of the political and religious landscape. This situation goes far to explain the conflicts and accommodations of the early Achaemenid period, especially Samarian hostility to the installation of a Judaeo-Babylonian elite controlling a rebuilt Jerusalem temple. It also helps to account for the conflicts and accommodations among priest families and factions that resulted eventually in Aaronites and Zadokites sharing hegemony. The almost complete absence of reference to priests claiming descent from Aaron in biblical texts with the exception of the Priestly source (P) in the Hexateuch and Chronicles,[44] and the association in the narrative tradition of Aaron with Bethel,[45] suggest the possibility that the 'sons of Aaron' (*benē ʾaharon*) profited by the Babylonian conquest and the destruction of the Jerusalem temple to obtain a foothold in the province of Judah. The patronymic of the Judaeo-Babylonian priest who claimed and apparently obtained control of the rebuilt Jerusalem temple, Jeshua ben-Jehozadak (Ezra 3:2 etc.), suggests further that he was the leader of the Zadokite party (the *benē-ṣādôq*) claiming descent real or fictitious from David's chief priest. However it came about, the accommodation reached between Aaronite and Zadokite priests in the late biblical period is reflected in the Aaronite genealogy of the Jerusalem priesthood in which Zadok occupies the midpoint between Levi and Jehozadak (1 Chr. 5:27–41).

Any attempt to assess the level and quality of religious life in Neo-Babylonian Judah is beset by two problems. The first and most obvious is the lack of data and the difficulty, or in some cases practical impossibility, of knowing the place of origin or date of the relevant biblical material. It is therefore advisable to consider most of these texts independently of the respective Judaean and diasporic situations. The other problem is that from the very beginning the historiographical tradition has decisively and unremittingly favoured the Judaeo-Babylonian element, which established itself in Judah (Yehud) as the dominant socio-economic elite and secured control of the rebuilt Jerusalem temple in the early Achaemenid period. All the significant religious initiatives are presented as originating in Babylonian Jewry and the native population, known as 'the peoples of the land' (*ʿammē hāʾªarāṣôt*, Ezra 3:3, etc.), are by contrast described as religiously and ritually polluted and compromised by intermarriage with outsiders. Influenced by this tradition, modern scholarship has until recently tended to locate practically all the more or less contemporaneous biblical texts – with the exception of Lamentations – in the Babylonian diaspora; and this despite the fact that as little as we know about what was happening in Judah, we know even less about the situation in Babylon.

LIFE IN THE DIASPORA

During the Neo-Babylonian and Achaemenid periods the Jewish diaspora spread around the Mediterranean rim and from the Caspian Sea in the north to Nubia in the south. The two major centres were the alluvial plain of southern Mesopotamia and Egypt from the Nile delta to the southern border (see, e.g., Jer. 44:1; Isa. 11:11; 19:18–25). We have practically no information on Jewish settlements in Lower Egypt. Judaean mercenaries had fought in Egyptian armies long before 586 BC and it is safe to assume that some of them settled in Egypt. Jeremiah 44:1 mentions Jewish settlements at Pelusium, Daphne and Memphis, and about that time we also hear of a Greek diasporic trading settlement at Naucratis in the same region. The Jewish military colony on the island of Elephantine at the first cataract of the Nile may have been established by this time – it certainly antedates the Persian conquest of Egypt in 525 BC – but the extant Aramaic documents all date from the fifth century BC.[46]

Successive waves of deportees following on the first conquest of Jerusalem in 597 were settled in the alluvial plain of southern Mesopotamia in the neighbourhood of the city of Nippur. Ezekiel reports a vision near the River Chebar (Ezek. 1:1, etc.), the *nār kabari* or 'grand canal' mentioned in contracts from the reign of Artaxerxes I (464–424), identified with the *shaṭṭ en-nîl* which makes a loop through Nippur on its way back to the Euphrates. The actual location of the experience, Tel Aviv, is unidentified, as are the names of settlements in the Judaeo-Babylonian census in Ezra 2:59 (= Neh. 7:61) – Tel Melah, Tel-Harsha, Cherub, Addan, Immer. The prominence of place names with 'tel' (Akkadian *tillu*), meaning the site of an abandoned ancient settlement, suggests a deliberate policy of settling ethnic minorities in areas earmarked for redevelopment, a kind of internal colonization, which agrees with what we know of the economic situation at that time and policies pursued by the Neo-Babylonian court.[47] It is also significant that Judaean and other deported groups were not enslaved. Slavery was not a major factor in the Neo-Babylonian economy except for temples, since slavery was not as cost effective a means of food production for an expanding population as leasing land to tenant farmers.[48] Moreover, ethnic minorities – Egyptians, Greeks, Phoenicians, Elamites and many others besides Judaeans – were permitted, probably even encouraged, to maintain their own distinct organization under Babylonian supervision, for obvious administrative and fiscal reasons. The fate of Judaean settlers was therefore very different from that of those deported by the Assyrians from the Kingdom of Samaria in the eighth century who had long since disappeared from the historical record.

Thousands of cuneiform tablets excavated at sites in southern Mesopotamia – principally Ur, Sippar, Uruk (the temple of the goddess Eanna), Nippur and Babylon – provide abundant information on social and economic conditions during the Neo-Babylonian and Achaemenid periods. Among these the most interesting from the point of view of Judaean presence in the region are the archives of the commercial house of Murashu (*bit murašū*) discovered more than a century ago at Nippur and dating from the mid to late fifth century BC. About a third of the names occurring in these texts are non-Babylonian and among these latter a significant percentage are Israelite–Judaean names, many of them theophoric formed with Yahweh (e.g. Banayaw, Zabadyaw, Tobyaw, Yahunatan) or otherwise familiar from biblical texts (e.g. Hanani, Shabbatai).[49] While conclusions based on onomastics call for caution – Judaeans could take Babylonian names (e.g. Zerubbabel, Mordecai) and presumably Babylonians could also take Yahwistic names – these data testify to a significant Judaean presence in the area occupying a variety of roles including tenant farmers on crown lands, fishermen, and estate managers.

Some ethnic minorities in the Nippur region were organized in a self-governing corporation (*ḫatru*) for the collective exploitation of land held in fief. Though direct evidence is lacking, this may have been the case with some Judaean settlers. A document from the region of Babylon in the early Achaemenid period records a transaction carried out in the presence of 'the assembly (*puḫru*) of the elders of the Egyptians' and we hear of a Jew bringing action against the house of Murashu before the *puḫru* of Nippur.[50] Biblical texts testify to the important organizational role played by elders (*zᵉqēnîm*) in the Babylonian diaspora (e.g. Jer. 29:1; Ezek. 8:1; 14:1; 20:1, 3; Ezra 5:5, 9 6:7–8), and there may be connections between a putative diasporic Judaean *puḫru* and organizational features of the *qᵉhal haggôlâ* (assembly of the diaspora group), which, according to the biblical sources, formed the dominant elite in Achaemenid Judah (Ezra 10:8). Other distinctive features of the post-exilic Judaean community may also have been imported or adopted from the Babylonian diaspora, including the social and economic role of the Jerusalem temple, land tenure, organization according to large (often fictive) kinship units (the *bēt 'ābôt*; cf. the Babylonian *bit abîm*),[51] and the practice of convening plenary sessions of the *qāhāl* (assembly) to decide important issues (e.g. Ezra 10:1–8; Neh. 8:1), rather like the Athenian *ekklēsia*.

The religious life of Judaeo-Babylonian communities is known to us only from occasional allusions in biblical texts (Jeremiah, Ezekiel, Isa. 40–55; Ezra–Nehemiah for the Achaemenid period) helped out by inference and conjecture. It has been suggested that the elders of the diaspora sought Ezekiel's approval for building a temple (Ezek. 20:1–3, 32) and that 'the place Casiphia' in Babylonia where Ezra recruited cult personnel (Ezra 8:17) was such a temple, comparable to the sanctuary at which the Elephantine Jews worshipped in Egypt.[52] While this is quite uncertain, we cannot explain the preservation of traditions on which the survival of the

Jewish ethnos depended without postulating some kind of infrastructure, perhaps in the form of a rudimentary synagogue network. The important role of the elders has already been noted, priests and Levites were still being educated (Ezra 7:6; 8:15–20), prophets were active, some of them apparently too active (Jer. 29:21–3), and instruction in religious traditions and practice was presumably going on. The frequent mention of settlements near running water (Ezek. 1:3; Ezra 8:15; Ps. 137) suggests an emphasis on rituals of purification accompanied by penitential prayer (Isa. 63:7–64:12; Ezra 9:6–15) and fasting (Zech. 7:3–7; 8:18–19; Ezra 8:21, 23), practices that reflect major concerns of the *bᵉnē haggôlâ* in early Achaemenid Judah. The circumstances in which diasporic Jews lived would have led those anxious to preserve their separate identity to give special importance to rituals of avoidance, dietary laws, circumcision and the observance of sabbath, all of which are much in evidence beginning about that time. Contacts with Judah were maintained through correspondence (e.g. Jer. 29) and movement back and forth, leading after the fall of Babylon (539 BC) to substantial numbers resettling in the province of Judah (Yehud). The practice of praying towards Jerusalem also dates from that time and place (1 Kgs 8:30, 35; Dan. 6:10), tesifying to close emotional and spiritual ties between the homeland and the diaspora.

REACTIONS TO POLITICAL DISASTER

The military conquests of the great empires in the Near East were sponsored by and carried out in the name of imperial deities, Ashur, Marduk and – for Xerxes in his unsuccessful campaign against the mainland Greeks – Ahura Mazda. In 701 the Assyrian Rabshakeh tried to persuade Hezekiah to capitulate by pointing out that the Judaean national deity could not hope to succeed where the gods of Hamath, Arpad and other conquered territories had failed to resist the Assyrian onslaught (2 Kgs 18:33–5; 19:12). Somewhat inconsistently, he added for good measure a very familiar kind of argument, namely, that Hezekiah had provoked the anger of the national deity by abolishing the high places (2 Kgs 18:22). At that time there was no Qoheleth to suggest that some things just happen and there is nothing to be done about it. One felt obliged to seek a *theological* reason for disaster, and the line of reasoning would tend to be either that the national deity had proved too weak, forgetful or negligent to save his devotees, or that he was using the Babylonians to punish his people for neglecting his cult or for other delinquencies. In any case, as Amos put it (3:7), the local deity had to be involved in some way any time evil befell a city – Samaria or Jerusalem, for example (Amos 3:7).

These are, more or less, the terms in which surviving representatives of and adherents to the national cult as opposed to local familial cults would have reacted to the disaster. The problem they faced was exacerbated by the crisis of prophecy in the last decades of Judah's existence, since it could at least be assumed that the deity endorsed the prophet's utterances. Nationalistic prophets like Hananiah, Ahab and Zedekiah who predicted trouble for Nebuchadrezzar (Jer. 28:1–4; 29:21–2) would obviously have lost their prophetic credentials in addition to losing their lives. But prophets of doom like Jeremiah would not have emerged unscathed, either because they were thought to have contributed to bringing about disaster by predicting it, or on account of their refusal to intercede for the people (Jer. 7:16; 11:14; 14:11–12). The crisis of prophecy in the years leading up to the fall of Jerusalem contributed substantially to the collapse of the cultic reforms of Josiah and the revival of syncretism. The state cult of the goddess Asherah, abolished by Josiah (2 Kgs 23:4, 6–7), was reinstated after 597 (Ezek. 8:3), and there were those in the Egyptian diaspora and no doubt elsewhere, among whom women are singled out, who attributed the disaster of 586 not to the anger of Yahweh but to the attempt to suppress the traditional and long-standing cult of the goddess (Jer. 44:15–19).

Whatever its origins, the idea that the nation's relationship with Yahweh rested on the basis of a contract or covenant, the terms of which were available in writing, came to mature formulation in writings emanating from the Deuteronomistic school both before and after the fall of Jerusalem. For the historian (Dtr) the idea had the advantage of providing a ready explanation of disaster by way of demonstrating that the people as a whole, and the rulers in particular, had broken the terms of their contract and had therefore forfeited divine protection. In the post-disaster period adherents of this Deuteronomistic theology attempted to modify the contractual character of the relationship somewhat by speaking in terms of a certain internalization of the moral requirements of the covenant, of the law written on the heart (Deut. 30:11–14; Jer. 31:31–4). For others, however, the experience of disaster on a massive scale appears to have revealed the inadequacy of this way of thinking in a more basic way. It seems that the authors of the Priestly source in the Pentateuch (conventionally designated by the siglum P), writing in the post-disaster period, abandoned altogether the idea of a bilateral agreement as a basis for moral obligation. Hence the absence of an account of covenant-making in the P version of the Sinai event. For others unable to abandon traditional religious thinking entirely the experience of disaster provoked reflection on the depths of moral incapacity – expressed in prophetic sayings about the inability of the leopard to change its spots (Jer. 13:23) and the desperate sickness of the human heart (Jer. 17:9–10).

The deportations confronted the deportees with the immediate question of the possibility of worshipping their deity outside the deity's jurisdiction and in territory in which the writ of other gods ran. We recall that David cursed those who drove him off his own turf to serve other gods (1 Sam. 26:19), and that Naaman the Syrian took back to Damascus a load of Israelite soil in order to be able to worship the God of Israel there (2 Kgs 5:17). The question about singing hymns to Yahweh in a foreign land (Ps. 137:4) was therefore not merely rhetorical. One solution at the symbolic level is presented in Ezekiel's vision of the mobile throne (Ezek. 1:1–28; 10:1–17), the base text in Jewish *merkābâ* mysticism, and the description of the migration of the divine 'glory' (*kābôd*) by stages from Jerusalem to Babylon where the vision could therefore take place (Ezek. 10:18–19; 11:23). Though subject to debate and controversy during the entire period of the Second Commonwealth (e.g. in Jonah who fled from the presence of Yahweh only to encounter him on the high seas and at Nineveh), the implications of breaking the link between deity and territory were far reaching. For Ezekiel and his 'school', however, the blueprint for a temple community in Judah (Ezek. 40–8), and the goal of repossessing land confiscated during the Babylonian conquest (Ezek. 11:14–17), reveal a limited and interim view of diasporic existence. Similar but more specifically political aspirations were entertained by those who still considered the restoration of the native dynasty a goal to be pursued, either in the person of Jehoiachin, detained at the Babylonian court, or one of his descendants.[53]

An anonymous seer preaching and writing during the last years of the reign of Nabonidus (Nabunaʿid 556–539), probably in the Babylonian diaspora,[54] turned the crisis of prophecy referred to earlier on its head by arguing that it was precisely the fulfilment of the prophecies of doom, which he refers to as 'the former things' (Isa. 41:22; 42:9; 43:9, 18; 46:9; 48:3), that provides the assurance that the prospect of liberation and a new beginning now being prophesied would indeed come about. This prospect is intimately tied in with the predicted collapse of the Babylonian empire and triumph of Cyrus who is even designated Yahweh's messiah (Isa. 45:1). The seer's 'argument from prophecy' is reinforced by a vigorous polemic against the cult of Babylonian deities as supplying religious legitimation for the Babylonian state and its imperial pretensions (Isa. 40:18–20; 44:9–20; 46:1–7). His presentation of Yahweh as world ruler and creator could be read as a mirror-image of the qualities attributed to the imperial deity Marduk in the canonical creation myth (*enuma elish*) recited at the autumnal New Year *akitu* festival, the high point of the Babylonian liturgical year.[55] To the Babylonian claim cited by the prophet – 'I am, and there is no one besides me' (Isa. 47:10) – corresponds the claim advanced by the 'Yahweh alone' party on behalf of their God that we begin to hear consistently from about that time and that will be the most characteristic feature of the Judaism to emerge under, successively, Iranian and Macedonian rule.

NOTES

1. Some commentators emend *šᵉbaʿ* (seven) to *šᵉbaʿ ʾeśrē* (seventeen), permitting the opinion that this larger number of deportees was culled from the provincial towns and villages that fell to the Babylonians while Jerusalem was still under siege, an opinion that can claim some support from the designation *yᵉhûdîm* (Judaeans) as opposed to the 832 Jerusalemites deported after the fall of Jerusalem. See Rudolph 1968: 322–5; Malamat 1956: 253–6. This is, I suppose, possible, though hardly obligatory. There is no support in the ancient versions for the alteration, and the seventh year fits the known date for the first surrender of the city to the Babylonians.

2. Whether the year in which city and temple were destroyed was 587 or 586 continues to be debated inconclusively. Arguments for the latter, adopted here, can be found in Hayes and Hooker 1988: 95–8.

3. E.g. Jer. 13:19b: *hoglat yᵉhûdâ kullâ hoglat šᵉlômîm* (or, with some versions, *gālût šᵉlēmâ*), anticipating that the Babylonians would do a thorough job of deporting the population of Judah; Jer. 40:11: the Babylonians left only a remnant (*šᵉʾērît*) in Judah. On exile as a ideological construct in biblical texts see Ackroyd 1968: 237–47; Carroll 1992: 79–93; Barstad 1996: *passim*.

4. Parpola and Watanabe 1988; Oded 1979. In describing the foreign land destined for the besieged inhabitants of Jerusalem in 701 BC, the Rabshakeh sounds like an enthusiastic travel agent (2 Kgs 18:32). The reality, I suppose, would have turned out to be rather different.

5. *ANET* 288. Oded 1979: 19–20 gives the total of forty-three Assyrian deportations accounting for 1,210,928 persons and, on the basis of their records, calculates that the Assyrians displaced some four and a half million people over a period of three centuries.

6. Blenkinsopp 1988: 79–93.

7. One of the most thorough discussions of the issue in the light of the Assyrian data, though naturally out of date in some respects, is that of Janssen 1956: 25–39. He comes out in favour

of the numbers in Jeremiah. Josephus, *Ant.* 10:98–101, counts 3,000 of the ruling class and 10,832 young men and artisans from Jerusalem. Since the larger figure has been reached by combining the 10,000 of 2 Kgs 24:14 with the 832 of Jer. 52:29 it has no independent value.

8   I have consulted Naroll 1962: 587–9; Heicksen 1975: 31–9; Hassan 1978: 49–103; Shiloh 1980: 25–35; Stager 1985: 1–35; Zorn 1994: 31–48.

9   There is broad agreement that these lists correspond to a situation no earlier than the seventh century BC. See Kallai-Kleinmann 1958: 134–60; Aharoni 1979: 347–51.

10 For Tell en-Naṣbeh stratum III (Iron II) Zorn estimates the population of the town, based on an exceptionally good ground plan, at about 1,000; see Zorn 1994: 31–48; and cf. Albright's estimate of 3,000 for eighth-century BC Tell Beit Mirsim; Albright 1960 [1949]: 105 n. 118.

11 Ofer 1993, 3: 815–16; 1994: 92–121.

12 Kochavi 1972 (in Hebrew).

13 In agreement with Weinberg 1972: 45–59 (total population 220,000 to 250,000, and 20,000 deportees), with which we can compare Kreissig 1973: 22–3 who postulates 15,600 deportees constituting one in eight of the population. While I still think Weinberg's figures err on the high side, I would now be more prepared to accept high figures than I was in Blenkinsopp 1991: 40–4.

14 B. Mazar's claim that stratum V of En-Gedi was completely destroyed by fire in 582 is a case in point since the date was chosen not on strictly archaeological grounds but rather on account of Jer. 52: 28–30, which refers to a deportation in the twenty-third year of Nebuchadrezzar; see Mazar 1993, 1: 402. We should also bear in mind that there was more than one Babylonian campaign in the Syro-Palestinian region during the reign of Nebuchadrezzar, on which see Wiseman 1985: 21–41. Can we really be sure, on archaeological grounds, that a particular site was destroyed in 586 and not 597 BC, for example? One solution to the periodization problem would be to interpose an Intermediate Period 600–550 between Iron III (Assyrian period, 700–600) and the Persian period (550–330).

15 Albright 1960 [1949]: 142.

16 Bunimovitz and Lederman, *NEAEHL* 1: 249–53 with bibliography; Emerton 1967: 197–206.

17 Greenberg 1993, 1: 177–80; Albright 1967: 207–20.

18 Arnold 1990: 50–4; Nancy L. Lapp 1993 2: 445–8.

19 Sellers 1968; Funk 1993, 1: 259–61.

20 E.g. Oded 1977: 475.

21 Herzog 1993, 1: 167–73; Manor 1992, 1: 641–5.

22 Aharoni 1993a 1: 82–7; Manor and Herion 1992 1: 331–6. Substantial doubts have been registered about Aharoni's stratigraphy by several archaeologists, including Ussishkin 1988, 142–57 who argues that the ceramic data suggest compressing Aharoni's strata X, IX and VIII into the eighth century. He also proposes to redate the casemate wall of stratum VI (Iron IIC) to the Hellenistic period. On the Arad ostraca, especially ostracon #24 referring to hostile Edomite activities in the region, see Aharoni 1981.

23 Kochavi 1993, 3: 934–6; Beit-Arieh 1993, 2: 642–6; Bartlett 1982: 13–24.

24 Biran 1993, 1: 89–92 summarizing numerous brief notices in *Israel Exploration Journal* and *Revue Biblique* from 1975 to 1982.

25 Oren and Morrison 1993, 2: 580–4 summarizing reports on 'Gerar' (1983, 1984, 1985, 1989/1990).

26 Helga Weippert 1988: 615.

27 A. Mazar, 1974: 276 and 1975: 266–8, stated that the fortress was destroyed by fire but withdrew this conclusion a few years later, 1982a. However, in 1993, 1: 15 he still maintained that the village at the foot of the hill on which the fortress stood was destroyed during the downfall of the Judaean Kingdom, but presents no evidence. One cannot help wondering why the Babylonians would leave the fortress standing and destroy the village.

28 The archaeological data on the fall of Jerusalem have been widely publicized; it will therefore suffice to refer the reader to the bibliography in Stern et al. 1993, 2: 716. Evidence for the destruction of Ramat-Rahel at the same time is less compelling. According to the

excavator, Y. Aharoni, who identified Ramat-Rahel with Beth-Haccherem, the late Iron II citadel was destroyed by fire in 597 or 586 BC. However, the evidence he cites seems to be confined to the stone paving of the gate passageway leading from the inner citadel together with a seal impression belonging to a certain Eliakim (*l'lyqm n'r ywkn*). This impression is identical with the one found at Tell Beit Mirsim, which, as noted earlier, persuaded Albright that stratum A2 of this site was destroyed in 586 BC. See Aharoni 1967: 171–84; 1993b, 4: 1261–7.

29 While Jer. 34:7 obviously alludes to a situation well into the Babylonian conquest of the country, the 'Hoshaiah file' preserved on the ostraca reflects the tense situation preceding the arrival of the Babylonian army rather than actual warfare, e.g., the mission of Coniah the army commander to Egypt presumably to solicit assistance (ostracon 3:13-16). See Ussishkin 1992, 4: 114–26; 1993, 3: 897–911; Weinberg 1969: 81.

30 Stern 1993, 1: 123–4 with bibliography.

31 Dever 1993, 2: 496–506.

32 Fargo 1993, 2: 630–4.

33 B. Mazar 1967a: 85–6; 1967b: 222–30; 1993, 2: 399–405; B. Mazar and Dunayevsky 1967: 133–43.

34 Pritchard's many publications on Gibeon are summarized in 1993, 2: 511–14. See also Eshel 1987: 1–17.

35 Broshi 1975b, 3: 912–18; Zorn 1993, 3: 1098–102; 1994: 31–48.

36 Here, too, Albright claimed to find evidence of destruction from 586 BC. The most recent account is Kelso 1993, 1: 192–4.

37 The inscription on the seal reads *lgdlyhw ('}šr 'l hbyt*, literally, 'belonging to Gedalyahu who is over the house [palace]'. On this Lachish bulla see Tufnell 1953: 348. Avigad 1986: 24–5 suggests that another bulla inscribed *lgdlyhw 'bd hmlk* ('belonging to the royal official Gedalyahu') may refer to the same person since the script is identical.

38 Badè 1933: 150–6.

39 *b'nôt hammelek*, the king's daughters, should probably be understood literally rather than referring to harem women.

40 See n. 35.

41 On the Assyrian provincial system Alt 1964 [1929]: 188-205 is still of basic importance. The provinces of Samerina, Magidu (corresponding to the Galilee), Duru (Dor, the coastal region) and Galazu (Gilead, east of the Jordan) were carved out of the Kingdom of Samaria between 732 and 722 BC.

42 Alt, 'Das System der Assyrischen Provinzen', 188, notes that the provincial system set up by the Assyrians remained basically unchanged down to the Seleucids.

43 Bethel continued as a cult centre *after* the Assyrian conquest of Samaria (2 Kgs 17:27–8) and together with Mizpah is the site of cultic activity in the tribal war against Benjamin (Judg. 20–1). A prophetic text from the early Persian period, before the rebuilding of the Jerusalem temple (518 BC) may indicate that it still had a role at that time (Zech. 7:1–3, reading 'Sareser, Regemmelek and his people sent to Bethel to entreat the favour of Yahweh . . .').

44 The silence is especially noticeable in texts from the Persian period including Ezra–Nehemiah. No 'sons of Aaron' appear in the census list of more than 4,000 priests in Ezra 2 (= Neh. 7), the Aaronite pedigree of Ezra is taken from the priestly genealogy in 1 Chr. 5:27–41, and the two allusions to Aaronite priests in Nehemiah (10:39–40 and 12:47) are later than the time of Nehemiah. The priests in the Jewish settlement on the island of Elephantine in Upper Egypt are never called Aaronite.

45 Exod. 32:1–29; 1 Kgs 12:28–33; Judg. 20:27–8.

46 Porten 1968; idem, in Davies and Finkelstein 1984: 372–400.

47 Adams and Nissen 1972: 55–7; Adams 1981: xiv, 186–90.

48 Eph'al 1978: 74–90; Bickerman 1984: 342–58; Dandamaev 1984: 330–42.

49 On the Murashu archive see Stolper 1985, and on Judaean names in the tablets Zadok 1988: 305–12.

50 Wiseman 1966: 154–8; Eph'al 1978: 76–80; Bickerman 1984: 349.

51 On the *bēt 'ābôt* see Weinberg 1973: 400–14.

52 The Elephantine temple was built before the Persian conquest and was destroyed in 411 BC. See Cowley 1923: 108–24.

53 Jehoiachin was exiled in 597 BC. by Nebuchadrezzar and released or paroled after thirty-seven years by Amel-marduk (2 Kgs 24:12, 15; 25:27–30). On the administrative documents from Babylon published by E. F. Weidner in 1939 that mention Jehoiachin (Ia-ku-u-ki-nu) and his five sons see *ANET* 308. Jehoiachin's return was being predicted – unsuccessfully – even before 586 (Jer. 28:4). For the post-disaster period see Jer. 23:5–6; 33:14–22; Ezek. 34:23–24; 37:4; Amos 9:11–12.

54 The alternative opinion that the so-called Second Isaiah lived in Judah and addressed Judaeans has been defended from time to time, most recently by Barstad 1982: 77–87; 1987: 90–110.

55 *ANET* 60–72.

BIBLIOGRAPHY

Ackroyd, P. R. (1968) *Exile and Restoration*, Philadelphia: Westminster Press.

Adams, R. M. (1981) *Heartland of Cities: Surveys of Ancient Settlement and Land Use on the Central Floodplain of the Euphrates*, Chicago: University of Chicago Press.

Adams, R. M. and Nissen, H. J. (1972) *The Uruk Countryside: The Natural Setting of Urban Societies*, Chicago: University of Chicago Press.

Aharoni, Y. (1962) *Excavations at Ramat Rahel*. Vol. 1: *Seasons 1959 and 1960*, Rome: Pontifical Biblical Institute Press.

—— (1964) *Excavations at Ramat Rahel*. Vol. 2: *Seasons 1961 and 1962*, Rome: Pontifical Biblical Institute Press.

—— (1967) 'Beth Haccherem', in D. Winton Thomas (ed.) *Archaeology and Old Testament Study*, Oxford: Clarendon Press.

—— (1970) *The Beer-Sheba Excavations 1–3*, Tel Aviv: Institute of Archaeology.

—— (1973) *Beer-Sheba I*, Tel Aviv: Tel Aviv University Press.

—— (1979) *The Land of the Bible: A Historical Geography*, Philadelphia: Westminster Press.

—— (1981) *Arad Inscriptions*, Jerusalem: Israel Exploration Society.

—— (1993a) 'Arad', in E. Stern et al. (eds) *New Encyclopedia of Archaeological Excavations in the Holy Land*, Vol. 1, New York: Simon & Schuster.

—— (1993b) 'Ramat Rahel', in E. Stern et al. (eds) *New Encyclopedia of Archaeological Excavations in the Holy Land*, Vol. 4, New York: Simon & Schuster.

Albright, W. F. (1932) 'The Seal of Eliakim and the Latest Preexilic History of Judah', *Journal of Biblical Literature* 5: 77–106.

—— (1934) 'The Kyle Memorial Excavations at Bethel', *Bulletin of the American School of Oriental Research* 56: 2–14.

—— (1960 [1949]) *The Archaeology of Palestine*, Baltimore: Penguin Books.

—— (1963) *The Biblical Period from Abraham to Ezra*, New York: Harper & Row.

—— (1967) 'Debir', in D. Winton Thomas (ed.) *Archaeology and Old Testament Study*, Oxford: Clarendon Press.

—— (1968) *Archaeology and the Religion of Israel*, Garden City, N.Y.: Doubleday.

Albright, W. F. and Kelso, J. L. (1968) 'The Excavation at Bethel 1934–60', *The Annual of the American School of Oriental Research in Jerusalem* 39, New Haven: Yale University Press.

Alt, A. (1914) *Kleine Schriften zur Geschichte des Volkes Israel*, Vol. 2, Munich: C. H. Beck.

Arnold, P. M., SJ (1990) *Gibeah: The Search for a Biblical City*, Sheffield: JSOT Press.

Avigad, N. (1986) *Hebrew Bullae from the Time of Jeremiah*, Jerusalem: Israel Exploration Society.

Badè, W. F. (1933) 'The Seal of Jaazaniah', *Zeitschrift für die alttestamentliche Wissenschaft* 10: 150–6.

Barstad, H. M. (1982) 'Lebte Deuterojesaja in Judäa?' A. Christofferson and H. M. Barstad (eds) *Veterotestamentica: Donum Natalicium A. S. Kapelrud a collegis et amicus XIV Iustra complenti*, NTT 83: 2: 77–87.

—— (1987) 'On the So-called Babylonian Literary Influence in Second Isaiah', *SJOT* 2: 90–110.

—— (1996) *The Myth of the Empty Land*, Oslo: Scandinavian University Press.

Bartlett, J. R. (1982) 'Edom and the Fall of Jerusalem, 586 BC', *Palestine Exploration Quarterly* 114: 13–24.

Beit-Arieh, I. (1989) 'New Data on the Relation between Judah and Edom towards the End of the Iron Age', in S. Gitin and W. G. Dever (eds) *Recent Excavations in Israel: Studies in Iron Age Archaeology*, Winona Lake: Eisenbrauns, *The Annual of the American School of Oriental Research in Jerusalem* 49.

—— (1993) "Ira, Tel', in E. Stern et al. (eds) *New Encyclopedia of Archaeological Excavations in the Holy Land*, Vol. 2, New York: Simon & Schuster.

—— (1996) 'Edomites Advance into Judah', *Biblical Archaeology Review* 22/6: 28–36.

Bickerman, E. (1984) *The Cambridge History of Judaism*. Vol. 1: *Introduction: The Persian Period*, Cambridge: Cambridge University Press.

Biran, A. (1993) 'Aroer', in E. Stern et al. (eds) *New Encyclopedia of Archaeological Excavations in the Holy Land*, Vol. 1, New York: Simon & Schuster.

Blenkinsopp, J. (1988) *Ezra–Nehemiah: A Commentary*, Philadelphia: Westminster Press.

—— (1991) 'Temple and Society in Achaemenid Judah', in P. R. Davies (ed.) *Second Temple Studies*. Vol. 1: *Persian Period*, Sheffield: JSOT Press.

Bliss, F. J. (1899) 'Excavations at Tell Zakarîya', *Palestine Exploration Quarterly* 31: 10–25, 89–111, 170–87.

—— (1900) 'Excavations at Tell Zakarîya', *Palestine Exploration Quarterly* 32: 7–16.

Boling, R. G. (1975) *Judges: Introduction, Translation and Commentary*, Garden City, N.Y.: Doubleday.

Bright, J. (1981) *A History of Israel*, Philadelphia: Westminster Press.

Broshi, M. (1975a) 'La population de l'ancienne Jérusalem', *Revue biblique* 82: 5–14.

—— (1975b) 'Nasbeh, Tell En-', in Michael Avi-Yonah (ed.) *Encyclopedia of Archaeological Excavations in the Holy Land*, Vol. 3, Englewood Cliffs, N.J.: Prentice-Hall.

—— (1978) 'Estimating the Population of Ancient Jerusalem', *Biblical Archaeology Review* 4: 10–15.

Bunimovitz, S. and Lederman, Z, 'Beth-shemesh', NEAEHL 1: 249–53.

Cagni, L. (1986) 'Le fonti mesopotamiche dei periodi neo-Babilonese, Achemenide e Seleucide (VI–III sec. A.C.)', *Rivista biblica* 34: 11–53.

Cardascia, G. (1951) *Les Archives des Murašu: Une famille d'hommes d'affaires babyloniens à l'époque perse (455–403 av. J-C.)*, Paris: Imprimerie nationale.

Carroll, R. P. (1986) *Jeremiah: A Commentary*, Philadelphia: Westminster Press.

—— (1992) 'The Myth of the Empty Land', in D. Jobling and T. Pippin (eds) *Ideological Criticism of Biblical Texts (Semeia 59)*, Atlanta: Scholars Press.

Clines, D. J. A. (1984) *Ezra, Nehemiah, Esther*, Grand Rapids: Eerdmans.

Cohen, R. (1981) 'Excavations at Kadesh-Barnea 1976–1978', *Biblical Archaeologist* 44: 93–107.

—— (1983) *Kadesh Barnea: A Fortress from the Time of the Judean Kingdom*, Jerusalem: Israel Museum Catalogue 233.

—— (1993) 'Kadesh Barnea: The Israelite Fortress', in E. Stern et al. (eds) *New Encyclopedia of Archaeological Excavations in the Holy Land*, Vol. 3, New York: Simon & Schuster.

Coogan, M. D. (1973) 'Patterns in Jewish Personal Names in the Diaspora', *Journal for the Study of Judaism* 4: 184–191.

—— (1974) 'Life in the Diaspora: Jews at Nippur in the Fifth Century', *Biblical Archaeologist* 37: 6–12.

—— (1976) *West Semitic Personal Names in the Murašu Documents*, Missoula: Scholars Press.

Cowley, A. E. (1967) *Aramaic Papyri of the Fifth Century BC*, Osnabrück: Otto Zeller (first published 1923).

Cross, F. M. and Wright, G. E. (1956) 'The Boundary and Province Lists of the Kingdom of Judah', *Journal of Biblical Literature* 75: 202–26.

Dandamaer, M. A. (1984) *Slavery in Babylonia from Nabapolassar to Alexander the Great (626–331 B.C.)*, DeKalb, Ill.: Northern Illinois University Press.

Davies, W. D. and Finkelstein (eds) (1984) *The Cambridge History of Judaism*, Vol. 1: *Introduction: The Persian Period*, Cambridge: Cambridge University Press.

Dever, W. G. (1970) *The 1964–1966 Seasons (Gezer I)*, Jerusalem: Hebrew Union College.

—— (1974) *The 1967–1970 Seasons in Fields I and II (Gezer 2)*, Jerusalem: Hebrew Union College.

Dever, W. G. and Richard, S. (1977) 'A Reevaluation of Tell Beit Mirsim Stratum J', *Bulletin of the American School of Oriental Research* 226: 1–14.

—— (1986) *The 1969–1971 Seasons in Field IV, 'The Acropolis' 1–2 (Gezer 4)*, Jerusalem: Hebrew Union College.

—— (1993) 'Gezer', in E. Stern et al. (eds) *New Encyclopedia of Archaeological Excavations in the Holy Land*, Vol. 2, New York: Simon & Schuster.

Diringer, D. (1967) 'Mizpah', in D. Winton Thomas (ed.) *Archaeology and Old Testament Study*, Oxford: Clarendon Press.

Emerton, J. A. (1967) 'Beth-Shemesh', in D. Winton Thomas (ed.) *Archaeology and Old Testament Study*, Oxford: Clarendon Press.

Eph'al, E. (1978) 'The Western Minorities in Babylonia in the 6th–5th Centuries BC: Maintenance and Cohesion', *Orientalia* 47: 74–90.

Eshel, H. (1987) 'The Late Iron Age Cemetery of Gibeon', *Israel Exploration Journal* 37: 1–17.

Fargo, V. M. (1993) 'Hesi, Tell el-', in E. Stern et al. (eds) *New Encyclopedia of Archaeological Excavations in the Holy Land*, Vol. 2, New York: Simon & Schuster.

Funk, R. W. (1993) 'Beth-Zur', in E. Stern et al. (eds) *New Encyclopedia of Archaeological Excavations in the Holy Land*, Vol. 1, New York: Simon & Schuster.

Giesebrecht, F. (1907) *Das Buch Jeremia*, Göttingen: Vandenhoeck & Ruprecht.

Gottwald, N. K. (1954) *Studies in the Book of Lamentations*, London: SCM Press.

Greenberg, R. (1993) 'Beit Mirsim, Tell', in E. Stern et al. (eds) *New Encyclopedia of Archaeological Excavations in the Holy Land*, Vol. 1, New York: Simon & Schuster.

Hammerhaimb, E. (1966) *Some Aspects of Old Testament Prophecy from Isaiah to Malachi*, Copenhagen: Dybwad.

Hassan, F. (1978) 'Demographic Archaeology', in M. B. Schiffer (ed.) *Advances in Archaeological Method and Theory*, Vol. 1, New York: Academic Press.

Hayes, J. H. and Hooker, P. H. (1988) *The New Chronology for the Kings of Israel and Judah*, Atlanta: John Knox Press.

Heicksen, M. N. (1975) 'Archaeological Light on Population Problems', *Bulletin of the Near Eastern Archaeological Society* 6: 31–9.

Hertzberg, H. W. (1929) 'Mizpa', *Zeitschrift für die alttestamentliche Wissenschaft* 47: 165–6.

—— (1959) *Die Bücher Josua, Richter, Ruth*, Göttingen: Vandenhoeck & Ruprecht.

Herzog, Z. (1993) 'Beersheba', in E. Stern et al. (eds) *New Encyclopedia of Archaeological Excavations in the Holy Land*, Vol. 1, New York: Simon & Schuster.

Hillers, D. R. (1972) *Lamentations: Introduction, Translation and Notes*, Garden City, N.Y.: Doubleday.

Hoglund, K. (1991) 'The Achaemenid Context', in P. R. Davies (ed.) *Second Temple Studies*, Vol. 1: *Persian Period*, Sheffield: JSOT Press.

Hyatt, J. P. (1937) 'A Neo-Babylonian Parallel to Bethel-Sar-Eser, Zech 7:2', *Journal of Biblical Literature* 56: 387–94.

Janssen, E. (1956) *Juda in der Exilzeit: Ein Beitrag zur Frage der Entstehung des Judentums*, Göttingen: Vandenhoeck & Ruprecht.

Jones, D. R. (1963) 'The Cessation of Sacrifice after the Destruction of the Temple in 586 BC', *Journal of Theological Studies* 14: 12–31.

Kallai-Kleinmann, Z. (1958) 'The Town Lists of Judah, Simeon, Benjamin and Dan', *Vetus Testamentum* 8: 143–60.

—— (1986) *Historical Geography of the Bible: The Tribal Territories of Israel*, Jerusalem: Magnes, Hebrew University; Leiden: E. J. Brill.

Kelso, J. L. (1943) 'The Excavation of Tell Beit Mirsim 3: The Iron Age', *Annual of the American School of Oriental Research in Jerusalem* 21–2, New Haven: Yale University Press.

—— (1993) 'Bethel', in E. Stern et al. (eds) *New Encyclopedia of Archaeological Excavations in the Holy Land*, Vol. 1, New York: Simon & Schuster.

Kenyon, K. M. (1976) 'The Date of the Destruction of Iron Age Beer-Sheba', *Palestine Exploration Quarterly* 108: 5–17.

Kochavi, M. (1967) 'Tell Malḥata', *Israel Exploration Journal* 17: 272–3.

—— (1968) 'Tel Malḥata', *Revue biblique* 75: 392–5.

—— (1972) 'Tel Malḥata', *Revue biblique* 79: 593–6

—— (1993) 'Tel Malḥata', in E. Stern et al. (eds) *New Encyclopedia of Archaeological Excavations in the Holy Land*, Vol. 3, New York: Simon & Schuster.

Kraeling, E. G. (1953) *The Brooklyn Museum Aramaic Papyri of the Fifth Century B.C. from the Jewish Colony at Elephantine*, New Haven: Yale University Press.

Kreissig, H. (1973) *Die Sozialökonomische Situation in Juda zur Achämenidenzeit*, Berlin: Akademie Verlag.

Lapp, N. L. (1993) 'Fûl, Tell el-', in E. Stern et al. (eds) *New Encyclopedia of Archaeological Excavations in the Holy Land*, Vol. 2, New York: Simon & Schuster.

Lapp, P. W. (1965) 'Tell el-Fûl', *Biblical Archaeologist* 28: 2–10.

Lemche, N. P. (1988) *Ancient Israel: A New History of Israelite Society*, Sheffield: JSOT Press.

Malamat, A. (1956) 'A New Record of Nebuchadrezzar's Palestinian Campaigns', *Israel Exploration Journal* 6: 253–6.

Manor, D. W. (1992) 'Beersheba', in David Noel Freedman et al. (eds) *Anchor Bible Dictionary*, Vol. 1, New York: Doubleday.

Manor, D. W. and Herion, G. A. (1992) 'Arad', in David Noel Freedman et al. (eds) *Anchor Bible Dictionary*, Vol. 1, New York: Doubleday.

Mazar, A. (1974) 'Khirbet Abu Twain', *Israel Exploration Journal* 24: 276.

—— (1975) 'Khirbet Abu Twain', *Revue biblique* 82: 266–8.

—— (1982a) 'Three Israelite Sites in the Hills of Judah and Ephraim', *Biblical Archaeologist* 45: 167–78.

—— (1982b) 'Iron Age Fortresses in the Judaean Hills', *Palestine Exploration Quarterly* 114: 87–109.

—— (1990) *Archaeology of the Land of the Bible 10,000–586 B.C.E.*, New York: Doubleday.

—— (1993) 'Abu Tuwein, Khirbet', in E. Stern et al. (eds) *New Encyclopedia of Archaeological Excavations in the Holy Land*, Vol. 1, New York: Simon & Schuster.

Mazar, B. (1967a) 'Chronique archéologique: En Gedi', *Revue biblique* 74: 85–86.

—— (1967b) 'En-Gedi', in D. Winton Thomas (ed.) *Archaeology and Old Testament Study*, Oxford: Clarendon Press.

Mazar, B. and Dunayevsky, I. (1967) 'En Gedi: Fourth and Fifth Seasons of Excavations: Preliminary Report', *Israel Exploration Journal* 17: 133–43.

—— (1993) 'En-gedi', in E. Stern et al. (eds) *New Encyclopedia of Archaeological Excavations in the Holy Land*, Vol. 2, New York: Simon & Schuster.

Miller, J. M. and Hayes, J. H. (1986) *A History of Ancient Israel and Judah*, Philadelphia: Westminster Press.

Moore, G. F. (1895) *A Critical and Exegetical Commentary on Judges*, Edinburgh: T. & T. Clark.

Meyers, C. L. and Meyers, E. M. (1987) *Haggai, Zechariah 1–8*, Garden City, N.Y.: Doubleday.

Naroll, R. (1962) 'Floor Area and Settlement Population', *American Antiquity* 27: 587–9.

North, F. S. (1954) 'Aaron's Rise in Prestige', *Zeitschrift für die alttestamentliche Wissenschaft* 66: 195–9.

Noth, M. (1960) 'Ap(h)eq(a) and 'Azeqa', *Biblica* 41: 41–63.

—— (1980 [1928]) *Die Israelitischen Personennamen im Rahmen der gemeinsemitischen Namengebung*, Hildesheim: Georg Olms Verlag.

Oded, B. (1977) 'Judah and the Exile', in J. H. Hayes and J. Maxwell Miller (eds) *Israelite and Judaean History*, Philadelphia: Westminster Press.

—— (1979) *Mass Deportations and Deportees in the Neo-Assyrian Empire*, Wiesbaden: Dr. Ludwig Reichert Verlag, 1979.

Ofer, A. (1993) 'Judean Hills Survey', in E. Stern et al. (eds) *New Encyclopedia of Archaeological Excavations in the Holy Land*, Vol. 3, New York: Simon & Schuster.

—— (1994) 'All the Hill Country of Judea', in I. Finkelstein and N. Na'aman (eds) *From Nomadism to Monarchy*, Washington, D.C.: Biblical Archaeology Society.

Oren, E. D. (1983) 'Gerar', in *Excavations and Explorations in Israel*, Jerusalem: Israel Antiquities Authority, 2: 33–5.

—— (1984) 'Gerar', in *Excavations and Explorations in Israel*, Jerusalem: Israel Antiquities Authority, 3: 27–30.

—— (1985) 'Gerar', in *Excavations and Explorations in Israel*, Jerusalem: Israel Antiquities Authority, 4: 31–3.

Oren, E. D. and Morrison, M. A. (1986) 'Land of Gerar Expedition: Preliminary Report for the Seasons of 1982 and 1983', *Bulletin of the American School of Oriental Research, Supplement* 24: 57–87.

—— (1989/1990) 'Gerar', in *Excavations and Explorations in Israel*, Jerusalem: Israel Antiquities Authority, 9: 69–73.

—— (1993) 'Haror, Tel', in E. Stern et al. (eds) *New Encyclopedia of Archaeological Excavations in the Holy Land*, Vol. 2, New York: Simon & Schuster.

Parpola, S. and Watanabe, K. (1988) *Neo-Assyrian Treaties and Loyalty Oaths*, Helsinki: Helsinki University Press.

Petersen, D. L. (1984) *Haggai and Zechariah 1–8*, Philadelphia: Westminster Press.

Porten, B. (1968) *Archives from Elephantine*, Berkeley: University of California Press.

Pritchard, J. B. (1955) *Ancient Near Eastern Texts Relating to the Old Testament*, Princeton: Princeton University Press.

—— (1993) 'Gibeon', in E. Stern et al. (eds) *New Encyclopedia of Archaeological Excavations in the Holy Land*, Vol. 2, New York: Simon & Schuster.

Rudolph, W. (1968) *Jeremia*, Tübingen: J. C. B. Mohr.

—— (1976) *Haggai–Sacharja 1–8–Sacharja 9–14–Malachi*, Neukirchen-Vluyn: Neukirchener Verlag.

Schofield, J. N. (1944) *The Religious Background of the Old Testament*, London: T. Nelson.

Sellers, O. R. (1968) 'The 1957 Excavations at Beth-zur', *The Annual of the American School of Oriental Research in Jerusalem* 38, New Haven: Yale University Press.

Shiloh, Y. (1980) 'The Population of Iron Age Palestine in the Light of a Sample Analysis of Urban Plans, Areas, and Population Density', *Bulletin of the American School of Oriental Research* 239: 25–35.

—— (1989) 'Judah and Jerusalem in the Eighth–Sixth Centuries BCE', in S. Gitin and W. G. Dever (eds) *Recent Excavations in Israel: Studies in Iron Age Archaeology*, Winona Lake: Eisenbrauns, *The Annual of the American School of Oriental Research in Jerusalem* 49.

Sinclair, L. A. (1960) 'An Archaeological Study of Gibeah (Tell el-Ful)', *The Annual of the American School of Oriental Research in Jerusalem* 34–5, New Haven: Yale University Press, 1–52.

—— (1964) 'An Archaeological Study of Gibeah (Tell el-Ful)', *Biblical Archaeologist* 27: 52–64.

Smith, R. L. (1984) *Micah–Malachi*, Waco: Word Books.

Soggin, J. A. (1981) *Judges: A Commentary*, Philadelphia: Westminster Press.

Stager, L. (1985) 'The Archaeology of the Family', *Bulletin of the American School of Oriental Research* 260: 1–35.

Stern, E. (1982) *Material Culture of the Land of the Bible in the Persian Period, 538–332 B.C.*, Jerusalem: Israel Exploration Society; Warminster, UK: Aris & Phillips.

—— (1993) 'Azekah', in E. Stern et al. (eds) *New Encyclopedia of Archaeological Excavations in the Holy Land*, Vol. 1, New York: Simon & Schuster.

Stern, E., et al (eds) (1993) *New Encyclopaedia of Archaeological Excavations in the Holy Land*, 3 vols, New York: Simon & Schuster.

Stolper, M. W. (1985) *Entrepreneurs and Empire: The Murašu Archive, the Murašu Firm, and Persian Rule in Babylonia*, Istanbul: Nederlands Historisch–Archaeologisch Instituut te Istanbul.

Toombs, L. E. (1990) 'The Joint Archaeological Expedition to Tell el-Hesi and the Results of the Earlier Excavations', *Palestine Exploration Quarterly* 122/2: 101–13.

Tufnell O. (ed.) (1953) *Lachish III: The Iron Age*, London: Oxford University Press.

Ussishkin, D. (1988) 'The Date of the Judaean Shrine at Arad', *Israel Exploration Journal* 38: 142–57.

—— (1992) 'Lachish', in David Noel Freedman et al. (eds) *Anchor Bible Dictionary*, Vol. 4, New York: Doubleday.

—— (1993) 'Lachish', in E. Stern et al. (eds) *New Encyclopedia of Archaeological Excavations in the Holy Land*, Vol. 3, New York: Simon & Schuster.

Vogt, E. (1957) 'Die neubabylonische Chronik über die Schlacht bei Karkemisch und die Einnahme von Jerusalem', *Vetus Testamentum Supplement* 4, Leiden: E. J. Brill, 67–96.

Weidner, E. F. (1939) 'Jojachin, König von Juda in Babylonischen Keilinschriften', *Mélanges syriens offerts à Monsieur René Dussaud secrétaire perpetuel de l'Académie des inscriptions et belles-lettres, par ses amis et ses élèves*, Vol. 2, Paris: P. Geuthner.

Weinberg, J. (1972) 'Demographische Notizen zur Geschichte der nachexilischen Gemeinde in Juda', *Klio* 34: 45–59.

—— (1973) 'Das Bēit 'ābôt im 6.–4. Jh. v.u.Z.', *VT* 23: 400–14.

Weinberg, S. S. (1969) 'Post-Exilic Palestine: An Archaeological Report', *The Israel Academy of Sciences and Humanities. Proceedings* 4/5.

Weippert, H. (1988) *Palästina in vorhellenistischer Zeit*, Munich: C. H. Beck.

Willesen, F. (1952) 'The Cultic Situation of Psalm 74', *Vetus Testamentum* 2: 289–306.

Williamson, H. G. M. (1985) *Ezra, Nehemiah*, Waco: Word Books.

Wiseman, D. J. (1966) 'Some Egyptians in Babylonia', *Iraq* 28: 154–8.

—— (1985) *Nebuchadrezzar and Babylon*, Oxford: Oxford University Press.

Zadok, R. (1988) *The Pre-Hellenistic Israelite Anthroponymy and Prosopography*, Leuven: Peeters.

—— (1992) 'Onomastic, Prosopographic and Lexical Notes', *Biblische Notizen* 65: 52–53.

Zorn, J. (1993) Nasbeh, Tell En-', in E. Stern et al. (eds) *New Encyclopedia of Archaeological Excavations in the Holy Land*, Vol. 3, New York: Simon & Schuster.

—— (1994) 'Estimating the Population Size of Ancient Settlements: Methods, Problems, Solutions, and a Case Study', *Bulletin of the American School of Oriental Research* 295: 31–48.

CHAPTER TWENTY-FOUR

ISRAEL UNDER PERSIA
AND GREECE

———•◆•———

Lester L. Grabbe

Many people think of the period of the Israelite monarchy as being the genuine time of Israel's history, and that the period after the exile – the 'post-exilic period' – is only an appendix to that history. Without going into the questions of terminology (since some would restrict the term 'Israel' to the northern kingdom which was conquered by the Assyrians about 722 BCE), one can say with some vigour that the post-exilic period was one of great importance and productivity for the literature, religion, and even self-identity of the Jewish people. More and more scholars are coming to regard the Hebrew Bible as by and large a product of this period.

The problem we have with the post-exilic period is that for the first couple of centuries our sources are brief, often of questionable reliability, and cover only a portion of the period even at their most optimistic reading. Many histories of this period either naively read the sources at face value or are very speculative – or even both together. It is important that historians make clear to the reader where we have evidence and where we are trying to fill in gaps by educated guesses.

Those readers used to histories and biographies relating to more recent times will be disconcerted to find how scanty are our sources and how little we really know about much of ancient history. We are dependent on a handful of sources, in some cases written long after the events they purport to describe and often with a clear bias. This means that different researchers will interpret some aspects of this history in quite different ways. Readers who read other accounts of the Jews in the Persian and Greek periods may find that my reconstruction differs considerably at some points from others. In some cases, this is because of new sources, but usually it depends on a question of methodology. On the whole, specialists for these periods are becoming more critical and sceptical of their sources and more alert to the biases contained in them. They are less likely to take the sources at face value but to question them closely and recognize the limitations on our knowledge. My chapter here reflects this more 'hard-headed' approach to writing the history of the Jews at this time.

We shall consider the period in question, which extends from Cyrus the Persian's conquest of Babylon to the taking of Jerusalem by the Roman general Pompey (c. 539–63 BCE), in five parts: the Persian period, the Greek conquest, the Ptolemaic period, Seleucid rule, and the Maccabean kingdom. Each section will begin with a brief outline of the sources available to us and the problems with writing a history of that particular period.

THE PERSIAN PERIOD

Jerusalem had been conquered in 587/586 BCE by the Babylonians. This was the time of the dominance by what is referred to as the Neo-Babylonian empire. The Neo-Babylonian control of Mesopotamia was relatively short lived, lasting less than a century (c. 612–539 BCE). Its most famous king was Nebuchadnezzar (called Nebuchadnezzar II, because another Nebuchadnezzar was a king of Babylon in 1126–1105 BCE) who ruled 604–562 BCE. His army took Jerusalem in 597 BCE and deported the king and his family and some of the upper class to Mesopotamia, according to the Bible (2 Kgs 24) and the *Babylonian Chronicles*. A decade later the Bible says that Jerusalem was destroyed after a long siege, the king blinded and taken captive, many of the leadership executed, and a large number of people transported to the Babylonian region (2 Kgs 25). Indeed, some biblical passages suggest that all the people were removed and the land left empty, but this disagrees with archaeology and also other biblical passages (cf. 2 Kgs 25:12). This period of 'the exile' lasted for about half a century. Then in 539 BCE Cyrus the Persian conquered Babylon, establishing the Persian empire from Afghanistan to the Mediterranean and from the Black Sea to Egypt.

The Persian period lasted two centuries and began a new phrase in Israel's history. The temple had been destroyed by the Babylonians and the king removed. The temple was eventually rebuilt under the Persians, but the kingship was not restored. Instead, Judah became a small and relatively unimportant province in the vast Persian empire, with a Persian governor appointed to oversee its affairs. Recent decades have seen an explosion of information on Persian rule. This comes partly from archaeology, though much of it is due to the finding, publication, and analysis of cuneiform texts from Mesopotamia and papyrus records in Aramaic and Egyptian from Egypt. Despite these valuable contemporary sources, for the broad outline of political events in Persian history we are still dependent on the classical Greek historians such as Herodotus, Thucydides, and Xenophon. The Greek writers are very important, but they also give everything from a Greek perspective; no native Persian histories have been found (even if they ever existed, which is not certain). The Greek writers tell us only what was important to the Greeks and do not attempt a comprehensive history of the Persians. They also have a strong bias against non-Greeks, whom they called 'barbarians' and thought inferior in many ways. We have to keep these points in mind in reading any Greek version of Persian history.

For the history of the Jews, we have Aramaic documents from a Jewish colony at Elephantine in Egypt, the evidence of archaeology, and a few inscriptions. Otherwise, we are dependent on biblical writings (the references to the Jews in Greek writings are mainly later than the Persian period), including the books of Ezra, Nehemiah, and some of the prophets (especially Haggai and Zechariah and probably Isaiah 56–66). Some other writings have also been suggested as coming from the Persian period, though there is disagreement among scholars: Esther, Jonah, Ruth, the Song of Songs, and Job in its final form. Although the books of Chronicles were most likely completed in the early Ptolemaic period, they can probably also be used as sources for the Persian period in certain respects. There are two problems with using the biblical literature to reconstruct history: (1) the biblical writers are not interested in history in the way that moderns are, as an accurate record of the past, but have a strong theological and ideological aim. They want to tell us *the way it should have been* rather than *the way it was*. (2) At their most optimistic reading the relevant biblical books cover only a few years – much of the Persian history of the Jews is a complete blank as far as literary sources are concerned.

When Cyrus took over Babylonia he issued decrees allowing the return of divine images to their cults because the last Babylonian king had gathered many of them to Babylon. Although these decrees are now seen as examples of royal propaganda, they fit with the general biblical picture that some Jews from Babylonia were allowed to return to Judah. The book of Ezra 1–6 describes the initial return in a particular fashion, including the rebuilding of the temple under quite adverse conditions, and many take it more or less at face value. However, there are reasons to query its picture. For one thing, it suggests that a largely empty Judah had to be resettled and ignores the fact that most Jews had not been deported but thousands of their descendants still continued to live in and farm the land. Also the sequence of Persian kings in Ezra 4–5 is very mixed up; documents dated to kings decades and even almost a century later are used to stop work on the temple in the time of Darius. The author is likely to have been writing long after the events and with few sources at his disposal.

We know two facts with reasonable certainty: (1) that a considerable number of Jews migrated from Babylonia and settled in Judah over a long period after 539 BCE, and (2) that the destroyed temple was rebuilt at an unspecified time (though probably before 600 BCE). Beyond these facts we can say little with confidence. The first governor of the province may have been a man named Sheshbazzar. Ezra 1:8–11 mentions him as being delegated to bring back to Jerusalem the temple vessels, which had been taken away to Babylon as booty, but then he disappears from the story. However, Ezra 5:14 quotes a Persian document which states that he was governor of the province and that he 'laid the foundations' of the temple. The contradictions between these two texts is a good example of the problems we have with trying to reconstruct a history of this period. Beyond these two problematic texts, we know nothing more about Sheshbazzar; it is almost as if the writer of Ezra 1–6 has deliberately wanted to play down his role and remove him from the narrative as far as possible, in favour of Zerubbabel and Joshua. These two early figures in leadership positions were Zerubbabel who was governor of the province and Joshua who was high priest of the cult (Hag. 1:1). They are associated with the rebuilding of the temple, which seems to have begun (or rebegun, if Sheshbazzar had already laid the foundations) in the reign of Darius I (522–486 BCE), perhaps about 520 BCE (Hag. 1:1–2:1). How long it took to build depended very much on the resources the people could muster, though the alleged help from the Persian treasury is unlikely (Ezra 6:8–10) and the date of completion in only four years is suspect (Ezra 6:15). Given the limits on resources of material and manpower, the completion probably took much longer.

The next we read in the biblical text of the Jewish community around Jerusalem is many decades later, in the middle of the fifth century. About this time, Ezra and Nehemiah are said to have to come to Jerusalem to introduce reforms in the religion, cult, administration, and practices of the community. Since the most trustworthy information is found in the book of Nehemiah, we begin our discussion there. At its heart, the book of Nehemiah seems to have an actual composition by Nehemiah himself (much of Neh. 1–6 and perhaps some of 13). Although events are given from his very particular perspective, which is highly partisan, he provided a contemporary account. Granted, his 'Memorial' or 'Memoir' has been edited and other material (mainly lists of various sorts) added to produce the present book of Nehemiah, but we are on surer ground here than with some other sources.

Nehemiah himself was sent as governor of the province of Judah (Neh. 5:14) with the specific commission to repair the city wall (Neh. 1–2). The building of this wall was more than just a chance to provide surer defences for the city: it furnished the means of a much more centralized and controlled administration. Nehemiah describes various 'enemies' who threatened his enterprise (Neh. 2:19–20; 4:1). One of these was Sanballat the governor of Samaria who would have been a natural rival to the governor of a neighbouring province. The Persian administration tended to permit semi-autonomous governors, who were allowed to function with considerable personal discretion. This encouraged rivalry among administrators of equal rank, especially among the satraps who ruled huge territories and were kings in miniature. Keep in mind that the terms 'satrap' and 'satrapy' were sometimes loosely used in ancient writings, even being applied to lesser provinces; but there were only about twenty genuine large satrapies in the Persian empire, with Judah in the one that took up all the region west of the Euphrates. Provincial governors had much less power, but they seem to have exercised it in their own province much as the satraps did. So for Nehemiah and Sanballat, as rulers of neighbouring provinces with a certain amount of power at their disposal, to be suspicious of one another and even adversaries is not surprising (though the satrap of the region would probably have kept some control to prevent this from getting out of hand). Another 'enemy' was Tobiah. Despite Nehemiah's attempts to slander him as an 'Ammonite slave', he was evidently the head of an old Jewish family with its ancestral home across the Jordan. Despite Nehemiah's fierce hatred of him, Tobiah had many friends and allies in Jerusalem who also co-operated with Nehemiah (Neh. 6:17–19). Therefore, we must not assume that Nehemiah's version of events was the only true one – as so often, there was more than one side to the story.

Among Nehemiah's aims seems to have been a desire to create a rather isolated religious community, governed by strict obedience to the law, which would have little to do with its neighbours and thus avoid 'foreign' influences. His first project, which was the repair of the city wall, as well as other measures he took, would have been a means to this end. As soon as he arrived he enlisted the community to help repair the wall, with stories of how Sanballat intended to threaten the community. Whether there was a real threat may be questioned – the satrap over the two of them is unlikely to have allowed things to go that far – but it would have helped to motivate the community. For this and other reasons, the people as a whole seem to have been behind the repair of the wall, which was done in a comparatively short period of time.

Nehemiah also brought in the community leaders and elders and a significant portion of the province's population to live in Jerusalem – and they seem to have had no choice in the matter (Neh. 7:4–5; 11:1–2). This would have allowed him to keep a close eye on the leadership and to exercise considerable control over the actions of the people (as the examples in Neh. 13 suggest). Thus, he seems to have succeeded in whipping the community into the shape of his own idealism, at least temporarily, but as soon as he was away for an extended period of time, the people reverted to a more relaxed way of doing things (cf. Neh. 13:4–31). This did not mean that they abandoned their religion or turned to pagan worship; it was just that they did not agree with Nehemiah's narrow 'fanatical' approach. If we look at the subsequent history of the community over the next 200 years or so, the people as a whole seem to have rejected Nehemiah's vision, even though, from all we can tell, they would still have regarded themselves as pious Jews. As has recently been pointed out, Nehemiah's actions look very much like those of a sect founder and leader. That is, he tried to treat fellow Jews as outsiders. Up until this time, Jews were all accepted as part of an ethnic community. The idea that ethnic Jews could be expelled from the community and from worship at the temple is characteristic of later sects like the Essenes. In certain ways, Nehemiah is the first Jewish sectarian known to us in history.

Unlike Nehemiah, Ezra is a shadowy figure. According to Ezra 7 he was given enormous personal power in the province and satrapy and unimaginable wealth to take to the Jerusalem temple. Yet he exercises none of the power when he has to address a crisis, and the 25 plus tonnes of silver and gold that he allegedly brought to Jerusalem is simply incredible. Ezra is supposed to have brought a law (but the law had been observed in Jerusalem and the temple for nearly three-quarters of a century); he was supposed to resolve a problem of mixed marriages (but others take the initiative; in any case, the women married were probably the descendants of Jews not taken captive; and Nehemiah had to deal with exactly the same problem a few years later); and he was in Jerusalem at the same time as Nehemiah (yet they seem to have had nothing to do with each other, and Nehemiah never mentions him). All in all, what we have in the story of Ezra (Ezra 7–10; Neh. 8) is a figure of legend rather than history.

So, if we cannot take Ezra 7–10 at face value, what are we to make of Ezra as a historical figure? No doubt an actual historical individual lies behind the legend. He was not as central to the history of Jewish law as the book of Ezra makes him, however, because he is ignored by Nehemiah and also by the later writing of Ben Sira (often known as Ecclesiasticus) about 200 BCE who mentions Nehemiah but not Ezra. Either Ben Sira did not know of Ezra or he did not consider him important. This ignorance would have been impossible in later Judaism when Ezra became a key figure as a lawgiver. Yet the legend that Ezra even restored the law after it was lost (*4 Ezra* [2 Esdras] 14) is indicative that he had something to do with the law. He was probably much less important than Nehemiah and only later became elevated to a position of prominence as the tradition developed.

One of the main emphases in Ezra and Nehemiah is the exclusivism of the Jewish community in Judah. According to these books the Jews should remain separate from the surrounding peoples (who are seen as 'foreigners', even though most were probably descended from Jews who had not been taken captive to Babylon). They assume that only the community created by the returned exiles has legitimacy. Having read these books, some people assumed that this was the only perspective of the biblical writers. However, if books such as Jonah and Ruth are from this period of time, as many argue, we have a quite different point of view. According to Ruth, even the great king David was descended from a Moabite woman, a foreigner who had nevertheless been in every way a model of faithfulness and loyalty. Similarly, the book Jonah tells how the Assyrians – the enemies of Israel – repented at Jonah's preaching and had been spared, something which the Israelites had not done according to many statements in the prophetic books. It has been strongly suggested that these books are deliberately opposing the policy of isolation and exclusivism espoused by the books of Ezra and Nehemiah.

Even using the biblical writings to their full we have at the most a history of the Jews at two brief points in the Persian period, with the entire last century of Persian rule a virtual blank. Josephus mentions an episode in which a high priest named Johanan killed his brother in the temple (*Ant.* 11.7.1 §§297–301). As a result the Persian governor Bagohi punished the Jews by placing a special tax on temple offerings. If historical, this episode would have been about 400 BCE (though some want to date it much later, about 340 BCE). Archaeology suggests two major catastrophes in which a number of cities and villages were destroyed. These would have been about the years 480 and 380 BCE, but there is no clear reference to them in the written records, a fact that emphasizes how little we know of the Jews in this period.

For this entire period Judah was a small province in a vast Persian empire. Through most or probably even all this period, there was a Persian governor over the province. In some cases, we know that this governor was Jewish, including Sheshbazzar, Zerubbabel, and Nehemiah. If a set of seals from the early Persian period is genuine, we also have the names of some other Judaean governors who were evidently Jewish as well, as indicated by their names. It has further been suggested, based partly on coins, that the high priest also held the office of governor of Judah in the latter part of the Persian empire. If so, this fits the situation we know of from the Ptolemaic and Seleucid periods in which the high priest was also the main administrative official of the province.

THE GREEK CONQUEST

Alexander the Great's army crossed into Asia Minor in 334 BCE and challenged Persian rule. The first Persian defeat at Issus in 333 showed that the Persian empire was coming to an end, and the last Persian king Darius III was defeated at Gaugamela in 331. Alexander continued to march east for several more years, reaching northern India, but by this time his troops had had enough. He returned to Babylon to consolidate his rule but died shortly afterwards in 323. Since he had designated no successor, a serious power vacuum was left. His generals (who became known as the *Diadochi*, 'successors') moved to fill it, and the next 40 years saw battles between great armies all over the ancient Near East as the power shifted and different leaders came and went. The final result was a threefold division of Alexander's empire between his general and companion Ptolemy in Egypt; the former chief of Alexander's elite bodyguard Seleucus over much of Asia Minor, northern Syria, and most of the eastern part of the empire; and the Antigonid dynasty over the mainland of Greece and Thrace. Although much of the eastern part of the Seleucid empire was lost from about 250, this division of rule remained in place for the most part until the Romans gained control in the mid-second century BCE.

Our knowledge of the Jews during this period is very skimpy, mainly a few literary bits and pieces whose information is not easy to evaluate. One story we can reject fairly easily. This is the legend that Alexander visited Jerusalem in the initial part of his conquest on his way to Egypt. This story is found in various versions, the earliest being that of Josephus (*Ant.* 11.8.1–6 §§304–45). According to it, the Jews refused to provide aid in the siege of Tyre. Alexander came to punish them but, because of a dream, instead bowed before the Jewish high priest and honoured the Jews. There are several reasons for doubting this account. Although the main history of Alexander by Arrian tells about this part of the campaign in great detail, he says nothing about a trip to Jerusalem, nor was there time between the siege of Tyre and the siege of Gaza for it to have taken place. Arrian has no bias against Alexander's interest in Oriental religions and would have had no reason to omit such a visit to Jerusalem. Also, the story has all the hallmarks of a piece of Jewish propaganda. In addition, Josephus claims that the high priest showed the book of Daniel to Alexander, but there is a strong consensus in modern scholarship that Daniel was written long after Alexander.

We also have the statement of Agatharchides of Cnidus (as quoted in Josephus, *Ant.* 12.1.1 §§3–10; *Ag. Apion* 1.22 §§209–12) that Ptolemy I captured Jerusalem at one point during the wars of the Diadochi, though he gives no reason why Ptolemy needed to capture the city nor when that took place. Josephus also tells us that a Jewish high priest named Ezekias (the Greek form of Hezekiah) came to Egypt with many of his people and asked to settle there, which Ptolemy I allowed. The most recent study of this text argues that this is the fabrication of a Jewish writer about 100 BCE; if this evaluation is correct, we cannot use this passage as historical information for the early Greek period.

The most valuable piece of information is a passage on the Jews that is supposed to have originated with Hecataeus of Abdera about 300 BCE (quoted by Diodorus of Sicily 40.3.1–8). It tells how the Jews left Egypt and came to Palestine under the leadership of Moses. There they set up an ideal state in which there was no king; rather, the priests chose the most pious of their number to be both high priest and civil leader of the country. They had no images of the gods but worshipped the heavens as divine. The people were willing to obey the instructions of the priests who also acted as judges and guardians of the law. If this description sounds rather utopian, it is because Hecataeus probably got much of his information from a source that ultimately goes back to Jewish priests. This is why he knows nothing of the monarchic period when there were indeed kings over the Jews. The Greeks were interested in exotic Oriental peoples who seemed to live a philosophical life, and Hecataeus appears to be giving an idealized version of Jewish history and government. Nevertheless, Hecataeus's account gives an important insight into the state and society of Judah shortly after the Greek conquest.

Apart from these brief notes we have no further direct references to the Jews. However, we can be fairly sure that the wars of the Diadochi between Alexander's death and about 280 BCE meant there was often military activity in and around Palestine. For example, the battle that allowed Seleucus to return from Egypt to Babylon, an event that began the use of the Seleucid era for calendar reckoning (a widely used means of dating before the BC/AD system developed about 600 CE), was fought at Gaza. It has been suggested that the 'giants' who devastated the earth in the book of *1 Enoch* (7:3–11; 9:21–9; 10:26–35) were modelled on the Diadochi and their armies.

PTOLEMAIC RULE

At various times during the wars of the Diadochi, the fighters would come to temporary agreements. But most of these lasted only a brief period of time before one or other of the parties broke the treaty and started the fighting once again. An important treaty was agreed to in 301, which assigned southern Syria and Palestine to the Seleucid territory; however, Ptolemy seized the territory and refused to give it up. Because Seleucus was in Ptolemy's moral debt he did not press his claim, but his successors did not give it up. The result was a series of 'Syrian wars' fought between the Seleucid and Ptolemaic empires thoughout the third century until the Seleucids finally about 200 BCE took what they always regarded as rightly theirs.

Under Ptolemaic rule Palestine and southern Syria were treated as if they were a part of Egypt. The main concern of the Ptolemaic rulers was to maximize tax revenue, and Syro-Palestine was a rich source for it. There were Ptolemaic officials down to the village level to supervise the collection of taxes. This meant that the foreign ruler was not just a dim and distant patriarchal figure but in some sense a daily presence for most Jews. At the lower level the Ptolemaic officials might be local people used by the administration, but the governmental supervision seems to have been much closer and omnipresent than under previous rulers. It is not clear whether there was a separate governor responsible for Syro-Palestine. Some scholars think so, but others argue that the region was supervised by the Ptolemaic court much as was any other region of Egypt. Whether it was one or the other probably made little difference to the average inhabitant of the region.

In some ways, Judah in the Ptolemaic period is as obscure as in the Persian period, but we do have two valuable sources. The first is the Zenon papyri. Zenon was an agent of the finance minister Apollonius who was next in power to the king himself. Apollonius had many personal as well as official interests in Syro-Palestine (Ptolemaic officials did not seem to make a distinction between personal and governmental business), and he sent Zenon on a year-long tour through the region in the year 259 BCE. Afterwards, Zenon kept up correspondence for a number of years with some of those he met. The documents from his tour and subsequent communications were collected in an archive that got buried and preserved in the Fayum area of Egypt where it was rediscovered about a century ago and has now been published. These papyri have provided valuable historical information, especially about the workings of the Ptolemaic administration and economic matters. There are also some references to individuals who can be identified as Jews.

The second main source for the Ptolemaic period is the history of the Tobiads found in Josephus (*Ant.* 12.4.1–11 §§157–236). The exact origin of this story is uncertain, though it was probably based on some sort of chronicle preserved by the Tobiad family. There are some problems since the story is clearly legendary in parts, yet the general outline has been confirmed at crucial points by references in other sources. This is why scholars have accepted the overall narrative while being somewhat sceptical of the details.

The Tobiads were an old Jewish aristocratic family living in the Transjordanian area who were important players in the Persian period (see above under 'Persian Period') and continued to be active at least into the Seleucid period. The Zenon papyri show a Tobias who was head of a military colony in the Transjordanian area and clearly an important local man. The troops under his control were by no means all Jews but a mixture of nationalities. This Tobias was of sufficient stature to host Zenon's large entourage and later to send gifts to the king.

In Josephus we find the continuation of the family history. A son (or possibly grandson) of Tobias was named Joseph. The Tobiads had married into the high priestly family (called the Oniads); the high priest seems to have continued his role as spokesman and representative of the Jews before the Ptolemaic government and apparently had some sort of official capacity in relation to tax collection. The high priest Onias refused to pay a sum of money to the Ptolemies. The exact reason for this is still debated, though it may well have had to do with pro-Seleucid views and the expectation that the Seleucids might soon take control of the Syro-Palestinian territory. However, the people were afraid that this would bring punishment on the whole province by the government. Joseph intervened to pay the money owed. He then bid for the tax farming rights over the province. (Tax farming was a system of collecting indirect taxes, such as those on buying and selling, which were hard to supervise. The tax farmer agreed to pay a certain amount to the king. If he did not collect that much, he had to make up the difference; if he collected more, that became his profit.) Having obtained the right to collect taxes, Joseph became a significant figure at court. He exercised this influential position and amassed great wealth for the next 20 years.

Joseph had eight sons, the youngest of whom showed the same entepreneurship as his father. This son, named Hyrcanus, borrowed money and went to the Ptolemaic court where he managed to displace his father as tax farmer and court presence. This created a family breach, with Hyrcanus on one side and Joseph and his other sons on the other. Many feel that the breach was more than just personal rivalry but involved strong political views, with Hyrcanus being pro-Ptolemaic while Joseph (despite being the former darling of Ptolemy) and his other sons had switched to supporting the Seleucids. Hyrcanus turned out to be wrong, and the others right, for not long after Hyrcanus obtained his position Antiochus III defeated the Egyptians and took control of all Syria and Palestine in 200 BCE. Hyrcanus retired to the Transjordanian estate but saw the handwriting on the wall when Antiochus IV became king in 175 BCE. According to Josephus, he then committed suicide.

SELEUCID RULE

The Seleucids claimed that Syro-Palestine was rightfully theirs and tried throughout the third century to retake it from the Ptolemies. When the dynamic ruler Antiochus III (223–187 BCE) came to the throne, he soon launched an attack on Egypt but was defeated at the battle of Raphia in 217. However, with a new ruler some years later (Ptolemy V [204–180]), Antiochus tried again and succeeded in 200 BCE. It has often been asserted that Seleucid rule was different from Ptolemaic rule, which it was to some extent, but there is no evidence that these differences mattered as far as the Jews were concerned, as we shall see below.

We have a number of sources for this period. The most important are the books of 1 and 2 Maccabees, but these will be discussed in the next section. Very important is the book of Jesus ben Sira, often referred to as Ecclesiasticus (cited as Ben Sira below). Written sometime between about 195 and 175 BCE, this is a wisdom book in the usual tradition and says little directly on political history. However, it tells us a lot about society in Palestine, and there is one important reference to the high priest Simon II. Josephus also has some significant material, including a decree of Antiochus III concerning the Jews (*Ant.* 12.3.3–4 §§138–46).

Many Jews welcomed Seleucid rule. As already noted, this was probably true for Joseph Tobiad and all but one of his sons. Some Jews helped Antiochus III to take Jerusalem. As a result, Antiochus issued a decree acknowledging this help and providing temporary relief from taxes to help in restoring the war damage to the city. The traditional Jewish religious rights were also reaffirmed by this decree, though it should be noted that this was by negotiation (2 Macc. 4:11). From all we know, the first quarter of a century of Seleucid rule was peaceful. Only one incident marred this tranquility: according to 2 Maccabees 3, Seleucus IV (187–175 BCE) sent a minister to confiscate the temple treasury. The reason for this is uncertain, though it is significant that Hyrcanus Tobiad (who was pro-Ptolemaic) had a large sum on deposit there (2 Macc. 3:10–11). For some reason, the task was apparently not carried out (2 Maccabees ascribes this to supernatural intervention).

Things changed when Antiochus IV (175–164 BCE) came to the throne, though not for the reasons many think. As far as we can tell, Antiochus had no particular interest in the Jews nor any ideological mission with regard to Hellenization. Because his father (Antiochus III) had been defeated by the Romans, he had had to spend many years in Rome as a hostage. He was returning home when his brother (Seleucus IV) was assassinated, so he seized the throne (Seleucus's son was only a boy). His main concern was to establish Seleucid control over Egypt, and he began immediate preparations to do this. He was hardly concerned to become involved with the small province of Judah in his empire; he had much more important things on his mind. Nevertheless, he became involved with the Jews in a way that caused great trauma not only to them but to himself, through the following circumstances.

When the Greeks conquered the ancient Near East, they brought Greek culture and language to the region. Most of those in the Greek armies did not return home but were given property in the conquered area by Alexander and his successors to settle. They founded cities on the model of those in the homeland. In such a city (called a *polis*) the citizens had many privileges, including government of the city

449

itself. Only the Greeks were citizens; even if natives were allowed to live in the city, they were not citizens. A gymnasium was established in each city. The gymnasium was more than just a place for exercises; it served as an important centre and focus for educational, cultural, and recreational activities, and the place where the trainee citizens were educated and prepared for their duties. Physical sport was an important part of this education, but the young men (and occasionally women) were trained in Greek language, literature, and rhetoric.

Initially, the Greeks were not interested in mixing with the natives and certainly not in spreading their own culture to them. (It is alleged that Alexander had just such a vision of a cultural synthesis between the Greeks and the Orientals but, if so, his premature death cut short any such development.) The impetus to participate in Greek culture arose from the side of the native populations. This came about first among the aristocracy who were in constant contact with the conquerors and also had the opportunity and means to gain a Greek education. But the Ptolemaic and then the Seleucid government and administration reached down to the village level. Although the native languages continued to be used in daily life and in the lower echelons of administration, the higher levels of government were carried out in Greek. Anyone wanting to advance beyond a certain point needed knowledge of Greek. There was another aspect, however: many Near Eastern peoples, the Jews included, found some or even many aspects of Greek culture attractive. People of intellect and education would have found pleasure in Greek literature and the various forms of Greek entertainment.

The process of Hellenization was a complex process. The elements of Greek culture did not displace the millennia-old ancient Near Eastern cultures; instead they became an addition to the diverse mixture to create a new synthesis we can call 'Hellenization'. Within the Hellenistic world, there were those who saw various aspects of Greek culture as symbolic of conquerors, occupiers, and oppressors; others perhaps opposed some parts of the Greek presence but welcomed other parts. Above all, many elements of Greek culture entered the common heritage and ceased to be recognized as foreign, so that Greek influence was widespread even below the recognition level.

After almost a century and a half of this process of Hellenization, the Jerusalem leadership decided it was time to joint the 'modern' world. Led by Jason, the brother of the high priest, they approached the new king Antiochus IV and proposed that Jason become high priest in place of his brother Onias (III), with the inducement of a large sum paid to the imperial coffers. In addition, they offered a further sum if Jerusalem was allowed to become a *polis*, a city organized along Greek lines. As far as we can tell, Antiochus had no particular interest in the Jews, and was not out to interfere in their internal affairs; however, he was interested in all the money he could get because of his plans to invade Egypt. He agreed to the request of the Jason faction, and the 'Hellenistic reform' began in Jerusalem. Onias was removed from office and replaced by Jason. The old constitution was removed, a list of citizens was drawn up, and a gymnasium was built for the training of new potential citizens.

Contrary to what you may read in many popular accounts, however, the temple worship and the Jewish religion as a whole was not affected. This is very clear from the hostile account of 2 Maccabees which is our main source about the Hellenistic reform. Despite its loathing of Jason and its colourful rhetoric, it cannot point to any concrete breach of the law on Jason's part. In any case, Jason's power base was still the temple and the cult, and it would not have been in his interest to tamper with their operation.

Jason's reform was short lived, however, lasting only about three years. Three brothers who were rivals to the Oniad family now intervened successfully. One of these was named Menelaus; he wrestled the priesthood away from Jason by offering even more money to Antiochus, and Jason fled the capital. The Hellenistic reform evidently came to an end. Also Menelaus was not careful to maintain Jewish law since he committed a number of acts that were definitely in violation of it (such as taking the Seleucid king into the temple).

THE MACCABAEAN REVOLT AND HASMONAEAN RULE

The Hellenistic reform and contest over the high priesthood moved quickly to the suppression of Judaism and the Maccabean revolt. (A new section is given here for convenience, but there is no real break in continuing events.) The main sources for this period are 1 and 2 Maccabees. Josephus gives only a somewhat garbled account in the *War*, and for the *Antiquities* he closely paraphrases most of 1 Maccabees. Although the revolt and later Hasmonean rule are referred to in Graeco-Roman sources, most of our detailed information is from the books of Maccabees. Both have quite useful information, but both have strong biases. Both were written after the revolt and restoration and see everything through the distorting lenses of these events. Both are also quite pro-Maccabaean and have a tendency to glorify their deeds and to slight the contribution of others.

In late 170 or early 169 BCE Antiochus put into effect plans that he must have had from the beginning. He had prepared for five years; now he launched an attack on Egypt. It does not appear that he wished to become king of Egypt (as well as of the Seleucid realm) as such, but he wanted to bring it under his control by placing a Ptolemy of his choice on the throne. The invasion was very successful. Antiochus made the arrangements about rule he wanted and returned with great spoils. It was probably at this time that he visited Jerusalem, was unlawfully given a conducted tour of the temple by Menelaus, and then took a great deal of money from the temple treasury before returning in triumph to Antioch (2 Macc. 5:1, 15–21 associates it with the second invasion, but it is confused about the two invasions).

Antiochus's political arrangements in Egypt did not last, however, and two years later (spring of 168 BCE) he invaded again. This time Rome intervened. A Roman mission was already in the area; when they received word of the sucessful Roman outcome at the battle of Pydna, they confronted Antiochus and required him to withdraw from Egypt or become an enemy of Rome. Antiochus knew he could not fight Rome, so he reluctantly withdrew in July of 168 BCE. As he did so, he heard of what he took to be a revolt in Judaea and sent an army to put it down. What had happened was that Jason had heard a rumour that Antiochus had died in Egypt; this seemed an opportunity not to miss, so he attacked Jerusalem with the intent of taking back the high priesthood from Menelaus. His supporters took Jerusalem but Menelaus holed up in the citadel and could not be dislodged.

Antiochus's army (it is not clear that Antiochus led it) drove off Jason and captured Jerusalem, killing or enslaving many of the inhabitants (2 Macc. 5:14 gives the unlikely figure of 80,000). This would have seemed to be the end of the matter. The revolt had been put down, Menelaus was reinstalled as high priest, and Jason removed once and for all. Yet the text goes on to give an inexplicable chain of events. First, a governor was placed over Jerusalem and also over the neighbouring province of Samaria. This is not surprising since Antiochus wanted to see that there were no further revolts. But then another Syrian army was sent to take the city of Jerusalem, to kill the men and enslave the women and children. But why? And was not the population of the city killed and enslaved once already? This army found the city peacable and used the Sabbath rest as the opportunity to carry out their terrible deed. This makes no sense (why attack a peaceable city?), and the text gives no hint as to why all this was supposed to have happened.

Finally, the king sent an Athenian to stamp out the practice of Judaism. This action was unprecedented in antiquity. We are used to centuries of religious persecution, but such persecution has normally been carried out by the monotheistic religions. The ancient polytheistic religions were inherently tolerant: if you accept many gods, there is no reason to deny genuine existence to the god of another people. Far from persecuting, even conquering armies often honoured the local deities, enlisting their aid as it were in defeating their worshippers (such conquests were often intepreted as punishment by the local deities for some sin or other). The Jews had revolted against Antiochus, but the revolt had been put down and things were calm once again. Why wake sleeping dogs? Why rouse the hostility of the Jews by trying to suppress their religion? Yet this is exactly what Antiochus did, and the reasons are still debated.

Some of the older suggestions of what Antiochus was trying to do by his attack on the Jewish religion have not stood up to investigation (though they are still widely repeated in popular literature). One is that he was trying to unify his empire by Hellenization, but there is no evidence that he undertook particular measures to impose Greek customs on the native people. In any case, Hellenization as a process was already 150 years old by his reign. It was once argued that he wanted the Jews to regard him as a god, but Antiochus did not act differently from other Seleucid rulers. It must be remembered that Antiochus initially became involved in internal Jewish affairs only because the Jews approached him, not the other way round. One suggestion is that Menelaus wanted to introduce an 'enlightened' form of Judaism that got rid of Judaism's 'superstitions'. Although this might make sense in a modern context, it does not fit well the ancient situation, and all we know about Menelaus does not suggest that he was an ideologue. Menelaus was probably in some way involved in the suppression, but his motives are unclear. Thus, despite a number of suggested solutions to the problem, the puzzle still remains.

Whatever the reasons for Judaism's being outlawed, it was a traumatic experience. Circumcision was forbidden, copies of the law scrolls were destroyed, and a pagan altar was built on the temple altar and swine were sacrificed on it. This came to be known in Jewish literature as 'the abomination of desolation' (perhaps a word play in Hebrew on the name of the Syrian deity whose worship was now introduced into the Jewish temple). This time the Jews revolted in earnest. According to the books of Maccabees, the Maccabaean family led the revolt, though many modern scholars are suspicious that the story is being told from a biased perspective that gives undue credit to the Maccabees. Nevertheless, the Maccabaean brothers had a great deal to do with subsequent Jewish history.

Judas Maccabaeus soon took the main leadership role, with many Jews from over the country joining him as soldiers. Although he achieved some significant victories, modern studies have tended to discount the 'miraculous' nature of them, contrary to the image of the books of Maccabees. The initial battles may have had to depend more on guerrilla tactics and improvised strategy, but Judas's victories are normally explicable by the standard canons of warfare. Judas's most important achievement was rapidly developing his band of irregular fighters into a trained and equipped regular army that fought in the standard mode of the time.

Despite these military facts, it was in a rather remarkably short time of three years that Judas was able to retake the city of Jerusalem, cleanse the temple, and reinstigate the regular cult. The 'abomination of desolation' was at an end, and it was not long afterwards that the prohibition of Antiochus was withdrawn (Antiochus IV himself died about December 164). The Seleucid government seemed ready to come to terms, but the Maccabees refused. The original goal of restoring religious rights seems to have expanded to include the desire for national independence. Fighting continued intermittently. Judas besieged the citadel (the acra) of the city held by Syrian troops but could not take it. Then Judas himself was killed in the fighting about 162. This was a major setback, and for the next five years or so the Maccabees were more or less on the run. Jonathan replaced Judas as leader. The majority of Jews seem to have been content with a return to the *status quo*. The Seleucids appointed a new high priest, Alcimus, and many Jews were happy to accept him.

The determination of the Maccabees began to pay off in the late 150s, however, when the Seleucid throne became the object of contest between two rival dynasties. Jonathan astutely exploited this to his own advantage. Alcimus died about 152 BCE, leaving the office of high priest vacant. Jonathan was appointed high priest by one of the rival claimants to the throne, and the other rival confirmed him in the office. This did not end Judah's troubles, but it was a major step forward in establishing Maccabaean leadership over the whole nation. Jonathan was eventually betrayed and executed by the Seleucids in 142 BCE and was succeeded by the third Maccabaean brother Simon.

If there is a point which we can use as a convenient date for when Judah became once more an independent state, it would be under Simon (see 1 Macc. 13:41–2). In 140 BCE, the third year of his leadership, a decree by the people was issued, confirming the Maccabaean leadership not only in the office of high priest but also in the role of political leadership (1 Macc. 14:27–47). This was a symbolic date and event, though the Seleucids had by no means given up their claims to Judah. Simon was assassinated by his son-in-law, and John Hyrcanus (Simon's eldest son) took the office of high priest. Jerusalem was besieged by a Seleucid army, and the siege was lifted only when John came to terms with Antiochus VII (138–129 BCE) – Seleucid rule was not yet dead. However, like his uncle, John exploited the rival Seleucid rulers to keep Judah's independence. John Hyrcanus's reign was probably one of the most successful of the Maccabaean rulers (or Hasmonaean rulers as they are known, from an ancestor called Hasmon). He began to expand Jewish territory, conquering Idumaea and Samaria.

John Hyrcanus had three sons. The eldest, Aristobulus, became priest and national leader after his father's death but held the office only a year (104–103 BCE). We know little about him, though he is alleged to have been the first to take the title of 'king'. The previous Hasmonaean rules had the title of 'high priest' but, even though acting like kings, they had not used that title. From Aristobulus I on, the title 'king' was used by Jewish rulers. The Judaean monarchy, which had ceased to exist in 587 BCE, was once again restored. Aristobulus extended the territory of Judah into Galilee, and he is said to have killed his brother who was a rival and put the other brother, Alexander Jannaeus, into prison.

When Aristobulus I died after a brief reign, his widow Alexandra released Alexander Jannaeus from prison and married him. Alexander's reign (103–76 BCE) was a long but troubled one. He proceeded to expand his territory even further, taking much of the Transjordanian territory and further portions of Galilee. By the end of his reign he probably ruled more territory than any other Jewish king in history (Solomon is alleged to have controlled more, but this is probably legendary). However, a revolt of his own countrymen developed early in his reign. He suppressed it, but after Alexander suffered a defeat fighting the Nabataean king, a new revolt began and developed into what amounted to a lengthy civil war. His opponents eventually persuaded one of the many Seleucid claimants to the throne at this time, Demetrius III, to invade Judah. Alexander was defeated by Demetrius, but then many of the Jews fighting on Demetrius's side got cold feet, perhaps realizing that Judah might come back under Seleucid rule. When they left Demetrius's cause, he decided the best course of action was to retire from the country. Jannaeus took revenge by crucifying 800 of his enemies while he and his concubines feasted. It is often alleged that those crucified were Pharisees, but Josephus does not say this, and there is no evidence that only Pharisees opposed him. The Pharisees constituted a part of his opposition, however, according to the testimony of Josephus.

Jannaeus was succeeded in his rulership role not by one of his sons but by his wife Alexandra Salome (76–67 BCE). In one of his accounts of Jannaeus, Josephus states that on his deathbed the king ordered his wife to favour the Pharisees. Whether that is true is a matter of debate since Josephus makes no such claim in his other account. According to both accounts, though, his wife's rule was dominated by the Pharisees. This is an important situation because this is the only period in Judaean history that we know of in which the Pharisees actually had *de facto* control of the government. We read that they tried to gain control at various other times, but as far as our sources tell us, it was only under Alexandra Salome that they succeeded. As a woman she could not be high priest but appointed her elder son Hyrcanus (II) to the office; her younger son who seems to have been a dynamic individual led a rebellion against her that lasted until her death. Otherwise, she appears to have been a good administrator and managed by negotiation to prevent Tigranes king of Armenia from invading Judaea after he had conquered Syria.

After Alexandra's death Aristobulus seized power. Hyrcanus at first agreed to let Aristobulus rule and himself to stay out of public life except to exercise the office of high priest. But an individual named Antipater suddenly appears on the scene and joins forces with Hyrcanus. Who this person was is not clear, though his father had apparently been the governor of Idumaea. In any case, he becomes an important figure in Jewish history at this point. He is also famous because his son Herod the Great became another king of the Jews. Antipater persuaded Hyrcanus that he would help him gain the Judaean throne. Hyrcanus and Antipater together assembled an army and attacked Aristobulus who holed up in Jerusalem under siege. In order to break the deadlock both sides appealed to the Roman legate in Syria, the general Pompey.

Up until this time the Jews had had friendly relations with Rome, but the Romans had gradually extended their control over the eastern Mediterranean for the past century or so. It is likely that the Romans would have found a reason to bring Judaea under their control fairly soon, but the two warring brothers presented one on a plate. Pompey accepted bribes from both brothers but then sided with Hyrcanus. Aristobulus set off for Jerusalem as if he were going to refuse Pompey's decision, but then surrendered to the army Pompey sent after him. His followers continued to hold Jerusalem, however, and the Romans besieged it in the summer of 63 BCE. Even as the city was being taken by the Romans, the priests continued to carry out the regular sacrificial cult, and many were slaughtered at their posts. Pompey himself went into the temple. The next day, though, he ordered the temple to be purified and the cult resumed. Judaean independence had come to an end. The Jews of Palestine would be ruled from Rome for another seven centuries until the Arab conquest.

CONCLUSIONS

The Persian and Greek periods saw great developments in Judaism and changes in the life and thought of the Jewish people. They had to adjust to living without a native monarch, becoming instead a small ethnic group centred on one of the many provinces of a great empire. The high priest functioned as the chief administrator and representative of the people, and under the Persians a provincial governor was appointed part or all of the time. Nevertheless, the Jews were free to practise their religion, and the temple and priesthood functioned without major hindrance through most of this period. As long as they paid their taxes and did not threaten rebellion they were allowed to get on with their lives. Most Jews seemed to accept this state of things. Yet it was impossible to entirely avoid becoming entangled in the broader political arena; what is more, some Jewish families were major players in the regional political games. For better or for worse, these families proved to be the catalyst to major changes in the life of the nation.

Although not part of a family as far as we know, Nehemiah was a dynamic individual who tried to create a Jewish state with strict adherence to a set of religious laws and greatly reduced ties with the external world. His vision prevailed for a time but was ultimately rejected by the people. One of Nehemiah's rivals, the Tobiad family, played a significant role in regional politics over many generations, at times even gaining considerable power and influence in the government of the Palestinian area. Another family was that of the Hasmonaeans who took over the high priesthood and rulership of the people for almost a century and continued to hold influence in the country at least until nearly the end of the first century CE. (Another family after our period is the Herodian; some want to deny the designation 'Jewish' to it but without good reason. Herod's father, Herod the Great himself, and Herod's descendants all identified themselves as Jewish as much as the Tobiads, Hasmonaeans, and many others.)

Significant religious changes and developments also occurred in these centuries. The temple and cult were restored in Jerusalem at the beginning of the Persian period, after lying desolate for a number of decades. Perhaps one of the most striking innovations was the rapid move to monotheism, a view of the divine world that was not the prevalent one during the period of the monarchy. Monotheistic trends can be observed at a much earlier time, perhaps being the view of some groups centuries before it spread to the whole of the Jews. But from the first part of the Persian period a monotheistic view seemed to prevail in Jerusalem and to make itself felt throughout Judaism fairly quickly; at least, evidence for the acceptance of other gods quickly disappears.

The centre of Israelite religion, like that of other north-west Semitic religions, was the altar and cult site. In Judah cultic rituals had become limited to the Jerusalem temple, at least by the Persian period. The temple cult was at the heart of Jewish worship during the entire Second Temple period. Without a king the Jews of Palestine looked to the priesthood for leadership. The high priest became the main representative of the Jews to the ruling powers and functioned as a political as well as religious leader through much of the period until the fall of the temple in 70 CE. The major threat to Jewish worship happened about 168 BCE with the attempt of Antiochus IV to suppress Jewish religion. The exact reason is uncertain, though the rivalry over the high priesthood preceded it and probably had something to do with it. With the restoration of the temple, however, another priestly family – that of the Hasmonaeans – resumed the traditional role of both political and religious leadership. Eventually, during Hasmonaean rule the high priest not only acted as, but even took the title of, 'king'.

Yet it was also probably during the Persian period that the written law, the Torah, began to become another focus of religious knowledge and worship. Many believe that much of the work of writing and editing what we now call the Hebrew Bible or Old Testament took place during this time, though many earlier traditions in both oral and written form were undoubtedly used. This allowed a unique development in Judaism not found elsewhere until many centuries later. Unlike other religions of the Mediterranean and Near Eastern world of this time, Judaism became a religion of the book. This process was not finalized until after the temple was destroyed for good in 70 CE, and we must not forget the importance of the temple until its destruction. Yet developments that had begun centuries earlier – in the Persian and Greek periods – put Judaism on a course that led finally to the evolution of a new entity, called rabbinic Judaism, which made the Torah and its study the core of religion.

FURTHER READING

Most of the history in this chapter is discussed in greater detail, with references to original sources and modern scholarly studies, in:

Lester L. Grabbe, *Judaism from Cyrus to Hadrian.* Vol. 1: *Persian and Greek Periods*; Vol. 2: *Roman Period* (Minneapolis: Fortress Press, 1992; London: SCM Press, 1994).

A good deal of history, religion, and literature is also discussed in the following work written for students and lay people:

Lester L. Grabbe, *An Introduction to First-Century Judaism: Religion and Politics* 539 BCE *to* 135 CE (Edinburgh: T & T Clark, 1996).

The religion of Jews in this period is also covered to a great extent in the books listed above; however, the most detailed recent treatment is:

Lester L. Grabbe, *Judaic Religion in the Second Temple Period: Belief and Practice from the Exile to Launch* (London/New York: Routledge, 2000).

These studies of mine will also serve to guide the reader to other relevant books and articles by modern scholars and will introduce the reader to original sources. Almost all the issues raised in this chapter will be discussed there in greater detail.

CHAPTER TWENTY-FIVE

JUDAEA UNDER ROMAN RULE: 63 BCE–135 CE

———— •◆• ————

Sarah Pearce

For knowledge of most of the first two centuries of substantial Roman involvement in Judaea, we owe the greatest debt to the Jewish historian Flavius Josephus (Rajak 1983). Thanks to him we have 'by far the most important contemporary account of any event in the history of the Roman Empire' (Millar 1994: 367). Nevertheless, for historians concerned with the reconstruction of an accurate portrait of the situation in Judaea in that period, Josephus's works are widely acknowledged as providing not only a goldmine but also a minefield (McLaren 1998). Josephus's personal situation was highly complex and has shaped his interpretation of this period in a variety of ways: for the period of the war, self-justification as a leading participant in the rebel side during the First Jewish Revolt against Rome, and then of his subsequent employment with the leaders of the Roman suppression of that revolt, Vespasian and Titus, as advocate for peaceful submission to Roman domination; in terms of his later position, apologist, in a hostile climate, for Jewish culture and especially for the Jewish political tradition, which his own class represented, of rule in Jerusalem by an aristocratic priestly class; and for the pre-war period, through his Hasmonaean ancestry, an inheritance of strong hostility towards the person of Herod the Great. (Rajak 1983; Feldman 1984).

Above all, however, Josephus's accounts of this period are dominated by his concern to explain the reasons for the First Jewish Revolt and the catastrophe of the destruction of the Second Temple in 70 CE. Thus, very much in the style of, and profoundly influenced by, deuteronomistic historiography, Josephus's history tends to highlight factors that, in his view, contributed to what he saw as a supremely catastrophic event in which all events are both part of the divine plan and to be seen as divine reponse to the fidelity or infidelity of Jews to the divine teachings contained in the Law of Moses. The result is, through his selection and organization of details and his commentary on those details, a near-consistent portrayal of at least first-century CE Judaea as dominated by 'turbulent times' (McLaren 1998) and a sense of the inevitability of revolt and catastrophe. A careful reading of Josephus must attempt to discern to what extent this conception of the first century CE reflects the true state of affairs in that period. To that end it is imperative that historians do not accept uncritically Josephus's portrait of Judaea as pregnant with the potential for revolt: the many details of conflict before 66 CE that he provides must be examined carefully to assess how far they can properly be seen as playing any significant part in the outbreak of revolt or rather as isolated incidents in a less extraordinary environment.

Yet, for all his problems, Josephus is without parallel in his value as a source for this period. The other major surviving Jewish writer of the first century, Philo of Alexandria, has relatively little to say of the situation in Judaea except in relation to the political crisis under Gaius (*Legatio*). Roughly contemporary with Josephus's works, the Gospels and Acts of the Apostles offer some details about the political and administrative situation in Judaea in the time of Jesus and the early Christian movement, marked by traditions of a fairly thoroughgoing hostility towards the Jewish political leadership of that period (Sherwin-White 1963). Sources of other evidence include various kinds of anonymous Jewish literature, though much of this is concerned primarily with internal religious questions and not with the wider political environment (Charlesworth 1985; Vermes 1998). Roman writers like Tacitus and Dio, writing from a chronological and cultural distance, preserve some details of Rome's involvement in Judaea (Stern 1974–84). Material evidence provides vital contemporary evidence shedding light on many aspects of Judaea under Roman rule: Jewish inscriptions, for the most part, attest the names and preoccupations of deceased members of the elite class, while Roman inscriptions shed light mainly on military activities in the provincial era (Frey 1936–52, 1975; Rahmani 1994; Williams 1999); coins provide indicators of such things as political and religious ideology and, to some extent, the economic condition of the region (Meshorer 1982); the abundant archaeology of the region provides vitally important information about wealth and cultural influences behind building projects under Herod the Great and in the first century, while also providing valuable evidence about both rebellions (Meyers and Strange 1981; Avigad 1984; Stern et al. 1993; Meyers 1997).

For the period beyond that covered by Josephus, we are much less well informed about the situation in Judaea. Of greatest significance are the history of Dio, which provides the fullest account of the Second Jewish Revolt (132–5 CE); fragments from other Roman and Christian historians; some details in the largely ahistorical rabbinic writings; and, above all, the contemporary evidence for the Second Revolt in the form of rebel coinage and documents, and the archaeological record associated with the rebels and with the Roman forces (Schürer 1973: 6–124).

ON THE EVE OF ROME'S ARRIVAL: HASMONAEAN FEUDING.

Like many of the Hellenistic states of the first century BCE, no longer dominated by the former superpowers of Egypt and Syria, Hasmonaean Judaea was torn apart by rival claimants to the throne (Jos., *BJ* 1.107–19; *AJ* 13.405–32). Even before the death of his mother Alexandra, Aristobulus, her younger son, had attempted to wrest power (or perhaps succeeded in doing so) from his brother Hyrcanus whom Alexandra had appointed as her sole heir, and who had assumed royal power during her lifetime in 69. On the queen's death in 67 BCE, Aristobulus backed his claim to Hyrcanus's position with military force, and an agreement was reached between the brothers that both monarchy and probably also the high priesthood were to be assumed by Aristobulus (Jos., *BJ* 1.121–58; *AJ* 14.1–79).

Hyrcanus's apparent acceptance of this situation was not, however, tolerated by the enemies of Aristobulus. Foremost among these was Antipater, a powerful Idumaean aristocrat, whose father had been *strategos* of Idumaea under Alexander Jannaeus. The status of Antipater himself is not clear at this period though he clearly had considerable influence in both Judaea and neighbouring Nabataea, as indicated by his marriage to a Nabataean royal, probably the daughter of King Aretas III. Antipater persuaded Hyrcanus to recover his throne through an alliance, based on acquiring military support in exchange for land, with Aretas. The success of Hyrcanus's cause now looked certain, as Aretas's forces easily overcame Aristobulus and looked set to take Jerusalem where Aristobulus had taken refuge and where his brother's supporters now besieged him during Passover. But the question of who would now take the throne was put on hold by the intervention of a much greater power, the Roman Republic.

Rome in the Near East

The Roman Republic had involved itself in the affairs of the East Mediterranean since the beginning of the second century BCE, defeating the Hellenistic kings of Macedon (197) and Syria (190). By the middle of that century Rome controlled large areas in the west of this region: Macedonia became a Roman province in 146, and in 133 the neighbouring kingdom of Pergamum was left to Rome by its late ruler and became the Roman province of Asia. Less than a century later, Rome had come to dominate the whole Mediterranean area with only the independent Parthian empire a plausible threat. This huge expansion resulted from measures to protect Rome's interests, to protect the new province of Asia and its Roman residents from external attack, and to clear the Mediterranean of the pirates who threatened the corn supply of the city of Rome (Crook et al. 1994).

Very different was the situation from the beginning of the first century BCE when Rome was faced with its most dangerous enemy since Hannibal. In Mithradates VI, powerful king of Pontus, Rome faced a formidable opponent who for nearly forty years exploited the various domestic and foreign crises that preoccupied the leaders of Rome to advance his ambition to expand his territory and to reduce Roman power in the region. The crisis posed by Mithradates was finally entrusted to the young general Pompey whose spectacular rise to influence depended on a remarkable record of successful military solutions to other major crises. In order to maintain that influence, which many in the Senate opposed, he depended on and sought further opportunities to show that Rome's security depended on him. Pompey's superior forces and strategies ensured that by the end of 66 Mithradates and his allies posed no further threat to Roman interests (Leach 1978: 78–101; Seager 1979; Sherwin-White 1994).

Pompey's attention now turned to other areas in the East, to ensure the security of newly acquired Roman territories and of independent but financially valuable places like Nabataea. Thus, under Pompey's direction, Rome intervened in the trouble spots of the region. Particular attention focused on the anarchic situation in

Syria on account of internal struggles between rival Seleucids, and the threat of Parthian invasion there; and the aggressive activities of Nabataea under Aretas, exploiting the troubles in Syria and in neighbouring Judaea where the civil war of the Hasmonaean brothers diverted Pompey's attention in 65.

Thus, the intervention of Scaurus, Pompey's general posted to Damascus in 65, in the affairs of Judaea was, as Josephus says, 'to snatch what seemed a god-sent opportunity' (Jos., *BJ* 1.127). Both Hasmonaean parties made representations for support to the Roman who, on receipt of a considerable gift of money from Aristobulus, (and no doubt because Hyrcanus was allied with the problematic Aretas), backed his cause. Scaurus removed the immediate threat to Aristobulus, ending the siege of Jerusalem with the mere threat of Pompey's intervention (Jos., *BJ* 1.126–58; *AJ* 14.29–76).

Meanwhile, Pompey arrived in Damascus in 64 to organize Syria's affairs as a new province of Rome and to try to ensure the stability of the surrounding region. As for Judaea, Pompey heard representations both from Hasmonaean parties but also from those who wanted an end to monarchy and instead government by priests (Jos., *AJ* 14.41ff; Diodorus, *Bibliotheca Historica* 40.2). No immediate decision about Judaea's government was taken on account of Pompey's concern to inspect the situation in Nabataea which, until recently, had held Damascus and intervened in Judaean affairs (Bowersock 1983). Aristobulus, however, spoiled his chances of maintaining power in Judaea: first, by abandoning Pompey on his way to inspect Nabataea; then by preparing forces who tried to keep Pompey out of Jerusalem. Pro-Hyrcanus supporters gave up the city and its royal palace to the Romans, while the followers of Aristobulus retreated to the Temple, the strong point of the city, where they were besieged for three months. Hyrcanus's friends assisted the Romans with preparing the assault on the Temple, which was eventually taken when Pompey, probably on the advice of Hyrcanus's side, took advantage of the Jews' abstinence from non-defensive hostilities on the Sabbath and erected the siege equipment that broke down the opponents' resistance.

Capture of the Temple

The Temple fell to the Romans in the third month of the siege 'on the day of the fast', probably the Day of Atonement (10 Tishri, September–October) (Jos., *BJ* 1.148–54; *AJ* 14.64–66; Strabo 16.2.40). Aristobulus's supporters, including many priests, perished in the assault, most at the hands of Hyrcanus's followers, many by their own hand. Among Jews, however, and for a long time to come, Pompey's assault on the Temple was remembered with horror for a different reason. In spite of his characteristic respect for non-Roman religions, unusual in a Roman of his time, Pompey caused huge offence by entering the 'Holy Place', forbidden to all but the high priest, in order to view the Temple's treasures (Jos., *BJ* 1.152; *AJ* 14.72; *Pss Sol.* 2.3; 8.12–14).

Pompey's settlement

Josephus, reflecting his Hasmonaean heritage, preserves a profoundly negative reflection on this period when he remarks that, through the Hasmonaeans' dissension, we lost our freedom and became subject to the Romans, and the territory which we had gained by our arms and taken from the Syrians we were compelled to give back to them, and in addition the Romans exacted of us in a short space of time more than ten thousand talents; and the royal power which had formerly been bestowed on those who were high priests by birth became the privilege of commoners

(*AJ* 14.77–8)

With the exception of the last point, his summary of the state of affairs in 63 is accurate. Judaea was treated like other states overcome by Rome: the former kingdom was made tributary to Rome, and it was stripped of various cities taken from the Seleucids (all coastal towns from Raphia to Dora; all 'non-Jewish towns' east of Jordan; Scythopolis and Samaria) by earlier Hasmonaeans. These were now incorporated into the province of Syria. That province and the whole area as far as Egypt and the Euphrates, including the land of Judaea, were left under the administration of Scaurus, governor of Syria (Jos., *BJ* 1.153–8; *AJ* 14.73–6). Territorial losses for Judaea were thus considerable, but the area ruled by its leader still reflected the legacy of the earlier Hasmonaeans' conquests in what remained to him of Idumaea, Peraea, Galilee and Samaritis.

The claim that rule was now transferred to 'commoners' does not hold true for 63, but reflects the realities of a later period under Herod the Great who could not claim royal ancestry. Under Pompey, Hyrcanus was reinstated as high priest and ethnarch (head of the country), but not as king. Looking at things from a broad perspective, Rome's settlement restored to Second Temple Period Judaea its traditional form of government, which many leading Jews had demanded of Pompey prior to the settlement. Hyrcanus' powers were not insignificant (including the charge of the army and of the country's revenue) and by many Jews he was indeed regarded as king.

By comparison with his administrative efforts in many places, Pompey's arrangements in the East were minimal. This was especially true of Judaea, as Pompey was drawn away to settle the affairs of Pontus following the death of Mithradates just before the siege of Jerusalem. Consequently, the region remained unstable in places, including Judaea. For the time being, the situation in Nabataea, which Pompey had been so anxious to investigate, was settled peacefully from Rome's point of view: with the aid of Antipater, Scaurus extracted money from Aretas in return for peace.

Josephus was right that the Hasmonaeans' quarrel was the immediate cause of Roman intervention. But there is no doubt, with or without Hasmonaean conflict, that Rome would have come to dominate Judaean affairs sooner or later. Before the First Revolt, all serious candidates for power in Judaea would appeal to Rome for support.

FROM HYRCANUS II TO HEROD THE GREAT

Though ethnarch of Judaea, Hyrcanus II was still answerable to the governors of Syria. In practice, however, because of the Romans' preoccupations with other parts of the region, there was no further Roman intervention in Judaea until 57 BCE. This allowed substantial opportunities for the Hasmonaean opposition to fight back. Though Aristobulus himself seemed finished, taken as prisoner to appear in Pompey's triumph of 61, his cause was not over yet. He and his sons, Alexander and Antigonus, continued to defy Rome's settlement of Judaea with a series of rebellions until Rome decided to install its own client king.

The early stage of the Hasmonaean opposition's efforts was countered by Aulus Gabinius, first governor of the now consular province of Syria (Appian, *Syr.* 51.256), appointed to deal with problems in the Syrian area, notably defending Roman-backed rulers in Egypt and Judaea. In Judaea he suppressed a series of unsuccessful revolts, led first by Alexander (57), and later, after their escape from Rome, by his father, Aristobulus, with the younger son, Antigonus (56). Their suppression was achieved with the aid of Jewish forces, showing that their claim was far from being universally supported in Judaea: indeed, the wife of Aristobulus is said to have offered express advice on preventing their revolutionary activities. The rebel Hasmonaeans were returned to Rome.

In the wake of the destruction caused by these serious disturbances Gabinius imposed a new regime aimed at ensuring peace: the restoration and resettlement of afflicted areas; a new government in which Hyrcanus's powers were confined to the Temple, a clear sign of no confidence in his political abilities, and five regional aristocratic councils were to take charge of the other affairs of the ethnarchy. Nothing more is known of these *synhedria* (on the model of regional federations in Macedonia), except that they disappeared altogether under the governorship of Antipater and may, indeed, never have functioned. Gabinius was also responsible for changes in tax-collection in Judaea, essentially a move to direct taxation by the governor's officials, part of a wider project to reorganize the tax system in Syria: this aimed at the fair treatment of provincials, but was later condemned by the Roman *publicani* for hampering their activities (Cic., *Prov. Cons.* 9.10; *Pis.* 41; Jos., *AJ* 14.104, 203).

Gabinius's efforts to restore Ptolemy Auletes in Egypt (backed by Rome and with the assistance of Hyrcanus's government) provided, in his distance from Judaea, an opportunity for more rebel activities there: Alexander once more attempted revolt, massacring 'all Romans in the country' (Jos., *BJ* 1.176). After suppressing his forces, Gabinius 'reorganized the government in accordance with Antipater's wishes' (Jos., *BJ* 1.178): it is likely that the latter was also appointed *epimeletes* at this time, perhaps giving him overall responsibility for tax-collection.

The activities of some of Rome's most powerful figures would have a major impact on Judaean affairs over the next two decades. The next governor of Syria, the triumvir and proconsul M. Licinius Crassus (54–53), anxious for military glory to rival that of his colleagues, equipped his disastrous expedition against Parthia by stripping the Jerusalem Temple of its wealth (Jos., *BJ* 1.179). This violation of the Temple's sanctity is likely to have fuelled further disturbances in Judaea in the following years. The revolt of Aristobulus's new-found ally Peitholaus was severely suppressed by the next governor of Syria, Cassius (53–51), called in by Antipater, and resulting in the decimation of the Galilean town of Tarichaeae and the enslavement of 30,000 of its men. This town would later prove one of the few Galilean centres of resistance to Rome during the First Revolt.

After the collapse of the first triumvirate (49 BCE), conflict between the surviving members, Julius Caesar and Pompey, dominated Judaean politics as it dominated the interests of others in the East. Caesar's attempt to exploit Hasmonaean opposition against Pompey failed: both Aristobulus, sent with two legions against Pompey in Syria, and Alexander were killed on Pompey's orders. However, following the death of Pompey (48), Antipater and Hyrcanus offered their support to Caesar, playing a key role in his campaign in Egypt against the young Ptolemy. Caesar's rewards were considerable. Hyrcanus was confirmed in his office as high priest and ethnarch, and granted exemption from tax in the sabbatical year, permission to rebuild the walls of Jerusalem and the restoration of some territory including Joppa and the Jezreel Valley taken away under Pompey. Relations with Rome were strengthened at a formal level: Hyrcanus received for himself and his children the title of *symmachos* (ally) of the Roman people, while Caesar's many decrees protecting the Jewish people included the guarantee of Jewish jurisdiction in Jewish affairs. Antipater received the title of *epitropos* (procurator) of Judaea, and, a rare privilege for a provincial at that time, Roman citizenship.

The rise of Herod

Josephus asserts that Antipater was the real ruler in this period, portraying Hyrcanus as too idle to play the part of king. Antipater's appointment of his sons, Phasael and Herod, to rule the tetrarchies of Jerusalem and Galilee respectively is also reported to have pleased many of the locals, and drawn the nation to treat him like a king. Indeed, the opposition among 'the leading Jews' accused the Antipatrids of taking on royal power. In particular, Herod's extermination of Galilean bandits caused tension with members of the Jerusalem elite, probably on the grounds that, in executing the bandits, he had superseded the powers of the ethnarch. As holder of the supreme power among the Judaean elite Hyrcanus was able to summon Herod to answer charges.

As on this occasion, so throughout the period of Roman domination until 66, supreme power in internal Jewish affairs in Judaean territory was maintained by the Jewish ruler of the time – ethnarch, king or high priest. On occasion, the ruler might call an assembly (*synedrion*), a picked assembly of associates and supporters, for consultative meetings or to try a particular case. These *synedria* were not, however, permanent institutions, but informally assembled from time to time on an *ad hoc* basis. Their members always included members of the upper priesthood and the 'powerful'; membership of a religious party such as the Pharisees was not, as some have thought, a determining factor for membership. In the trial of individuals, the *synedrion*'s role seems to have been that of confirming the ruler's decision. Under Hyrcanus, Herod, his descendants, and perhaps the high priests of the provincial era, the power of trial and execution lay in the hands of the Jewish ruler of Judaea (Goodman 1987; McLaren 1991; Sanders 1992).

Nevertheless, the outcome of the showdown between Hyrcanus and Herod demonstrated Hyrcanus's weakness as Herod was let go under pressure from the governor of Syria, Sextus Caesar, an early sign of Rome's favour towards Herod, a point which was confirmed when his powers were extended yet further by Rome to include the governorship of Coele Syria, covering a considerable area of the Palestinian region, and probably also Samaria.

In the period leading up to his appointment as king, Herod is pictured as a loyal servant of Rome and a great soldier, favoured by God and by no means without support from Jews. In Josephus's later work, the *Antiquities*, which is markedly more hostile to the king than the account in *Jewish War*, Herod is still portrayed overall as an impetuous and passionate, but on the whole reasonable, man: damning statements stand alongside records of his humanity and generosity to the end of his life. The hostility of our sources and of Josephus's personal position must be viewed alongside the relatively little evidence they supply for contemporary active opposition to his rule.

Herod's ability to win Roman approval was largely the key to his success. After Caesar's assassination (44 BCE), Herod's family transferred allegiance to his assassins, Cassius and Brutus, who had gone to the East where they tried to build up support against Caesar's party, led by Mark Antony. The Antipatrids' support of Cassius, based in Syria, won Herod the office of *strategos* of Coele-Syria, and the promise of the monarchy of Judaea. Fears over the complete demise of Hasmonaean influence were behind the assassination of Antipater (43), but neither this nor subsequent attempts at rebellion against his sons proved effective. Indeed, the death of Antipater, in removing Hyrcanus's greatest ally, also destroyed 'the best surety for the continued existence of the Hasmonaeans' (Schalit 1975: 53). Cassius's favour towards the Antipatrids was clear in his support for Herod's destruction of his father's assassin.

The situation under Cassius was not easy for either Judaea or its neighbours whose finances were severely stretched by the Roman's need for funds for his military campaign, now facing the opposition of the newly formed Triumvirate of Mark Antony, Caesar's heir Octavian, and Lepidus. In the task of fund-raising, Herod proved an excellent servant.

However, following the triumvirs' victory at Philippi (42 BCE), the surviving Antipatrids backed those loyal to Caesar's cause, represented in the East by Mark Antony. Under his authority, Antipater's sons Phasael and Herod were appointed as tetrarchs with the administration of the whole of Judaea (and responsibility for funding Antony). In this, they were not without support among Jews, notably Hyrcanus, in need of a defender against the threat of his brother's surviving son, Antigonus. This role was, for the time being, taken on by Herod: his ability to repel Antigonus's invasion of Galilee was rewarded by the closest alliance with Hyrcanus, the promise of his daughter Mariamme in marriage. The problem of Antigonus was not yet over, however.

Herod's move from the office of tetrarch to that of monarch by 40 owed much to the Triumvirate's defence policy in the East and to Mark Antony in particular who, under the terms of the Treaty of Brundisium (40), retained charge of the East. Sometime before Philippi, Q. Labienus, a former general of Caesar, had been sent by Cassius to the Parthian court: resulting from this strange alliance of Roman republicanism and Parthia, Labienus invaded Asia Minor while Pacorus, son of the king of Parthia, took most of the Roman province of Syria, and supported against the Roman-backed rule of Herod and Phasael the claims of Antigonus, the last Hasmonaean ruler, whom they installed in 40 as 'king and high priest' (Jos., *BJ* 1.274–375; *AJ* 14.370–491; Schürer 1973: 281–6; Smallwood 1976: 44–59).

Parthian custody ended the careers of Herod's closest allies in Jerusalem: Phasael was driven to suicide, while Hyrcanus II, Rome's approved high priest in Jerusalem, was taken prisoner by the Parthians and mutilated personally by Antigonus. Mutilation disqualified him permanently, following the traditions of the Torah, which insists on the physical integrity of the priesthood, from the office of the high priesthood.

Herod turned first to Nabataea for assistance. When this was not forthcoming, on account of political considerations towards Parthia, Herod fled to Rome. His mission there was ostensibly to secure the Judaean throne for his future brother-in-law, Aristobulus III. That this was his original aim is not entirely unlikely: he must have been aware that Rome's usual policy was to back claimants from native royal families, not commoners like himself. However, this was not always the case, as the example of Herod shows: the triumvirs and the Senate declared him king of Judaea and Samaria, an appointment celebrated in the traditional way by ritual sacrifices to Jupiter, supreme god of the Roman Capitol.

Meanwhile, the *de facto* king of Judaea remained Antigonus. The Senate's appointment of Herod was of great advantage to them, in the face of the Parthian crisis, at a time when armed forces were stretched in the aftermath of Philippi. They also had reason to trust him in view of his father's friendship with Caesar and his loyal service to Roman powers in the East. No substantial military assistance, however, was given to Herod until 37 CE by which time he, with considerable support in Judaea, had accomplished much of the task of taking his kingdom by conquest. By 37, however, Antony's forces had driven the Parthians out of Syria. Sossius, governor of Syria, arrived to assist the conclusion of Herod's five-month siege of Jerusalem and the brief rule of Antigonus, abandoned by the Parthians and failing to win Roman support for his cause. Herod persuaded Sossius to remove his forces to prevent sacrilege, plunder and murder in Jerusalem, and Antony to dispose of Antigonus. Herod's conquest of his kingdom gave further legitimacy, in Roman eyes, to his right to the throne. His marriage to Mariamme the Hasmonaean, during the course of the siege, gave support to that claim for his children by right of royal descent.

HEROD THE GREAT

Herod's successful maintenance of power over a long reign (37–4 BCE) stands in marked contrast to the civil unrest that marred the rule of the later Hasmonaeans, and the almost immediate breakdown of social control in Judaea after Herod's death, exacerbated by the failure of his son Archelaus, and the growth of Jewish objections to Roman or Roman-dominated rule.

Despite his evidence for some support for Herod among Jews, Josephus gives much space to underlining Herod's general lack of popularity in his kingdom. In characteristically deuteronomic fashion, his accounts of Herod frequently attack Herod as a 'bad' king, on account of alleged transgressions of Jewish law and association with idolatry. But at the heart of this approach is Hasmonaean opposition: playing on Herod's origins as an Idumaean, labelled as a 'half-Jew' by his rival Antigonus, arguing on these grounds that Herod's kingship violated Jewish custom. Certainly it was contrary to Hasmonaean notions of right, and Hasmonaean ambitions proved a constant problem throughout his reign. However, opposition to Herod was relatively muted during his lifetime and minimal by comparison with the huge uprisings against the later Hasmonaeans.

Herod's relative success as king of Judaea was due to several factors. For security at home, a fundamental need was the creation of a ruling class not dominated by the Hasmonaeans (Stern 1976). While it is not clear that he destroyed the Hasmonaean aristocracy altogether, his court was constituted of imported advisers and officials or family members: loyalty was more probable, though not always forthcoming, from such quarters. In addition, the execution of prominent and wealthy Jews opposed to him ensured vital funds from the confiscation of their property.

Herod's recovery of Hyrcanus II from the hands of the Parthians was not entirely an altruistic act towards his father-in-law: while he remained their 'guest', he also remained a source of danger, as a potential Hasmonaean rival, to Herod's position. Nevertheless, Hyrcanus's days as high priest were over. Appointment to the crucial office of the high priesthood was filled by candidates from abroad, with no links to the Hasmonaeans. The exception to this rule was the brief interlude in which Herod was persuaded by his Hasmonaean mother-in-law to appoint her son, through the influence of Cleopatra on Antony, Aristobulus III, to this office. The popularity of this boy priest and his potential as a figurehead for pro-Hasmonaean discontent led to his early removal (35), reportedly by deliberate drowning under Herod's authority. Under Herod, the office of high priest was controlled by the king, with frequent changes of incumbent. By the first century CE, as a consequence of this policy, considerable rivalry existed within the high priestly families.

Decision-making in internal affairs was controlled by the king, as it had been in principle under Hyrcanus as ethnarch, who might act alone or in collaboration with others. On rare occasions, involving highly sensitive decisions such as the execution of respected teachers, Herod called on a public assembly to confirm his decision.

Less successful were Herod's attempts to absorb the Hasmonaean problem at a personal level by marriage to Mariamme, a union that incorporated a descendant of both Jannaeus's sons into his family. This did not prevent Mariamme's mother, Alexandra, from conspiring to increase Hasmonaean power against Herod, through intrigues with her royal neighbour in Egypt, Cleopatra. The coincidence of Hasmonaean ambitions to weaken Herod and the Egyptian queen's continuation of Ptolemaic designs on Judaea led Cleopatra to pressure her lover Mark Antony to give her a huge amount of territory governed by Herod, which he was obliged to lease back from her. In addition, her demands for Nabataean territory also made Herod responsible for collecting revenues due to her there and, in due course, for invading that territory when its king, Malichus I, defaulted on his payments (31 BCE).

The further story of Herod's dealings with the Hasmonaeans, exacerbated by the suspicions of other parts of his family, including the execution of Hyrcanus II, Mariamme, and Alexandra, all of whom were believed, with good reason, to be destabilizing forces, illustrates the continuing struggle for power centring on Hasmonaean claims throughout Herod's reign. Herod's plans to be succeeded by his Hasmonaean sons were abandoned on evidence suggesting their disloyalty to their father, eventually executed on Roman recommendation (7 BCE); similarly, his Idumaean son Antipater who played a key role in destroying his half-brothers and in trying to destroy his father (5 BCE). Of close family members, Herod's sister Salome seems to have remained the most constant in loyalty. Thus, Herod's removal of many of the old aristocracy who had emerged under the Hasmonaeans transformed the nature of the Jewish governing classes who would dominate in the following century (Stern 1982).

The policing of Herod's kingdom was undertaken very seriously and with good reason in view of the Hasmonaean revolts before 40 and the threat of territorial encroachment from external forces like Egypt and Parthia. Of Herod's many defensive structures, the most notable are a series of military forts including a fortified royal palace in Jerusalem, the reconstruction of the fortress Antonia, honouring Antony, to the north of the Temple, and the refortification of many others including Masada.

Herod was also careful to maintain a substantial and loyal army. He reinforced his rule at home, and his potential to assist Rome when called upon, with an army composed of mercenaries including both Jews and non-Jews from Judaea, but also soldiers from as far afield as Thrace, Germany and Gaul (Shatzman 1991). Their settlements increased the importance of non-Jews among the population of his kingdom (Stern 1975: 96). The Hasmonaeans would not have been able to expect loyalty from such a force.

Thirdly, and most importantly, Herod's power was derived from and sustained by the support he received from his Roman allies. In the struggles that developed among Caesar's party, Herod initially supported Mark Antony against Octavian. However, after Antony's defeat at Actium (31 BCE) Herod switched his support to Octavian, blocking the arrival of vital reinforcements for Mark Antony. Both Herod and Malichus I of Nabataea were fortunately absent from Actium itself, engaged in the struggle Cleopatra and Antony had determined for them. Herod now successfully offered his services to Octavian.

The victorious Octavian, soon to become Augustus, the supreme ruler of the Roman Empire, confirmed Herod's status at this time and granted him considerable extensions to his territory both now and later so that by his death the extent of his territory almost equalled that of the Hasmonaeans. From the Roman point of view, Herod was primarily valuable for his ability to keep Judaea at peace under overall Roman rule and so to control the region between Egypt and Syria.

As a 'friend and ally of the Roman people', Herod played an important role in other respects too. Like other client kings, he was responsible for supplying military aid when occasionally needed; providing revenues and personal gifts to the senior representatives of the Roman State; and cultivating Roman alliances at a personal level and by ostentatious displays of devotion to Rome. His powers within his own territory were supreme with the exception that critical decisions concerning the royal family of Judaea were subject to the emperor's consent. Actions outside his kingdom, on the other hand, could not be undertaken without Roman approval. Good relations were maintained with the governors of Syria in whose decisions, after 20 BCE, Herod was invited to take part (*AJ* 15.360; *BJ* 1.399). A temporary deterioration in his relations with Rome occurred only when Herod undertook a campaign, without the emperor's authority, outside his own kingdom, attacking hostile forces based in Nabataea, and thus exceeding his mandate as a client king.

As such, Herod represented the interests of the Roman State and the people of Judaea to one another. He also greatly increased the standing of Judaea in the Empire through the maintenance of Roman alliances and the influence that brought, through alliances with other local dynasties (Sullivan 1978), through benefactions to many of the cities of the Empire, and through his great display of power and wealth manifested in the unrivalled scale of his building programmes within Judaea and in many other parts of the Roman world. Within his own territory Herod was responsible for the refounding of Sebaste in honour of Augustus; the rebuilding of Caesarea as a city to rival Jerusalem, supplied with a world-class harbour to benefit Judaea's economy; and, most spectacularly, the rebuilding of the Jerusalem Temple as one of the greatest wonders of the contemporary world, drawing Jews and non-Jews alike to Jerusalem to express their devotion to God and to spend money there (Braund: 1984). The financing of such projects may have drawn on tax revenues, but there is no certainty that Herod imposed a severe tax burden in his kingdom. Much of his wealth was derived from other sources including inherited lands, the confiscated property of enemies, and benefits from Rome.

Thanks principally to Josephus, Herod's rule is frequently seen as that of an 'outsider', the first challenge to the established ruling class of Judaea since the Hasmonaeans themselves took power. Doubts about Herod's loyalty to Judaism are, however, misplaced. Undoubtedly he was very Hellenized, as his cultural endeavours and personal relationships show. But in this he was like many Jews of the Empire, and especially those of elite classes – a process that intensified during and beyond Herod's reign. Accusations that Herod altered or broke Jewish law are recorded with emphasis by Josephus. Most examples of this refer to aspects of Herod's Hellenization programme such as the theatre in Jerusalem (in which objectors failed to show signs of idolatry), and temple buildings for his non-Jewish subjects. Certainly, if Josephus is to be trusted, there were objections to such phenomena, but, in a time of great diversity over the interpretation of Jewish law, they should not be taken as representative of Jewish opinion, nor of Herod's deliberate flouting of the law. Such opposition as existed over these practices appears to have roused the active opposition of very few. Moreover, the very accusation that Herod broke Jewish law implies an acceptance of his identity as Jewish: such accusations could not be levelled at a non-Jew. Indeed, Josephus does not avoid representing Herod as a self-proclaimed Jew and attributes to him speeches exhorting others with piety. It is also Josephus who supplies evidence for Herod's own piety in many ways: the rebuilding of the Temple according to strict tradition; his maintenance of the prohibition of 'images of men' in the buildings of Jerusalem and on his coins; his serious undertaking of the Jewish duty of charity; his defence of Jews' legal right to observe their laws in the Empire; and his insistence on conversion for males marrying into his family. Significantly, Herod was remembered by non-Jews as the epitome of Jewishness.

The general view is that Herod was deeply unpopular with his subjects. This was undoubtedly true for pro-Hasmonaeans whose sentiments are preserved in Josephus and others. But we should not forget that hostility towards the Hasmonaeans themselves had been very deeply felt during their period of rule. It has also been suggested that Herod was regarded with hostility on religious grounds. The same had also been true, as the sectarian Dead Sea Scrolls and Josephus reveal, of the Hasmonaeans.

Josephus records that some Pharisees influenced the Jewish population against Herod, on the grounds that he was a 'half-Jew' and a friend of the Romans. Josephus's desire to show the Pharisees as a destabilizing party under both Hasmonaeans and Herod must be taken into account here, and we should not read this as evidence for systematic rejection of Herod by religious groups (Mason 1991). He is, after all, reported as having received the friendship of some Pharisees. Some degree of religious hostility is suggested by incidents such as the incitement by two religious teachers to tear down the Roman eagle from Herod's Temple gate, an act that expresses primarily hostility towards Roman rule. Herod's lack of popularity is also suggested by the story that he is said to have ordered the execution of certain distinguished men on his death (4 BCE) so that there should be widespread mourning at the time of his funeral. But, we must remember, this comes mainly from Josephus who deeply regretted the end of the Hasmonaean dynasty that Herod's rule had brought. Accusations brought against Herod after his death were not, as Nicolas of Damascus pointed out in his defence, voiced during his lifetime.

HEROD ARCHELAUS

After Herod's death, the succession was decided in Rome by the emperor. In the interim, serious disturbances erupted in Judaea: revolutionary demands for the avenging of those killed for their protest over the Temple eagle and for a new high priest; provocations by the Roman procurator of finances, preying on the treasuries of Judaea; rival claims over the kingship aimed at promoting various Herodians or less conventional claimants, some with anti-Herodian and anti-Roman programmes. Roman reprisals were severe and a legion was installed to garrison Jerusalem. Protests against Herodian rule were also voiced in Rome by Jewish representatives with requests for the incorporation of Judaea into the province of Syria.

In the end, no king was appointed. Augustus appointed Archelaus as ethnarch of Judaea, Samaria and Idumaea with the cities of Strato's Tower and Sebaste, and the promise of monarchy should he prove capable. Greek cities such as Gaza and Gadara, however, were incorporated into the province of Syria. Other territories were divided among Herod's sister Salome and his surviving sons: to Antipas, Peraea and Galilee (deposed 39 CE); to Philip, Batanaea, Trachonitis, Auranitis and part of the domain of Zenodorus (d. 33 CE); to Salome, Jamnia, Azotus, Phasaelis and the palace at Ascalon, all in Archelaus's domain.

Archelaus, Herod's son by a Samaritan woman, remained ethnarch until 6 CE, a rule of ten years, which impressed neither the leaders among his subjects nor the authorities in Rome (Dio 55.27.6). Little is known about his rule and none of it is positive. Charges of cruelty and tyranny brought against him by the leading men of the Jews and Samaritans were accepted in Rome and he was exiled to Vienna in Gaul. Local protests against rulers were not unusual at this period: at around the same time, the deaths of the kings of Commagene and Philopator of Cilicia 'disturbed the peace of their countries, where the majority of men desired a Roman governor, and the minority a monarch' (Tac., *Ann.* 2.42). It is likely that Archelaus's removal was advantageous to Rome: the new revenues from his property and from the tribute imposed would prove useful as they did in other former kingdoms.

DIRECT ROMAN RULE

The territory of Archelaus was added to the province of Syria. From now on, except for the brief return of monarchy under Agrippa I (41–4 CE), this area would be ruled directly by Roman officials until the outbreak of revolt in 66 CE, which saw the temporary collapse of Roman rule in Judaea. For the administration of Judaea, Augustus appointed the legate of Syria, P. Sulpicius Quirinius, to undertake a census of property, the normal Roman method of ensuring efficient taxation of new territories in the Empire (in the whole province of Syria), and to sell the estates of Archelaus. This census is well known from the Gospel of Luke, which mistakenly assigns it to the reign of Herod the Great.

For reasons that remain unclear, the census in Judaea coincided with an uprising among some Jews. If the revolt was over the census, it was not a peculiarly Jewish objection: similar protests accompanied the imposition of the census in other regions (Goodman 1991). Josephus characterizes the Jewish protesters as members of a coherent movement, 'the Fourth Philosophy'. But the fact that he can attribute them no real name – they are called the 'Fourth Philosophy' in relation to the three authentic and named philosophies of Judaism (Essenes, Pharisees and Sadducees) – and no clear definition of their principles, shows that the evidence is unclear. Whatever the nature of their objections, their aim, according to Josephus, was to achieve independence from Roman rule before it took proper effect. The quick suppression of this movement suggests that the rebels found little real support. But, in Josephus's interpretation of history, this movement, in its antagonism towards foreign rule, represented a fatal innovation in the ancestral traditions that sowed the seed of the disaster to come sixty years later in the Jewish Revolt.

Jewish attitudes to Roman rule

In spite of long-cherished traditions, based on promises in Scripture that looked forward to freedom from foreign rule, there is little sign before 70 CE that most Jews objected to Roman rule as such. A few charismatic figures appear from time to time in first-century Judaea, advocating grand gestures of political defiance against Rome. But they did not prove at all effective. Banditry continued to be a problem but it is by no means clear that it was primarily motivated by opposition to Roman rule.

Among the Jewish elite about whose views we are, thanks to Josephus, best informed, there was positive enthusiasm for the arrival of Roman government. It was members of their class, after all, who had requested direct Roman rule in 6 CE, no doubt looking forward to relative freedom for themselves. Among other things, the demise of the monarchy freed them from involvement in the internecine conflicts of the Herodians, which had caused such unrest in recent years. Jews took many complaints to the Roman authorities in the years of direct rule in Judaea, yet their objections were not to Roman rule as such but to usually local Roman actions perceived to be hostile to the Jews politically or religiously. State protection of the Temple and of Jewish customs, established under Julius Caesar, remained in force under direct rule in so far as Jews appealed to Rome with confidence over infringements of these decrees, and senior Roman officials continued to punish such infringements severely when asked to do so. Rome's goodwill towards the Jewish people was expressed through gifts to the Temple, and sacrifices offered in Jerusalem on behalf of the emperor and the Roman people were treated as the Jews' expression of devotion to their rulers. Nevertheless, the actions of several of the Roman governors of Judaea and their military forces put great strain on this relationship in their blatant disregard for Jewish religious sensibilities, especially where the Temple was concerned. Otherwise, religious ideology, in spite of Josephus's efforts to show the contrary, was not a major factor in the outbreak of revolt in 66 CE (though it undoubtedly helped to raise and to sustain support). When and where it appeared, Jewish resistance to Roman rule was not extraordinary in the context of the times: other regions like Judaea, on the edge of the Empire, and especially, as in 66, at times of Roman weakness, were also prone to sometimes long periods of rebellion (Goodman 1991).

Roman government

The government of pre-revolt Judaea was not, as Rome's appointment policy shows, regarded as one of the better jobs in provincial administration. In contrast to most provinces, to which members of the senatorial class were appointed, the governors of Judaea were drawn from the equestrian class or lower, the pattern of appointment for rebellious or newly acquired regions (Sherwin-White 1963: 6), and did not enjoy substantial military support within their territory. Governors were appointed and removed from office by the emperor, far distant from the province's affairs, and allowed relative freedom: only in exceptional cases did the senatorial legate of Syria, the nearest senior representative of Rome, interfere. The first governors were comissioned as prefects, suggesting their military functions. In practice, however, major military matters were left to the legate of Syria, while Judaea had a very small military presence made up of local auxiliaries, suggesting that Rome did not view this area as especially problematic. Based in Caesarea, Judaea's governors had three main responsibilities: policing; fiscal duties; and judicial government, with the power to impose the death penalty. The only laws limiting the governors' power with regard to provincial subjects guarded against extortion and perhaps also excessive cruelty on the governors' part (Sherwin-White 1963: 3). Even then, protests to the emperor could only be undertaken by the upper classes among the provincials.

Overall control in Judaea was held by Rome through military force. The supreme representative of the Jews for most of the pre-war provincial period was the high priest, appointed, with regular changes, by Roman governors or Herodian princes. Other decision-making, though probably not the power to impose the death penalty, was in the hands of the high priests and the powerful. If the high priest occasionally exceeded the formal limits of his power, for example by authorizing executions without Roman approval, the phenomenon was not without parallel in other relatively remote parts of the Empire (Sherwin-White 1963: 42). Thus, the leadership of Judaea enjoyed a large degree of independence from interference by Roman officials: 'Under Roman rule the Jewish community [of Judaea] maintained its identity and sense of independence in terms of administrative affairs' (McLaren 1991: 224). Most of the time, Roman governors sought to resolve problems by negotiation: only in rare cases, and, tellingly under the governor under whom revolt broke out, did they seek to break down Jewish resistance by violence.

The main threats to the power of the high priest came from rival claims to this office. Most serious rivalries over leadership came from within the ruling elite just as the most serious threat to Herod's rule had been from within his family. Otherwise, the chief priests and the lay 'powerful' were apparently generally well supported by the rest of the Jewish community: there is, as one recent study puts it, 'no evidence of any long-standing tension between prominent Jews and the remainder of the community' (McLaren 1991: 224). That is not to ignore the various attempts by non-elite individuals or groups to get prominence throughout this period (e.g. Judas the Galilaean), but most failed to get much support.

No contemporary source has much good to say about the provincial governors of Judaea. Those who did well did so, according to Josephus, because they refrained from interfering with the customs of the country: of these, he mentions only two, Cuspius Fadus and Tiberius Julius Alexander. The failure of others to keep the peace was precisely linked to their ability to provoke Jews on religious grounds. Their failure in government, so Josephus, was a serious cause for the move towards revolt in 66.

Virtually nothing is known of the situation in Judaea for the first decade of direct Roman rule. Of Judaea under Tiberius (14–37), Tacitus informs us that 'all was quiet' (Tac., *Hist.* 5.9.2). For this period he merely reports complaints over the excessive burden of taxation in Syria and Judaea at the beginning of Tiberius's reign, but there is no suggestion that such complaints were made exclusively by Jews nor that they were accompanied by disturbances.

However, the impression of peace at this time is contradicted by evidence of the insensitive and sometimes savage rule of Pontius Pilate in Judaea (26–36) (for a more sympathetic portrait of Pilate, see Schwartz: 1992). The Gospels' image of Pilate as a thoughtful judge, sensitive to the wishes of Jews, is supported by no non-Christian source, and is a function of the Gospels' apologetic purpose to downplay conflict between Christianity and Rome. Both Philo and Josephus, however, stress Pilate's offences, unprecedented in Roman practice, against Jewish religious sensibilities in Jerusalem that provoked serious unrest there: the introduction of legionary standards in the city, and the use of sacred money to build an aqueduct, on which occasion protest was crushed with savage violence. Pilate's rule ended with his suspension from office to answer charges by Vitellius, governor of Syria, for responsibility in the massacre of Samaritans, allegedly refugees from Pilate's persecution of them. By Roman standards of provincial government, which prohibited extortion and cruelty, Pilate had failed.

The brief rule of Gaius Caligula (37–41) (Barrett 1989) marked Judaean history in two important ways. First, by his patronage of M. Julius Agrippa, grandson of Herod the Great by Aristobulus, and who had grown up at the imperial court in Rome. With the considerable resentment of other Herodians, the emperor awarded Agrippa the title of king and territories north of Judaea, previously in the hands of his uncles Philip and Antipas (the latter deposed after demanding kingship for himself). This was the beginning of Rome's last efforts to govern the East through client kings (Millar 1994: 56). However, Gaius's friendship with Agrippa does not seem to have been accompanied by sympathy for Judaism. In retaliation for a Jewish attack on an imperial cult shrine in Jamnia, Gaius, inspired by a conviction of his own divinity, planned to convert the Jerusalem Temple into an imperial shrine with a colossal statue of himself as Jupiter in the Holy of Holies (Philo, *Leg.* 188.207–333; Jos., *AJ* 18.261–309; Tac., *Hist.* 5.9; Smallwood 1976 : 174–80; Barrett 1989: ch. 12). The situation was deemed so serious that the legate of Syria took over affairs in Judaea. Widespread opposition, voiced by elite Jews like Philo and Agrippa himself, and the cautious attitude of the legate of Syria, kept the project at bay until Gaius's assassination in 41.

AGRIPPA I

For his key role in ensuring Claudius's succession after Gaius (41), Agrippa was rewarded with the territories of Judaea and Samaria. In his brief but firm rule, this last king of Judaea asserted strong control over the ruling class and the military of Judaea, and suppressed dissident movements like Christianity (Acts 12.1–11). Agrippa's tendency to independent actions, however, raised some suspicion in Rome of revolutionary aspirations. His reputation for piety and defence of Judaism was marred by behaviour reminiscent of his patron Gaius when, in the theate at Caesarea, he failed to reject the flattery of those who hailed him as a god (Jos., *AJ* 19.343–6; Acts 12.19–23). He died soon afterwards, apparently repenting of this impiety, and much mourned by his Jewish subjects.

No more Herodians would rule Judaea. But Herodian influence continued in Jerusalem with their power over the administration of the high priest: only the last high priest, appointed by the rebels, was not a royal appointee. The kingdom of Agrippa was split up on his death (44), and the territories of Galilee, Peraea, Judaea, Samaritis and Idumaea were brought together as the province of Judaea under equestrian governors with the title 'procurator'. Agrippa's son, Agrippa II, reckoned too young to rule at this time, was later awarded various lands to the north of Judaea and, eventually, the right to control the administration of the Temple.

The first procurators of Judaea exercised extreme vigilance over potential subversion. Cuspius Fadus (?44–6), perhaps suspecting subversive activities among the Jerusalem elite, came into conflict with them over the guardianship of the high priest's vestments, a powerful symbol of their authority. The situation was later resolved by giving control of Temple affairs to Herod of Chalcis, brother of the late Agrippa I. Other disturbances in this period were severely suppressed: a border conflict between Jews of Peraea and the city of Philadelphia, and the activities of Theudas who promoted himself as a leader in the style of Moses with the professed ability to make the waters of the Jordan part.

In contrast with that time is the breakdown of order under the later procurators, attributable in part to the continuing presence of locally recruited auxiliaries hostile to Judaism. Ventidius Cumanus (48–52) proved a damaging failure for all concerned due to his failure or unwillingness to control forces hostile to the Jews of his province: individual soldiers were responsible for grave provocations, and his mishandling of bloody Samaritan–Jewish conflicts led to the intervention of the legate of Syria and Cumanus's removal and punishment by Claudius who decided in favour of the Jews.

The last procurators of Judaea were all appointments of Nero (54–68) under whom provincial maladminstration was notoriously widespread and its results visible in unrest not only in Judaea but also in places like Britain, Gaul, Africa, Egypt and Greece. The first of these, Antonius Felix (?52–?60), was of low social origins, but, in spite of the sneers of Josephus and Tacitus, very well connected at Rome and Jerusalem. His period of rule is characterized by disorder, possibly intensified by Rome's preoccupation with Armenia and Parthia (Millar 1994: 68–9). Banditry in Judaea, and popular independence protests, were constant problems: Felix's policy of severe repression did not bring peace and such activities continued to 66. In Jerusalem, on the other hand, apparently no restraint was imposed, resulting in a wave of political assassinations by the so-called *sikarii* (dagger-men) (Jos., *BJ* 2.254–7), hired by Jews and Romans alike, and gang-warfare between members of the ruling class.

The governor exercised relatively moderate intervention after riots between Jews and Syrians over the question of citizenship in Caesarea, each side claiming it for themselves. The issue was decided in favour of the non-Jews: in 60, Nero cancelled Jewish citizen rights there, a move that, in Josephus's view, proved critical in the outbreak of war (Jos., *AJ* 20.184).

Subversive activities among the Jerusalem ruling class increased in the last years before the war. The brief absence of a governor, through the death in office of Porcius Festus, was exploited by the high priest Ananus, son of the Ananus who had deliberately contravened Roman authority by executing some Christians (Jos., *AJ* 20.200). This relatively small sign of independent intentions brought the younger Ananus's immediate removal by the next representative of Rome, Luceius Albinus.

Despite evidence for considerable efficiency on Albinus's part, his years in Judaea saw an intensification of struggles for personal power among prominent members of the Jewish ruling class including Ananias, other high priests, and members of the Herodian family (Jos., *AJ* 20.205–7, 213–14). The clear involvement of members of the ruling class in the revolt, characterized by internal power struggles, and less than ten years away, is not surprising against this background.

Gessius Florus, the last Neronian procurator of Judaea, stands condemned by both Josephus and Tacitus for pushing the Jews into war against Rome. As Josephus puts it, 'we preferred to perish together rather than by degrees' (Jos., *AJ* 20.257; cf. Tac., *Hist.* 5.10.1). While Florus's appointment had been secured through the influence of Poppaea, friendly to Josephus and other Jews, his actions showed great contempt for the Jewish subjects of his province. His prime motivation (like that of many of Nero's provincial governors) was self-enrichment, achieved allegedly through widespread plunder of communities either by himself or by brigands charged with providing the governor with 'his quota of the spoils' (Jos., *AJ* 20.255). These activities caused many in the province, and especially the wealthy, to go abroad. In Josephus's earlier account, which provides the only specific details about Florus's activities, he claims that the governor deliberately provoked the Jewish revolt in order to cover up his own crimes from his superiors (Jos., *BJ* 2.282–3).

Events in the first six months of 66 proved critical for the breakdown in order in the province and especially for the extreme souring of relations between the governor and members of the Judaean ruling class. First, Florus failed the Jews, and especially the 'leading Jews', of Caesarea. Despite having taken bribes from the 'Jewish notables of Caesarea' to protect their synagogue from the hostile activities of their non-Jewish neighbours, Florus did nothing to help them. His sympathies, no doubt shaped by his own background as a native of a Greek city himself, were with the Greeks of Caesarea. Florus's hostility towards the Jews went further, however, than doing nothing: when the Jews of Caesarea fled the city and brought their protest before Florus, he responded by arresting the delegation of leading men on the charge of having removed a Torah scroll from Caesarea. It is not difficult to see why Florus's action was seen as deeply provocative, and as signalling the governor's complete lack of sympathy with the leading Jews of his province.

Even greater outrage was provoked by Florus's seizure of funds from the Jerusalem Temple, allegedly to make good some aspect of the imperial finances. This was probably overdue tribute, given the size of the sum, but nevertheless perceived as sacrilegious because money devoted to the service of God was being put instead to the service of the emperor (Jos., *BJ* 2.282–3). This proved the critical point for widespread Jewish disaffection with the governor, though not yet for revolt. One group mocked what they took to be his greed by collecting coppers in the street for him, as if for a beggar. When the Jerusalem authorities failed to hand over the culprits, Florus took revenge on an uncooperative ruling class. His troops sacked the upper city with much slaughter, and many of the 'peaceable citizens', some of them of equestrian rank, were treated like brigands, scourged and crucified (Jos., *BJ* 2.301–14; Goodman 1987: 170–2).

One further provocation elicited the first rebel action. Florus's troops, on his instruction, ignored the salute of the Jerusalem populace. On this occasion, some Jews took action to prevent the capture of the Temple by destroying its porticoes. It was clear by now that revolt was in the air. At the request of Jerusalem priests, a cohort was left behind in the city to keep the peace. Florus, meanwhile, filed a report to Cestius Gallus, legate of Syria, accusing the Jews of revolt.

At this stage, Josephus's record suggests, revolt might have been avoided had Florus been seen to be dealt with justly. However, nothing materialized of the protests made to Gallus by leading members of Jerusalem society, including Berenice, nor of the legate's promises to investigate the matter (Jos., *BJ* 2.280–1). King Agrippa's failure to have Florus removed, and his advice that the governor should be appeased for the meantime, led to his expulsion from the city.

THE FIRST JEWISH REVOLT

Rebel action against Rome began on two fronts. Unidentified rebels, perhaps members of the ruling class (McLaren 1998: 283), took Masada and wiped out its Roman garrison, thus acquiring substantial weaponry (Jos., *BJ* 2.408). This Herodian fort was the first of the rebels' prizes, and the only place to stay in rebel hands for the duration of the revolt. Meanwhile in Jerusalem, Eleazar, son of the high priest Ananias and captain of the Temple, called on the Temple priests to reject any gift or sacrifice from a foreigner (Jos., *BJ* 2.409–10). In Josephus's view, this laid the foundations for war: what Eleazar demanded, and got, was the rejection of sacrifices on behalf of the emperor and the people of Rome; it was a strong signal of hostility by members of the Jewish elite towards the centre of power in Rome.

In Jerusalem those leading citizens, including the high priest Ananias, who, according to Josephus, were urging peace, resorted to calling in the pro-Roman forces of Agrippa. The results, from their point of view, were catastrophic: targeting both Romans and pro-Roman Jews, the rebels destroyed the properties of Ananias, Agrippa and Berenice, expelling or recruiting Agrippa's army, and massacring the small Roman force remaining in the city. The destruction of the debt archive at this time was a symbolic strike against the money-lending rich, but also a calculated spur to win the poor over to the rebel cause.

The rebels had been joined in their actions by Menahem, a descendant of Judas the Galilean, now equipped with forces and arms from Masada. He took the leading role in attacking the Roman forces and their Jewish supporters: his purge of pro-Roman Jews took the lives of Eleazar's father and uncle, Ananias and his brother. The radical coalition of Menahem and Eleazar rapidly dissolved, however. Eleazar's determination to protect his leading role in the revolt led quickly to the assassination of Menahem and many of his followers. The survivors among this group fled to Masada and would play no further part in the war in Jerusalem.

Josephus claims that the trigger for much wider disturbances, at this time, was the rebels' Sabbath-day massacre of the surrendered Roman forces in Jerusalem, holed up in the royal towers. In his interpretation this sinful action received immediate punishment at the hands of Providence (*pronoia*): the entire Jewish population of Caesarea was massacred by other citizens. This proved the catalyst for many more ferocious conflicts initiated by Jews and gentiles on each other. The pattern of mutual hostility was not entirely uniform: in some places gentiles gave strong protection to their Jewish neighbours; and, in others, notably the Greek cities of the Decapolis, Jews gave their lives in loyalty to their local city, fighting against the Jewish rebels. Life for such Jews was precarious, as Josephus's tragic story of the Jews of Scythopolis shows very clearly: there, Jews who had fought Jewish rebels were nevertheless massacred by their non-Jewish Scythopolitan allies (Jos., *BJ* 2.466–76; Goodman 1992b: 53). Disorder in this region also intensified the long-running tensions between Jews and Greeks in Alexandria, resulting in the massacre of huge numbers of Jews there at the order of Philo's nephew, Tiberius Julius Alexander. One major outcome of these conflicts was, among the survivors, a supply of Jews to join the rebel cause.

Roman reaction to these events was slow and ineffectual. Cestius Gallus, governor of Syria since 65 and consul of more than twenty years before, did not approach Jerusalem until October 66. Realizing the need for better preparations, he withdrew his forces, only to be pursued by the rebels, who killed 6,000 of his soldiers near Beth Horon (Jos., *BJ* 2.499–555). The rebels' achievement was extraordinary by the standards of the time: as Fergus Millar puts it, 'There is no other example of a comparable defeat of Roman regular forces by the population of an established province' (Millar 1994: 71).

The rebel regime

Jerusalem remained under rebel control until 70. A provisional government emerged in 66, lasting over a year, and headed by Joseph son of Gorion and Ananus the ex-high priest. Military leaders were appointed to conduct the war in other areas from

Idumaea to Galilee: among these were sons of the chief priests and Josephus, also of the priestly aristocracy, who was given the charge of Galilee (Jos., *BJ* 2.562–8).

The pattern of elite leadership continued throughout the revolt: many members of the ruling class did not leave Jerusalem for the duration of the war; leading citizens made up the Zealots' criminal court; while individual rebel leaders and many of their supporters were aristocrats. Individual aristocrats' struggle for greater power became clear in the years leading up to revolt, while in 66 Florus's actions in Caesarea and Jerusalem signalled manifest contempt for their class, and loss of faith on both sides. For an aristocracy that had relied on Roman support that now appeared to have been withdrawn, the prospect of independent power, built on a national revolt, must have seemed the best chance of survival (Goodman 1987).

Because of Josephus's role in Galilee we are best informed for this early period about the situation there. Galilee presented a difficult task for the rebels, being the area most vulnerable to attack from Roman forces in Syria. But defence was not made easy by the fact that many Jews of the most important cities (Tiberias, Sepphoris, Gabara) were ambivalent about or opposed to the war. Josephus's personal task was also made difficult by the rivalry of John of Gischala who, with some backing from Jerusalem, sought the rebel leadership for himself and to obstruct Josephus.

Minting of rebel coinage, for sacred and ordinary purposes, began at the beginning of the revolt and continued until 70 (Meshorer 1982). This is not mentioned by Josephus, but is attested in large quantities in Judaea, Galilee and Samaria. It is not clear who was responsible for this, but the priests' access to the Temple treasuries indicates that responsibility lay in their circles. The issue of silver coins, in particular, a right denied to provinces, signalled the claim to independence not just from Rome but from the Tyrian mint, which had previously supplied silver coins for the Temple. Rebel symbols represent the land and the Temple. Slogans proclaim no particular leadership, but recall in different ways the glorious past of the country when free from foreign rule: Palaeo-Hebrew script represents the standard for coins of the autonomous Hasmonaean era; proclamation of the 'freedom of Zion' recalls the ancient name of Jerusalem; the 'shekel of Israel', the currency and the name of the land belonging to a distant past. The rebels represented a new future based on the past in which the name of Judaea, associated with previous regimes, did not figure (Goodblatt 1998). The coins also proclaim independence in the traditional Hellenistic manner by proclaiming a new era, lasting to year 5 (70).

In early 67, from his base in Greece, Nero made two new appointments to the region: C. Licinius Mucianus to replace Gallus, who had died the previous winter, and, to suppress the Jewish revolt, 57-year old Flavius Vespasianus, a trusted man from Nero's circle in Greece, and a first-generation senator with military distinctions in a now rather distant past (Rudich 1993: 194).

With his son Titus as second-in-command, Vespasian was given forces of around 60,000 including three legions (around twice the size of Gallus's forces). The repression of Galilee, begun in June 67, was quick and ruthless. Very few places offered resistance: in Jotapata, Josephus was one of just two males to survive, captured after a 47-day siege; other rebel centres in Galilee and in Agrippa's territory of Gaulanitis were crushed. Vespasian's successes of 67 were completed with a brief visit to Judaea, taking Jamnia and Azotus, and installing garrisons there. Action was resumed in early 68, and by June only Jerusalem and the forts of Herodion, Machaerus and Masada remained untouched. Nero's suicide (June 9) ended Vespasian's mandate in Judaea, and he halted his actions in Judaea, pending Rome's advice, until the following year. For most of that year, Vespasian waited, watching from a distance in Alexandria, the bloody struggles over the succession to Nero. Apart from a brief intervention in June 69 to suppress Simon's forces in south Judaea, he waited until spring 70 to begin finishing off the revolt.

In the meantime, the Roman political scene changed dramatically. Vespasian's own bid for the position of emperor was declared in July 69 (Jos., *BJ* 4.592–620; Tac., *Hist.* 2.79–80; *P. Fouad* 8 = *CPJ* 418a), supported by the legate of Syria, Mucianus, and the prefect of Egypt, Tiberius Julius Alexander. At this point, the former rebel general Josephus was released as a reward for his now fulfilled prophecy of Vespasian's rise (Jos., *BJ* 3.399–408). This move eventually brought Josephus into the close circle of Vespasian, and thus into the position from which he could begin his career as apologetic historian. In December 69, Vespasian was acknowledged as emperor by the Senate.

New factions in Jerusalem

Vespasian's successes in 67 had a major impact in Jerusalem. Loss of faith in the leadership of Ananus fuelled the rise of the Zealots, a self-designation apparently denoting their religious zeal, in 68 (Jos., *BJ* 4.160–1): led by Ananus's rival, the priest Eleazar son of Simon, its membership was composed of upper-class priests and refugees from Vespasian's victories. The Zealots asserted their control over the Temple with the election of a new high priest: Phanni son of Samuel, an unknown from an unknown village and, according to Jewish tradition (Jos., *BJ* 4.138–57, 160; *t. Yoma* 1.6), not of high-priestly descent. Joined by John of Gischala, a refugee since 67 from the suppression of his home town, and a force of Idumaeans, the Zealots also took control of Jerusalem, destroying the previous leadership with the murder of Ananus. In Josephus's view, this murder sealed the fate of the city, since Ananus alone represented the possibility of a compromise solution with Rome (Jos., *BJ* 4.318).

Some of those who had fled the Zealot takeover joined forces with Simon bar Gioras, a former rebel general in Acrabatene: in spring 69, having gained an army of refugees from the Zealot cause, Simon took control of the whole city, except for the Temple, and remained in charge to the moment of defeat. After the fall of Jerusalem it was he who was recognized by Rome as the leader of the enemy.

From then until their brief unity at the beginning of the Roman siege of the city, the rebels were divided. A new party led by Eleazar son of Simon with men of 'weight' and 'distinction' (Jos., *BJ* 5.5–7), many of them Zealots, split from John and occupied the Temple. John and some of the Idumaeans took the outer precincts, while Simon, with much the greatest support, held the rest of the city. All the factions warred with each other and the rest of the Jerusalem population. John eventually took the inner court at Passover: two factions became one with the murder of Eleazar. Only when the battering-rams arrived at Jerusalem did John agree to recognize Simon's leadership.

Famine was assured, once the siege was underway, since the factions had burned the storehouses for provisions: 'all the environs of the Temple were reduced to ashes' (Jos., *BJ* 5.25). Josephus paints a dire picture of life, reminiscent of the horrors accompanying the curses at the end of Deuteronomy, in the city in this period: his interpretation of these events as divine punishment for impiety is emphasized again and again. Roman writers shared another of Josephus's much stressed perceptions, that the rebels' own divisions defeated them. Nevertheless (as in other terrors), he provides evidence for a considerable degree of organization of the city's life under some kind of council. The rebels continued to maintain the daily sacrifice until July 70 (Jos., *BJ* 6.94; *m. Taanit* 4.6), and, though with severe risk to the visitor, the Temple as a place of pilgrimage (Jos., *BJ* 5.18). Further signs of organization appear in the continued issue of coinage until the fall of Jerusalem, the burial of the dead, and the assembly of courts by the Zealots to assert their power (which they certainly did when the verdict went against them (see Jos., *BJ* 4.334–44; Goodman 1987: 178–9).

From 68 onwards the rebels might reasonably have had 'great expectations': other revolts (especially at the borders of Empire), had succeeded, and the leadership of Rome was in chaos. What they did not anticipate was the marvellous opportunity their suppression offered to a newly elected emperor in need of a victory.

The Roman reconquest of Jerusalem was undertaken by Titus in March 70, appointed by his father Vespasian to take over the war. Supported by massive forces of four legions (against an estimated rebel force of 24,000), with assistance from forces including Agrippa II and Tiberius Julius Alexander, the Roman forces took the city after a brief siege culminating in the destruction of the Temple in late August and the suppression of the rebel forces.

According to Josephus, anxious to defend the reputation of Titus to Jews and Romans alike, the Temple was burned against Titus's express orders (itself improbable; cf. Smallwood 1976: 325) that it should be spared. There are good reasons, however, to believe the opposite: the propaganda of the victors, which gloats over the destruction, and Roman sources, which make clear that the destruction was deliberate. While there are no signs before 70 that the Romans found the cult objectionable, its use as a rebel fortress in the war, and perhaps its long-standing role as a focus for protest, decided its fate.

The date of the Second Temple's destruction was remembered as coinciding with that of the first under the Babylonians (10 Ab: Jos., *BJ* 6.250; 9 Ab: *m. Taanit* 4.6). Within a month, on Titus's orders, the city was virtually razed to the ground. Only the Herodian towers and part of the city's western wall, where future Jewish pilgrims would lament the Temple's loss, were spared. The devastation would lead visitors, so Josephus, to suppose Jerusalem had never been inhabited (Jos., *BJ* 7.3). For the time being, the city served mainly as the headquarters of the Legion X Fretensis.

Jewish losses were enormous. Many had lost their lives already in the famine, or at the hands of the rebels or, captured by the Romans, had been crucified outside the city to terrorize the rebels into submission (Jos., *BJ* 5.420ff.). The remains of burnt houses in Jerusalem (the only remains to be associated with this period of destruction) testify to the devastation of the period (Avigad 1984: 123). Survivors not freed by Titus faced enslavement or, for proven rebels, and the old and the ill, execution (Jos., *BJ* 6.414–20). Many Jewish prisoners were later killed in Titus's celebratory games held in Caesarea Philippi, Berytus and the cities of Syria (Jos., *BJ* 7.23–4, 37–9, 96).

In hindsight, seeking to explain the catastrophe of the revolt, Josephus pointed to many causes. He is undoubtedly right that Roman maladministration, especially under Nero, and especially with regard to offences against the Temple, was a major factor. His attempt to identify the chief rebels with marginal groups – rural bandits, urban assassins and deluded ideologues – is less convincing. Josephus's own evidence does not show that any of these groups aimed at the active destruction of Roman rule in Judaea. The *sikarii*, on whom Josephus blamed the beginning of war (Jos., *BJ* 7.253–8, 262), operated, by his own admission, as assassins for Jew and Roman alike, and took no real part in the war itself. Menahem, with whom, like the *sikarii*, Josephus links the Fourth Philosophy, does not emerge as a rebel leader until after the outbreak of revolt and, even then, is quickly suppressed by elite rebel forces. Antagonism from the local non-Jewish elements in the governors' armies and, much more so, the bloody hostilities between Jews and non-Jews in Greek cities in 66 undoubtedly fired the mood for revolt. So perhaps did the widespread poverty and unemployment of the province. However, while, in the economic conditions of first-century Judaea, there was much reason to expect hostility to the regime to come from the poor (Goodman 1982; 1996: 758–61), there is little evidence that the inspiration for revolt came from such quarters. Their contribution to the revolt seems largely to have been as hirelings in the armies of the Jewish aristocrats who led the revolt. Despite Josephus's efforts to place the blame elsewhere, he provided strong testimony to the ambition for power among the Judaean elite as a decisive factor in promoting war against Rome (Goodman 1987; Price 1992; cf. Brunt 1977).

Exploitation of victory

Suppression of the Judaean revolt was exploited by Vespasian and his sons, keen to show off their central role in defending Rome from disorder at home and in the provinces. Accordingly, in 71, they celebrated a triumph in common (Jos., *BJ* 7.121–57), to display the treasures of the peoples they had crushed into submission. Josephus naturally gives special prominence to the display of conquered Judaea and especially to the captured treasures of the Jerusalem Temple. The climax of the procession, following Roman practice, saw the execution of the enemy's general, Simon bar Gioras (Jos., *BJ* 7.148–54). Triumphal arches and a new temple for the goddess Pax, in which were housed the Temple's treasures, provided more permanent commemorations of the victory in Rome. From 71, and sporadically until 81, vast quantities of special coins were issued to commemorate the capture and humiliation of Judaea. Such propaganda, like the triumph, was unprecedented after the suppression of a revolt: the 'Judaea Capta' coins provided important reminders of the Flavians' greatest victory while no doubt also designed to deter further revolt (Smallwood 1976: 330). Some tact was shown in the coins issued for the province, which display markedly less insulting images of Jews than those issued in Rome (Meshorer 1982: 194).

Very few details survive concerning the taxation of the province after 70, though evidence for tax exemptions in the 80s suggests early signs of economic recovery. As a direct result of the war, however, a new annual tax of two drachmas (the *didrachmon*) was imposed from 70 onwards on all Jews of the Empire who 'followed their ancestral customs' (Dio 66.7.2). The financial burden of this tax was not slight, but the 'psychological burden' is likely to have been more significant: the tax not only associated all Jews, regardless of their involvement in the war, with a failed rebellion, but its use in the restoration of the temple of Capitoline Jupiter made them pay for the practice of their religion by supporting the cult of the victor's chief deity (Jos., *BJ* 7.218). One important consequence of the new tax was the development of an official Roman definition of Jewish identity as conferred by practice of Jewish customs rather than by ancestry (Goodman 1989).

For all their propaganda against the rebels, the Flavians' good relations with some of the Jewish aristocracy continued after 70. However, literary evidence from elite Roman writers like Tacitus and Juvenal suggests a markedly more contemptuous mood towards Judaism than is evident in earlier Roman writers, stressing the un-Roman qualities of Judaism (Tac., *Hist.* 5.2–5; Juv., *Satires* 14.96–106). To counter this mood, and to persuade those who mattered in Roman society that Judaism was indeed compatible with Roman values, was the enterprise with which Josephus was to engage himself for the rest of his life. Other Jewish writings post 70 CE, however, illustrate the development of a much more ambivalent, often very hostile, mood towards Rome that was not present in earlier Jewish culture.

Suppression of further resistance

After the fall of Jerusalem, rebels still held out in Herodian forts and in caves near the Dead Sea. Josephus reports that the surrender of the forts of Herodion and Machaerus was quickly achieved by the legate Lucilius Bassus, second governor of the new administration (71–3), wiping out surviving rebel refugees from Jerusalem and Machaerus at the 'forest called Jardes' (Jos., *BJ* 7.163–215).

By the time of Bassus's death in office in 73, only Masada remained as a rebel stronghold. The reduction of this fortress, housing around 1,000 rebels, was rigorously undertaken by the new legate, L. Flavius Silva. What actually happened at Masada is not known for sure (Jos., *BJ* 7.304–401; Yadin 1966; Feldman 1975; Ladouceur 1987). Josephus's famous account of the rebels' last days makes for exciting reading but some aspects of its reliability are far from certain. In particular, his story of the rebels' mass suicide is hard to sustain, for lack of material evidence: while it is plausible that the rebels, like other Jews in the war, had indeed committed suicide, it is quite possible that Josephus's story is a cover-up for a Roman massacre, while also lending some dignity to the final exit of the Judaean rebels. The primary purpose of the story, as it stands in Josephus, is to make these rebels, with their ideological links to the Fourth Philosphy, accept responsibility for the war and admit defeat: the rebel leader, Eleazar ben Yair, is made to acknowledge, through the words of Josephus, that God now stands on the side of Rome (Jos., *BJ* 7.360). Resistance within Judaea was, for the time being, over: a garrison was installed at Masada; and determined rebels made new homes in Egypt and Cyrene, where they and their descendants may well have contributed to the Jewish revolts there under Trajan.

Settlement of Judaea

Very little is known about Judaea in the early years after the fall of Masada. We do know that a new Roman order was established in the province: in place of low-ranking procurators and meagre military resources, government was entrusted to an imperial legate of praetorian rank, assisted by a procurator in charge of finance, and with the military force of a legion (X Fretensis) stationed in Jerusalem, reckoned the likely trouble spot for the future as it had been in the past. Auxiliary units composed of local gentiles, who had caused much friction with local Jews in recent years, were posted well away from the province.

After 70, Vespasian disposed of territory confiscated from rebel landowners (Jos., *BJ* 7.216; Isaac 1984): there is no reason to exclude the possibility that other Jews bought this land. Indeed, it is clear that Jews continued to own land in Judaea after the revolt. Within Judaea, Emmaus was renamed Nicopolis in honour of Vespasian's victory, and land there was used to settle 800 veterans from the war, a useful supplement to defences around Jerusalem (Jos., *BJ* 7.217). Otherwise, Vespasian founded a new city, Flavia Neapolis, in Samaria, with predominantly non-Jewish settlers. To accompany the introduction of the legion to the province, Caesarea was promoted to the status of a colony with exemption from *tributum capitis*.

Josephus's efforts to promote the upper-priestly class and Agrippa II in his *Jewish War* suggest that, at first, enough of this class survived to make a plausible bid for power; but, if so, he no longer reckoned their chances by the time of his *Antiquities* (Schwartz 1990). There, like other Jews writing in the aftermath of the war, and following in the fundamental tradition of Judaism, he advocates the life lived according to the words of Moses: he does not, however, indicate any particular authority to mediate those words.

There were undoubtedly many groups at this period seeking to fill the authority vacuum that the crushing of the priestly leadership and its cultic centre had left. The best known of these are those figures, from a variety of backgrounds, whose traditions are collected in the earliest rabbinic literature (Strack and Stemberger 1991; Neusner 1994). This reflects, among other things, the early rabbis' attempts to gain an authoritative position among Jews, initially in Judaea, and later in Galilee (Goodman 1983). However, the evidence of their own writings, depicting conflicts with other Jews, together with other literary and archaeological evidence, shows that the rabbis were not to play a leading role in Jewish society before at least the third century. On the other hand, it is clear from inscriptional evidence that members of priestly families continued to consider, long after 70, the great importance of their status (Williams 1999).

While literary evidence makes clear that, from very early on after its destruction, Jews expected the eventual restoration of the Temple cult (*4 Ezra*; *2 Baruch*), and some, in that expectation, wrote about it as though it still existed (Jos., *Ap.* 2.193–8), neither the cult nor its high priesthood were in fact restored after 70 (Guttmann 1967). The economic, political and religious significance of Jerusalem was severely diminished as a consequence.

TO THE SECOND JEWISH REVOLT

At the end of Trajan's reign (115–17), Jewish revolts erupted in various parts of the eastern Empire: Cyrene, Egypt, Cyprus and Mesopotamia (Dio 68.32.1–3; Euseb., *Hist.* 4.2; Appian, *Frg.* 19; *Civil Wars* 2.90; *SHA, Hadrian* 5.8). Conducted with ferocity and crushed with huge Jewish losses, no ancient writer could find an explanation for these rebellions, though resentment at the destruction of the Temple and the imposition of the *didrachmon* for Jupiter's temple may well lie behind widespread Jewish attacks on gentile cult centres in Cyrene and Egypt (Goodman 1992a). These revolts do not seem to have been accompanied by comparable disturbances in Judaea where there are no clear signs of disturbance prior to 132 (though cf. Horbury 1996).

In the aftermath of Trajan's Parthian war (113–17) and Jewish revolts in neighbouring countries (115–17), however, Rome's military presence in Judaea was substantially reinforced, no doubt in anticipation of potential problems there. Under the rule of Hadrian, Trajan's successor, Rome's interests in Judaea were protected by a governor of consular rank and by two legions (Lifshitz 1960; Isaac and Roll 1979a, 1979b).

Like the rest of the region, Judaea experienced the impact of Hadrian's programme of promoting the Hellenization of the East (Birley 1997). The most enduring evidence of this in Judaea is connected with the emperor's visit to the province in 130: new roads and buildings were constructed, and the visit was commemorated with the 'conventional expressions of honour' found in other provinces including the building of Hadrianea at Caesarea and Tiberias, and coins celebrating the *adventus* of the emperor to Judaea.

The foundation of cities and colonies was part of Hadrian's policy of restoration and promotion of Hellenism in the East. The refounding of Jerusalem as the *colonia* Aelia Capitolina, honouring Hadrian's family as well as the gods of the Capitoline, was probably intended to commemorate Hadrian's visit (Bowersock 1980: 134). (Around this time, nearby Sepphoris, with a largely Jewish population, was also renamed in honour of the emperor and his supreme God as Diocaesarea.) No doubt the introduction of a second *colonia* in Judaea also served other practical needs: the second legion, now in Judaea for at least ten years, required a local supply of citizen recruits (Isaac and Roll 1979a: 66; Birley 1997: 233).

Paucity of evidence makes it very difficult to gauge reaction in Judaea to this event. If, as seems likely, the new *colonia* was founded in 130, there is no sign of immediate protest over this move, nor at other aspects of Hadrian's programme of Hellenization through building in Judaea and other areas with Jewish populations (Bowersock 1980: 134). Indeed, Hadrian's special honouring of Jerusalem may well have been regarded positively by some Jews at this stage (Schäfer 1990).

THE SECOND JEWISH REVOLT

Nothing in the sources prepares us for the outbreak of a well-organized revolt in Judaea, probably confined only to Jews, lasting from 132–5 CE, and remembered as one of the chief disasters of Hadrian's reign (sources in Dio 69.12.1–15; Euseb. *Dem.*

6.18.10; *Hist.* 4.5.2; 5.12.1; Fronto, *Parthian War* 2). The causes of this revolt seem not to have been well understood in antiquity. The fullest account of the revolt, derived from Xiphilinus's epitome of Dio, gives the foundation of Aelia and the construction there, in place of 'the temple of the god' (Dio 69.12.1), of a temple dedicated to Zeus as the immediate cause of rebellion. As we have seen, however, cause and effect do not meet so spontaneously in this case (Bowersock 1980). Revolt began no earlier than 132, two years after the likely date of the foundation of the *colonia*. Based on Jewish reactions to Roman violations of Jerusalem's sanctity in the previous century, the *colonia*'s introduction of a Roman temple on the site of Jerusalem might well (as Dio claims it did) have been expected to provoke uproar. If so, it did not do so immediately. It is also striking that Hadrian, an emperor who generally sought to promote peaceful rule, did not anticipate significant protest over this development of Jerusalem.

Dio's explanation of the revolt does not account for its timing. A more immediate provocation is required between the foundation of Aelia (130) and the outbreak of revolution (132). That is supplied by the slender evidence of Hadrian's supposed biographer, Pseudo-Spartianus, in the fourth-century *Historia Augusta*. There it is claimed that 'the Jews began war, because they were forbidden to mutilate their genitals' (*SHA*, *Hadrian* 14.2). A universal ban on circumcision, part of Hadrian's development of earlier imperial prohibitions of castration, is probably to be connected with his tour of the East in 130–2. Its historicity is confirmed by a subsequent law exempting Jews from the prohibition under the reign of the next emperor, Antoninus Pius (*Dig.* 48.1.11pr.). This special exemption may reflect a Roman sense that the ban was a factor behind the revolt. Although Jews were by no means the only people affected by such a ban, many will undoubtedly have seen it as a hostile action by the Roman State against their religious practice. However, opposition to circumcision may have been a policy that some Jews supported prior to the revolt: rabbinic evidence refers (at this time) to the recircumcision of Jews (probably under the compulsion of the rebels) who had previously reversed their circumcision (*t. Shab.* 15.9; Schäfer 1981, 1990; Birley 1997: 271).

The documentation left behind by the rebels themselves provides no straightforward cause for the revolt (Benoit et al. 1961; Avigad 1961, 1962; Yadin 1963, 1971; Lewis 1989; Cotton and Yardeni 1997). Their slogans and activities, military and administrative, suggest, however, that the primary motivation was independence. Their propaganda is preserved in their coins, overstrikes of previous mints, which publicized their aspirations and that, through symbols of the land and the Temple cult, sought to exploit the patriotic and religious feelings of other Jews (Meshorer 1982: ch. 8; Mildenberg 1984).

Like the rebels of the First Revolt, these rebels styled their land as 'Israel', a proclamation of the ancient independent land as defined by Scripture. The coins proclaimed the liberation of this land and of Jerusalem. However, the rebels' real territorial gains were much more limited, and these proclamations of freedom must, to a large extent, be taken as programmatic statements (but cf. Eck 1999: 81). The evidence is clear that they did control territory to the south of Jerusalem, with centres at Herodion and Bethar, but it does not put them, at any time, in Jerusalem or any other major urban centre in or outside Judaea.

The coins and documents also proclaim a new political regime, marked by the beginning of a new calendrical era. The leadership of this regime, in contrast to that of the First Revolt, appears to have been centred on one man, Shimeon bar Kosiba, styled in the rebel documentation as '*nasi* (prince) of Israel'. Coins dating to the first two years of revolt also proclaim the co-leadership of one 'Eleazar the priest', about whom nothing else is known for sure. In later rabbinic and Christian writings, Shimeon is connected with the messianic title 'Bar Kokhba' or 'son of the star', derived from messianic interpretation of Numbers 24.17 (*y. Taanit* 4.8; *Lam. Rabbah* 2.4; Euseb. *Hist.* 4.6.2). (This prophecy was read as a promise by many Jews in antiquity of a future leader who would defeat the foreign enemy: 'a star shall come forth out of Jacob, and a sceptre shall crush the forehead of Moab and break down all the sons of Seth'.) These same sources, Jewish and Christian, remembered him as a failed messianic pretender. It is unclear whether Shimeon regarded himself as a messiah: the title he attached to himself, *nasi*, may represent a claim to messianic status but it is also used of Jewish leaders without implying that claim. Similarly, the acclamation of a *nasi* and a priest may reflect messianic beliefs such as those found in the Qumran *War Scroll*, but it also may have been intended to replicate the pattern of government under the ancient kings of Judah with no such implication.

As a leader, Shimeon's own documents reveal him as very strict both in demands for support and for correct observance of the Sabbath and festivals (*IEJ* 1961: 42 no. 3; *DJD* II no. 44, pl. xlvi). Jewish support for the revolt never appears to have been very widespread: the huge scale of Jewish casualties should not be taken as an indication of the victims' participation in the war. Towards the end of the revolt, Shimeon's letters indicate the level of difficulty just in maintaining the support of his armed followers (*IEJ* 1961: 46 no. 12). Little else is known of the identity of the rebels though their documents hint that at least some of them were wealthy.

In view of their resources, the rebels' achievements were remarkable. A substantial amount of territory near Jerusalem came under their control, to the extent that Shimeon was able to issue administrative documents recording the leasing and tithing of this land. What is most striking, however, is the rebels' ability to keep massive Roman forces occupied from spring 132 until autumn 135. Their construction of a sophisticated system of underground hiding-places appears to have been crucial in this temporary success (Kloner 1983).

Hadrian's actions during and after the revolt show this was regarded as a very serious crisis: the best general of the day, Julius Severus, was brought in from Britain (133/34) to replace the ineffective efforts of the governor Tineius Rufus; extra recruits were drummed up in Italy; and, after victory, a grateful emperor bestowed the highest honours on his leading generals. For the first time in his rule, Hadrian marked a victory with an alteration in his title: from 135, Hadrian presented himself as Imperator II (Birley 1997: 275).

The revolt cost a huge loss of life on both sides (Dio 69.14.1). Roman casualties were excessive and Roman memories of these losses would last a long time (Fronto, *Parthian War* 2). Of the Jews, Dio reports that very few survived. The human cost on the Jewish side is revealed in microcosm in the sad remains of skeletons, clothes and documents recovered at Nahal Hever, the victims of Roman blockade and massacre (Avigad 1961, 1962; Yadin 1961, 1971: 60–5; Aharoni 1962). Later Jewish writers also remembered the enormous devastation of Jewish life in the siege of the final rebel stronghold of Bethar. Many Jewish survivors ended up on the slave market.

JUDAEA AFTER 135

The development of the new colony of Aelia Capitolina continued, representing until the time of Christian emperors, a relatively minor provincial centre of which little is known. Caesarea, as the provincial capital, would soon become an important Jewish centre in the post-Temple era. Four years after the revolt, the province of Judaea acquired a new official name, Syria Palaestina. Though Hadrian was dead by then, the move may be attributed to him. Its rationale is unknown, though it may have been meant as a punitive measure, erasing the distinctly Jewish nature of the province's name. If so, it was an unprecedented form of punishment in the history of the Roman Empire.

For the most part, the memory of Hadrian in Jewish tradition is profoundly negative. The vilification of Hadrian, 'May his bones rot', is probably to be linked to his measures for the suppression of the revolt rather than for any later punitive actions. Rabbinic evidence for the prohibition of certain communal practices (*m. Shabb.* 4.11; *b. B. Bat.* 60b; *b. San.* 14a; *b. Ber.* 61b), if authentic, is likely to reflect measures taken during rather than after the revolt. The same is probably true of the stories of Jewish martyrdom under Hadrian (Schäfer 1995: 159–60; though cf. Herr 1973).

Early Christian claims that Hadrian banned Jews from Aelia Capitolina and its environs after 135 are widely accepted as true (Euseb., *Hist.* 4.6.3–4; Tert., *Adv. Iud.* 13; cf. Justin, *Apol.* 1.47; *Dial.* 16.2). If authentic, the ban must, according to the contemporary Roman definition of Jewishness, have applied only to Jews who publicly practised their religion. It is by no means certain, however, that the ban should be considered authentic (Krauss 1996: 18). The evidence for a ban has no clear support in Roman sources, a remarkable silence in view of the unprecedented nature of this punitive measure (but cf. Rendell-Harris 1926). Moreover, the evidence of early rabbinic writings and archaeology points to both continued Jewish visits to former Jerusalem and a continued Jewish presence there in the late second century and beyond (Safrai 1975; Schwartz 1986). The Christian claim, first attributed to Ariston of Pella in Eusebius, may represent an exaggeration of some other punitive measure in the immediate aftermath of the revolt. The exaggerated presentation of this measure as a ban on all Jews was, as early Christian writers show clearly, influenced by the desire to attribute divine prophecies of doom, including Isaiah's prophecy of exile from Jerusalem, to the Jews (Isa. 33.17; cf. Euseb. *Chronicle of Hadrian* Year 18). It is not clear then that former Jerusalem did become thoroughly non-Jewish after 135.

There is no doubt, on the other hand, that Jewish presence throughout the province was significantly diminished as a result of the revolt. Death and enslavement account for much of the 'devastation' that Dio records (Dio 69.13.2). Substantial emigration by Jews was seen as a serious problem by some rabbis who, after the revolt, demanded that Jews return to inhabit the land. Others, whether under the rabbis' influence or not, began a new trend in Jewish practice and reflected their sense of identity with the Land by choosing to be buried there (Gafni 1997: chs 3–4). At the same time, however, the impact of the new colony of Aelia and its religious culture, together with the loss of the Temple, meant that, for many Jews, former Jerusalem became a much less significant place as a place to live (or to aspire to do so) than it had been. But signs of Jewish life are by no means lacking in this region after 135: substantial Jewish communities continued in much of former Judaea, and signs of recovery appear already in the second century (Schwartz 1986).

Defeat did not end Jewish hopes for the restoration of the holy city and the Temple, hopes that later had some support in the attempts of the Emperor Julian to rebuild it. Further afield, Jewish life continued to flourish – in the West in Rome and in Asia Minor; and the rabbinic movement began to develop its programme for renewing Judaism without a Temple and without access to the holy city, in Babylonia, the place of the first exile from Jerusalem.

BIBLIOGRAPHY

Aharoni, Y. (1962) 'Expedition B – the Cave of Horror', *IEJ* 12: 186–99.

Alexander, L. (ed.) (1991) *Images of Empire*, Sheffield: JSOT Press.

Avi-Yonah, M. (1976) *The Jews of Palestine: A Political History from the Bar Kokhba War to the Arab Conquest*, Oxford: Basil Blackwell.

Avi-Yonah, M. (ed.) (1975) *The World History of the Jewish People*, Vol. 7: *The Herodian Period*, London: W. H. Allen.

Avigad, N. (1961) 'The Expedition to the Judaean Desert, 1960', *IEJ* 11: 3–72.

—— (1962) 'The Expedition to the Judaean Desert, 1960', *IEJ* 12: 167–262.

—— (1984) *Discovering Jerusalem*, Oxford: Basil Blackwell.

Barnes, T. (1989) 'Trajan and the Jews', *JJS* 40: 145–62.

Barrett, A. A. (1989) *Caligula: The Corruption of Power*, London: Batsford.

Benoit, P., Milik, J., de Vaux, R. (eds) (1961) *Les Grottes de Murabba'at: Discoveries in the Judaean Desert 2*, Oxford: Clarendon Press.

Bilde, P. (1979) 'The Causes of the Jewish War according to Josephus', *JSJ* 10: 179–202.

Birley, A. R. (1997) *Hadrian: The Restless Emperor*, London: Routledge.

Bowersock, G. W. (1980) 'A Roman Perspective on the Bar Kokhba War', in W. S. Green (ed.) *Approaches to Ancient Judaism 2*, 131–41.

—— (1983) *Roman Arabia*, Cambridge, Mass.: Harvard University Press.

Bowman, A., Champlin, E., Lintott, A. (eds) (1996) *The Cambridge Ancient History*, Vol. 10: *The Augustan Empire 43 BC–AD 69*, Cambridge: Cambridge University Press.

Braund, D. (1984) *Rome and the Friendly King: The Character of Client Kingship*, London: Croom Helm; New York: St. Martin's Press.

Brunt, P. (1977) 'Josephus on Social Conflicts in Roman Judaea', *Klio* 59: 149–53.

Cancik, H. et al. (eds) (1996) *Geschichte – Tradition – Reflextion*, Tübingen J. C. B. Mohr.

Charlesworth, J. (1985) *The Old Testament Pseudepigrapha 1–2*, New York: Doubleday.

Cohen, S. J. D. (1982) 'Masada: Literary Tradition, Archaeological Remains, and the Credibility of Josephus', *JJS* 33: 385–405.

Cotton, H. and Yardeni, A. (1997) *Discoveries in the Judaean Desert 27: Aramaic and Greek Texts from Nahal Hever and Other Sites*, Oxford: Clarendon Press.

Crook, J., Lintott, A., Rawson, E. (eds) (1994) *The Cambridge Ancient History*, Vol. 9: *The Last Age of the Roman Republic 146–43 BC*, Cambridge: Cambridge University Press.

Davies, P. R. and White, R. (1990) *A Tribute to Geza Vermes*, Sheffield: Sheffield Academic Press.

Dunn, J. (ed.) (1992) *Jews and Christians: The Parting of the Ways* AD 70 to 135, Tübingen: J. C. B. Mohr.

Eck, W. (1999) 'The Bar Kokhba Revolt: The Roman Point of View', *JRS*: 76–89.

Feldman, L. (1975) 'Masada: A Critique of Recent Scholarship', in J. Neusner (ed.) *Christianity, Judaism and Other Greco-Roman Cults*, Part 3, 218–48.

Feldman, L. (1984) *Josephus and Modern Scholarship* (1937–80), Berlin: de Gruyter.

—— (1986) *Josephus: A Supplementary Bibliography*, New York: Garland.

Feldman, L. and Hata, G. (eds) (1987) *Josephus, Judaism and Christianity*, Detroit: Wayne State University Press.

Frey, J.-B. (1936–52) *Corpus Inscriptionum Iudaicarum*, 2 vols, Rome: Pontificio Istituto di archeologia cristiana; vol. 1 revised with prologue by B. Lifshitz (1975), New York: Ktav.

Gafni, I. (1997). Vol. 1: *Land, Center and Diaspora: Jewish Constructs in Late Antiquity*, Sheffield: Sheffield Academic Press.

Goodblatt, D. (1998) 'From Judeans to Israel: Names of Jewish States in Antiquity', *JSJ* 29: 1–36.

Goodman, M. (1982) 'The First Jewish Revolt: Social Conflict and the Problem of Debt', *JJS* 33: 417–27.

—— (1983) *State and Society in Roman Galilee, AD 132–212*, Totowa: Rowman & Allanheld.

—— (1987) *The Ruling Class of Judaea: The Origins of the Jewish Revolt Against Rome*, Cambridge: Cambridge University Press.

—— (1989) 'Nerva, the *Fiscus Judaicus* and Jewish Identity', *JRS* 79: 40–4.

—— (1991) 'Opponents of Rome: Jews and Others', in L. Alexander (ed.) *Images of Empire*, 222–38.

—— (1992a) 'Diaspora Reactions to the Destruction of the Temple', in J. Dunn (ed.) *Jews and Christians: The Parting of the Ways* AD 70 to 135, 27–38.

—— (1996) 'Jews in the Decapolis', *Aram* 4: 49–56.

—— (1996) 'Judaea', in A. Bowman, E. Champlin, A. Lintott (eds) *The Cambridge Ancient History*, Vol. 10: *The Augustian Empire, 43 BC–AD 69*, 737–81.

Grabbe, L. L. (1992) *Judaism from Cyrus to Hadrian*, London: SCM Press.

Green, W. S. (ed.) (1980) *Approaches to Ancient Judaism* 2, Atlanta: Scholars Press.

Griffin, M. (1984) *Nero: The End of a Dynasty*, London: Batsford.

Guttmann, A. (1967) 'The End of the Sacrificial Cult, *HUCA* 38: 137–48.

Herr, M.-D. (1973) 'Persecutions and Martyrdom in Hadrian's Days', *Scripta Hierosolymitana* 23: 85–125.

Horbury, W. (1996) 'The Beginnings of the Jewish Revolt under Trajan', in H. Cancik et al. (eds) *Geschichte – Tradition – Reflexion*, 283–304.

Horbury, W., Davies, W. D., Sturdy, J. (eds) (1999) *The Cambridge History of Judaism*, Cambridge: Cambridge University Press.

Isaac, B. (1984) 'Judaea after 70', *JJS* 35: 44–50.

Isaac, B. and Oppenheimer, A. (1985) 'The Revolt of Bar Kokhba: Ideology and Modern Scholarship', *JJS* 36: 33–60.

Isaac, B. and Roll, I. (1979a) 'Judaea in the Early Years of Hadrian's Reign', *Latomus* 38: 54–66.

—— (1979b) 'Legio II Traiana in Judaea', *ZPE* 33: 149–56.

Kasher, A., Rappaport, U., Fuks, G. (eds) (1990) *Greece and Rome in Eretz Israel: Collected Essays*, Yad Izhak Ben-Zvi: Israel Exploration Society.

Kloner, A. (1983) 'The Subterranean Hideaways', *The Jerusalem Cathedra* 3: 83–96.

Krauss, S. (ed. and rev. W. Horbury) (1996) *The Jewish-Christian Controversy*, Vol. 1: *History*, Tübingen: J. C. B. Mohr.

Ladouceur, D. (1987) 'Josephus and Masada', in L. Feldman and G. Hata (eds) *Josephus, Judaism and Christianity*, 95–113.

Leach, J. (1978) *Pompey the Great*, London: Croom Helm.

Lewis, N. (1989) *The Documents from the Bar Kokhba Period in the Cave of Letters: Greek Papyri*, Jerusalem: Israel Exploration Society.

Lifshitz, B. (1960) 'Sur la date du transfert de la legion VI Ferrata en Palestine', *Latomus* 19: 109–11.

McLaren, J. (1991) *Power and Politics in Palestine: The Jews and the Governing of Their Land 100 BCE–AD 70*, Sheffield: Sheffield Academic Press.

—— (1998) *Turbulent Times? Josephus and Scholarship on Judaea in the First Century CE*, Sheffield: Sheffield Academic Press.

Mason, S. (1991) *Flavius Josephus on the Pharisees: A Composition-Critical Study*, Leiden: E. J. Brill.

Meshorer, Y. (1982) *Ancient Jewish Coinage*, 2 vols, Dix Hill: Amphora Books.

Meyers, E. (1997) *The New Encyclopaedia of Archaeology in the Near East*, New York: Oxford University Press.

Meyers, E. and Strange, J. (1981) *Archaeology, the Rabbis and Early Christianity*, London: SCM Press.

Mildenberg, L. (1984) *The Coinage of the Bar Kokhba War*, Aarau: Sauerlaender.

Millar, F. (1994) *The Roman Near East 31 BC–AD 337*, Cambridge, Mass.: Harvard University Press.

Neusner, J. (1994) *Introduction to Rabbinic Literature*, New York: Doubleday.

Neusner, J. (ed.) (1975) *Christianity, Judaism and Other Greco-Roman Cults*, Part 3, Leiden: E. J. Brill.

Price, J. (1992) *Jerusalem Under Siege: The Collapse of the Jewish State, 66–70 CE*, Leiden: E. J. Brill.

Rahmani, L. (1994) *A Catalogue of Jewish Ossuaries in the Collections of the State of Israel*, Jerusalem: Israel Academy of Sciences and Humanities.

Rajak, T. (1983) *Josephus: The Historian and His Society*, London: Duckworth.

Rawson, E. (1994) 'Caesar, Civil War and Dictatorship', in J. Crook, A. Lintott, E. Rawson (eds) *The Cambridge Ancient History*, Vol. 9: *The Last Age of the Roman Republic 146–43 BC*, 424–67.

Rendell-Harris, J. (1926) 'Hadrian's Decree of Expulsion of the Jews from Jerusalem', *HTR* 19: 199–206.

Rudich, V. (1993) *Political Dissidence Under Nero: The Price of Dissimulation*, London: Routledge.

Safrai, S. (1957) 'Kehalah Kadisha de-Ve-Yerushalayim', *Zion* 22: 183–93.

Safrai, S. and Stern, M. (eds) (1974–6) *The Jewish People in the First Century* 2, Compedia Rerum Iudaicarum ad Novum Testamentum, Assen: Van Gorcum.

Sanders, E. P. (1992) *Judaism: Practice and Belief*, London: SCM Press.

Schäfer, P. (1981) *Der Bar Kokhba-Aufstand*, Tübingen: J. C. B. Mohr.

—— (1990) 'Hadrian's Policy in Judaea and the Bar Kokhba Revolt: A Reassessment', in P. R. Davies and R. White (eds) *A Tribute to Geza Vermes*, 281–306.

—— (1995) *The History of the Jews in Antiquity*, Luxembourg: Harwood Academic Publishers.

Schalit, A. (1969) *König Herodes: der Mann und sein Werk*, Berlin: de Gruyter.

—— (1975) 'The End of the Hasmonaean Dynasty and the Rise of Herod', in M. Avi-Yonah (ed.) *The World History of the Jewish People*, Vol. 7: *The Herodian Period*, 44–70.

Schürer, E. (1973) (rev. G. Vermes, F. Millar, M. Black, M. Goodman) *The History of the Jewish People in the Age of Jesus Christ*, Vol. 1: Edinburgh: T&T Clark.

Schwartz, D. (1990) *Agrippa I, the Last King of Judaea*, Tübingen: J. C. B. Mohr.

—— (1992) 'Pilate', in *ABD* 5.

Schwartz, J. (1986) *Jewish Settlement in Judaea: After the Bar Kokhba War until the Arab Conquest, 135ce – 640ce*, Magnes Press: Jerusalem.

—— (1998) 'Urban Synagogues', in D. Sperber (ed.) *The City in Roman Palestine*, 149–87.

Seager, R. (1979) *Pompey, a Political Biography*, Oxford: Oxford University Press.

Shatzman, I. (1991) *The Armies of the Hasmonaeans and Herod from Hellenistic to Roman Frameworks*, Tübingen: J. C. B. Mohr.

Sherwin-White, A. N. (1963) *Roman Society and Roman Law in the New Testament*, Oxford: Clarendon Press.

—— (1994) 'Lucullus, Pompey and the East', in J. Crook, A. Lintott, E. Rawson (eds) *The Cambridge Ancient History*, Vol. 9: *The Last Age of the Roman Republic 146–43 BC*, 229–73.

Smallwood, E. M. (1976) *The Jews under Roman Rule*, Leiden: E. J. Brill.

Sperber, D. (1998) *The City in Roman Palestine*, Oxford: Oxford University Press.

Stern, E., Lewinson-Gilboa, A., Aviram, J. (eds) (1993) *New Encyclopaedia of Archaeological Excavations in the Holy Land*, 4 vols, New York: Simon & Schuster.

Stern, M. (1974–6) 'Aspects of Jewish Society: The Priesthood and Other Classes', in S. Safrai and M. Stern (eds) *The Jewish People in the First Century*, Vol. 2, 561–630.

—— (1975) 'The Reign of Herod', in M. Avi-Yonah (ed.) *The World History of the Jewish People*, Vol. 7: *The Herodian Period*, 71–123.

—— (1974–84) *Greek and Latin Authors on Jews and Judaism*, 3 vols, Jerusalem: Israel Academy of Sciences and Humanities.

—— (1982) 'Social and Political Realignments in Herodian Judaea', *The Jerusalem Cathedra* 2: 40–62.

Strack, H. and Stemberger, G. (1991) *Introduction to the Talmud and Midrash*, Edinburgh: T&T Clark.

Sullivan, R. D. (1978) 'The Dynasty of Judaea in the First Century', *ANRW* 2/8: 262–94.

—— (1990) *Near Eastern Royalty and Rome, 100–30BC*, Toronto: University of Toronto Press.

Vermes, G. (1998) *The Complete Dead Sea Scrolls in English*, London: Penguin Books.

Williams, M. (1999) 'The Contribution of Jewish Inscriptions to the Study of Judaism', in W. Horbury, W. D. Davies, J. Sturdy (eds) *The Cambridge History of Judaism*, 75–93.

Yadin, Y. (1961) 'Expedition D', *IEJ* 11: 36–52.

—— (1962) 'Expedition D', *IEJ* 12: 227–57.

—— (1963) *The Finds from the Bar Kokhba Period in the Cave of Letters*, Jerusalem: Israel Exploration Society.

—— (1966) *Masada*, London: Weidenfeld & Nicolson.

—— (1971) *Bar Kokhba: The Rediscovery of the Legendary Hero of the Last Jewish Revolt Against Imperial Rome*, London: Weidenfeld & Nicolson.

CHAPTER TWENTY-SIX

ISRAEL'S NEIGHBOURS

———•◆•———

Bustenay Oded

THE PHILISTINES

General

Studies of the Philistines' history and culture combine textual, pictorial, and archaeological information. Most of the written information on the Philistines speaks of them pejoratively (cf. the derogatory term 'Philistinism'). This negative image emerges from their adversaries who fought prolonged wars with them, mainly the Israelites for whom the Philistines were the implacable foe. Nevertheless, archaeological excavations in Philistia and material remains uncovered at Philistine settlements, combined with the copious scholarly studies of the extant sources, provide clear insights into their cultural world and their proper place in the history of the ancient world. One must, however, be aware that the circumstances of the Philistines' appearance in Palestine, the exact connection of the monochrome and 'Philistine bichrome' ware with the Philistines, and the population composition of Philistia are still controversial.

Origins

The biblical sources state that the Philistines came from Caphtor, which may be a synonym for Crete, or from Cilicia in Anatolia (e.g. Amos 9:7; Ezek. 25:16). The Egyptian hieroglyphic inscriptions and their associated pictorial reliefs, especially those from the mortuary temple of Ramesses III in Medinet Habu, in which the Philistines are mentioned for the first time, describe the impending invasion by the 'Sea Peoples', as modern scholars call them. These texts (*ANET*: 262–3) present the Philistines as arriving from the islands in the north (the Aegean basin) by land and by sea, together with allied peoples, to invade Egypt in massive numbers (not just a few invaders or mercenaries), probably through the Nile Delta, looking for a new land to settle on the eastern shores of the Mediterranean Sea. Names of several groups of 'Sea Peoples' mentioned in the Egyptian records and in the Bible can be associated with names found in the records and literature from the Aegean world, and so provide a clue to their origins: *Ikwš* = Achaia; *Šrdn* = Sardinia; *Luka* = Lykia; etc. The unique Philistine title *seren* (always plural, *seranim*) probably derived from the Hittite *Tarwanis* (Greek *Tyranos*). Achish, the king of Gath (Septuagint Anchus, cuneiform Ikausu) is similar to the Trojan hero Anchises (*Iliad* II, 819). Goliath can be compared with Alyattes, king of Lydia. Hence, the Sea Peoples, were Indo-Europeans. Among them the Philistines were not of Semitic but of Indo-European origin. There are many similar cultural traits that verify hereditary relationship and historical connections between the Philistines' customs and those known in the Aegean–Mycenaean world. Goliath's battle gear is similar to typical Aegean armour, and hand-to-hand combat to decide the issue is reminiscent of the challenge to a duel described in the Homeric epic.

The very detailed reliefs of Medinet Habu illuminate the physical appearance of the Philistines as well as their dress, vehicles, and weapons, and demonstrate similarities between the Sea Peoples and the Mycenaean and Anatolian world. The reliefs depict scenes of land and naval battles against different groups of Sea Peoples. The vessels bear a remarkable resemblance to the Aegean vessels of that time (Stager 1995: 338). Some of the Sea People soldiers wear the so-called feathered headdress helmet with chinstraps very similar to one of the signs on the yet-undeciphered script on the clay disc known as the Phaistos Disc from Crete (fifteenth century BCE). The Aegean context of the material found in Philistia, primarily the pottery, establishes the Philistines' Aegean origins. In conclusion, the entire range of evidence relating to the Philistines points to the Aegean orbit as the place from where they migrated by land and sea at the turn of the thirteenth century BCE, when the Hittite empire and the Aegean civilization collapsed, marking the transition from the Late Bronze Age to the Iron Age.

The initial settlement

Papyrus Harris I relates that Ramesses III defeated the Sea Peoples and stationed them 'by hundred-thousand' in Egyptian strongholds providing them with food and clothing 'from the treasuries and granaries every year' (*ANET*: 262). Despite the exaggeration of the description, most scholars take this information as evidence that Ramesses III recruited the defeated invaders as mercenaries and garrisoned them in settlements in Canaan, such as Gaza, Dor, Megiddo, and Beth-Shean. The Bible mentions the five city-states (Pentapolis) of the Philistines – Gaza, Ashkelon, Ashdod, Ekron, and Gath (not yet identified) – with their agricultural periphery and subsidiary settlements. Archaeological excavations contribute the major part in identifying Philistine settlements on the plausible assumption that the Iron Age I monochrome IIIC:1b and the bichrome (red and black decoration) should be associated with the Philistines (Stone 1995: 24). On the basis of textual and archaeological evidence, we can generally demarcate the extent of Philistia. It stretched from the southern coast of Palestine in the west to the western slopes (Lower Shephela) of Judaea in the east, and from Gaza and its environs in the south to Tell Qasile near the Yarkon River in the north.

History

Soon after the initial period of settlement, the Philistines extended their territory to the north and east, exerting pressure on the Israelite tribes. This is the age of the

Figure 26.1 A Philistine captive. From the reliefs of Ramses III at Medinet Habu. Twelfth century BCE. Copyright AKG Berlin/Erich Lessing.

Philistines' political and military hegemony in Canaan. They were better organized than the Israelites, who failed to maintain technological parity with the Philistines. The latter were superior in smithery and produced advanced weapons, and even monopolized metalwork (1 Sam. 13:19–20). They controlled the highway, known later as the Via Maris, up to Megiddo and Beth-Shean. They built garrisons at strategic points (1 Sam. 10:5; 1 Sam. 23:14) and defeated the Israelites in several skirmishes, oppressing them and even destroying the foremost holy shrine at Shiloh and capturing the Ark of the Covenant. Their pressure forced the tribe of Dan to move to northern Galilee (Judg. 18), and was a factor in the transition to monarchy in Israel. They crushed Saul's army on the slopes of Mount Gilboa, where the first king of Israel was killed.

The balance of power changed completely during the first years of David as king of all Israel. He defeated the Philistines in three battles (2 Sam. 5:17–25; 8:1; 25:15–22), broke their confederation, drove them out of the central hill region, restricted their territories to Philistia proper, and subjugated them as vassal states.

The splitting of the united monarchy of Israel freed the Philistines from Israelite control, but they did not regain primacy in Palestine. Continuous conflict with the kingdom of Israel and mainly Judah altered the frontiers (1 Kings 15:27; 16:15–17). One or more of the Philistine cities rendered tribute to Jehoshaphat, king of Judah

(2 Chron. 17:11), but they probably threw off Judaean control during Jehoram's reign (see 1 Kings 8:23; 2 Chron. 21:16–17).

Important information about Philistia during the eighth and seventh centuries BCE can be drawn from the Assyrian records. Adad-nerari III (809–783 BCE) claimed that he imposed tax and tribute on *Palastu* (Philistia), while Tiglath-pileser III (745–727 BCE), campaigned against Hanun, king of Gaza (734 BCE), and against Mitinti (I), king of Ashkelon (732 BCE). Hanun made a formal submission to Assyria, and paid tribute. Silbel, who was enthroned in Gaza by Sargon II, was a loyal subordinate to Assyria. Sargon II settled deportees on the border of the 'Brook of Egypt' (716 BCE) in order to consolidate the Assyrian hold on the southern border of Philistia. In 713 BCE Azuri, king of Ashdod, rebelled against Assyria. Sargon II deposed Azuri and enthroned Ahimiti, Azuri's brother. But the Ashdodites hated his (Ahimiti's) reign and elevated Iamani (a Greek from Cyprus) instead (*ANET*: 286). This rebellion is also referred to in Isaiah 20:1 and on a dark basalt fragment of a stele erected in Ashdod by Sargon II (T. and M. Dothan 1992: 143). Ashdod suffered a terrible massacre at the hand of Sargon when he put down the revolt, deported many Ashdodites and organized the city as a province. Two reliefs in the palace of Sargon II that commemorate his siege on Ekron and Gibbethon are probably connected with the campaign against Ashdod in 712 BCE (Yadin 1963: 418–19). Nevertheless Ashdod is mentioned as a metropolis ruled by a local king named Mitinti who paid tribute to Sennacherib on his military expedition against Tyre, Judah, Ashkelon, and Ekron in 701 BCE. This expedition, which is known from the Bible (2 Kings 18–19; Isa. 36–7; 2 Chron. 32) and from the inscriptions of Sennacherib (*ANET*: 287–8), took place after Sidqa, king of Ashkelon, and the nobility of Ekron conspired together with Hezekiah against Sennacherib. Padi, the king of Ekron, who remained loyal to Assyria, was deposed by the Ekronites who handed him over to Hezekiah. Sennacherib conquered Ashkelon and its enclave in the north of Philistia, deported Sidqa and his family, and enthroned Sharruludari, the son of Rukibtu, who had earlier been deposed by the rebellious Sidqa. On his way to conquer Ekron, Sennacherib met a large Egyptian force *en route* to help the rebels. Sennacherib defeated the Egyptians on the plain of Eltekeh, north of Ekron, continued to Ekron, and punished the rebels. He released Padi from Jerusalem and reinstated him as king of Ekron. As for Hezekiah, Sennacherib claims that his towns 'which I have plundered, I took away from his country and gave them (over) to Mitinti, king of Ashdod, Padi, king of Ekron and Silbel, king of Gaza. Thus I reduced his country' (*ANET*: 288). The men from Philistia who did forced labour in Nineveh during the reign of Sennacherib were probably deportees from Ashkelon and Ekron (*ARAB*: 383).

There is no explicit evidence that the kings of Philistia made any attempt to rebel again during the reigns of Esarhaddon (680–669 BCE) and Ashurbanipal (668–633 BCE). On the contrary, Silbel of Gaza, Mitinti (son of Sidqa) of Ashkelon, Ikausu (Achish, son of Padi) of Ekron, and Ahimilki the Ashdodite are mentioned among the kings who provided Nineveh with labour and building materials in 679 or 677 BCE (*ANET:* 290–1). They took part in the building of Kar-Esarhaddon on the Phoenician coast in 678 BCE (*ANET*: 290). Ashurbanipal required these four kings, and others, to supply troop contingents to join his first military expedition to Egypt in 667 BCE (*ANET*: 294). Assyrian documents relating to taxation and conscription from various vassals (e.g. *SAA* I, no. 110; ND 2672) refer to taxes and tributes paid by Philistine cities. Padi of Ekron is mentioned in an Assyrian bulla dated 699 BCE as delivering one talent of silver to the king's palace (*SAA* XI, no. 50).

Towards the end of Ashurbanipal's reign the Assyrian empire disintegrated. The major powers that exploited the vacuum and struggled over the Assyrian inheritance were Egypt and Babylonia. Evidently, from the last third of the seventh century and during the early sixth century BCE the Philistines' settlements suffered destruction from the kingdoms of Judah, Egypt, and Babylonia. According to Jeremiah 47:5 Pharaoh (probably Psamtik I) attacked Gaza and Ashkelon. According to Herodotus (II:157) the pharaoh besieged Ashdod for 29 years and conquered it with the help of Greek mercenaries (around 640 BCE). The archaeological finds indicate that Ashdod suffered destruction, probably at the hands of Psamtik I (T. and M. Dothan 1992: 138, 187). Egypt controlled the Syro-Palestinian area until 605 BCE, the year when Nebuchadnezzar II crushed the Egyptian army at Carchemish and reduced all the land 'from the river of Egypt unto the river of Euphrates, all that retained to the king of Egypt' (2 Kings 24:7; Jer. 25:8–11; *ABC*: 99). Philistia came under the rule of the Babylonian empire.

According to the Babylonian Chronicles, in 604 BCE Nebuchadnezzar captured and plundered Ashkelon (cf. Herodotus, I:105). The survivors were deported. Two sons of Aga, king of Ashkelon, and other Ashkelonites were taken into captivity (*ANET*: 308). There are references to exiled Philistines in Mesopotamia (Gitin et al. 1998: 180). In an Aramaic royal letter, found at Saqqara/Memphis, a king named Adon, probably the king of Ekron, informed pharaoh about the advance of the Chaldaean armies and appealed for urgent military aid against the impending Babylonian attack (around 603 BCE: *KAI* no. 266). A thick layer of destruction debris at Ekron indicates that the city was destroyed by Nebuchadnezzar II, whereas Ashdod was reduced to a very small town (T. and M. Dothan 1992: 187–8).

Evidently, Gaza, Ashkelon, and Ashdod were no longer distinctive Philistine cities with a political, ethnic, and cultural identity from the Persian period on. Philistia was organized as a province of Ashdod by the Babylonians, or perhaps later as administrative units by the Persians. At long last, the Philistines of non-Semitic origin gave their name (Palastinoi, Palastium), to the country; it was first used by Herodotus (I:105; II:104) for the southern coast and subsequently became the geographical–administrative designation for the entire country: Palaestina, Palestine.

Culture and acculturation

The intrusion of the Philistines from the Aegean basin to Palestine involved transplanting their Mycenaean (pre-Helladic) culture to their new abode. In the first phase of their presence in Palestine (twelfth century BCE) they maintained a distinctive ethnic and cultural identity among the various groups in Palestine, which were mainly of Semitic origin. Nevertheless, already from the late twelfth century BCE their initial Aegean culture became permeable to outside influences (Iacovou in Gitin et al. 1998: 332–44). The Philistines were farmers, herders, and city dwellers. The townspeople concentrated mainly in the Philistine Pentapolis in well-fortified cities that were divided into public, residential, cultic, and industrial quarters. The temples, palaces, and other large buildings discovered at the urban centres indicate the existence of skilled architects, artisans, and builders. A unique architectural feature was the hearth at the centre of public buildings, as found in Tell Qasile and Ekron (twelfth–eleventh centuries BCE), reminiscent of the hearths in the shrines and palaces in Cyprus and the Aegean world.

The Philistines had the technology and skill to produce metal implements for military and agricultural purposes. The uncovered furnaces for melting ores at Ekron, Tell Qasile, and Tell Jemmeh, and metal tools found in large quantities, hint at many metalworkers and smelters engaged in industrial activities. Highly skilled pottery makers preserved the main artistic features of their homeland Mycenaean prototypes, and produced very delicate and finely crafted ceramic artefacts. The monochrome Mycenaean IIIC:1b (twelfth century BCE) is a scholarly and technical designation for locally made monochrome (black or red) pottery. It is Mycenaean in shape and style, but made of local clays (Stager 1995: 344–55). The typical decorations and motifs are horizontal bands, streamers, loops, birds, and fishes. The typical vessels are kraters, bell-shaped bowls, stirrup jars, and jugs with a strainer spout. This monochrome pottery soon evolved into elaborate bichrome ware, designated by the archaeologists as 'Philistine bichrome' (red and black) or neo-Philistine, decorated with patterns of concentric, circular, or semi-circular horizontal bands, stylistic birds looking backwards, and fishes, all reminiscent of the original Mycenaean and Cypriot motifs and traditions. The abundance of loomweights found at Ekron, Ashkelon, and Tell Qasile indicate the existence of a textile industry. Ekron was a large centre for olive-oil production (Gitin 1995; 1997). Archaeological excavations at several sites demonstrate that under Assyrian domination Philistia enjoyed an economic and cultural revival (Gitin 1997: 82–3).

The excavations at Tell Qasile, Ashdod, and Ekron have yielded an abundance of cult structures and artefacts, a combination of Aegean cultic traditions with religious elements of neighbouring societies. The Philistines' religion was polytheistic and syncretic (Judg. 10:6; 1 Sam. 31:9). Dagon (the god of grain) a prominent god worshipped all over the Semitic world, was adopted into the Philistine pantheon (Judg. 16:23; 1 Sam. 5:1–5). They worshipped Ashtaroth/Astarte (1 Sam. 31:10), a Canaanite goddess. A god called Baal Zebub, a Semitic name, was worshipped at Ekron (2 Kings 1:2–3, 6, 16). A large storage jar found at Ekron bears the inscription 'sanctified to Asherat' (a Canaanite/Phoenician goddess). The inscription of Achish, the son of Padi, discovered at Ekron, written in a local Canaanite script and a Semitic language, commemorates the dedication of a sanctuary to a non-Semitic female deity possibly called *ptgyh* (Dothan et al. 1997; A. Damsky reads *ptnyh*). In the temple complex in Ashdod was found a unique long-necked figurine in the stylized image of a seated female, probably a Philistine goddess, very similar to the Aegean figurines of seated goddesses of the Late Bronze Age. Throned cultic figurines in the form of a female were also found at Tell Qasile (Mazar 1986: 12–13), Ekron, and Ashdod (T. and M. Dothan 1992).

The Philistines worshipped their gods at sanctuaries (Judg. 16:23–30; 1 Sam. 31:10). The excavations at Tell Qasile of the twelfth and eleventh centuries BCE, and those at Ashdod and Ekron of the seventh century BCE, uncovered sanctuaries

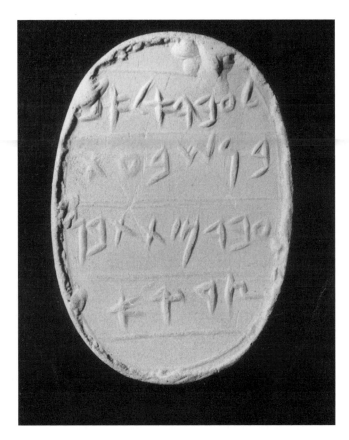

Figure 26.2 A Philistine seal with the inscription 'Belonging to ʿAbdiliab son of Shibʿat servant of Mitinti son of Sidqa'. Seventh century BCE. Copyright British Museum.

with cultic objects among which are bronze wheels with eight spokes each, known from Cyprus as part of a cult stand (cf. 1 Kings 7:27–30; T. Dothan 1995:48). The Philistines had diviners, priests, and soothsayers as part of their cultic personnel (1 Sam. 5:5; 6:2–5; 2 Kings 1:2; Isa. 2:6). In several places, such as Tell el-Farah, Beth-Shean, Lachis, and Deir el-Balah, human-shaped clay coffins (anthropoids) with detachable lids in the shape of faces were found in the context of Egyptian artefacts and Philistine bichrome pottery. One of the lids from Beth-Shean has the shape of the feather headdress. Evidently this is an Egyptian manner of interment. Another burial custom, Mycenaean in origin, is the rock-cut communal tomb.

Surprisingly, no clear example of early Philistine script has been found. Hence, we have no substantial evidence of original Philistine writing, although a few inscriptions from about the eighth and seventh centuries BCE were found in Philistia (Naveh 1985). The script is a local version of Hebrew/Phoenician script, in a Semitic language that may be called 'Neo-Philistine' (Stager et al. 1996: 65). The biblical narratives supply some indications about their original language. The names Achish and Goliath and the term *seren* relate to Aegean or old Anatolian dialects. Most of the known names of kings of Philistia from the eighth to seventh centuries BCE, such as Hanun, Azuri, Rukibtu, Sidqa, and Matat (Mitinti) are west-Semitic (Dothan et al. 1997).

The adoption of foreign cultural traits was a long historical process. The Aegean heritage started to fade by the eleventh century BCE. The process of acculturation was completed during the Persian period, from which point no further ethnic or cultural distinction could be made between the inhabitants of Philistia and the surrounding population.

THE PHOENICIANS

Name and sources of information

Phoenicia is a later substitute Greek name for Canaan in its limited sense of the narrow coastal strip stretching from Mount Cassius (Gebel Arqa) in the north to the plain of Acco in the south. The coast is indented and has excellent natural harbours. In Homer (*Odyssey*, IV:85), where the geographical term 'Phoenicia' appears for what seems to be the first time, the name 'Sidonians' is used to designate the inhabitants of Phoenicia. In the Bible the names 'Canaan' and 'Tyre' or 'Sidon' sometimes mean the Phoenician coast and sometimes its inhabitants (Gen. 10:19; Num.13:29; Josh. 13:2–6; Isa. 23:8). Many scholars believe it derives from 'Phoinix', which means dark red, purple, since the Phoenicians were renowned for producing and trading in purple dye. The Phoenicians themselves called their land by the general name 'Canaan' or after the city-state in which they dwelt or whence they came, such as 'Tyrian', 'Sidonite', 'Byblian' (original 'Sori', 'Sidoni', 'Gabli'). The Phoenician language and script, the names of the Phoenician kings, and their culture's origin, all prove that the Phoenicians were Canaanite in origin (cf. Gen. 10:15).

The reconstruction of the Phoenician history (twelfth–sixteenth centuries BCE) combines several sources: Phoenician/Punic records, the Bible, Egyptian and cuneiform documents, classical Hellenistic and Latin compositions, and archaeological material. The corpus of Phoenician inscriptions found in Phoenician and Punic settlements (*KAI* nos 61–173, 277) is composed almost entirely of stereotype-style dedicatory or tombstone inscriptions. Nevertheless, a wealth of evidence about the existence of major historical literature is to be found. From the Wen-Amon report it seems that Byblos had chronicles of the kings (*ANET*: 27). Josephus Flavius tells of scrolls kept in Tyre that recount events in Tyre and foreign countries (*Against Apion*, I:17; *Ant.*, IX:283–4). Josephus also quotes from such authors as the Greek Dio, who composed a history of Tyre, and Menander of Ephesos (*Ant.*, VIII:144) who used Tyrian chronicles. Philo of Byblos (first century CE) used the composition of a Tyrian writer Sanchuniyaton (seventh century BCE). The major cities of Phoenicia are archaeologically unknown. Sarepta (Sarafand), Tell 'Arqa, Tell Kazal, Khaldé (south of Beirut), Tell el Burak and other sites along the coast of Palestine (such as Achziv, Acco, Dor, Athlith, Sharon Valley) have yielded remains that shed little light on the history of the Phoenicians but contribute to the study of the material culture.

Political history

The Phoenician city-states

The history of the Phoenicians is the history of individual city-states. The major city-states were Tyre, Sidon, Byblos, and Arvad, all ruled by kings. By conflation of several sources, ancient and late, it is possible to reconstruct the king-lists of Byblos, Tyre, and Sidon (Katzenstein 1997: 349). The authority of the Phoenician kings was limited, and subject to municipal and civic bodies whose precise nature is not yet clearly known. The 'Elders of Byblos' (Ezek. 27:9) were the wise men (Ezek. 27:8) who helped to direct the state. The kings maintained small armies because they relied on the natural defences of their cities and their strong surrounding walls. The wars in which the Phoenicians engaged were generally in defence of their cities, and they rarely participated in distant military campaigns. Because of their international sea trade they possessed fleets of merchant vessels and warships, which were used by the imperial power such as the Assyrians, and later the Persians.

The most important cities in Phoenicia during the Iron Age period were Tyre and Sidon. Apart from its strong surrounding walls, Tyre enjoyed the advantage of a natural defence against attack from the sea (Ezek. 27:32). The mainland sector facing the island was called Palaetyrus in the Hellenistic sources, probably Ushu in the Assyrian records. Palaetyrus supplied the Tyrians with water, timber, and agricultural products, and was used as a graveyard. Tyre dominated towns such as Achziv, Acco, and Dor (Stern in Gitin et al. 1998), called by Ezekiel (26:6) 'her daughters which are in the field'.

It seems highly likely that Tyre and Sidon were incorporated as one kingdom during the tenth to eighth centuries. Tyre became the capital of the Sidonians (1 Kings 5:15, 20; 1 Chron. 22:4). Hiram I strengthened and enlarged the capital, renovating its temples and increasing its fleet. He suppressed a rebellion in the Tyrian colony in Cyprus, and made an alliance and established trading relations with both King David and King Solomon (2 Sam. 5:11; 1 Kings 5:15). The richness, grandeur, and splendour of Tyre and its kings are outlined in the prophecies of Ezekiel, chapters 26–28.

Figure 26.3 Tyre, depicted as an island fortress, on one of the bronze strips that decorated the residence of Shalmaneser III (859–824 BCE) at Balawat (Imgur-Bel) near Nimrud. The scene shows Tyrians bearing tribute to the Assyrian king. Copyright British Museum.

Phoenicia and Israel

The kingdom of Tyre/Sidon had good relations with David and Solomon, and later with Ahab, king of Israel, and Jehoshaphat, king of Judah (ninth century BCE) owing to common political and economic interests. David's victories over the Philistines and the Aramaeans enabled the Phoenicians to develop their trade and establish a maritime economic empire. The great building projects undertaken by David and Solomon – the Temple, the royal palace and the fortified cities – were planned and executed with the aid of Phoenician artisans, technology, and building material. Hiram I supplied David and Solomon with timber from the Lebanon (2 Sam. 5:11). In return, Hiram I received agricultural products, mainly oil and wheat (2 Kings 5:26; and cf. Ezek. 27:17). The Israelite kingdom was a prime market for the Phoenicians' industrial products and technological knowledge. The Phoenicians, skilled in art and ship-building, were 'shipmen that had knowledge of the sea', and the uninterrupted passage from the Mediterranean to the Red Sea gave them access to raw material in the distant south. Hiram and Solomon launched a joint mercantile expedition in the Red Sea (1 Kings 9:26–8; 10:11–22).

When the united monarchy was divided into two rival kingdoms of Israel and Judah, Phoenicia lost the advantage of the presence of a single political entity extending from the borders of Phoenicia to the Red Sea. Moreover, the Phoenician kingdom of Tyre itself underwent internal crisis when Abdastratus, the grandson of Hiram I, was murdered and, after a period of anarchy, the throne was seized by Ethbaal, the priest of Ashtoreth (*Against Apion*, I:18). Later, the rise to power of Omri in Israel and Ethbaal I in Tyre (c. 887–856 BCE) created conditions suitable for the renewal of economic relations between the two states. Omri made peace with the kingdom of Judah, so once again the Phoenicians had free access to the Red Sea. Ahab, son of Omri, was married to Jezebel, the daughter of Ethbaal, 'the king of the Sidonians' (1 Kings 16:31). Their daughter Athaliah was the wife of Jehoram, king of Judah. The triple alliance of Phoenicia, Israel, and Judah, strengthened by marriage ties among the royal houses, brought economic benefits to all three. Jehoshaphat planned to renew the route to Ophir with Israel, which had close relations with Tyre (1 Kings 22:49–50). Ahab's palace in Samaria and the city walls were built by Phoenician masons and under their supervision. Because of the economic and political ties between the two countries Phoenician culture, as indicated by the biblical texts, filtered into Israel (1 Kings 18:19; 16:32; 2 Kings 10:21; 11:18). Nevertheless, the success of Jehu's revolt in Israel and of Jehoiada in Judah weakened Phoenician influence in Samaria and Jerusalem and impaired relations among the kingdoms of Israel, Judah, and Tyre.

Phoenicia and Assyria

The Phoenicians did not oppose Tiglath-pileser I and there is no evidence of any opposition on their part to the campaign of Ashurnasirpal II (883–859 BCE) along the coast. In the battle of Qarqar in central Syria (853 BCE), Byblos, Irqanata (Arqa), Arvad, Usanata (Ushnu), and Siyanu joined an anti-Assyrian coalition of 12 kings, among them Hadadezer the Aramaean, king of Damascus, and Ahab the Israelite

(*ANET*: 278–9). In 841 BCE, on his campaign against Hazael of Damascus, Shalman-
eser III took tribute from Tyre, Sidon, and Jehu king of Israel (*ANET*: 280). Like
Shalmaneser III, Adad-nirari III does not mention any campaign against the
Phoenician coastal cities. He records that he levied tribute from Tyre, Sidon, and
Joash, king of Israel, and erected a royal stele at Arvad in the context of his mili-
tary campaign against Damascus in 802 or 797 BCE (RIMA 3/2: 211).

The Assyrians asserted various forms of direct control over Phoenicia from the
time of Tiglath-pileser III (745–727 BCE), whose policy was to establish a stable
Assyrian suzerainty as far as 'the brook of Egypt'. Ethbaal (or Hiram II) of Tyre,
Shiptibaal the Byblian, and Matanbaal of Arvad paid tribute between 743 and 738
BCE (*TPIII*: 68, 171). Tiglath-pileser III established the province of Simirra at the
foot of Mount Lebanon, which included the northern shore of Phoenicia, and deported
many inhabitants (*TPIII*: 67, 105, 136, 148). Tiglath-pileser III mentions in his
inscriptions, as Assyrian officials do in letters to Calah (Nimrud), Assyrian trading
stations (*karum*) and emporia (*bit-kari*) in Philistia and Phoenicia (*TPIII*: 104).

In 734 BCE Hiram II, together with Israel and Damascus, plotted against Assyria.
Tiglath-pileser III set out on a rapid expedition against the rebellious kings and
Hiram paid heavy tribute (*TPIII*: 187). Later on, Matenna (Matan II) of Tyre, perhaps
a usurper, paid a huge amount of gold and silver to Assyria as tribute (*TPIII*: 171,
191). Tiglath-pileser III established a new province on the coast of Palestine, whose
capital was *Du'ru* (Dor), tightened the Assyrian grip, and restricted the autonomy
of the coastal cities. Assyrian officials were appointed as supervisors of the key port
cities to assure the payments of taxes and tributes, to watch the political behaviour
of the local kings, and to control the export–import trade. A letter (ND 2715) from
an Assyrian official in Phoenicia confirms that the timber trade, the basis of the
Phoenician economy, was under Assyrian control, much to the resentment of the
local population and Egypt. According to Menander, the Assyrians besieged Tyre
for five years with the help of ships from the neighbouring Phoenician cities (*Ant.*,
IX:283–7). There is no record of how the campaign ended, but it is possible that
Sargon II (722–705 BCE) came to terms with Tyre since neither a war between
Sargon and Elulaios nor the surrender of Tyre is mentioned.

In 701 BCE Sennacherib set out to subdue the rebellion in the west. His annals
relate that Luli, king of Sidon (Tyre), fled from Tyre far overseas to Yadnana (Cyprus),
as depicted also in a relief in the palace of Sennacherib in Nineveh. Sennacherib
installed Tuba'lu (Ethbaal) on the throne of Tyre and imposed on him a tribute to
be paid annually. The kings who had not participated in the rebellion, among them
Abdili'ti of Arvad and Urimilki of Byblos, received the king of Assyria near Ushu
with heavy tribute.

The relations between Phoenicia and Assyria were quite different in the time of
Esarhaddon (680–669 BCE) and Ashurbanipal (668–627 BCE), who both adopted a
policy of complete control over the sea trade of the Phoenician coastal cities. In 677
BCE Abdimilkuti, king of Sidon, revolted against Esarhaddon (*ANET*: 290–1). The
Assyrian king conquered Sidon, looted its treasures, destroyed the city and cut off
the head of Abdimilkuti. He built a new city near Sidon, which he called Kar
Esarhaddon (fortress of Esarhaddon), and organized a new Assyrian province where
he settled exiles from various conquered lands. Tyre now regained its prominence

among the Phoenician cities. Moreover, Baal, the Tyrian, had a treaty with Esarhaddon according to which Tyre apparently received certain trading rights along the Phoenician and Palestinian coast (*ANET*: 533–4). Baal of Tyre, Matan-Baal of Arvad, and Milkiashapa of Byblos are mentioned among the '22 kings of Hatti, the mainland and the islands', who were forced to transport building material to Nineveh (*SAA* II: 5). The failure of Esarhaddon's campaigns in Egypt in 674 BCE had repercussions in Phoenicia: Baal, king of Tyre, who relied on Tirhakah, king of Egypt, as well as Iakinlu, king of Arvad, apparently broke free of Assyria. In 671 BCE Esarhaddon set out on a campaign against Tyre and Egypt, captured the cities of Baal and annexed them, taking from Tyre heavy tribute and reorganizing part of the territories of Tyre on the mainland as a province (*ANET*: 291). Baal surrendered but continued to rule Tyre. Ashurbanipal, like his father Esarhaddon, lists the kings of Tyre, Byblos, and Arvad among the 22 kings who were compelled to support him with troops and ships in his first campaign against Egypt (667/6 BCE). The inscriptions of Ashurbanipal (*ANET*: 295–6) mention a second campaign to Egypt (663 BCE) as well as a war against Baal, king of Tyre, who had good relations with Egypt. Ashurbanipal deported the members of the royal family, as well as Iahimilki, son of Baal, but said, 'I had mercy upon him and returned to him the son, the offspring of his loins'. Between 651 and 646 BCE Ashurbanipal punished the inhabitants of Acco and Ushu 'who did not obey their (Assyrian) governors', conscripting some into his armies and deporting others to Assyria (*ANET*: 300). This is the last Assyrian expedition to Phoenicia that we know about.

Phoenicia in the Egyptian–Babylonian maelstrom

During the last years of Ashurbanipal, the Assyrian control over the Syrian and Palestine area eventually collapsed, creating a political gap that allowed Egypt to reimpose its political supremacy over them, especially over the seaports. It is likely that Necho II (610–595 BCE), who went north to help the Assyrians against the Babylonians, had some sort of control over Phoenicia, as well as over Philistia and Judah.

After the decisive victory of Nebuchadnezzar II (605–562 BCE) over the Egyptian armies in 605 BCE, the Babylonian king led several campaigns to bring all the Syro-Palestinian region ('Hatti Land') under his control. Phoenicia succumbed to him and paid the tribute demanded, but attempted to cast off the Babylonian yoke at the instigation of Egypt. According to Jeremiah (27:3), delegations from Tyre and Sidon came to Jerusalem contemplating an anti-Babylonian act (probably in 593 BCE).

Ezekiel's prophecies about the destruction of Tyre and Sidon by Nebuchadnezzar II (26:7; 28:20–3; 32:30), were presumably connected with the siege of Tyre by Nebuchadnezzar II. Josephus relates that in the time of Ithobaal III, Nebuchadnezzar II besieged Tyre for 13 years (*Against Apion*, I:156), probably from 586/5 to 573 BCE (Katzenstein 1997: 325–32). According to Ezekiel (29:17–18) he did not capture the city. The kings of Tyre, Sidon, and Arvad are listed in a certain document (?570 BCE) from the court of Nebuchadnezzar as exiles (*ANET*: 308), indicating that the Babylonian king conquered the Phoenician city-states. All Phoenicia was under Babylonian dominance (Katzenstein 1997: 333–7), until 539 BCE, when Cyrus conquered Babylonia. The territories 'beyond the river Euphrates' became part of the Fifth Satrapy (Herodotus, III, 19:91). Yet the Persians did not abolish the monarchies of the Phoenician city-states which provided the Persians with naval power. Because of its special ties with Persia Sidon became the most important kingdom in Phoenicia. Nevertheless, the centre of the sea trade moved westwards to Carthage and Greece.

Culture

The Phoenician culture is a development of the second-millennium Canaanite culture, with inevitable changes caused by commercial and political contacts with foreign peoples and lands, and by technological advances (Markoe 1990).

Language and script

Phoenician belongs to the family of North-western Semitic languages, and is a Canaanite dialect of the Iron Age period. Punic is the designation of the Phoenician language as spoken in Carthage and elsewhere in the west Mediterranean, mainly from the sixth century BCE onwards. Like the language, the script too is a development of the proto-Canaanite writing of the Late Bronze Age.

Religion

Details about the religious practices are mainly from second-hand sources. All the evidence indicates that the Phoenician religion was rooted in the ancient Canaanite cult and influenced by Egyptian, Mesopotamian, Syrian, and Aegean religions. The Phoenician deities were associated with individual city-states, each with its chief god. The principal goddess of Byblos was Baalat Gebal (Mistress of Byblos), probably a fertility goddess. Sidon's most important deity is Eshmun, also called Baal-Sidon. His mate was Astarte (Ashtoreth), 'the goddess of the Sidonians' (1 Kings 11:5; 2 Kings 23:13).

The chief deity of Tyre was Melqart, the 'Lord of Tyre'. In addition, the Phoenicians worshipped Baal-Shamem/n, Baal-Zephon, Baal-Rosh, Baal-Lebanon, Dagon, Adonis (known only from Greek sources and identified with Eshmun), Resheph, and Ashera. The Phoenicians took their gods and goddesses with them wherever they established colonies in foreign countries. In the Phoenician/Punic colonies the chief deities were Baal-Hamon and his mate Tanit. The Phoenicians tended to worship their gods on hilltops and to link a certain god to a certain place (mountain peaks, springs, and lakes) as his abode (e.g. Baal-Lebanon). Temples/ shrines to the Phoenician/Punic deities are mentioned mostly in dedicatory-type inscriptions (e.g. *KAI* nos 62, 72, 81). The priesthood had priests and priestesses among whom were the king and the queen. The calendrical feasts were connected with the agricultural cycle. Details of Phoenician cosmogony are preserved in late compositions, mainly of Philo of Byblos (Clifford 1990: 58–9; Culican 1991: 472).

A special issue is the problematic and much debated subject of child sacrifice (Clifford 1990: 58; Gras et al. 1991: 150–74). The archaeological finds are inconclusive. On the basis of biblical references (Lev. 18:21; 23:10; 2 Kings 16:3; 21:6; Jer. 32:35) scholars explain 'tophet' as graveyards in which are cinerary urns containing bones of children and/or bones of animals. A tophet (with stelae) from the eighth to sixth centuries BCE was found at Tyre (Sader 1991). The sanctuary of Tanit and Baal-Hamon in Carthage, where urns containing calcined bones of children and lambs were buried, is also called by scholars 'tophet', or 'the Precinct of Tanit'. Beside the urns were stelae dedicated to Tanit and Baal-Hamon. The tophets in the Phoenician and Punic world indicate, according to scholars, the existence of an institution of ritual infanticide. This view is supported by the biblical phrase 'passing through fire' to Molech, by classical sources, and by the phrase *mlk 'dm* in the Punic inscriptions, where the term *mlk* is interpreted as a kind of sacrifice. Others think that child sacrifice was practised only at times of great calamities (Gras et al. 1991: 159); or perhaps these graveyards are only for infants who died, for example, from disease.

Art and craft

There are many references to the 'cedars of Lebanon' in the Egyptian, biblical, and cuneiform texts (e.g. 1 Kings 5:24[10]; Isa. 14:8). The supply of cedar and fir timber necessitated a skilled infrastructure for cutting and transporting the large beams (1 Kings 5:20 (English versions 5:6). The Phoenician artisans produced carved woodwork and excelled in shipbuilding and navigation (cf. Ezek. 27). The Assyrian reliefs show several types of Phoenician ship (Aubet 1993: 146–51).

An important, widely known Phoenician speciality was the large-scale production of purple dye (blue-purple and red-purple) produced from secretions of the murex marine snails common in the shallow waters along the rocky shore of Phoenicia (Ward in Hoerth 1994: 200). In addition, the sand along the Phoenician coast was especially suited to the industry of multicoloured glass bottles and flasks (Uberti in Moscati 1988: 474–91; Aubet 1993: 269–70). Best known of the Phoenicians' art and craft are their artistic ivory carvings, metal utensils, and various precious objects, mostly discovered outside Phoenicia proper (see 2 Chron. 2:14; 1 Kings 7:14) as far as Spain.

The special features of Phoenician handicraft were the workmanship, design, and combination of borrowed motifs of various origin, mainly Assyrian and Egyptian (Markoe in Bikai et al. 1990: 31–5). The Phoenician pottery profile is represented by archaeological finds in Phoenicia (Sarepta, Tyre, Khalde) and the northern coast of Palestine (Achziv), Cyprus, and throughout the Mediterranean basin. First (before the tenth century BCE) appears bichrome ware, with reddish-purple bands influenced by the Cypro-Aegean fashion (Anderson 1990). Then follows 'black on red' ware with decorations in black (Bartoloni in Moscati 1988: 492–510; Culican 1991: 473–5; Anderson 1990)

Figure 26.4 A Phoenician ivory plaque with gold leaves and lapis-lazuli, depicting a lioness devouring a Nubian negro. Found at Nimrud, probably brought to Assyria as booty or tribute. Eighth century BCE. Copyright British Museum.

International trade and colonial expansion

The diffusion of Phoenician culture corresponded with Phoenician mercantile activity and colonial expansion. The maritime trade along the shores of the Mediterranean basin became the linchpin of the Phoenician economy. Ezekiel 27 reflects the thalassocracy of Tyre during the eighth to seventh centuries BCE and its commercial activity all over the ancient world.

The Phoenicians developed a mercantile economy based on industry and export. The large-scale export of goods necessitated a search for raw materials from which these goods were produced; in addition, new overseas markets were sought. The Phoenicians sailed to Ophir for gold (1 Kings 22:49), to the kingdom of Sheba for perfumes and spices, to Gadir (Spain) for silver and other metal ores. The fact that the Phoenicians excelled in long-voyage navigation and were skilled in the manufacture of expensive small objects ('minor arts') made transportation and widespread trade and distribution easier and increased profitability. The westward seafaring necessitated the establishment of victualing stations along the coasts as far as Spain. Although opinions differ about the beginning of Phoenician colonial expansion to the Mediterranean islands and along the Mediterranean coast (Aubet 1993: 170–87), some date this as early as the twelfth century BCE and others as late as the sixth century with regard to the western Mediterranean and the shift from trade to colonization. Another question is which western settlements were established by

Phoenicians who came from the homeland, and which by settlers from Carthage. Modern research appears to vindicate the view that the Phoenician penetration of the western Mediterranean must have begun no later than the late ninth century BCE.

Phoenicians traded with Cyprus (Alashiya), from where they imported copper (Muhly in Gitin et al. 1998: 323). From Cyprus and the coast of Anatolia they could sail west and trade with the Aegean islands' inhabitants, before reaching the gold mines of Thrace (Herodotus, VI:47). In Sicily too there are traces of Phoenician presence. An important settlement was Motya on the western coast of Sicily facing Sardinia in the north, where there was copper to be mined; and Malta, Carthage, and the Moroccan coast in the south. In Nora (Sardinia) two Phoenician inscriptions have been found, which most researchers consider ancient. One of them, 'The Nora stone', probably dates to the ninth century BCE (*TSSI* no. 11). In it is a reference to *tršš* (Tarshish), the location of which is much debated.

The most famous Phoenician settlement is Carthage on the Tunisian coast. The original form of the name was *qrthdšt* (New City). Many scholars believe that Carthage took over the thalassocracy from the city-states of Phoenicia from the sixth century BCE on, and established its own network of colonies in Sicily, Sardinia, and elsewhere.

The quest for metals brought the Phoenicians to Spain with its metalliferous sites, yielding silver, copper, lead, tin, and mercury (cf. Ezek. 27:12; 1 Macc. 8:3; Pliny, *Nat. Hist.* III:30; Aubet 1993: 64, 75–6, 118–19, 236–41. For another view see Muhly in Gitin et al. 1998). Although Strabo says that the Phoenicians sailed beyond the Pillars of Hercules, explored Iberia, excavated the silver mines of Tartessos and founded Gadir (Gades, modern Cadiz), all before Homer (Strabo, III.2:14; Pliny, *Nat. Hist.* III:30), scholars date the Phoenician infiltration into Spain between the ninth and eighth centuries BCE, some even later. In Portugal the Phoenicians (or Punic merchants) found excellent timber, tin, and gold. A few sites on the Atlantic coast of Morocco have been identified as Phoenician/Punic settlements from the sixth to fifth centuries BCE (Aubet 1993: 247–9).

Phoenician history proves that a relatively small population in a small country, with a small army, can achieve much by exploiting natural conditions and by industry and ability. The international commerce and colonial expansion also generated mutual cultural influences. The biblical narratives about the Tyrian–Sidonian influence on Israel and Judah are only one example.

ARAM-DAMASCUS

Origins

The Aramaeans of ancient Syria are the western branch of the Aramaean tribes that spread across Syria and Mesopotamia from the twelfth century BCE. No Aramaean traditions about their origins are known. The biblical tradition assumes a close relationship between the Aramaeans and their Israelite ancestors (Gen. 22:21). According to Amos 9:7 the Aramaeans came from Qir, an unidentified place. Aramaean tribes are first mentioned by Tiglath-pileser I (1114–1076 BCE) as *Aḫlamû*

Aramayya. He claims that he pursued the Aramaeans across the river Euphrates as far as Mount Bishri (RIMA 2/1: 34, 37–3). From the eleventh century BCE on the Aramaeans constituted the major part of the population in Syria and a considerable ethnic element in Mesopotamia. Among the dozens of Aramaean tribes and states, Aram-Damascus played a major role in the political history of Syria and Palestine during the ninth to eighth centuries BCE, until its destruction in 733–732 BCE.

No Aramaean historiography concerning the Aramaean states in southern Syria has survived. Most information on the Aramaean states comes from the Bible, the Assyrian inscriptions, and from a few archaeological finds (Lemaire 1991: 91–5).

History

By the end of the 11th century BCE a series of kingdoms in Syria were ruled by Aramaean dynasties. Hadadezer, king of Aram-Zobah, established a union of Aramaean kingdoms under his hegemony, as a first step towards creating a single Aramaean kingdom in Syria. His realm encompassed the Ante-Lebanon mountains and the northern Lebanon valley. The term 'kings of Zobah' in 1 Samuel 14:47 apparently refers to kings who were vassals of Hadadezer and his 'servants' (2 Sam. 8:7). The hegemony and influence of Aram-Zobah extended from the Euphrates to the land of the Ammonites (2 Sam. 8:3; 10:16–19; 2 Chron. 18:3; 19:6–8, 18–19). Saul's efforts to block Aramaean penetration in Transjordania were continued by David, who put an end to Hadadezer's expansionist ambitions (2 Sam. 8:5–6). The Bible ascribed to David decisive victories over Aram-Zobah and its vassals (around 1000 BCE). He annexed the kingdom of Aram-Damascus as a province to be ruled by Israelite governors. Northern Transjordania became a source of conflict between Aram and Israel.

During the reign of Solomon, Rezon, who had been a servant of the king of Zobah, seized Damascus and proclaimed himself king there. This kingdom rapidly became a major factor in Syria–Palestine, and Israel's most dangerous neighbour. The king of Damascus adopted Aram-Zobah's goal of unifying Aramaean states in Syria around a single centre (Damascus) and Aramaeizing northern Transjordania. The division of the united kingdom of Israel into two inimical kingdoms (Israel and Judah) only helped the kings of Damascus to realize their goal for hegemony over all Syria and Palestine. The penetration of Ben-Hadad into Galilee (1 Kings 15:18–20) was not an isolated event but an episode in a series of similar developments in the mutual relations of Aram and Israel.

The Assyrians had continuous conflicts with the Aramaean states in Syria, mainly during the ninth and eighth centuries BCE, especially with the major kingdom of Aram-Damascus against which Shalmaneser III led several campaigns. Hadadezer, king of Damascus, presided over an anti-Assyrian league of '12 kings', among them Ahab king of Israel. The purpose of the coalition was to block the Assyrian imperial advance towards Syria and Palestine. The battle took place at Qarqar (853 BCE), in the vicinity of Hamath. The alliance of the '12 kings' appears to have been successful in halting Shalmaneser III's advance. In fact, the Assyrian king was obliged to fight Damascus again and again. Hadadezer and Ben Hadad (II), who was involved in bitter conflicts with Ahab of Israel, are two names that seemingly refer to the same king (Pitard 1987: 125–32; 133–8). Jehoahaz and Jehoash, kings of Israel, waged several wars with Aram-Damascus, half a century later, when Israel was bitterly pressed by Hazael and his son Ben-Hadad (III) (Pitard 1987: 115–20). Hazael conquered all of Israelite Transjordania as far as the Arnon, and may have extended Aramaean influence to Edom and to Philistine cities (2 Kings 10:32–3; 12:18–19; Amos 1:3; Lemaire 1991: 101–2). Samaria became subservient to Aram (1 Kings 20:1–11; 2 Kings 5:6–24). An Aramaean inscription from Tel Dan commemorates the victory of the king of Aram over Israel (Biran and Naveh 1995: 1–18). Evidence of the activities of the kings of Aram-Damascus in Syria is present in the stele of Zakur king of Hamath and Lu'ash (Pitard 1987: 170–4). The title 'king of Aram' given to Bar-Hadad, the son of Hazael, in Zakkur's stele, and Bar-Hadad's position as leader of the allied Aramaean and neo-Hittite forces fighting against the king of Hamath, clearly demonstrate that from the beginning of the ninth century the kings of Aram-Damascus generally played the primary role among the Syrian states from Arpad in the north to Bashan in the south to the degree of that of 'empire' (Lemaire 1991: 104–6). Moreover, the inscriptions of Adad-nerari III (809–782 BCE) call the king of Aram-Damascus 'lord' (RIMA 3/2: 211, 213) which was the title used by the vassal governors in addressing the king of Aram, and not a proper name (for the inscription from Samos see Dion 1995: 485). Hazael assassinated the former king (Bar-Hadad/Hadadezer) and ascended the throne sometime between 844 and 842 BCE. Shalmaneser III fought against Damascus during the reign of Hazael (841, 838, 837? BCE), besieged Damascus, took much booty, destroyed many towns, but did not conquer the capital or enthrone another king instead of Hazael (RIMA 3/2: 54, 60, 62, 77, 118). Nevertheless, as soon as the Assyrian pressure on Damascus subsided, Hazael and his son Ben-Hadad (III) seized their opportunity and again started to oppress Israel (2 Kings 8–12; 13:3–7), reaching even Philistia and Judah in the south (2 Kings 12:18–19).

According to the biblical narratives, 'the Lord gave Israel a saviour so that they went out from under the hand of Aram' (2 Kings 13:5). Most scholars identify this 'saviour' with Adad-nerari III, who fought against Mari'/Bar-Hadad, the son of Hazael, between 802 and 796 BCE. Adad-nerari claims that he besieged Damascus, conquered it, and took heavy tribute (RIMA 3/2: 209, 211, 213). According to a stele found near Maras (in Turkey), Shamshi-ilu, the field-marshal of Shalmaneser IV, marched to Damascus and took heavy tribute from Hadianu (*ha-di-a-ni*) the Damascene (RIMA 3/2: 240).

Aram-Damascus enjoyed a further short period of strength before its final destruction by Assyria. Rezin (*Ra-hi-a-nu; Ra-qi-a-nu; Rdyn*) who seized the throne in Damascus, planning to reinstate it as the metropolis of a great Aramaean kingdom, is mentioned in the list of kings who paid tribute to Tiglath-pileser III, apparently in 738 BCE (*TPIII*: 55, 107). Rezin initially allied himself with the usurper Pekah, king of Samaria, against Jotham, king of Judah (2 Kings 15:37). During the reign of Ahaz, the son of Jotham, an Aramaean–Ephraimite coalition, in which Rezin was the dominant partner, invaded Judah, preparing to besiege Jerusalem and to crown a certain Ben-Tabeel, apparently a Judean from Transjordan near the Ammonite border (Isa. 7). Tiglath-pileser III's campaigns in southern Syria and Palestine were primarily directed against Damascus, because Rezin was the leader of an anti-Assyrian coalition consisting of Damascus, Israel, Gaza, and Ashkelon. Tiglath-pileser III conducted a grisly reprisal against Damascus (733–732 BCE), besieged Damascus, and captured 'the wide land of Bit Hazaeli' (i.e. the kingdom of Damascus; *TPIII*: 81): He deported the population and killed Rezin (2 Kings 16:9) and annexed the kingdom of Damascus to Assyria (Tadmor 1994: 139, 187), dividing it into several provinces, one of which was the province of Damascus.

Culture

Our knowledge of the culture of the Aramaeans is very limited. The Aramaeans certainly used Aramaic for various purposes, but owing to the perishability of papyrus and parchment in the Syro-Mesopotamian climate these documents are lost. The lack of archaeological excavations in the territories of the ancient kingdom of Damascus,

Figure 26.5 Horse's forehead ornament with an Aramaic inscription according to which the blinker was given 'to our lord Hazael'. Found at Samos (Greece) but is of north Syrian origin. Ninth century BCE. Copyright Deutsches Archäologisches Institut-Athen.

including Damascus, make the investigation of Aramaean culture more difficult. As the Aramaeans were scattered throughout Mesopotamia and Syria, even from their initial appearance, there is no unique Aramaean civilization. On the basis of extant data it is impossible to discern distinct Aramaean features. It would not be far wrong to assume that the culture of the Aramaean tribes and kingdoms was a blend of their west-Semitic Amorite or *Ahlamû* legacy, their autochthonic predecessors, and foreign influences, mainly neo-Hittite, Phoenician, Egyptian, and Mesopotamian. No specifically Aramaean pottery, metalwork, or seals can confidently be isolated as uniquely Aramaean. The most one can say is that the Aramaeans made only slight contributions to art and craft and to political and social systems and practices.

Hadad was the pre-eminent deity and the head of the Aramaean pantheon. He was already worshipped by the west Semites (Amorites) in Mesopotamia and northern Syria during the Old Babylonian period, and was considered to be the storm god, equivalent to the Assyrian god Adad. His cognomen is Ramman (biblical Rimmon) 'the thunderer' (2 Kings 5:18; Zech. 12:11). 'Hadad' and 'Ramman' appear as theophoric elements in personal names (1 Kings 15:18; Greenfield 1987: 68). Bar-Hadad, an Aramaean king (probably of Damascus) revered Melqart (*ANEP*: 499). From the old Aramaic inscriptions and the Aramaean nomenclature we can include in the Aramaean pantheon deities like El, Rakib-El, Baal, Shamash, Resheph, Dagan, and Sahar (equivalent to the moon god, Sin). Hadad–Ramman had a temple in Damascus called Beth-Rimmon (2 Kings 5:18), possibly under the present Great Mosque (Lemaire 1991: 95). In the Tell Fakheriye (north Syria) inscription of an Aramaean ruler named *hdysʿy* (Hadad is my salvation) there is a reference to the temple of Hadad, the bestower of fertility (Greenfield 1987: 68). Rites of mourning the dead and of appeasing them were among the religious practices. A mortuary rite connected with the deity Hadad–Ramman is mentioned in Zecheriah 12:11.

The Aramaeans borrowed their alphabetic script from the Canaanite/Phoenician script during the eleventh century BCE. Only during the eighth century BCE was the independent characteristic Aramaic cursive script developed (Layton 1988: 174–5). The Aramaean version of the alphabetic script spread all over the ancient Near East, supplanting the complicated cuneiform system of writing. The diffusion of the Aramaean script led to the spread of Aramaic as a medium of communication, starting from the eighth century BCE and widely used during the Neo-Babylonian and Persian periods. The earliest phase of the Aramaic, labelled generally as 'Old Aramaic', is represented by inscriptions from the tenth to seventh centuries BCE, as distinct from 'Imperial Aramaic' (Persian period), 'Biblical Aramaic', and later dialects. Aramaic is the major contribution of the Aramaeans to the civilizations of the Levant because it became the lingua franca, used for commercial, legal, administrative, diplomatic, and literary purposes. Documents in Aramaic language and script have been discovered all over the Near East.

THE KINGDOMS OF TRANSJORDANIA: AMMON, MOAB, AND EDOM

General

The nature of the country

The term 'Transjordania' refers to an extensive territory that abuts to the west on the River Jordan, the Sea of Galilee, the Jordan Valley, the Dead Sea, and the Arabah between the Dead Sea and the Gulf of Elath, and to the east on the Syrian–Arabian desert. The Yarmuk flows between the Golan and Bashan in the north, and Gilead in the south. The Jabbok (Wadi Zerqa) divides northern Gilead (al Ajlun) from southern Gilead (al-Belqa). The Arnon (Wadi Mujib) flows into the Dead Sea; to its north is the tableland called the Land of the Plain (Mishor, Jer. 48:21) and to its south are the mountains of Moab. The Zered (Wadi el-Hasa) makes its way between the plateau of Moab and the plateau of Edom/Seir, which extends southwards to the Gulf of Elath.

The economy of Transjordania was based on pasturage and cultivation of field corn and various kinds of vegetables and fruits. Some of the inhabitants were semi-nomad pastoralists (especially in Moab and Edom) and some sedentary, living in farms, villages, towns, and fortified urban centres. In the Arabah a metallurgy industry developed. In the forests of Gilead and the high mountains of Edom (Seir) trees were felled for building and fuel, and for balsam for pharmaceutical purposes (Gen. 37:25; Jer. 8:22; 46:11; Ezek. 27:17).

The Transjordanian kingdoms also benefited economically from controlling the trade routes that traversed their countries. Alongside the main routes settlements arose. The 'King's Highway' linked Egypt and the Arabian peninsula with Syria and Mesopotamia. But as a frontier land, bordering the Great Desert, the extent of the security that could be given by the central government to persons and property against the desert brigands determined whether the land would prosper or decline.

Sources and problems

The Bible still remains the major source for the history of the Transjordanian peoples and kingdoms and for our knowledge about the origins of the three kingdoms, Ammon, Moab, and Edom, and their populations before the ninth century BCE. The biblical traditions relate that before these three peoples settled in the land and established their ethnic–national kingdoms, others were present there (Gen. 19:30–8). When the tribes of Israel arrived from Egypt the Transjordanian kingdoms already existed (Num. 21:10–20; Deut. 2:9–10). Nevertheless, the biblical authors/redactors lived many generations after the period they purported to describe. Moreover, the biblical accounts pertaining to the Transjordanian peoples and kingdoms were written from an Israelite/Judaean standpoint. Hence, despite its importance as a source of information, the Bible should not be taken entirely at face value but should be read critically and in the light of the epigraphical and archaeological evidence.

Egyptian and Mesopotamian sources provide occasional glimpses into the Transjordanian state of affairs. The Egyptian sources are important for supplying details about Transjordania during the second millennium BCE, while the Akkadian sources, mainly the neo-Assyrian royal inscriptions and administrative archives, are helpful for the study of the history of Transjordania in the first half of the first millennium BCE.

Archaeological surveys cover a considerable area from the River Yarmuk down to the Gulf of Aqaba, but few sites have been excavated in the regions of Ammon, Moab, and Edom. The beginning of modern scholarly archaeological exploration in Transjordania is marked by Nelson Glueck's work (Bienkowski 1992, *passim*). He concluded that a break in sedentary occupation had occurred during the Middle Bronze and Late Bronze Age (approximately nineteenth–fourteenth centuries). Southern Transjordania was no man's land. During the thirteenth century BCE the land was resettled by new groups who came from the east, and established their kingdoms just before the Israelites settled in Canaan, namely, the Ammonites, the Moabites, and the Edomites (For Glueck's hypothesis see Sauer 1985: 206–8).

The archaeological explorations undertaken after Glueck (for archaeological surveys and excavations see Mattingly in Hoerth 1994: 330–3) show generally that (1) during the Middle Bronze and Early Late Bronze Ages Transjordania was sparsely populated (LaBianca and Younker 1995: 406–7). (2) Towards the end of the Late Bronze Age and in the Early Iron Age the number of settled sites, some of them fortified, gradually increased, but no surge of resettlement took place. (3) The number of settlements increased dramatically during the eighth to sixth centuries BCE and the land enjoyed remarkable prosperity. This is why scholars are inclined to theorize that the Transjordanian kingdoms as united states did not emerge before the eighth century BCE (Dornemann 1983: 165–70; Adams in Bienkowski 1992: 184; Dearman 1997: 206–12).

'Before any king reigned over Israel'

Although the information from various sources is still sparse, from a socio-political viewpoint it is reasonable to assume that the organized ethnic–national kingdoms developed out of confederated tribes and chiefdoms for defence purposes. This historical development is reflected in the biblical list (Gen. 36) of *allûphim* (tribal chieftains) and tribal kings (cf. 'Midianite kings' in Num. 31:8; Judg. 8:12). It seems that at the background of the emergence of the Transjordanian kingdoms, not necessarily concurrently, were several clans/tribes, which later united on the basis of common historical traditions. First to undergo the process were the Ammonites, who were more densely settled and more cultivated than the Moabites; and later the Edomites, whose terrain was sparsely occupied (LaBianca and Younker 1995: 399, 406–7, who prefer the definition 'tribal kingdoms' to true 'nation-state kingdoms'). The first mention of one of the peoples/lands known in Transjordania is found in the Egyptian inscription of Ramesses II (thirteenth century), *mu'bu* = Moab (Timm 1989: 5–9). The first to mention Edom is Merneptah (Bartlett 1989: 77), the same king who mentioned Israel (in Canaan) for the first time (thirteenth century). Extra-biblical texts mention the nomadic pastoral Shasu tribes of Edom and of Seir (thirteenth–twelfth centuries BCE), reflecting the pre-monarchic period in Edom (Worschech 1997: 230–4).

The relationship between Israel and the Transjordanian peoples

'So Saul took the kingdom over Israel and fought against all his enemies on every side, against Moab, and against the children of Ammon, and against Edom, and against the kings of Zobah, and against the Philistines . . .' (1 Sam. 14:47). This verse shows that, at its outset, the period of the Israelite kingdom was marked by a war between the Israelites and their neighbours in Transjordania. The history of this enmity preceded the rise of kingship in Israel and lasted until after the destruction of Jerusalem. Such mutual hatred and vindictiveness (Ezek. 25:2–14; Mal. 1:3; Ps. 83:108–9) might at first seem surprising in view of the tradition of blood kinship between the two sides (Gen. 25:19–26; 19:37–8; Deut. 2–9; cf. Ps. 83:9). The idea of 'brotherhood' is in contrast to the Israelites' attitude towards their western neighbours, the Canaanites and the Philistines (Bartlett 1989: 175–86).

Ammon

The Ammonites settled on the central Transjordanian plateau, along the upper and lower course of the Jabbok and its streams, with the desert their natural frontier in the east. In the Bible their country is called Ammon or Bene-Ammon, and in two Ammonite inscriptions their country is called *bn'mn* (Hübner 1992: 21–2, 27). The earliest explicit extra-biblical reference to Ammon is in the inscriptions of Tiglath-pileser III, who mentions Sanipu, the king of *Bit-Am-ma-na-a* (*TPIII*:171). The form (*mat*) *ba-an-am-ma-na-a* appears in a report from the time of Sargon II (SAA 1, no. 110). The corpus of the Ammonite inscriptions (Aufrecht 1989) sheds much light on Ammonite culture, and the Assyrian records mention episodes in Ammonite history. Archaeological excavations in the territory of Ammon include significant settlements such as Amman, Um ed-Dannanir, Tell Safut, Tell Siran, Sahab, Tell el-Umeiri, and Hesban on the border of Ammon with Moab. Most of the archaeological finds are from the eighth to seventh centuries BCE, the period when the Ammonites flourished under the aegis of the Assyrian empire. The capital was Rabbath Bene-Ammon (Deut. 3:11; today Amman). The city's acropolis was built on a hill today called Al Qal'a (the citadel) surrounded by deep wadis. The reconstruction of the frontiers of the land of Ammon in the north, west, and south depends on interpreting general biblical definitions of the territory of Ammon and the land of Sihon (Num. 21:24; Deut. 2:37; Josh. 12:3; etc.); on explaining the descriptions of the areas settled by the tribes of Gad and Reuben with reference to the border with Ammon (Num. 32:1–4, 33–8; Josh. 13:16–28); on determining the historical background of the prophecies about Ammon; and on defining a certain kind of structure that might have been round (*rujm el-malfuf*), rectangular, or square (Kletter 1991: 41; Hübner 1992: 150–8). From the biblical data, the array of Ammonite material, and the topographic conditions, it appears that the northern boundary was formed by the upper reaches of the River Jabbok (Deut. 2:37; 3:16; Josh. 12:2), which flows east–west to the point where the Wadi er-Rumeimin empties into it. From here the frontier goes south towards es-Salt. The upper channels of Wadi Shueib, Wadi es-Sir, Wadi Kafrein, and Wadi Hisban formed a partition between the land of the Ammonites and the Israelite settlements. The south extremity of the land of Ammon reached the vicinity of Heshbon, which formed a buffer land between Ammon and Moab (Hübner 1992: 131–57).

The nature of the Ammonites' country – a fortified urban centre (Rabath-Ammon) surrounded by 'daughter settlements' within a wide agricultural periphery (Jer. 49:2; Amos 1:14) – and the international commerce in the ancient Near East, which was generally a royal monopoly, facilitated the unification of the Ammonites as a national state administered from their capital (2 Sam. 12:26). The corpus of the Ammonite written material combined with biblical texts and Assyrian records help to reconstruct an incomplete list of Ammonite kings (Hübner 1992: 208–9). The first one known by name is Nahash (1 Sam. 11:1). His son is Hanun (2 Sam. 11:1). Sanipu reigned in the time of Tiglath-pileser III (733 BCE). A certain Yarih-azar is mentioned in a statue from the eighth century BCE. He is the son of Zakkur, the son of Sanipu, possibly the same Sanipu mentioned above (Hübner 1992: 23–6). Sennacherib and Esarhaddon's inscriptions (end of eighth and first half of seventh century BCE) mention Puduilu. Amminadab (I) was the king of Ammon during the time of Ashurbanipal (mid-seventh century BCE). He is probably the father of Hasilel and the grandfather of Amminadab (II) who reigned towards the end of the seventh century BCE (according to a Tell Siran inscription: Hübner 1992: 27–30). Amminadab II (or I?) is known from two seals discovered in tombs near Amman (see below). The last king whose name has been preserved is Baalis (Jer. 40:14) probably the same *b'lyš'* known from a seal found in Tell el-Umeiri (Younker in Hoerth 1994: 313). The Ammonite king was supported by a ramified administration of military commanders and officials (2 Sam. 10:3; 1 Chron. 19:3; Amos 1:15; Jer. 49:3; and several Ammonite seals). Archaeological explorations provide abundant evidence about the Ammonite culture. Ammonite pottery, usually found in graves, bears witness to the high technical level achieved by Ammonite potters. Typical were red burnished vessels decorated with white bands framed by black lines (Dornemann 1983: 171; Herr 1993: 29). The Canaanite alphabetic script used by the Ammonites was well formed and influenced by Aramaean lapidary writing (van der Kooij in Hadidi 1987: 115; Aufrecht 1989: 21–3). The Ammonite language belongs to the West-Semitic family. The national god of the Ammonites was Milkom who is known from the Bible (1 Kings 11:5; 2 Kings 23:13; Zeph. 1:4–6) and from Ammonite inscriptions and seals. The name Milkom serves as a theophoric element in personal names (Hübner 1992: 127). The Amman Citadel Inscription most likely concerns a temple construction for Milkom, whose command to build him a sanctuary was probably delivered by a seer.

According to the biblical account the hostility between Israel and Ammon started during the period of the Judges (twelfth–eleventh centuries BCE) (Judg. 3:12–14; Hübner 1992: 167–8). Nahash's friendly attitude to David (2 Sam. 10:2; 1 Chron. 19:2) was intended to harm Saul by giving refuge to his opponents. Ammonite suspicions of David's expansionist ambitions, especially after he had defeated the Philistines and Moabites (2 Sam. 8:1–2), was their main reason for making war on him, while the insulting attitude towards the Israelite delegation only added provocation for conflict. After David had decisively defeated the Aramaean–Ammonite coalition (2 Sam. 1:8; cf. 2 Sam. 12:28), it is unclear whether he crowned himself king of Ammon in place of Hanun son of Nahash, or took the Ammonite king's crown as booty and left the local dynasty on the throne.

The enthronement of Rehoboam, whose mother was an Ammonitess, must have formed a link between Rabbath-Ammon and Jerusalem, this does not prove that the Ammonites were subservient to Judah. Apparently, the wars between Israel and Judah, and the rise of Aram-Damascus encouraged the Ammonite rulers to seek independence.

Repercussions of the Ammonite incursions across the frontiers of Israel and Judah can be found in 2 Chronicles 20 and Amos 1:13. Uzziah, and later Jotham, subjugated the Ammonites (2 Chron. 26:8; 27:5). At that time the king of Ammon was Sanipu, mentioned in the list of kings who paid tribute to Tiglath-pileser III during the Assyrian campaign in Palestine in 734–732 BCE.

Moab

The Moabites inhabited the rolling plateau immediately east of the Dead Sea, and their land initially encompassed territories on both sides of the Arnon river. North of the river, Moab included the plain (Mishor, Josh. 13:9; Jer. 48:21) up to the 'plains of Moab opposite Jericho' (Num. 22:1; 33:48), and south of the river it extended over the mountain ranges as far as the Zered (Wadi el-Hasa) valley. The eastern border of Moab was confined by the Arabian desert.

According to the biblical tradition, by the time of the first Moabite king, the Moabites had been ejected from the territory north of the Arnon by Sihon king of Heshbon (Num. 21), and the Arnon and the brook Zered became the two geographical barriers that marked their borders to the north with Israel and to the south with the Edomites (Num. 21:13; Judg. 11:18; Deut. 2:12–13). The northern plateau, from the Arnon as far as Nebo and Heshbon, was inhabited by a mixed population – Moabites, Israelites, and Ammonites.

The royal city of Moab was Kir-Hareseth (Kir of Moab, 2 Kings 3:25; Isa. 15:1, 16:11; Jer. 48:31–6). The commonly accepted identification of this city with Kerak is challenged and open to question (Miller in Bienkowski 1992: 85–6). The most important cities north of Arnon were Dibon and Medeba.

Although the land of Moab, including the Mishor, was suitable for pastorage (sheep and goats), for growing cereal crops, and for orchards and vineyards (cf. Isa. 16 and the story of Ruth), herd husbandry remained the economic basis of the region (Dearman in Bienkowski 1992: 73; and see Judg. 5:16; 2 Kings 3:4). The Moabites benefited from the international 'King's Highway' that traversed their land (Num. 20:17; 21:22; Dearman 1997: 206).

The reconstruction of the Moabites' history is based on the biblical narratives, the epigraphic material from Moab and other places, and archaeological explorations in Moab (Timm 1989; Bienkowski 1992; Miller 1997). The most important Moabite source is the Moabite inscription of Mesha, king of Moab (Dearman 1989). The general conclusion from the various excavations is that 'none of the excavated sites in Moab has a substantial occupational history in the Late Bronze period' (Dearman

Figure 26.6 The inscription of Mesha, king of Moab (ninth century BCE). Discovered in 1868 at Dibon, Transjordan. Mesha commemorating his victories over Israel. Louvre Museum. Copyright Photo RMN, Paris.

in Bienkowski 1992: 70). It is not far-fetched to assume that the inhabitants who occupied the land of Moab during the Late Bronze Age originated from a mixture of 'pre-Moabite' indigenous clans with new settlers from the north ('Amorites') and from the east (Kitchen in Bienkowski 1992: 21–34; Mattingly in Hoerth 1994: 324; Worschech 1997: 231).

Events after the Israelite conquest show clearly that the Moabites did not give up the Plain, which became an area of conflict between Israel and Moab in the period of the Judges and of the monarchy. Moab rose up against Israel at the end of the period of the Judges (Judg. 3:12–29; Ps. 83:7, 9; 1 Sam. 14:47), only to be subjugated later by David. Yet he did not abolish the Moabite monarchy (2 Sam. 8:2). The Mesha inscription discovered at Dibon provides important first-hand information on relations between Moab and Israel in the ninth century BCE. The stele commemorates Mesha's military and building activities, even though many details in it are unclear (Dearman 1989: 196–203). According to 2 Kings 1:1, 3:5, Moab revolted when Ahab died. The inscription states that 'Omri had occupied the land of Medeba' imposing his authority on the king of Moab, who lived in Dibon. The subjugation lasted throughout the reign of Omri 'and half the time of his son' (Ahab). Mesha withheld his tribute from Ahab as an act of liberation of Moab from Omri's dynasty, and strengthened Dibon by building the *qrhh* (the acropolis), preparing to withstand a long siege. When Ahab died in the battle of Ramoth-Gilead, Mesha marched northwards and annexed the land of Ataroth and the land of Medeba, which he conquered together with Bezer and Nebo. Mesha presents his wars against Israel as a reconquest of Moabite territories and mentions an expedition to Horonaim in southern Moab. This would mean that he almost entirely restored the borders of Greater Moab, from the River Zered to the 'Plain of Moab'. Nevertheless, in the time of Jeroboam II Israelite rule became established in the Land of the Plain (2 Kings 14:25; Amos 6:14). But after the fall of Aram-Damascus and Samaria Moab accepted the suzerainty of the Assyrian empire. Tiglath-pileser III mentions Salamanu the Moabite among the kings who paid him tribute during his campaign in Palestine (734–732 BCE).

Mesha's inscription shows clearly that the Moabite language is closely akin to Hebrew, and the script is essentially not different from Hebrew script (Timm 1989: 277–302). During the reign of Mesha, the king resided in Dibon, which was fortified. Excavations in Dibon, the archaeological survey in greater Moab, and epigraphic finds disclose outstanding technical ability in building fortresses, watchtowers, and installations for water collection (Daviau 1997: 223–4).

Kemosh was the national god of the Moabites (Num. 21:29; 1 Kings 11:17, 33; Jer. 48:46). The divine name constitutes a theophoric element in Moabite personal names (Timm 1989: 162–74). The Moabites had statues of their national god (Jer. 48:7). The worship of Kemosh in the land of Moab continued well into the third century BCE (Mattingly in Dearman 1989: 220–1). Kemosh was worshipped at high

Figure 26.7 A Moabite seal with the inscription 'Belonging to Kemosh'am (son of) Kemosh'el, the scribe'. Eighth–seventh century BCE. Copyright Israel Museum.

places (*bamah*) and in temples (1 Kings 11:7–8; 2 Kings 23:13; Isa. 16:12; 'house of Kemosh' in a basalt fragment from Dibon). The ban, the sacrifice of burnt-offerings of animals, or, on special occasions of humans (Num 23:1; 2 Kings 3:27), and circumcision (Jer. 9:24–5) were some of the Moabite ritual customs. The names Ashtar-Kemosh (Mesha inscription), 'House of Baal-Peor', 'High-place of Baal', little clay figurines found in abundance in various Moabite settlements, and the combination of star and crescent moon on seals all attest to the pagan character of the Moabite religion (Mattingly in Dearman 1989). Priests, seers, and diviners are mentioned in Num. 22–4; Jer. 48:7).

Edom

The land of Edom stretched from the brook of the Zered (Wadi el-Hasa) in the north along the high plateau to the shore of the Gulf of Aqaba/Elath in the south. Edom is bound on the east by the Great Desert and to the west by the Arabah valley. Certain biblical passages indicate that the land of Edom stretched west of the Arabah (Num. 34:3; Deut. 2:8; Josh. 11:7, 12:7; etc.). The territory is referred to as the land of Seir (Gen. 32:4; Num. 24:18; Josh. 24:4; Judg. 5:4; Ezek. 25:8; 35:15; 2 Chron. 25:14). Seir and Edom are mentioned in the Egyptian sources from the thirteenth to twelfth centuries BCE as the land of the nomadic tribes called Shasu who lived in tents and roamed vast regions from Seir/Edom westwards across the Negev and Sinai (Kitchen in Bienkowski 1992: 26–7, 31). Shasu is a nickname for Bedouin tribes. The Assyrian records of Adad-nirari III mention the name Edom for the first time (*u-du-mu*), but it is not certain if it refers to a kingdom or just to a land. Several sites have been excavated, such as Buseirah (Bosrah), Tawilan, Umm el-Biyara, and Tell el-Kheleifeh (north of Aqaba). The general conclusions are that (1) there is no evidence of permanent settlement in Edom during the Late Bronze Age (Parr in Bienkowski 1992: 42); (2) there are some Early Iron Age remains, mainly from the northern region of Edom (MacDonald in Bienkowski 1992), meaning that some settled occupation existed in the Wadi el-Hasa region during Iron Age I; (3) almost all settled sites, including major settlements such as Buseirah, Tawilan, Umm el-Biyara, and Tell el-Kheleifeh, failed to produce any significant Iron Age material predating the eighth century BCE (Hart in Bienkowski 1992: 94). The prevailing conclusion is that in the Late Bronze Age Edom was apparently inhabitated by various nomads and semi-nomads: tent-dwellers and pastoralists. It is less likely that all Edom, from Wadi el-Hesa as far as the Gulf of Aqaba, was at that time organized as a centralized kingdom with a capital. It is not probable that the tribes had been united in the framework of a kingdom as early as the tenth century BCE (Finkelstein 1992: 164).

The economy of Edom was based on pasturage. The Edomites exploited the trading routes that traversed their land, controlled the port on the Gulf of Aqaba, and exploited the copper resources. The copper industry was a factor in the economy of Edom. Copper mining and smelting took place in the Wadi Feinan region, between Tafile and Petra (Knauf-Lenzen in Hadidi 1987: 86; MacDonald 1994: 241), and by controlling Elath/Ezion-Geber the Edomites could benefit from the trade centres in Arabia.

The assemblage of Edomite pottery shows that 'typical Edomite ceramics can be divided into three main groups: (a) decorated vessels, mostly bowls and kraters painted with black and red strips in geometric designs; (b) perforated and fenestrated cups and bowls, sometimes with denticulated decoration; (c) cooking pots with stepped rims produced from clay with Nubian sandstone temper' (Beit-Arieh 1995: 303 n. 1; Parr in Bienkowski 1992: 44).

The Edomite language was a version of north-west Semitic. The script developed from the Canaanite/Phoenician script, and was strongly influenced by the Aramaic script.

The national god of Edom was Qaus/Qos (?bow). His name appears in inscriptions and seals, mainly as a theophoric element. 2 Chronicles 25:14 intimates the polytheistic nature of the Edomite religion. Female figurines found in Edomite sites may symbolize a goddess, perhaps Astarte. Of special interest is the figurine of a goddess with a triple-horned headdress, found at Horvat Qitmit, 10 km south of Arad. This site, which offers the clearest reflection of the Edomite religion, is defined by the excavator as an open-air Edomite cultic site (Beit-Arieh 1988). In Ein Hasebah a shrine with ceramic vessels of cultic character similar to those at Horvat Qitmit was uncovered (Cohen and Yisrael 1995). A scarab seal from Tawilan depicting a crescent on a pole may represent Sin, the moon god, whose principal centre was at Harran in northern Syria. A cuneiform tablet that was written and signed at Harran and discovered at Tawilan is another argument for the assumption that the moon god was worshipped by the Edomites. Scholars believe that several verses in the Bible point to Edom/Seir as the original dwelling of YHWH (Judg. 5:4; Hab. 3:3; Isa. 63:1–6), thus indicating that the Edomites worshipped YHWH before Qaus was accepted as the chief god. Like the Moabites, the Ammonites, and others, Edomite males were circumcised (Bartlett 1989: 196–7).

Edom was among the enemies of Israel during the time of Saul (1 Sam 14:47–8). David subjugated the Edomites and appointed governors in Edom (2 Sam. 8:13–14), namely he brought them under direct control. Hadad, of the 'seed of the (Edomite) royal family', fled to Egypt and married into the Egyptian royal house (1 Kings 11:14–22), but it is not explicitly stated that he returned to Edom. By subjugating the land of Edom David secured the south-east border of his kingdom and controlled the trade route to the Gulf of Aqaba, where Solomon built a fleet of ships 'in Ezion-Geber, which is beside Eloth, on the shore of the Red Sea, in the land of Edom' (Bartlett 1989: 46–9). Edom gained its independence sometime between 848 and 841 BCE (Weippert in Hadidi 1987: 98) in the light of the tribute to Adad-nirari III (RIMA 3: 213). Judah's recovery, which began in the reign of Amaziah and continued with Uzziah and Jotham, led to its renewed control over the Arabah valley and Ezion-Geber and possibly to the subjugation of the land of Edom (2 Kings 14:7, 22; 2 Chron. 25:11–12, 14; 26:2). Specific mention of a king of Edom in the inscription of Tiglath-pileser III can serve as evidence that Edom was liberated from Judah. From this time on Judah faced a well-organized and centralized Edom, whose capital was Bosrah (Buseirah).

TRANSJORDANIA UNDER ASSYRIA'S RULE

The expeditions of Tiglath-pileser III to southern Syrian and Palestine in 734–732 BCE marked the beginning of a new era in the history of Transjordania. Tiglath-pileser III founded several provinces, among them Qarnini in Bashan, Haurina in the Hauran, and Gal'ad (Gilead) in Transjordania (*TPIII*: 139, 192). He mentions the tributes received from Qausmalaku of Edom, Salamanu of Moab, and Sanipu of Ammon (*TPIII*: 171). Several Assyrian administrative letters and lists refer to tributes accepted from the Transjordanian kingdoms (Weippert in Hadidi 1987: 100; ND 2765; *SAA* 1, no. 110; VII/1, no. 57; XI, no. 33). The king of Ashdod applied to the neighbouring states, including Moab and Edom, for help against Sargon II (711), but none responded (*ANET*: 287). In a long list of precious items issued to visiting delegations in the time of Sargon II, Padû-il of Bit-Ammon and his servants (*SAA* VII/1: no. 58, col. 1:4–10) are mentioned. This is probably the same *pd'l* referred to in a seal of an Ammonite official (Hübner 1992: 75–6). Sennacherib mentions that Puduilu from Bit-Ammon, Kammusu-nadbi from Moab, and Ayaramu from Edom welcomed him with many gifts at the time of his campaign in Palestine against Hezekiah king of Judah and his allies (701 BCE, *ANET*: 287). In 673 BCE Esarhaddon king of Assyria ordered '22 kings of Hatti, the seashore and islands', including Qausgabri of Edom, Musuri of Moab, and Puduilu of Beit-Ammon, to transport to Nineveh long beams of cedar and pine trees from the mountains of Lebanon for his palace (*ANET*: 291). Qausgabri, king of Edom, Musuri, king of Moab, and Amminabbi II, king of Ammon, provided him with military service on his first expedition to Egypt in 667 BCE (*ANET*: 298). A seal impression with the inscription 'Qausge[ber] king of E[dom]' was found in Umm el-Biyara (Bartlett 1989: 213).

From the eighth century on, the inhabitants of the desert increased their pressure on the countries of the Fertile Crescent bordering on the desert, so frontier states such as Ammon, Moab, and Edom were exposed to extreme danger. The Transjordanian kingdoms sought Assyrian protection from the nomads. The three following episodes are illustrative: (1) An Assyrian official reported to the Assyrian king about a raid on Moabite territory by men of the land of Gidir (ND 2773; Weippert in Hadidi 1987: 100 n. 42). The Moabites relied on Assyria to protect them against intrusions from any direction. (2) Ashurbanipal sent his armies to attack Arabian tribes along the eastern borders of Transjordania, defeating them 'in bloody battles' in the territories of Ammon, Moab, and Edom and in other places bordering on the desert (*ANET*: 298). (3) In one of the encounters with the Arabian tribes during the reign of Ashurbanipal, Kamushaltu, king of Moab, a loyal vassal of Assyria, inflicted a defeat upon Ammuladi king of Qedar who had revolted against Assyria and made forays against the kings of the Westland (*ANET:* 298). The Assyrians were interested in strengthening the frontier states against the desert brigands, and integrated them into the imperial defence system.

The general stability in Transjordania under the Assyrian empire improved the economy of the region. The flourishing economy of Transjordanian kingdoms in this period of *pax Assyriaca* (eighth–seventh centuries BCE) is emphasized by the plethora of archaeological and epigraphic finds (especially seals) in Ammon, Moab, and Edom.

Fortified and unfortified settlements greatly increased in number, indicating a growth of the settled population (Hübner 1992: 196; Weippert in Hadidi 1987: 102). The excavations at Buseirah, Umm el Biyara and Tawilan attest that the period of vassaldom to Assyria (Iron Age II) marked the most developed and prosperous period in Edom's history (Bartlett 1989: 136; Bienkowski 1992: 104; 1995: 139). Amos mentions the 'palaces of Bosrah'. Intimations of the prosperity of the Transjordanian kingdoms at this time can be heard in the words of Jeremiah to Ammon, the 'backsliding daughter that didst trust in thy treasures' (49:4), and to Moab that 'trusted in thy works and in thy treasures' (48:7, 29). The Edomite penetration west of the Arabah to the Judahite Negev, beginning from the seventh century BCE and intensifying during the sixth, are expressions of the change of the balance of power between Edom and Judah. The prophecies in Zephaniah 2:8 and Jeremiah 49:1 about the expansion of Moab and Ammon were probably made against the background of the hard times in Judah after the death of Josiah (609 BCE).

THE END OF THE TRANSJORDANIAN KINGDOMS

In 605–604 BCE Nebuchadnezzar II, king of Babylonia, subjugated Syria–Palestine as far as the border of Egypt. The kings of Ammon, Moab, and Edom were apparently among 'all the kings of the land of Hatti' who brought gifts to Nebuchadnezzar when he was fighting Ashkelon (604 BCE) (Lemaire 1994: 11). Forces from Moab and Ammon, and probably also from Edom, served the Babylonian king and helped him quell the rebellion of Jehoiakim in 599/8 (2 Kings 24:1–2). A few years later the Transjordanian kingdoms changed their policy and joined other countries in an attempt to throw off the Babylonian yoke. In the fourth year of Zedekiah's reign (594/3 BCE), the kings of Edom, Moab, and Ammon sent messengers to Zedekiah to elaborate a plot against Babylonia (Jer. 27:3), but for unknown reasons this revolt did not materialize. Open rebellion broke out in 589/8, but Edom and Moab remained aloof (see Obad. 11; Lam. 1:7) when the Chaldean army suddenly approached. Probably only Tyre and Ammon rebelled with Judah against Nebuchadnezzar (2 Kings 21:23–7). The Transjordanian states nevertheless neither failed to profit from the plight and destruction of Judah nor to conceal their delight in its difficulties (e.g. Ezek. 25:3–4; Obad. 10–14; Lam. 4:21–2). A Hebrew ostracon from Arad (no. 24) speaks of soldiers dispatched from Arad and Kinah to the city of Ramoth-Negeb 'lest the Edomites come thither' (Bartlett 1989: 149–50). Indeed, the archaeological excavations in the Judahite Negev uncovered an abundance of Edomite material, epigraphic and non-epigraphic, at several sites, mainly Ein-Hasebah, Horvat Uza, Tel Malhata, Tel Ira, Horvat Qitmit, and Beer-Sheba (Beit-Arieh 1988; 1995; Lemaire 1994: 23–6; Cohen and Yisrael 1995).

From Ezekiel 35:10–12 it is clear that the Edomites benefited from Judah's destruction (Bartlett 1989: 175–86). Ammonite involvement in Judah's rebellion against Babylonia is substantiated by Ezekiel 21:23–7 and by the episode relating to Gedaliah, the Babylonian-appointed governor of the Judaeans (Jer. 40–3), who was assassinated by Ishmael, son of Nethaniah 'of the seed royal' (of Judah), under the instigation of Baalis, the last Ammonite king. Baalis hoped to gain influence in

Judah by this intrigue. His policy of expansion is probably reflected by his taking over Heshbon from Moab (Jer. 48:2; 49:3).

A Babylonian punitive campaign against rebellious states, including the Transjordanian kingdoms, came a few years later. Josephus relates (*Ant.* X:181) that five years after the destruction of Jerusalem, namely 582/1 BCE, the king of Babylonia launched a major campaign against Syria and Palestine. He fought and defeated the Moabites and the Ammonites, and then continued his campaign against Egypt. He probably deported a section of the population. Commentators connect this expedition to the reference in one of Nebuchadnezzar's inscriptions about a campaign in Lebanon (*ANET:* 307), with the information in Jeremiah 52:30 about a further deportation of men from Judah in 582/1 BCE, and with Jeremiah's prophecy on Moab that Kemosh would be taken captive with his priests and princes (48:7).

On the final phase of the Transjordanian kingdoms we have little information. The Chaldeans are nowhere explicitly said to have conquered the Transjordanian kingdoms and transformed them into Babylonian provinces. A rock relief portraying Nabunaid in southern Transjordan hints at a campaign undertaken by the Babylonian king but of this campaign we cannot know the outcome. However, the absence of clear information about these kingdoms as independent or semi-independent political entities after the reign of Nebuchadnezzar II, makes it reasonable to suppose that they were organized as Babylonian provinces (Lemaire 1994).

Incursions of the desert nomads constituted one factor that pushed the Edomites westwards. The prophet Ezekiel (25:4–10; 35:15; Jer. 49:1–22; and also Isa. 11:14) accurately prophesied the punishment that was to befall the settlements in Transjordania during the sixth century BCE, a calamity reflected in the hold gained there by the nomads. The end of the kingdoms did not mean, however, that the land became completely desolate. Archaeological finds demonstrate continuity of occupation in several settlements from the neo-Babylonian period to the Persian period (Sauer 1985: 213), not as kingdoms but as Persian provinces (Weippert in Hadidi 1987: 102; Herr 1993: 34–5; Hoglund in Hoerth 1994: 343–4). The names of Ammon and Moab continued to survive as eparchies named Ammonitis and Moabitis (Hellenistic period). Edom was part of the province of Arabia (Lemaire 1994: 14, 26–7), and the name Edom moved westwards as the name of the eparchy of Idumea, south of the province of Judah.

BIBLIOGRAPHY

Anderson, W. P. (1990) 'The Beginning of Phoenician Pottery', *BASOR* 279: 35–49.

Aubet, M. E. (1993) *The Phoenicians and the West*, Cambridge.

Aufrecht, W. E. (1987) 'The Ammonite Language of the Iron Age', *BASOR* 266:85–95.

Aufrecht, W. E. (1989) *A Corpus of Ammonite Inscriptions*, Lewiston.

Bartlett, J. R. (1989) *Edom and the Edomites* (JSOTSup 77), Sheffield.

Beit-Arieh, I. (1988) 'New Light on the Edomites', *BAR* 14: 28–41.

—— (1995) *Horvat Qitmit: An Edomite Shrine in the Biblical Negev*, Tel Aviv.

Bienkowski, P. (1992) (ed.) *Early Edom and Moab: The Beginning of the Iron Age in Southern Jordan*, Sheffield.

—— (1995) 'The Architecture of Edom', in K. 'Amr et al., *Studies in the History and Archaeology of Jordan*, 5: 135–43.

Bikai, P. M. et al. (1990) 'The Phoenicians', *Archaeology* 43: 22–35.

Biran, A. and Naveh, J. (1995) 'The Tel Dan Inscription: A New Fragment', *IEJ* 45: 1–25.

Brown, S. (1992) 'Perspectives on Phoenician Art', *BA* 55: 6–24.

Clifford, R. J. (1990) 'Phoenician Religion', *BASOR* 279: 55–64.

Cohen, R. and Yisrael, Y. (1995) 'The Iron Age Fortresses at "En Haseva"', *BA* 58: 223–35.

Culican, W. (1991) 'Phoenicia and Phoenician Colonization', in CAH 3/r, 2nd edn, 461–546.

Daviau, P. M. N. (1997) 'Moab's Northern Border', *BA* 60: 222–8.

Daviau, P. M. M. et al. (2001) *The World of the Aramaeans*, Vols I–III, Sheffield.

Dearman, J. A. (1989) *Studies in the Mesha Inscriptions and Moab*, Atlanta.

—— (1997) 'Roads and Settlements in Moab', *BA* 60: 205–13.

Dicou, B. (1994) *Edom, Israel's Brother and Antagonist*, Sheffield.

Dion, P. E. (1995) 'Syro-Palestinian Resistance to Shalmaneser III in the Light of a New Document', *ZAW* 107: 482–9.

—— (1997) *Les Araméens a l'âge du fer: Histoire politique et structures socials* (EBib 34), Paris.

Donner, H. and Röllig, W. (1962) *Kanaanäische und Aramäische Inschriften I–II*, Wiesbaden.

Dornemann, R. H. (1983) *The Archaeology of the Trans Jordan in the Bronze and Iron Age*, Milwaukee.

Dothan, T. (1995) 'Tel-Miqneh: The Aegean Affinities of the Sea Peoples' (Philistines') Settlement in Canaan in Iron Age I', in S. Gitin (ed.), *Recent Excavations in Israel: A View to the West*, Dubuque, 41–59.

Dothan, T. and Dothan, M. (1992) *People of the Sea: The Search for the Philistines*, New York.

Dothan, T. and Gitin, S. (1990) 'Ekron and the Philistines', *BAR* 16: 20–42, 59.

Dothan, T. et al. (1997) 'A Royal Dedicatory Inscription from Ekron', *IEJ* 47: 1–16.

Ehrlich, C. S. (1996) *The Philistines in Transition: A History from ca. 1000–730 BCE*, Leiden.

Finkelstein, I. (1992) 'Edom in the Iron I', *Levant* 24: 159–66.

—— (1998) 'From Shreds to History: Review Article', *IEJ* 48: 120–31.

Gibson, C. L. (1971) *Textbook of the Syrian Semitic Inscriptions*, Oxford.

Gitin, S. (1995) 'Tel Miqne-Ekron in the 7th century BCE', in S. Gitin (ed.), *Recent Excavations in Israel: A View to the West*, Dubuque, 61–79.

—— (1997) 'The Neo-Assyrian Empire and its Western Periphery: The Levant, with a Focus on Philistine Ekron', in S. Parpola and R. Whiting (eds), *Assyria 1995*, Helsinki, 77–103.

Gitin, S. et al. (eds) (1998) *Mediterranean Peoples in Transition*, Jerusalem.

Gras, M. et al. (1989) *L'Univers Phénicien*, Paris.

—— (1991) 'The Phoenicians and Death', *Berytus* 39: 127–76.

Grayson, A. K. (1975) *Assyrian and Babylonian Chronicles*, New York.

—— (1987) *The Royal Inscriptions of Mesopotamia, Assyrian Periods*, Toronto.

Greenfield, J. (1987) 'Aspects of Aramaean Religion', in P. D. Miller et al. (eds), *Ancient Israelite Religion* [in Honor of F. M. Cross], Philadelphia, 67–8.

Hadidi, A. (ed.) (1987) *Studies in the History and Archaeology of Jordan*, Amman, Vol. 3.

Herr, L. G. (1993) 'Whatever Happened to the Ammonites?', *BAR* 19/6: 26–35, 68.

Hoerth, A. J. et al. (eds) (1994) *Peoples of the Old Testament World*, Grand Rapids.

Hübner, U. (1992) *Die Ammoniter*, Wiesbaden.

Jacobsen, D. M. (1999) 'Palestine and Israel', *BASOR* 313: 65–74.

Katzenstein, H. J. (1997) *The History of Tyre* (rev. edn), Jerusalem.

Kletter, R. (1991) 'The Rujm El-Malfuf Buildings and the Assyrian Vassal State of Ammon', *BASOR* 284: 33–50.

LaBianca, Ø. S. and Younker, R. W. (1995) 'The Kingdoms of Ammon, Moab and Edom: The Archaeology of Society in Late Bronze/Iron Age Transjordan, ca. 1400–500 BCE', in T. E. Levy (ed.), *The Archaeology of Society in the Holy Land*, London, 399–415.

Layton, S. C. (1988) 'Old Aramaic Inscriptions', *BA* 51: 172–89.

Lemaire, A. (1991) 'Hazaël de Damas, roi de Aram', in D. Charpin and F. Joannes (eds), *Marchands, Diplomates et Empereurs*, Paris, 91–108.

—— (1994) 'Les transformations politiques et culturelles de la Transjordanie au VIᵉ siècle av. J.-C.', *Transeuphraténe* 8: 9–27.

Lipiński, E. (ed.) (1991) *Phoenicia and the Bible*, Leuven.

Lipiński, E. (2000) *The Aramaeans. Their Ancient History, Culture, Religion*, Leuven.

Luckenbill, D. D. (1927) *Ancient Records of Assyria and Babylonia*, Chicago.

MacDonald, B. (1994) 'Early Edom: The Relation Between the Literary and Archaeological Evidence', in M. D. Coogan et al., *Scripture and Other Artifacts*, Louisville, 230–46.

Markoe, G. E. (1990) 'The Emergence of Phoenician Art', *BASOR* 279: 13–26.

Markoe, G. E. (2000) *Phoenicians*, London.

Mazar, A. (1986) 'Excavations at Tell Qasile, 1982–1984: Preliminary Report', *IEJ* 36: 1–15.

Mazar, A. (2001) *Studies in the Archaeology of the Iron Age of Israel and Jordan*, Sheffield.

Miller, J. M. (1997) 'Ancient Moab: Still Largely Unknown', *BA* 60: 194–204.

Moscati, S. (1988) *The Phoenicians*, New York.

Na'aman, N. (1997) 'King Mesha and the Foundation of the Moabite Monarchy', *IEJ* 47: 83–92.

Na'aman, N. and Zadok, R. (1988) 'Sargon II's Deportations to Israel and Philistia', *JCS* 40: 36–46.

Naveh, J. (1985) 'Writing and Scripts in Seventh Century BCE Philistia: The New Evidence from Tell Jemmeh', *IEJ* 35: 9–21.

Oren, E. D. (2000) *The Sea Peoples and Their World: A Reassessment* (University Museum Monographs 108), Pennsylvania.

Parpola, S. (ed.) (1987–) *State Archives of Assyria*, Helsinki.

Pitard, W. T. (1987) *Ancient Damascus*, Winona Lake.

Pritchard, J. B. (1954) *Ancient Near East in Pictures*, Princeton.

Pritchard, J. B. (ed.) (1969) *Ancient Near Eastern Texts Relating to the Old Testament*, Princeton.

Sader, H. (1991) 'Phoenician Stelae from Tyre', *Berytus* 39: 101–26.

Sauer, J. A. (1985) 'Ammon, Moab and Edom', *Biblical Archaeology Today*, Jerusalem, 206–14.

Singer, I. (1994) 'Egyptians, Canaanites and Philistines', in I. Finkelstein and N. Na'aman (eds), *From Nomadism to Monarchy*, Jerusalem, 295–338.

Stager, L. E. (1995) 'The Impact of the Sea Peoples in Canaan (1185–1050 BCE)', in T. E. Levy (ed.), *The Archaeology of Society in the Holy Land*, London, 332–48.

Stager, L. E. et al. (1996) 'The Fury of Babylon: Ashkelon and the Archaeology of Destruction', *BAR* 22: 56–69, 76–7.

Stone, B. J. (1995) 'The Philistines and Acculturation: Culture Change and Ethnic Continuity in the Iron Age', *BASOR* 298: 7–32.

Tadmor, H. (1991) 'On the Role of Aramaic in the Assyrian Empire', in M. Mori et al. (eds), *Near Eastern Studies*, Leiden, 419–25.

Timm, S. (1989) *Moab zwischen den Mächten*, Wiesbaden.

Treumann-Watkins, B. (1992) 'Phoenicians in Spain', *BA* 55: 28–34.

Worschech, U. (1997) 'Egypt and Moab', *BA* 60: 229–36.

Yadin, Y. (1963) *The Art of Warfare in Biblical Lands*, London.

Younker, R. W. (1997) 'Moabite Social Structure', *BA* 60: 237–48.